Methods of Matrix Algebra

MATHEMATICS IN SCIENCE AND ENGINEERING

A Series of Monographs and Textbooks

Edited by

Richard Bellman

The RAND Corporation, Santa Monica, California

In preparation

Methods of
MATRIX ALGEBRA

MARSHALL C. PEASE, III

Stanford Research Institute
Menlo Park, California

1965

ACADEMIC PRESS   New York and London

ACADEMIC PRESS INC.
111 Fifth Avenue, New York, New York 10003

United Kingdom Edition published by
ACADEMIC PRESS INC. (LONDON) LTD.
Berkeley Square House, London W.1

LIBRARY OF CONGRESS CATALOG CARD NUMBER: 65-19017

PRINTED IN THE UNITED STATES OF AMERICA

Foreword

In writing this book, it has been my hope to make available to the physical scientist and engineer some of the more sophisticated techniques of matrix algebra.

There have been many books on matrix algebra and related topics, some quite excellent. Yet it seemed to me that none of them suited the needs of the reader I had in mind—the student in physics, electronics, and similar fields. Some are too much of the "cookbook" variety; others go deeply into the subject, but treat it as a mathematical discipline rather than as a tool for analysis. It is true that matrix algebra is a valuable discipline, and that it has significance as a point of entry into the higher algebras. But, for the reader I had in mind, this is not its primary relevance.

This book is primarily directed toward the student at or near the graduate level in physics or some related field who is interested in any mathematical subject principally because he hopes to make use of it in his own research.

The problems that occur in modern science and engineering often demand a mode of analysis that is quite sophisticated. Further, the connection between the problem and the mathematics that will handle the problem is often quite unobvious. It is therefore not enough that the researcher be given the formal rules of manipulation. He must also have a sense of their general significance and a feeling for why they are the appropriate manipulations to make. It is only by such an understanding of the mathematics that he will be able to perceive how his problem can be approached.

This kind of understanding cannot be communicated directly. It comes only as the result of hard study, of "beating your head against the wall." But it is up to the teacher, or author, to help.

To help the student develop this understanding, a textbook should emphasize the *why* even more than the *what*. The structure of logic should be built up gradually from what the student already knows. The movement should be from the particular to the general, with the reasons for each step being given, where possible, in advance. The development should create the illusion that each step is inevitable.

The inevitability of a particular route is an illusion, at least for the student. For the author, or teacher, who already has a developed understanding, the choice may indeed be an inevitable consequence of his

v

own viewpoint. But until the student has obtained a thorough understanding of the field as an organic whole—until he has discovered in
himself a mode of thought that fits the whole—he can have no real
sense of what is inevitable. Left to himself, he would be lost in a maze
of separated facts. It is up to the author, or teacher, to give him the
shelter of an illusion in which he can confidently search for his own
subjective realization of meaning. The organization and style of this
book has been developed with this need in mind—the need to develop
in the student a coherent understanding of the field as a whole. It asks
of the student that he brings to its study only a certain maturity of mind,
both in terms of mathematical and conceptual openness, and of physical
understanding.

In the organization of this book, I have started with premises that
differ from those of most authors. I have assumed, first, that the student
is thoroughly familiar with complex numbers. Most texts start with
real matrices, sometimes for mathematical reasons; sometimes, apparently
with the thought that the real numbers are more familiar to most
students. This is not true of the student I have had in mind. He, in
fact, has been so thoroughly exposed to complex numbers that a restriction to the real number field strikes as being arbitrary, and since it is
only the complex number field that is algebraically complete, restriction
to the real number field introduces some complications that are quite
serious.

Also, I have chosen as the basis of development the concept of eigenvectors and eigenvalues, rather than quadratic forms as is more custo-
mary. This has been done not only because of my own prejudice, but
also because I felt that it was more appropriate for the particular student
I had in mind. This is certainly true of the student of electronics. He
has "cut his teeth" on characteristic and iterative impedances, which
immediately define eigenvectors, and on phase delays, which are eigenvalues. In the case of the physicist, it depends on his particular interest.
If he has been interested in such subjects as crystallography or stress-
strain theory, he is thoroughly familiar with the concept of principal
axes, which leads directly to eigenvectors. If his field is quantum
mechanics, he was probably introduced to eigenvectors through the
Schroedinger formulation and the concept of the pure state. Such a
state, again, defines an eigenvector. On the other hand, it has also been
pointed out to him that all observable quantities are describable as
quadratic forms of a particular class, i.e., hermitian forms. But at least
I felt that the concept of eigenvectors would not be alien to him.

If the primary emphasis is placed on eigenvectors, complications are
introduced. It results, particularly, in the introduction of generalized

eigenvectors almost as soon as the eigenvectors themselves. If the primary emphasis were on quadratic forms, an initial restriction to hermitian or symmetric operators could be made quite reasonably, thus deferring the need for generalized eigenvectors.

I have found that those who have had only a slight exposure to matrix analysis, or the theory of linear operators, tend to stand in awe of generalized eigenvectors, but that this is quickly and easily dissipated by more specific exposure. In my opinion generalized eigenvectors have been given an unnecessary aura of mystery, and there is no real pedagogical need to avoid them.

I also think that there is an unnecessary aura of mystery about the general inner product relation. The basic idea of metricizing an abstract linear vector space seems quite natural. It seems more unnatural to restrict attention to the unitary or euclidean inner product. After all, what is the "natural" definition of the length of a vector, some of whose components may have the dimensions of volts, and some of amperes? I have, therefore, not hesitated to introduce the general (proper) inner product in Chapter II at almost the same time as the unitary inner product is developed.

From these premises, the material in Chapters I through VIII flows more or less logically. They contain the techniques that are generally pertinent to any problem involving matrix analysis.

Chapter IX represents a significant departure from conventional theory. It contains what is admittedly a pet concept of my own, which I call the "improper inner product." Specifically, this is a nonsingular hermitian quadratic form that plays the same role as the inner product defining a Hilbert space, except that it is not required that it be positive definite. Mathematicians may object to my calling such a form an inner product at all. In deference to them I call it "improper."

The value of the improper inner product relation is that it can be used to express certain important constraints in a very convenient form. This is perhaps most easily illustrated by electronic systems. Different kinds of systems exhibit various important conservation laws—the Manley-Rowe relations, Chu's kinetic power theorem, etc. It is a very useful device to consider that these relations specify a metric for the abstract space involved. Then the fact that these quantities are conserved means that the length, so defined, of a signal vector is constant, and the system must be described by an operator that, in the appropriate sense, is rotational. If this is done, the resulting inner product relation is improper.

This concept leads to complications; particularly that the space is "hyperbolic" like Minkowski space-time rather than "elliptic" like euclidean space. However, these complications already exist in the problem, so that what we achieve is a transference of existing complications from the problem to the underlying vector space. This seems a useful generalization of viewpoint.

In Chapter X, the improper inner product is employed to develop what I call the "dyad expansion" of a matrix. It has been my experience that this is a very useful device in physics problems which include knowledge of a conservation law, so that a suitable metric for the system is known. In cases of this type, the dyad expansion is the easiest method of handling problems such as determining a function of a matrix, or the effect of a perturbation.

Chapter XI on projectors consists of concepts and theorems that are well known. However, their significance for the practical solution of problems does not seem to have been generally appreciated. Rather, they have been used for the abstract development of theory. I have used abstract methods in developing their relations, so as to free them from dependence on a proper metric, but my purpose has been their development as tools of analysis. It is very useful that the projectors on the eigensubspaces can be determined from the eigenvalues and structure of an operator alone, without reference to the eigenvectors involved. In some cases, this is a very important simplification of the process of analysis.

Chapter XII deals with the problem of solving the vector equation $\mathbf{u} = \mathbf{Tv}$ when $\mathbf{T}$ is singular or rectangular—i.e., of obtaining what is sometimes called the "pseudo inverse" of a singular matrix. The methods used here seem to be new, although similar results have been obtained before by other methods. Those used in this book have the advantage that they are based on the properties of the minimum polynomial. This often simplifies the numerical solution of particular problems. Also and more importantly, it connects this type of problem to the more abstract parts of matrix theory, and so opens the way to the formal study of general situations that may involve singular operators.

In Chapter XIII, the theory of commutators is developed to some extent. The problem in writing this chapter was to know how completely to treat this subject. Any attempt to cover it thoroughly, even in summary, would have extended the chapter into a book all by itself. (The theory is properly the subject of Lie algebras.) I have, therefore, largely restricted my attention to a particular kind of problem for which the exponentially tapered transmission line can be considered the prototype. The general class I call the class of systems with "simple nonuniformity." The class is of considerable importance in its own right. I also hope that its study will be valuable to the student in that at least a glimpse is given him of what can be accomplished by generalizing matrix analysis into the study of abstractly defined linear operators of finite dimensionality.

Chapter XIV, on the direct product and the Kronecker sum, might have been presented earlier, since the techniques involved are pure matrix methods. However, their most important application is probably to the development of the representation theory of Lie .groups and algebras. Therefore, their treatment has been deferred until after Chapter XIII so that this relation could be pointed out.

Periodic systems, which are studied in Chapter XV, consist of problems which are of great practical importance. Partly because of this importance, and partly because they are more tractable than the general nonuniform problem, they have been studied intensively by many people since Lyapunov's time. The theory, however, is usually barely touched upon in books which do not specialize in this aspect of it. While the subject has not by any means been exhausted here, I have attempted to cover it to the extent that the interested student will know how the theory can be applied and to make him aware of the existence of this body of theory.

Chapters XVI and XVII on applications of matrix theory to electromagnetic theory and to Sturm-Liouville systems are intended to illustrate some of the important ways in which the basic techniques of analysis can be extended. Again, these chapters are not intended as exhaustive treatments, either of the physical theory or of the mathematical techniques, but rather to stimulate thought on the kinds of approaches possible to practical problems.

Chapter XVIII, on Markov matrices, has a similar purpose. It covers briefly an important subfield of matrix algebra, and another type of application, this time to probability theory. Again the intent is to illustrate rather than to give a thorough exposition of the subject which could hardly be done in less than book length.

The final chapter, on stability theory, is one about which I have had reservations. The problems involved here are of such great practical importance that I felt I could not avoid giving at least a brief outline of the subject. Yet much of the theory is not really a part of matrix analysis at all, but instead is a part of the theory of rational polynomials. But again, I felt that I had to give the student at least some idea of the methods that are available to him when he finds himself faced with a question of stability.

In summary, it is my hope that there will be students who will be able to use this book as an aid to gain insight into the substance and nature of matrix analysis. If so, they derive it, not *from* this work, but *through* it; it will, I hope, prove to be a useful guide.

Science and engineering have reached levels of subtlety which require sophisticated methods of analysis, and there is no reason to think that the future will not make this continually more true. The rewards of accomplishment are more apt to go to those with the deepest insight into the available methods of analysis.

In conclusion, I would like to acknowledge the many sources of help I have had. Unfortunately, it would be impossible to list them all in detail. I would like, however, to make special mention of Dr. Clarence W. Barnes who has been my co-worker in this field for several years. I would also like to thank Mrs. E. Mock who, with my wife, did most of the backbreaking job of typing the manuscript.

I would also like to acknowledge the support of the Stanford Research Institute during the preparation of the book and the role of the U.S. Air Force in supporting the research that has been part of my own reason and excuse for studying the subject.

M. PEASE

Symbols and Conventions

A   Bold face capital letters—a matrix.

x   Bold face lower case letters—a vector expressed as a column matrix.

$\mathbf{x}^*$ or $\mathbf{A}^*$ Superscript asterisk—complex conjugate of $\mathbf{x}$ or $\mathbf{A}$.

$\mathbf{x}^T$ or $\mathbf{A}^T$ Superscript T—transpose of $\mathbf{x}$ or $\mathbf{A}$.

$\mathbf{x}^\dagger$ or $\mathbf{A}^\dagger$ Superscript dagger—complex conjugate transpose or hermitian conjugate of $\mathbf{x}$ or $\mathbf{A}$.

$\oplus$ Direct sum (see p. 193).

$\in$ "Is a member of ..."

$\mathbf{x}_{\sim i}$ The vector conjugate to $\mathbf{x}_i$ in the sense of Chapter IX, Section 4, pp. 220–223.

$\langle \mathbf{x}, \mathbf{y} \rangle$ An inner product relation, proper or improper, pp. 49, 217.

$[\mathbf{A}, \mathbf{B}]$ The commutator of $\mathbf{A}$ and $\mathbf{B}$, $(\mathbf{AB} - \mathbf{BA})$, p. 279.

Ad_A The commutator operator, $[\mathbf{A}, -]$, p. 305.

Contents

IV. Hermitian, Unitary, and Normal Matrices

V. Change of Basis, Diagonalization, and the Jordan Canonical Form

X. The Dyad Expansion and Its Application

XI. Projectors

XII. Singular and Rectangular Operators

XIII. The Commutator Operator

XIV. The Direct Product and the Kronecker Sum

XV. Periodic Systems

XVI. Application to Electromagnetic Theory

XVII. Sturm-Liouville Systems

XVIII. Markoff Matrices and Probability Theory

XIX. Stability

CHAPTER I

Vectors and Matrices

In this chapter, we shall lay the foundations of the rest of our work. We shall define what we mean by a vector (which is not the same thing, although it is a generalization, as the vectors one meets in, for example, vector analysis). We shall introduce the concept of a matrix as an operator that expresses a linear homogeneous relation between two vector spaces (a mapping of one vector space onto or into another). Finally, both as an example and because the problem is an important one, we shall briefly discuss the analysis of reciprocal ladder networks.

1. VECTORS

The basic element that we shall consider is the vector. As we use the term, a vector is a generalization of the concept that we use in vector analysis or in elementary physics. It has some of the properties of a vector in physical 3-space, but not necessarily all of them. To avoid confusion, we must take pains to know exactly what we mean by the term.

We start with a partially abstract definition:

Definition. *A* **vector** *is a set of n numbers arranged in a definite order.*

To be completely general, we should say "a set of n numbers of a field,[1] F," or of symbols that stand for members of the field.

The set of numbers so arranged are called the *components* of the vector. The number n is the *dimensionality* of the vector.

---

[1] A *field* is defined, roughly, as a collection of elements within which the operations of addition, subtraction, multiplication, and division, except by zero, are always possible and give a unique element of the field.

The positive real numbers are not a field since subtraction is not always possible. Neither is the set of all integers, since division is not always possible.

The two fields that will concern us are the field of all real numbers and the field of all complex numbers.

The elements of the field being considered are called *scalars*.

1

We shall take a column as the standard form for a vector. That is, we shall write

$$\mathbf{x} = \begin{pmatrix} x_1 \\ x_2 \\ \vdots \\ x_n \end{pmatrix}, \qquad x_i \in F \tag{1}$$

where F is the field and the symbol $\in$ means "is a member of." We shall use parentheses around the array, and boldfaced lower case letters when we represent the vector by a single symbol.

We shall also, on occasion, write Eq. (1) as

$$\mathbf{x} = \mathrm{col}(x_1 \quad x_2 \quad \dots \quad x_n) \tag{1'}$$

to save space.

We shall also use, at times, a row representation:

$$\mathbf{x}^T = (x_1 \quad x_2 \quad \cdots \quad x_n) \tag{2}$$

This, however, we shall consider a secondary, or alternative representation, with the column form being the basic one. The superscript T (indicating the *transpose* as we shall discuss later) indicates its secondary role.

These standardizations are quite arbitrary. Between the column and row representations there is complete duality. The designation of one of them as fundamental and the other as secondary is purely arbitrary. It is, however, convenient to make such a standardization.

Furthermore, we shall later have occasion to use other forms for the representation of abstract vectors. In particular, we shall find that it is sometimes useful to consider a square array—i.e., a matrix—as a vector. It is, therefore, important to realize that the particular form used is not intrinsic to the definition. It is simply as a matter of convenience that we take the column form as being the ordinary one.

This definition says nothing about the physical significance of a vector. The numbers may represent any physical quantities in any units that are convenient. As indicated in the definition, the order is defined so that the position of a particular number in the array has significance. Hence, the different elements of the array, its *components*, may measure very different quantities, quite possibly in different units.

To illustrate, consider a box containing some kind of network with a pair of wires—a "port"—at each end, as in Fig. 1. This box may be connected at one end to some kind of generator, and at the other to

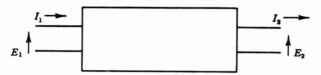

FIG. 1. A 2-port network.

some kind of load. We ask ourselves how we can describe conveniently what is happening at each end.

One way of doing this is to record the voltage and current at each end, measured according to the arrows. A convenient way of arranging these data is in the form of two vectors

$$\mathbf{x}_1 = \begin{pmatrix} E_1 \\ I_1 \end{pmatrix}, \qquad \mathbf{x}_2 = \begin{pmatrix} E_2 \\ I_2 \end{pmatrix} \tag{3}$$

It may be noted that the first component of each vector has the dimensions of volts, and the second of amperes.

This is by no means the only way vectors can be defined for this system. In particular, we could record any two linearly independent combinations of the voltage and current, such as

$$\mathbf{y}_1 = \begin{pmatrix} E_1 + RI_1 \\ E_1 - RI_1 \end{pmatrix}, \qquad \mathbf{y}_2 = \begin{pmatrix} E_2 + RI_2 \\ E_2 - RI_2 \end{pmatrix} \tag{4}$$

where R is a constant with the dimensions of ohms.

In fact, the decision to describe what is happening at each port, as implied by the above, is itself dictated by other considerations, and other descisions are possible. For example, if we are going to consider what happens when we connect batteries or voltage generators at each end, then it may be convenient to define the vectors

$$\mathbf{e} = \begin{pmatrix} E_1 \\ E_2 \end{pmatrix}, \qquad \mathbf{i} = \begin{pmatrix} I_1 \\ I_2 \end{pmatrix} \tag{5}$$

The vector $\mathbf{e}$ then describes the voltage components at *both* ports, and $\mathbf{i}$ the currents.

If we are concerned with the response of the system to signals at frequency ω, the E's and I's may be taken as the complex amplitude of the appropriate exponentials. That is, we write the actual voltage at port #1 as the real part of $E_1 \exp(j\omega t)$, and record only E_1. (The ability to do this is a consequence of linearity which we have not so far assumed, but which we will, shortly.)

In fact, we must go further. In the system of Fig. 1, what is happening at port #1 is a physical event. It is this event that, properly speaking is the *abstract vector*. It cannot be described until we have established a *basis*, or a *coordinate system*—i.e., until we have decided, for example, that the first component shall be the voltage, and second the current, and decided on the units to be used. It is only after these decisions have been made that we can actually write down the vector. The $\mathbf{x}_1$ so obtained is then, properly speaking, a *representation of the abstract vector*.

This distinction between the abstract vector and its representation is fundamental. It is important because, as we have seen, the physical event at port #1 can be described in many ways. The event—i.e., the abstract vector—is the same, but it may be given many different representations.

We can state the process broadly. The system is described by a certain number, N, of variables. Of these, only a certain number, n, can be independently specified, the remaining $(N - n)$ then being determined by the dynamics of the system. We may separate the whole set into two sets of sizes n and $(N - n)$ in whatever way is convenient for our purposes, and define a *driving vector* from the variables that are considered as the independent ones, and a *response vector* from the others.

The problem of matrix algebra is to study the relation between such vectors.

The same mathematical problem arises in many contexts. We have described the problem as it arises in a 2-port network. But suppose we wish to study the probability of an electron tunneling a thin barrier. The boundary conditions at the edges of the barrier require continuity of the psi-function and of its first derivative. But the two edges are related by Schroedinger's equation for the potential function in the barrier. This provides a linear relation between the edges. We establish the vectors col(ψ, ψ') at the two edges. There is, then, a matrix relating these two vectors. We can find this matrix by solving Schroedinger's equation, analytically if possible, otherwise numerically. With this matrix, we can find what wave functions in the two outer regions will simultaneously match the conditions on the edges of the barrier. The problem, when set up in this form, becomes formally similar to the 2-port network of Fig. 1.

Many other examples could be cited, including problems in heat-flow, stress-strain theory, the deflection of beams, vibrations, chemical processes, and so on, almost without limit. All that is required is that the equations involved be linear, and that the problem be one-dimensional at least in a piecewise manner. If there are two degrees of freedom, the problem becomes formally similar to the 2-port network discussed. If there are more degrees of freedom involved, then it becomes analogous to a larger network, say $2n$-port.

The vectors that are involved in these problems are not geometric in the sense of a vector in ordinary space. They are representations of possible real physical processes. In elementary texts on physics, a vector is often defined as an entity that has both direction and magnitude. These abstract vectors have neither, at least without further interpretation and definition. What, for example, is the magnitude of a vector that is 2 volts along one axis, and 3 amp along the other? What is its direction? We do not know until we define what we mean by either magnitude or direction.

We regard a vector as an abstract entity. We assign to it only those properties that are needed to make it a convenient way of describing the physical processes under study. The geometric concept of a vector as something that has magnitude and direction in ordinary space is both an example of a specific application and a geometric model that is sometimes useful and sometimes not. To make vectors applicable to a wide variety of problems, we need a flexible concept of their nature. It is the abstract approach that gives us the flexibility that we need.

2. ADDITION OF VECTORS AND SCALAR MULTIPLICATION

To make use of the representation of a complex situation as an abstract vector, we need to have rules for manipulating such entities. The two simplest operations are the addition of two vectors and the multiplication of a vector and a scalar. These are defined in the obvious way:

Definition. *The* **sum** *of two n-dimensional vectors* $\mathbf{x}$ *and* $\mathbf{y}$ *is the vector whose components are the sums of the components of* $\mathbf{x}$ *and* $\mathbf{y}$. *That is, if*

$$\mathbf{x} = \begin{pmatrix} x_1 \\ x_2 \\ \vdots \\ x_n \end{pmatrix}, \quad \mathbf{y} = \begin{pmatrix} y_1 \\ y_2 \\ \vdots \\ y_n \end{pmatrix} \tag{6}$$

then

$$\mathbf{x} + \mathbf{y} = \begin{pmatrix} x_1 + y_1 \\ x_2 + y_2 \\ \vdots \\ x_n + y_n \end{pmatrix} \tag{7}$$

Since the components of each vector are in a field F, and since addition is always possible in a field, any two vectors of the same dimensionality may be added.

We also note that the definition does not apply to two vectors of different dimensionality. We find we have no need or interest in being able to add vectors of different dimensionality.

Definition. *The* **product** *of a scalar a, in a field F, and a vector* **x**, *whose components are in F, is the vector whose components are a times the components of* **x**. *If*

$$\mathbf{x} = \begin{pmatrix} x_1 \\ x_2 \\ \cdot \\ \cdot \\ \cdot \\ x_n \end{pmatrix} \tag{8}$$

then

$$a\mathbf{x} = \begin{pmatrix} ax_1 \\ ax_2 \\ \cdot \\ \cdot \\ \cdot \\ ax_n \end{pmatrix} \tag{9}$$

Since a and all the x_i are in the field F, and since multiplication is always possible in a field, this definition is always applicable.

From the abstract definition of a field, it follows that these operations have the properties that we would expect:

1. Addition is *commutative* and *associative*:

$$\mathbf{x} + \mathbf{y} = \mathbf{y} + \mathbf{x}$$
$$\mathbf{x} + (\mathbf{y} + \mathbf{z}) = (\mathbf{x} + \mathbf{y}) + \mathbf{z} \tag{10}$$

2. The set S_n of all possible n-dimensional vectors formed from the field F contains a unique zero element, or *null vector* **0**, such that for any **x** in S_n,

$$\mathbf{x} + \mathbf{0} = \mathbf{x}$$

The null vector is, evidently,

$$\mathbf{0} = \begin{pmatrix} 0 \\ 0 \\ \cdot \\ \cdot \\ \cdot \\ 0 \end{pmatrix} \tag{11}$$

3. Each vector **x** in S_n has a unique *negative*, designated as $(-\mathbf{x})$ such that

$$\mathbf{x} + (-\mathbf{x}) = \mathbf{0}$$

The negative of **x** is evidently given by

$$-\mathbf{x} = \begin{pmatrix} -x_1 \\ -x_2 \\ \vdots \\ -x_n \end{pmatrix} \quad \text{if} \quad \mathbf{x} = \begin{pmatrix} x_1 \\ x_2 \\ \vdots \\ x_n \end{pmatrix} \tag{12}$$

4. Scalar multiplication is *associative*:

$$a(b\mathbf{x}) = (ab)\mathbf{x} \tag{13}$$

5. Scalar multiplication is *distributive* with respect to addition of both the scalar and the vector:

$$(a + b)\mathbf{x} = a\mathbf{x} + b\mathbf{x}$$
$$a(\mathbf{x} + \mathbf{y}) = a\mathbf{x} + a\mathbf{y} \tag{14}$$

6. There exists a unique element of F, designated as 1, such that

$$1 \cdot \mathbf{x} = \mathbf{x} \tag{15}$$

7. Scalar multiplication is *commutative*:

$$a\mathbf{x} = \mathbf{x}a \tag{16}$$

All these properties can be obtained immediately from the definition of the operations and of a field. For the detailed definition of a field, the student can go to any text on number theory.

It might be more elegant, mathematically, to start from these properties as postulates and go from there to the actual operations. For our purpose here, however, we are not concerned with abstract development *per se*, and it is these particular operations that will be useful to us. It is comforting to find that they do have the properties that one expects from addition and multiplication by a number.

3. LINEAR VECTOR SPACES

From these operations, we are led to the very important definition:

Definition. *A set S of n-dimensional vectors is a* **linear vector space** *over the field F if the sum of any two vectors in S is in the set and if the product of any vector in S times a scalar in F is in S.*

We can combine these two requirements into one and say that if **x** and **y** are any vectors in S, and α and β any scalars in F, then $(\alpha\mathbf{x} + \beta\mathbf{y})$ is in S.

We recall that the components of a vector are elements of a field. Generally, but not necessarily, this will be F, the field defining the linear vector space. It is possible to consider vectors whose components are in F_1, and which form a linear vector space under linear combination over a field F_2. For example, we might have vectors with complex coefficients which form a linear vector space under combinations of the form $(a\mathbf{x} + b\mathbf{y})$ where a and b are in the field of real numbers.

We shall not have occasion to use this generality in this book, and will confine our attention to the situation where both fields are the same—generally the field of complex numbers. The student, however, should recognize that the possibility exists. If he carries his studies further into the abstract higher algebras, he will find important situations where different fields are involved in the different roles.

While speaking of the more abstract possibilities, we should also mention the use of different fields. The finite set of numbers modulo p, where p is prime, form a field (a field with *characteristic p*). Much of what we have to say, but not all, will be true for vectors or linear vector spaces formed from such fields. In particular, if $p = 2$, so that we have the *binary field*, there are some quite important differences.

We should also mention the possibility of defining a linear vector space over collections of elements that do not form a field. The usual definition only requires F to be a ring. While such generality is of great importance in the study of certain classes of operators, we shall limit our attention to the case where F is a field. This will give us sufficient generality for our present purposes.

We shall, throughout the book, assume that all fields contain an infinite number of elements (have characteristic zero). In particular, we shall consider only the fields of real numbers and of complex numbers. This should be understood, even when not explicitly stated.

4. DIMENSIONALITY AND BASES

We have specified that the vectors are n-dimensional, but this does *not* say what is the dimensionality of the vector space. In ordinary 3-space, we have 3-dimensional vectors, but certain sets of them form 2-dimensional subspaces—i.e., planes—or one-dimensional subspaces, which are lines. To define the dimensionality of a space, we need the concept of linear independence.

Definition. *The set of k n-dimensional vectors* $\mathbf{x}_1$, $\mathbf{x}_2$, ..., $\mathbf{x}_k$ *are said to be* **linearly independent** *in the field F if and only if there exists no set of scalars* c_1, c_2, ..., c_k *of F, not all zero, such that*

$$c_1\mathbf{x}_1 + c_2\mathbf{x}_2 + \cdots + c_k\mathbf{x}_k = 0 \tag{17}$$

If this equation has any solution for the scalar constants c_i other than the trivial one in which all c_i equal zero, then the vectors are said to be linearly dependent. Otherwise they are linearly independent.

From this we obtain the dimensionality of a linear vector space S.

Definition. *A linear vector space S has the* **dimension k** *if S contains at least one set of k vectors, none of which are the null vector, that are linearly independent, but does not contain any set of* (k + 1) *linearly independent vectors.*

Definition. *If S is k-dimensional, then a set of vectors in S,* $\mathbf{x}_1$, $\mathbf{x}_2$, ..., $\mathbf{x}_k$ *that are linearly independent is called a* **basis** *for S.*

It can be proven that the dimensionality of a space S is a property of the space and not of the particular vectors chosen.

Properly speaking, the space is *generated* by taking all linear combinations of a set of generators. The space is then said to be the *linear envelope over the field* of the vectors. The vectors, in turn, are said to *span* the space S. Of this set, we find a subset, which may be the whole set, that is linearly independent and such that all other members of the set can be expressed as linear combinations of the subset. The subset is a basis, and, if it contains k members, the space is k-dimensional. It follows, although it requires careful development to show rigorously, that any other basis for the space will also contain exactly k vectors, neither more nore less.

The terms *basis* is used to indicate the fact that any arbitrary vector in the space $\mathbf{y}$ can be expressed uniquely as a linear combination of the basis vectors:

$$\mathbf{y} = c_1\mathbf{x}_1 + c_2\mathbf{x}_2 + \cdots + c_k\mathbf{x}_k \tag{18}$$

where the set c_i are scalars in the field being used. If no such set existed, then $\mathbf{y}$ would be linearly independent of the set $\mathbf{x}_i$ over the field, contrary to assumption; and, if the set c_i for a given $\mathbf{y}$ were not unique, then the difference of the two expansions would give a nontrivial linear relation between the $\mathbf{x}_i$, so that the set $\mathbf{x}_i$ would not be linearly independent, contrary to assumption.

A set of vectors $\mathbf{x}_i$ which is a basis for the space being considered is said to be *complete* in the space. The representation of an arbitrary vector **y** as a linear combination of the $\mathbf{x}_i$ as in Eq. (18) is called the *expansion* of **y** on the basis, or in terms of the complete set $\mathbf{x}_i$.

The dimensionality of a linear vector space S may be less than that of the vectors it includes, but cannot be more. That is, the individual vectors may be represented as an array of n elements of the field. If the space is k-dimensional, we can have n greater than or equal to k but not less than k. If S has the same dimensionality as the vectors, it is said to be *the whole space*. If it is of dimension $0 < k < n$, but not zero, it is said to be a *proper subspace* or, loosely, a *subspace*. The *null space*, or space containing no vectors (except the null vector), has dimension zero and is a subspace, but not a proper one. Also, the whole space is a subspace, but not a proper one.

In the 3-space of ordinary geometry, a vector is an array of three real numbers which are the components of the vector along three chosen axes, not necessarily orthogonal. As a basis for the whole space, we may take any three vectors that are linearly independent—i.e., are not coplanar since an equation of the form

$$ax + by + cz = 0 \tag{19}$$

defines a plane. Any plane through the origin is a subspace of dimension two. As a basis for it, we may take any two vectors on the plane that are not co-linear.

Any line through the origin is a subspace of dimension one. As a basis for it, we may take any vector on the line.

It would be more precise, in some respects, to use the term *linear manifold* instead of subspace. The distinction, however, has significance only in infinitely dimensional spaces. In such cases, we can have a manifold, defined as above, that is not closed—i.e., does not contain the limit of all sequences of vectors in it. A subspace, then, is a closed linear manifold. Since we shall here deal only with finitely dimensioned subspaces, this is an unnecessary complication of terminology for our purposes.

The concept of linear spaces and subspaces is a fundamental one. In the immediate context it may seem like an unnecessary abstraction serving no useful purpose. It is, however, of crucial importance in the development of the underlying theory. We shall meet it again when we consider general canonical forms whose theory is largely based on the concept of invariant subspaces.

5. LINEAR HOMOGENEOUS SYSTEMS—MATRICES

We must now consider what we want to do with our vectors. Obviously there is a considerable range of possible desires. However, we may take as an example of at least a broad class of problems the one that has been suggested in connection with Fig. 1. In Fig. 1 we had a simple 2-port network. We defined, for example, the vectors

$$\mathbf{x}_1 = \begin{pmatrix} E_1 \\ I_1 \end{pmatrix}, \qquad \mathbf{x}_2 = \begin{pmatrix} E_2 \\ I_2 \end{pmatrix} \tag{20}$$

We suggested that one of these, say $\mathbf{x}_2$, might list the variables which are known from the boundary or initial conditions, and the other those that are determined by the system and $\mathbf{x}_2$. In other words, the variables of $\mathbf{x}_2$ are considered as independent, with the variables of $\mathbf{x}_1$ being dependent on those of $\mathbf{x}_2$. Formally,

$$\mathbf{x}_1 = f(\mathbf{x}_2) \tag{21}$$

As long as we do not specify what is in the box of Fig. 1, we have no information regarding the nature of this functional dependence. However, for a great many physical systems of interest, the dependence of Eq. (21) in the range of interest is very well approximated by a particularly simple kind of relationship—i.e., linear dependence. Equation (21) is said to be *linear* if, for any $\mathbf{x}_1$ and $\mathbf{x}_2$ that satisfy Eq. (21) and for any scalar a, in the field of interest

$$f(a\mathbf{x}_2) = a\mathbf{x}_1$$

Note that this must be true for all solutions of Eq. (21).

Even when the particular system or problem cannot be taken as linear over the range of interest, it is very often true that the questions that must be answered first are linear. We may be seeking the large signal behavior of an amplifier. This is not a linear problem if the question of saturation is involved. But, before even tackling this problem, we will certainly want to know what is the small-signal behavior of the device, and this is, by definition, the linear approximation to the actual system.

The general subject of network analysis, as usually defined, is an example of a linear type of problem. This is true because the elements of the structures being studied are themselves linear, including such things as resistances, capacitors, inductors, and even nonreciprocal elements such as ferrite isolators under small-signal conditions. These elements are closely linear over a very wide range of applied conditions. The range is not infinite. None of them are good for an indefinitely high voltage or unlimited current. But within the range of their usual application, they are linear. In fact, this defines and limits the range of usual application.

On the other hand, if we add an electron beam or a semiconductor diode or varistor to the system, the problem is nonlinear, and may be very nonlinear. However, it is still true that our first question very often is: What happens if an equilibrium state is slightly disturbed? Does the disturbance grow or decay, and how fast? We may want it to grow as in a traveling wave tube, or we may want it to decay as in a control system for which we want stability. But in either case, it is the growth or decay of an infinitesmal disturbance or perturbation that interests us, and this question can usually be expressed as a linear problem.

Matrix algebra is designed primarily for the study of linear problems. It is sometimes useful in nonlinear ones as well, but this is not its primary purpose or application.

We shall assume linearity. We assume either that the system itself is approximately linear or, if not, that it is being perturbed from an equilibrium state so that the problem can be approximated as a linear one.

We shall also generally assume *homogeneity*. That is, we assume that if the independent vector $\mathbf{x}_2$ is the null vector, so is the dependent vector. If it is not, then we subtract the inhomogeneous part of the problem, and reduce it to a homogeneous problem. We can, for example, measure the voltage at port #1 from a reference level such that the meter reads zero when $\mathbf{x}_2$ is null. Likewise, we can offset the current meter appropriately. We can always make $\mathbf{x}_1$ null when $\mathbf{x}_2$ is.

If the 2-port system of Fig. 1 is linear and homogeneous, then the only possible form of the relation between $\mathbf{x}_1$ and $\mathbf{x}_2$ is

$$E_1 = AE_2 + BI_2$$

$$I_1 = CE_2 + DI_2$$

(22)

where A, B, C, and D are independent of E_2 and I_2. Note that we avoid calling them constants. They might be functions of time or some other parameter of the system. But they are not functions of the independent variables E_2 and I_2.

We say that the vector $\mathbf{x}_2$ is *mapped onto* the vector $\mathbf{x}_1$. If $\mathbf{x}_1$ is a vector in the linear vector space S_1, and $\mathbf{x}_2$ any vector in the linear vector space S_2, we say that Eq. (22) *maps S_2 into S_1*. If any vector in S_1 can be obtained by substituting in Eq. (22) some vector in S_2, then we say that Eq. (22) *maps S_2 onto S_1*.

If the system had many ports, some of which were labeled as dependent and some as independent, then we would have more and longer equations of the same type:

$$y_1 = a_{11}x_1 + a_{12}x_2 + \cdots + a_{1n}x_n$$
$$y_2 = a_{21}x_1 + a_{22}x_2 + \cdots + a_{2n}x_n \qquad (23)$$
$$\vdots$$
$$y_m = a_{m1}x_1 + a_{m2}x_2 + \cdots + a_{mn}x_n$$

If the variables are the complex amplitudes of a sinusoidal wave of given frequency—if, e.g., the physically measurable voltage equals the real part of $E \exp j\omega t$, where E is complex—then we must also allow A, B, C, D, or a_{11}, etc., to be complex.

The question now is: What do we wish to do with these equations? If we simply want to calculate the result of E_2 and I_2, or $x_1, ..., x_n$, then these equations are quite adequate.

More often, though, we want something more. Perhaps we want to know if there is *any* signal that the system will, or will not, amplify. Or we want to know the maximum input standing wave ratio for *any* load impedance. Or we have some other question, involving what the system can do for *any* set of values of the independent variables subject, perhaps, to certain constraints. Our interest is in the system, not in the particular values of the variables.

Since the effect of the system is contained in the coefficients of Eq. (22) or (23), we are led to extract the coefficients from the equations. We define what we shall call the *matrix* of the coefficients of Eq. (22):

$$\mathbf{M} = \begin{pmatrix} A & B \\ C & D \end{pmatrix} \qquad (24)$$

or of Eq. (23):

$$\mathbf{A} = \begin{pmatrix} a_{11} & a_{12} & \cdots & a_{1n} \\ a_{21} & a_{22} & \cdots & a_{2n} \\ \vdots & & & \\ a_{m1} & a_{m2} & \cdots & a_{mn} \end{pmatrix} \qquad (25)$$

We shall use boldfaced capital letters for matrices.
We shall also use the symbology

$$\mathbf{A} = (a_{ij}) \qquad (26)$$

to indicate Eq. (25) where, conventionally, the first index indicates the row and the second the column.

The elements on the diagonal running from the top left to the bottom right corner of the matrix of Eq. (25) play a special role, as will become evident later. This set of elements is called the *main diagonal* of **A**. It is the set of elements of the form a_{ii} .

If all elements of a square matrix are zero except those on the main diagonal, the matrix is called *diagonal*. This form is very important because of its extreme simplicity, and we shall have much use for it. We will, on occasion, specify such matrices by writing

$$\mathbf{A} = \text{diag}(a_{11}\,,\,a_{22}\,,\,...,\,a_{nn}) \tag{27}$$

where we simply enumerate the elements on the main diagonal in order from that in the top left corner to the one in the lower right.

The *dimensionality* of a matrix is specified by the two numbers giving its shape. The matrix **A** is called an $m \times n$ (read "m by n") matrix. If **A** is obtained from a system of equations as in Eq. (23), then it operates on the n quantities $(x_1\,,\,...,\,x_n)$ and produces the m quantities $(y_1\,,\,...,\,y_m)$.

We emphasize that a matrix is not a number. This is obvious, but causes confusion. A determinant also is written as an array, but it is a single number. A matrix, however, is a new kind of thing whose display as an array has, itself, significance.

We shall use parentheses, as in Eq. (24) or (25), to indicate a matrix. Other authors use other forms, such as, in the 2×2 case:

$$\begin{bmatrix} A & B \\ C & D \end{bmatrix} \qquad \left\Vert \begin{matrix} A & B \\ C & D \end{matrix} \right\Vert \qquad \begin{array}{c|c} A & B \\ \hline C & D \end{array} \qquad \boxed{\begin{array}{c|c} A & B \\ \hline C & D \end{array}}$$

Parentheses, however, seem to be slowly winning the contest, and we will use them.

Determinants, on the other hand, are almost always indicated by vertical lines, either around the array, or around the symbol for the entire matrix if the determinant is obtained from the matrix. For the 2×2 case, we write, for example,

$$|\mathbf{M}| = \begin{vmatrix} A & B \\ C & D \end{vmatrix} = AD - BC$$

To summarize, we are here concerned with linear homogeneous operators that map one linear vector space onto or into another. It is an operator, in other words, that acts on a vector $\mathbf{x}_2$ in the linear vector space S_2 and yields a vector $\mathbf{x}_1$ in the linear vector space S_1 .

If, we have chosen a particular representation for the two linear vector spaces, then the abstract vectors $\mathbf{x}_1$ and $\mathbf{x}_2$ become particular column arrays. In this case, the operator can be specified by the rectangular array developed from the coefficients of Eq. (22) or (23). This array we call the matrix that is the appropriate representation of the abstract operator.

6. PARTITIONED MATRICES

We will also, on occasion, find it convenient to consider a matrix as being made up of elements that are themselves matrices. We can, for example, write

$$A = \begin{pmatrix} M & R \\ S & N \end{pmatrix} \tag{28}$$

where M is an $m \times m$ matrix and N an $n \times n$ one. R, then, must be a rectangular matrix with dimensions $m \times n$, and S $n \times m$. The whole matrix A is $(m + n) \times (m + n)$.

Such a matrix of matrices is no different from the usual kind, at least not in practice. There is a conceptual difference in that, in Eq. (28), the underlying field is one step further removed. However, we generally bring the form of Eq. (28) back into that of Eq. (25) for computational purposes.

A matrix that is written as a matrix of matrices is said to be *partitioned* as indicated.

If A is square and can be partitioned into the form

$$A = \begin{pmatrix} A_1 & 0 & \cdots & 0 \\ 0 & A_2 & & 0 \\ & & \ddots & \\ 0 & 0 & \cdots & A_k \end{pmatrix} \tag{29}$$

where all the A_i are square, and the zeros indicate the appropriately dimensioned null matrices, then we say that A is *quasidiagonal*. We will, on occasion, write Eg. (29) as

$$A = \text{quasidiag}(A_1, A_2, \cdots, A_k) \tag{30}$$

Such a matrix is an obvious generalization of the class of diagonal matrices. It is an extremely important type of matrix. (See, specifically, Chapter V for the Jordan canonical form.)

We have, so far, implied that the matrices on the diagonal of a partitioned matrix are square. This is by no means necessary, but it does seem to be the most useful case. One exception, however, that is of considerable value is the partitioning of an $m \times n$ matrix into a sequence of $m \times 1$ matrices—i.e., into column vectors:

$$\mathbf{A} = (\mathbf{x}_1, \mathbf{x}_2, \cdots, \mathbf{x}_n) \tag{31}$$

Here, each $\mathbf{x}_i$ is an n-dimensional column vector. The $\mathbf{A}$, in this case, takes on the appearance of a row vector.

Likewise, we can partition $\mathbf{A}$ into a column of row vectors:

$$\mathbf{A} = \begin{pmatrix} \mathbf{y}_1{}^T \\ \mathbf{y}_2{}^T \\ \vdots \\ \mathbf{y}_m{}^T \end{pmatrix} \tag{32}$$

We shall find both of these partitionings useful on occasion.

In general, partitioned matrices can be handled very much as ordinary matrices, providing the dimensionalities both of $\mathbf{A}$ and of the component matrices are appropriate to the operations involved. One exception, however, should be carefully noted. The determinant of the matrix of Eq. (28) cannot, in general, be computed easily from the determinants of the component matrices. It generally must be computed from the original matrix, Eq. (25). (Quasidiagonal matrices form a significant exception to this.)

7. ADDITION OF MATRICES AND SCALAR MULTIPLICATION

To be able to manipulate these things that we call matrices we need certain basic operations. The simplest of these are the addition of two matrices and multiplication times a scalar. We define these two operations in ways that will probably seem thoroughly reasonable:

Definition.   *The sum of* $\mathbf{A} = (a_{ij})$ *and* $\mathbf{B} = (b_{ij})$ *of the same dimensions is the matrix whose terms are the term-by-term sum of the terms of the separate matrices*:

$$\mathbf{A} + \mathbf{B} = \begin{pmatrix} a_{11} + b_{11} & a_{12} + b_{12} & \cdots \\ a_{21} + b_{21} & a_{22} + b_{22} & \cdots \\ & \cdots & \end{pmatrix} \tag{33}$$

Definition.   *The* **product** *of* $\mathbf{A} = (a_{ij})$ *times a scalar* α *is the matrix* $\alpha\mathbf{A} = (\alpha a_{ij})$:

$$\alpha\mathbf{A} = \begin{pmatrix} \alpha a_{11} & \alpha a_{12} & \cdots \\ \alpha a_{21} & \alpha a_{22} & \cdots \\ & \cdots & \end{pmatrix} \tag{34}$$

Both definitions imply a given field.

It may be noted that the addition of matrices is defined only for two matrices of the same shape—i.e., that have both the same number of rows and the same number of columns. It turns out we do not need any more general definition than this.

It follows immediately from the properties of a field that these operations have the same properties that we listed for the addition of two vectors and multiplication of a vector by a scalar.

8. MULTIPLICATION OF A MATRIX TIMES A VECTOR

Given the matrix of Eq. (24) and the vectors defined before, how can we reconstruct Eq. (22)? In the first place, we can say that the 2-port of Fig. 1 *maps* the space of possible x_2's *onto* the space of possible x_1's. The expression "Eq. (22) maps x_2 onto x_1" suggests that we should regard the matrix of Eq. (24) as *operating on* x_2 to produce x_1, which implies some sort of multiplicative process.

This is true since ordinary multiplication can be described as doing just this sort of thing. If $y = 2x$, we can say that y is obtained by "doubling" x, or that x is "operated on" by the operator "twice," or that the space of possible x's is mapped onto the space of possible y's by the operation of doubling.

It is therefore reasonable to write, formally,

$$x_1 = Mx_2 \tag{35}$$

and to call the resultant operation the multiplication of the matrix M times the vector x_2.

But what is this process?

Inspection of Eq. (23) shows what the process is. We see that these equations can be written

$$y_i = \sum_j a_{ij}x_j \tag{36}$$

In other words, the equation

$$y = Ax \tag{37}$$

indicates that the ith component of y is obtained by multiplying term by term the ith row of A by the components of x and adding. For example,

$$\begin{pmatrix} \vdots \\ y_i \\ \vdots \end{pmatrix} = \begin{pmatrix} \vdots & \vdots & & \vdots \\ a_{i1} & a_{i2} & \cdots & a_{in} \\ \vdots & \vdots & & \vdots \end{pmatrix} \begin{pmatrix} x_1 \\ x_2 \\ \vdots \\ x_n \end{pmatrix}$$

$$y_i = a_{i1}x_1 + a_{i2}x_2 + \cdots + a_{in}x_n \tag{38}$$

We may note that the definition has meaning only if the number of columns of **A** is the same as the number of components of **x**—i.e., the dimensionality of **x**. Likewise, the number of rows of **A** must be the same as the dimensionality of **y**.

We find no need for any more general definition.

It can be easily seen that multiplication is distributive with respect to addition of either matrices or vectors:

$$(\mathbf{A} + \mathbf{B})\mathbf{x} = \mathbf{A}\mathbf{x} + \mathbf{B}\mathbf{x}$$
$$\mathbf{A}(\mathbf{x} + \mathbf{y}) = \mathbf{A}\mathbf{x} + \mathbf{B}\mathbf{y} \tag{39}$$

and with respect to multiplication by a scalar:

$$\alpha(\mathbf{A}\mathbf{x}) = (\alpha\mathbf{A})\mathbf{x} = \mathbf{A}(\alpha\mathbf{x}) = (\mathbf{A}\mathbf{x})\alpha \tag{40}$$

However, multiplication of a matrix times a vector is not commutative. In fact, **xA** has, in general, no meaning in matrix analysis. (It can be given a meaning, however, in a form of tensor algebra.)

We indicated before that a vector could be equally well represented as a row array, which we symbolized $\mathbf{x}^T$. We can easily see that Eqs. (23) are equally well obtained by

$$(y_1 \quad y_2 \quad \cdots \quad y_m) = (x_1 \quad x_2 \quad \cdots \quad x_n) \times \begin{pmatrix} a_{11} & a_{21} & \cdots & a_{m1} \\ a_{12} & a_{22} & \cdots & a_{m2} \\ \vdots & \vdots & & \vdots \\ a_{1n} & a_{2n} & \cdots & a_{mn} \end{pmatrix}$$

$$\mathbf{y}^T = \mathbf{x}^T \mathbf{A}^T \tag{41}$$

where the ith component of $\mathbf{y}^T$ is now obtained by multiplying term by term the coefficients of $\mathbf{x}^T$ by the ith column of the matrix and adding:

$$y_i = x_1 a_{i1} + x_2 a_{i2} + \cdots + x_n a_{in} \tag{42}$$

We note that the matrix of Eq. (41) is not the same as that of Eq. (38), and cannot be if we are to obtain Eqs. (23) by the same sort of process. It differs in having corresponding terms on opposite sides of the main diagonal (i.e., the diagonal through a_{11}, a_{22}, etc.) interchanged. The term in the ith row and jth column in Eq. (38) is a_{ij}, but in Eq. (41) it is a_{ji}.

These two matrices are said to be *transposes* of each other. The process may be visualized as "flipping over" around the main diagonal as pivot, or as "reflection on the main diagonal."

If **A** is an $m \times n$ matrix—i.e., m rows, n columns—then $\mathbf{A}^T$ is an $n \times m$ matrix with n rows, m columns.

As suggested by our symbology, a column vector $\mathbf{x}$ can be considered as an $n \times 1$ matrix. Hence, its transpose $\mathbf{x}^T$ is a $1 \times n$ matrix—i.e., a row vector. Hence the symbology of Eq. (2) is consistent.

We note that if we take the transpose of Eq. (37) and compare it to Eq. (41) we must have

$$(\mathbf{Ax})^T = \mathbf{x}^T\mathbf{A}^T \tag{43}$$

Formally, then, the operation of transposition reverses the order of a product. We shall see later that this is generally true.

9. MATRIX MULTIPLICATION

Finally, we come to the problem of defining, usefully, what we mean by the product of two matrices.

We saw that we could interpret the product of a matrix times a vector as the effect of a linear homogeneous operator acting on the vector $\mathbf{x}$. Since the result is a vector $\mathbf{y}$, we can now act on it with another linear homogeneous operator to obtain a third vector $\mathbf{z}$. Since the operators are linear and homogeneous, $\mathbf{z}$ must be a linear homogeneous function of $\mathbf{x}$. Hence $\mathbf{z}$ can be expressed as some matrix times $\mathbf{x}$. It is reasonable to consider this operator as the *product* of the original operators. And it is reasonable to take the appropriate representation of the product of the operators as defining the product of the matrices which are their representations.

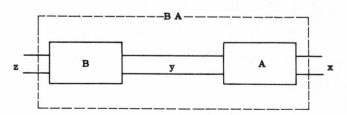

FIG. 2.   Series connection of 2-ports.

Let us consider first the simple system of Fig.2. Let

$$\mathbf{y} = \mathbf{Ax} \tag{44}$$

i.e.,

$$y_1 = a_{11}x_1 + a_{12}x_2$$
$$y_2 = a_{21}x_1 + a_{22}x_2 \tag{45}$$

and

$$\mathbf{z} = \mathbf{By} \tag{46}$$

or

$$z_1 = b_{11}y_1 + b_{12}y_2$$
$$z_2 = b_{21}y_1 + b_{22}y_2 \tag{47}$$

We are not here specifying just what is the basis of the vectors, but we are requiring that the physical situation be described in such a way that the vector $\mathbf{y}$ is written so that it can serve both as the dependent vector of the subsystem $\mathbf{A}$ and as the independent vector of the subsystem $\mathbf{B}$. As an illustration of the pitfall that exists here, we may note that we could have reversed the direction of I_1 in Fig. 1 without changing anything that we have said up to this section. We could have measured the outward flowing currents at both ends. At the middle position of Fig. 2, however, a current flowing outward from $\mathbf{A}$ is flowing inward to $\mathbf{B}$. Hence, the sign of the current component of $\mathbf{y}$ would be incorrect and Eqs. (47) would not represent the physical situation.

As another example, if we are using the basis of Eq. (4), which is sometimes called a wave basis if R is the characteristic impedance, then we must use the same value of R throughout.

Assuming that we have chosen a basis such that we can describe the whole system of Fig. 2 by the two sets of equations (45) and (47), we now wish to express $\mathbf{z}$ in terms of $\mathbf{x}$. Formally,

$$\mathbf{z} = \mathbf{By} = \mathbf{B(Ax)} = \mathbf{(BA)x} \tag{48}$$

Substituting Eqs. (45) into Eq. (47) we obtain

$$z_1 = (b_{11}a_{11} + b_{12}a_{21})x_1 + (b_{11}a_{12} + b_{12}a_{22})x_2$$
$$z_2 = (b_{21}a_{11} + b_{22}a_{21})x_1 + (b_{21}a_{12} + b_{22}a_{22})x_2 \tag{49}$$

More generally, if

$$y_i = \sum_j a_{ij}x_j \tag{50}$$

$$z_i = \sum_j b_{ij}y_j$$

then

$$z_i = \sum_j b_{ij} \left(\sum_k a_{jk}x_k \right)$$

$$= \sum_k \left(\sum_j b_{ij}a_{jk} \right) x_k \tag{51}$$

We therefore define the elements $(\mathbf{BA})_{ij}$ of the product of the two matrices $\mathbf{B}$ and $\mathbf{A}$ to be

$$(\mathbf{BA})_{ij} = \sum_k b_{ik} a_{kj} \tag{52}$$

so that

$$z_i = \sum_j (\mathbf{BA})_{ij} x_j \tag{53}$$

Operationally, we can say that to obtain the ijth term of $\mathbf{BA}$ we multiply term by term the components of the ith row of $\mathbf{B}$ by the jth column of $\mathbf{A}$ and add:

$$\begin{pmatrix} & \vdots & \\ \cdots & c_{ij} & \cdots \\ & \vdots & \end{pmatrix} = \begin{pmatrix} & \vdots & \\ b_{i1} & b_{i2} & \cdots & b_{in} \\ & \vdots & \end{pmatrix} \begin{pmatrix} & a_{1j} & \\ \cdots & a_{2j} & \cdots \\ & \vdots & \\ & a_{nj} & \end{pmatrix}$$

$$c_{ij} = b_{i1} a_{1j} + b_{i2} a_{2j} + \cdots = \sum_k b_{ik} a_{kj}$$

$$\mathbf{C} = \mathbf{BA} \tag{54}$$

For example,

$$\begin{pmatrix} 2 & 3 \\ 4 & 5 \end{pmatrix} \cdot \begin{pmatrix} 6 & 7 \\ 8 & 9 \end{pmatrix} = \begin{pmatrix} 2 \cdot 6 + 3 \cdot 8 & 2 \cdot 7 + 3 \cdot 9 \\ 4 \cdot 6 + 5 \cdot 8 & 4 \cdot 7 + 5 \cdot 9 \end{pmatrix}$$

$$= \begin{pmatrix} 12 + 24 & 14 + 27 \\ 24 + 40 & 28 + 45 \end{pmatrix} = \begin{pmatrix} 36 & 41 \\ 64 & 73 \end{pmatrix}$$

This, then, is the definition of matrix multiplication that is pertinent to this problem. It has meaning only if the number of columns in the first matrix equals the number of rows in the second—i.e., as the product of an $n \times m$ matrix times an $m \times p$ matrix, which then yields an $n \times p$ matrix.

It can be readily verified that multiplication so defined when applicable has all the usual properties of multiplication except commutivity. If we consider, for example, the set of $n \times n$ square matrices so that multiplication is always meaningful, then it is *distributive* with respect to addition from both sides:

1. $$(\mathbf{A} + \mathbf{B})\mathbf{C} = \mathbf{AC} + \mathbf{BC}$$

2. $$\mathbf{A}(\mathbf{B} + \mathbf{C}) = \mathbf{AB} + \mathbf{AC}$$

3. It is *associative*:
    $$\mathbf{A}(\mathbf{BC}) = (\mathbf{AB})\mathbf{C}$$

4. There exists a zero element, called the *null matrix*, such that, for any **A**,

$$0 \cdot \mathbf{A} = \mathbf{A} \cdot 0 = 0$$

which, clearly, is the matrix all of whose terms are zero:

$$0 = \begin{pmatrix} 0 & 0 & 0 & \cdots \\ 0 & 0 & 0 & \cdots \\ \vdots & & & \end{pmatrix}$$

5. There exists a unit element, called the *identity matrix*, such that, for any **A**,

$$\mathbf{IA} = \mathbf{AI} = \mathbf{A}$$

Inspection of Eq. (51) or (54) shows that **I** is the matrix with zeros everywhere except on the main diagonal where it has ones:

$$\mathbf{I} = \begin{pmatrix} 1 & 0 & 0 & 0 & \cdots \\ 0 & 1 & 0 & 0 \\ 0 & 0 & 1 & 0 \\ 0 & 0 & 0 & 1 \\ \vdots & & & \end{pmatrix} = (\delta_{ij}) \tag{55}$$

where δ_{ij} is the so-called Kronecker delta:

$$\begin{aligned} \delta_{ij} &= 0 \qquad \text{if} \quad i \neq j \\ &= 1 \qquad \text{if} \quad i = j \end{aligned} \tag{56}$$

Also, as we would expect, matrix multiplication combines with scalar multiplication and addition.

10. AN ALGEBRA

It is a consequence of the preceding that we say that the set of $n \times n$ matrices "form an algebra under matrix multiplication."

An *algebra* is defined as a set of entities which is a linear vector space and over which a rule of binary combination, a *product relation*, has been defined with respect to which the set forms a ring.[2] In other words,

---

[2] A *ring* is, briefly, a set with addition and multiplication. It differs from a field in that (a) subtraction and division need not be always possible within the ring, (b) multiplication is not necessarily commutative, and (c) it need not have a unit element. For example, the set of all integers is a ring but not a field since division is not always possible. The set of positive numbers is still a ring even though subtraction is not always possible. The set of even integers is a ring even though it contains no unit element.

it is a set that is closed with respect both to linear combination and to the defined product relation.

It may sound strange to call the set of $n \times n$ matrices a linear vector space when we have taken as our standard form for a vector the column matrix. However, we emphasized at the time that this was a choice dictated by convenience only. An $n \times n$ matrix is also "a set of (in this case) n^2 numbers arranged in a definite order." More particularly, if $\mathbf{A}$ and $\mathbf{B}$ are any two $n \times n$ matrices whose coefficients are elements in the field F and α and β are any two scalars of F, then $(\alpha\mathbf{A} + \beta\mathbf{B})$ is also an $n \times n$ matrix formed from F, Therefore, the set of all such matrices fills the definition of a linear vector space.

It is also a ring under matrix multiplication, because, if $\mathbf{A}$ and $\mathbf{B}$ are any matrices of the set, so is $\mathbf{AB}$.

Hence, the set is an algebra.

(Some additional care is needed if one wishes to consider matrices of infinite size. We are restricting ourselves throughout to finitely dimensional entities, however, for which the above is sufficient.)

We should also add that the algebra so defined is an *associative algebra*. We sometimes have occasion to use a product relation that is non-associative, so that $\mathbf{x(yz)} \neq \mathbf{(xy)z}$. We shall see an example of this in Chapter XIII.

Finally, we will remind the student of the fact that a collection of elements in a linear vector space implies that we can choose a basis for that space. One possible basis of the set of all $n \times n$ matrices in the field F is the set of matrices E_{ij} that have 1 as the ij component, and zeros elsewhere. Then, evidently, if $\mathbf{A} = (a_{ij})$ is any $n \times n$ matrix,

$$\mathbf{A} = \sum_{ij} a_{ij}\mathbf{E}_{ij} \tag{57}$$

so that $\mathbf{A}$ has been "expanded on the basis."

Furthermore, the set of $\mathbf{E}_{ij}$ is evidently linearly independent, i.e., there exists no set of scalar c_{ij} not all zero such that

$$\sum_{ij} c_{ij}\mathbf{E}_{ij} = \mathbf{0} \tag{58}$$

We shall have occasion to consider, in Chapter X, other bases that, for many purposes, are much more useful than this.

11. COMMUTATIVITY

As we mentioned previously, matrix multiplication is not, in general, commutative. Obviously, the two matrix factors in a product are treated differently—the rows of the first being multiplied into the columns of the second. We can most easily see that this does, in fact, cause non-commutativity with a specific example:

$$\begin{pmatrix} 0 & 2 \\ 3 & 0 \end{pmatrix}\begin{pmatrix} 5 & 0 \\ 0 & 7 \end{pmatrix} = \begin{pmatrix} 0 & 14 \\ 15 & 0 \end{pmatrix}$$

$$\begin{pmatrix} 5 & 0 \\ 0 & 7 \end{pmatrix}\begin{pmatrix} 0 & 2 \\ 3 & 0 \end{pmatrix} = \begin{pmatrix} 0 & 10 \\ 21 & 0 \end{pmatrix}$$

In this case $\mathbf{AB} \neq \mathbf{BA}$.

As another example, consider the matrix product given on page 21. If we reverse the order of the factors, we obtain

$$\begin{pmatrix} 6 & 7 \\ 8 & 9 \end{pmatrix} \cdot \begin{pmatrix} 2 & 3 \\ 4 & 5 \end{pmatrix} = \begin{pmatrix} 6 \cdot 2 + 7 \cdot 4 & 6 \cdot 3 + 7 \cdot 5 \\ 8 \cdot 2 + 9 \cdot 4 & 8 \cdot 3 + 9 \cdot 5 \end{pmatrix} = \begin{pmatrix} 40 & 53 \\ 52 & 69 \end{pmatrix}$$

which is different from the result obtained before.

This does not say, of course, that the product of two matrices *never* is independent of order, only that it may not be. We shall have occasion, later, to consider the conditions under which matrices do commute. We shall also have occasion to consider sets of $n \times n$ matrices, all pairs of which commute and which therefore form a *commutative subspace* of the linear vector space of all $n \times n$ matrices. An example of such a subspace is the set of all $n \times n$ diagonal matrices—i.e., those whose only nonzero elements are the ones on the main diagonal. Any two such matrices commute. Other less obvious examples can also be found.

Physically, noncommutativity means that the system of Fig. 2 is different if we interchange the blocks—i.e., that it looks different from the two ends. Since this is obviously true unless the circuit is carefully chosen to be symmetric, noncommutativity of matrix multiplication should not be surprising.

We may find noncommutativity disturbing. We are so used to dealing with numbers—i.e., a field—in which multiplication is commutative that it comes as a bit of a shock when we first come up against a non-commutative situation. If, however, we view multiplication as the application of two operations in succession, there is really no reason why we should expect commutativity.

In point of fact, lack of commutativity is not too serious. It does prevent us from doing certain things that can be done with numbers, but a great deal of the manipulative operations of ordinary number theory can be taken over, providing we take care to preserve order. As a simple example, we have already encountered the distributive law, which states that $\mathbf{A}(\mathbf{B} + \mathbf{C})$ equals the sum of $\mathbf{AB}$ and $\mathbf{AC}$, where order has been preserved.

As another example, consider the square of $(\mathbf{A} + \mathbf{B})$. By the square, we mean the product with itself. Hence we see that

$$(\mathbf{A} + \mathbf{B})^2 = (\mathbf{A} + \mathbf{B})(\mathbf{A} + \mathbf{B}) = \mathbf{A}^2 + \mathbf{BA} + \mathbf{AB} + \mathbf{B}^2 \qquad (59)$$

which is different from the usual formula only in that we have no assurance that $\mathbf{BA}$ and $\mathbf{AB}$ are the same.

Noncommutativity requires caution but is, usually, not a major stumbling block.

12. DIVISORS OF ZERO

We should note another property of matrix multiplication that does not have its counterpart in the algebra of ordinary numbers—i.e., that the product of two nonnull matrices may be the null matrix. This can be easily shown by example:

$$\begin{pmatrix} 1 & 0 \\ 0 & 0 \end{pmatrix}\begin{pmatrix} 0 & 0 \\ 1 & 0 \end{pmatrix} = \begin{pmatrix} 0 & 0 \\ 0 & 0 \end{pmatrix}$$

We can even have a nonnull matrix whose square is the null matrix:

$$\begin{pmatrix} 1 & j \\ j & -1 \end{pmatrix}\begin{pmatrix} 1 & j \\ j & -1 \end{pmatrix} = \begin{pmatrix} 0 & 0 \\ 0 & 0 \end{pmatrix}$$

The latter property is described by saying that the matrix is *nilpotent*. It is a property that we shall encounter later (Chapter X).

We must therefore assiduously avoid concluding that because a given matrix expression equals the null matrix, some one of its factors must be null. It need not be true. A comparable pitfall occurs in the product of a matrix and a vector. We see, for example, that

$$\begin{pmatrix} 1 & j \\ j & -1 \end{pmatrix}\begin{pmatrix} 1 \\ j \end{pmatrix} = \begin{pmatrix} 0 \\ 0 \end{pmatrix}$$

We can *not* conclude that because $\mathbf{Ax} = 0$, either $\mathbf{A}$ is the null matrix or $\mathbf{x}$ the null vector.

If, however, $\mathbf{Ax} = 0$ for *any* vector in the space, then it is indeed true that $\mathbf{A}$ must be the null matrix. Or, if the set $\mathbf{x}_i$ is a basis for the space—i.e., a set of linearly independent vectors that span the space—and if $\mathbf{Ax}_i = 0$ for all i, then, again, we can conclude that $\mathbf{A}$ is the null matrix.

13. A MATRIX AS A REPRESENTATION OF AN ABSTRACT OPERATOR

Finally, we observe that the remarks we made on page 4 regarding the distinction between an abstract vector and its representation apply here as well. In Fig. 1, we have specific events happening at ports #1 and #2. The relation between these events is a property of the system, and quite independent of how we choose to describe the system—i.e., independent of the coordinate axes we use to represent the events. We speak of this relation between the physical events as the *abstract operator*. When we choose coordinate axes so that the abstract vectors are represented by column vectors (or other arrays) with specific entries, then, and then only, we obtain a matrix that is a *representation of the abstract operator*.

As an example, the 2-port network of Fig. 1 can be described in many ways. If we relate E_1 and I_1 to E_2 and I_2, then the matrix is called the *ABCD matrix* or the *transmission matrix*, whether the E's and I's are the actual physical voltages or the complex amplitudes. (The names of various matrices are not completely standardized, and some authors use them in different senses than that given here. The student should take care that he knows what the author means. Particularly since not all authors take the care that they should!) The system is then said to be described on an *E-I basis*. If we use vectors such as those of Eq. (4), the matrix is often called the *wave matrix* and the system said to be described on a *wave basis*. The name comes from the interpretation of a component of the form $E + RI$ as the amplitude of a wave traveling to the right in a transmission line with characteristic impedance R. A component of the form $E - RI$ is, then, the amplitude of a wave traveling to the left.

If we use these same components, which we have indicated schematically in Fig. 3, we can make the division into dependent and independent variables differently. In particular, it is sometimes useful to relate the outflowing waves to the inflowing ones, and write

$$\begin{pmatrix} v_1 \\ u_2 \end{pmatrix} = \begin{pmatrix} a & b \\ c & d \end{pmatrix} \begin{pmatrix} v_2 \\ u_1 \end{pmatrix} = \mathbf{S} \begin{pmatrix} v_2 \\ u_1 \end{pmatrix} \tag{60}$$

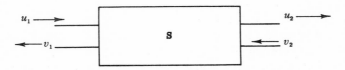

Fig. 3.   Waves at the terminals of a 2-port network.

The matrix of Eq. (60) is called the *scattering matrix* and the system said to be described on a *scattering basis*.

We can also redivide the E's and I's. If we relate E_1 and E_2 to I_1 and I_2, the matrix is called the *impedance matrix*. If we relate I_1 and I_2 to E_1 and E_2, the matrix is the *admittance* matrix.

All of these different matrices describe the same physical situation. They are different ways of saying the same thing. Where the same division of the variables is involved, we say that the different descriptions are different *representations* of the same *abstract operator*. For example, the transmission or $ABCD$ matrix and the wave matrix are such different representations of the same abstract operator. The scattering matrix is not, however, since it involves a different convention regarding which are the independent operators. The boundary conditions that must be applied in this case to fix the situation are different.

We are generally concerned with the properties of the physical system. These properties are properties of the abstract operator and will be true regardless of the particular representation being used. To study such properties, we will need to know how to change from one representation to another, so that we can see if a given property is, in fact, independent of the representation. This is a limited form of the principle of gauge invariance that is so powerful a tool in certain areas of modern physics. We shall discuss this process in detail in Chapter V.

14. OTHER PRODUCT RELATIONS

We have developed the product of two matrices in terms of a particular type of problem—i.e., the analysis of a series connected system such as that shown in Fig. 2. It would be more satisfactory if it could be developed from the postulates (associativity, distributivity with respect to addition, etc.) that we expect a product to obey. This is not possible, however, for a very simple reason. This is not the only way to define a product that will meet these postulates.

In fact, the product we have defined is not even the only kind that is useful. For example, consider a 2-port network described as a scattering matrix as in Eq. (60).

If we connect two such elements in series, we have the system of Fig. 4.

The scattering matrix equations of the two elements are

$$\begin{pmatrix} v_1 \\ u_2 \end{pmatrix} = \begin{pmatrix} a_1 & b_1 \\ c_1 & d_1 \end{pmatrix} \begin{pmatrix} v_2 \\ u_1 \end{pmatrix} \tag{61}$$

$$\begin{pmatrix} v_2 \\ u_3 \end{pmatrix} = \begin{pmatrix} a_2 & b_2 \\ c_2 & d_2 \end{pmatrix} \begin{pmatrix} v_3 \\ u_2 \end{pmatrix} \tag{62}$$

where the order of the components in the vectors is arranged so that the matrix becomes the identity if the element is a simple connection of one port to the other.

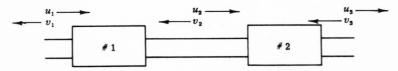

FIG. 4.   Series connection of two 2-port networks.

What we want to find is the scattering matrix of the whole system, i.e., the matrix S such that

$$\binom{v_1}{u_3} = S\binom{v_3}{u_1} \tag{63}$$

The vector on the right of Eq. (61) is not the same as that on the left of Eq. (62). Hence we cannot simply substitute and obtain S as the matrix product. If, however, we write out the four scalar equations symbolized by Eqs. (61) and (62), we can eliminate u_2 and v_2 from them, and write the result in the form of Eq. (63). We obtain

$$S = \frac{1}{1 - b_2 c_1} \begin{pmatrix} a_1 a_2 & b_1 + b_2 \Delta_1 \\ c_2 + c_1 \Delta_2 & d_1 d_2 \end{pmatrix} \tag{64}$$

where Δ_1 and Δ_2 are the determinants (generally unity but not necessarily so if the waves are differently normalized):

$$\Delta_1 = a_1 d_1 - b_1 c_1, \qquad \Delta_2 = a_2 d_2 - b_2 c_2 \tag{65}$$

We define S as the *star product* of the matrices in Eqs. (61) and (62), S_1 and S_2, and write

$$S = S_1 * S_2 \tag{66}$$

It can be shown directly, if tediously, that this rule of binary combination has all the properties we enumerated in Section 9 for a product. It provides a completely satisfactory product, which is, however, quite a different one from that we called "matrix multiplication."

This is intended to illustrate that there is nothing magic about matrix multiplication. It happens to be the product relation that is convenient for most purposes, but it is very far from being the only one that can be used or that may be useful.

The choice of a particular product relation is based wholly on pragmatic considerations. A particular relation is used only if, and when, it fits the particular physical situation.

15. THE INVERSE OF A MATRIX

Before proceeding to the more detailed study of the properties of matrices, we will briefly discuss the problem of inverting a matrix.

Suppose, again, we are considering the circuit of Fig. 1. We have considered, in Eq. (22) and following, the situation when we know what is happening at port #2, and want to discover what is happening at port #1. That is, we took x_2 to be the independent vector, and x_1 the dependent one related to x_2 through the matrix A:

$$x_1 = Ax_2 \qquad (67)$$

Suppose we choose to invert this picture. Suppose we ask how x_2 depends on x_1. Formally, we can write

$$x_2 = A^{-1}x_1 \qquad (68)$$

where A^{-1} is defined as the *inverse* of A.

Formally, then, if we substitute Eq. (67) in to Eq. (68), we find that

$$x_2 = A^{-1}x_1 = A^{-1}(Ax_2) = (A^{-1}A)x_2 \qquad (69)$$

or, if we substitute Eq. (68) in Eq. (67),

$$x_1 = Ax_2 = A(A^{-1}x_1) = (AA^{-1})x_1 \qquad (70)$$

If Eq. (69) is to be true for any x_2, or Eq. (70) for any x_1, it follows that we must have

$$A^{-1}A = AA^{-1} = I \qquad (71)$$

where I is the identity element defined in Eq. (55).

The problem now is whether A^{-1} exists or not; if so, whether it is unique; and, finally, if so, what it is.

Going back to the expressions that lead to defining the matrix in the first place, Eqs. (22) and (23), the problem is to solve Eq. (22) for E_2 and I_2 in terms of E_1 and I_1, or Eq. (23) for $x_1, ..., x_n$, in terms of $y_1, ..., y_n$ where we are now assuming that $m = n$. These are sets of linear inhomogeneous simultaneous equations. Equation (23), for example, is a set of n such equations in the n unknowns $x_1, ..., x_n$.

From elementary algebra, we know that if the set, y_1, ..., y_n are not all zero, Eq. (23) is uniquely soluble for the unknowns x_1, ..., x_n *if and only if* the determinent of the coefficients does not vanish:

$$| \mathbf{A} | = \begin{vmatrix} a_{11} & a_{12} & \cdots & a_{1n} \\ \vdots & \vdots & & \vdots \\ a_{n1} & a_{n2} & \cdots & a_{nn} \end{vmatrix} \neq 0 \tag{72}$$

Further, we know that the solution can be obtained from the cofactors of the terms of the original equations. Specifically, we know that

$$\mathbf{A}^{-1} = \left(\frac{A_{ji}}{| \mathbf{A} |} \right) \tag{73}$$

where A_{ij} is the cofactor, or algebraic complement, of the ijth term of $\mathbf{A}$. That is, to determine the jith term of A^{-1}, we eliminate the ith row and jth column from the determinant, multiply by -1 if $i + j$ is odd, or by $+1$ if $i + j$ is even, and divide by $| \mathbf{A} |$. Note, however, the transposition that occurs here. The ij term of $\mathbf{A}^{-1}$ is determined by the jith cofactor, not the ijth.

In particular, if

$$\mathbf{A} = \begin{pmatrix} A & B \\ C & D \end{pmatrix}$$

as in Eq. (22), then

$$\mathbf{A}^{-1} = \frac{1}{(AD - BC)} \begin{pmatrix} D & -B \\ -C & A \end{pmatrix} \tag{74}$$

We have the following definition:

Definition. *A square matrix* $\mathbf{A}$ *is* **singular** *if its determinant is zero. It is* **nonsingular** *if its determinant is not zero.*

We also have the following:

Theorem. *Given a nonsingular square matrix* $\mathbf{A}$, *its inverse exists uniquely. Furthermore, its left inverse is the same as its right.*

The rigorous derivation of this theorem would carry us too far into the postulational foundations of abstract algebra. We shall therefore simply rest on the arguments already given. It should be noted, however, that those arguments depend entirely on the properties of the fields involved. Matrices can be constructed from other elements, however, including noncommutative operators. The question of whether or when the theorem applies to such matrices we will leave open.

The second statement of the theorem, that the left inverse equals the right inverse, has already been proven in Eq. (71).

From elementary algebra, we know that the product of two determinants $| a_{ij} |$ and $| b_{ij} |$ is given by

$$| a_{ij} | \cdot | b_{ij} | = \left| \sum_k a_{ik} b_{kj} \right| \tag{75}$$

The correspondence of this to Eq. (54) for matrix multiplication is evident. Hence, it follows that the determinant of the matrix product of two determinants $\mathbf{A}$ and $\mathbf{B}$ is the product of their determinants:

$$| \mathbf{AB} | = | \mathbf{A} | \cdot | \mathbf{B} | \tag{76}$$

This, of course, may not be, and in general will not be, true of any other product relation than the matrix multiplication defined by Eq. (54).

From Eq. (76), it follows that if $\mathbf{A}$ and $\mathbf{B}$ are nonsingular, so is $\mathbf{AB}$. Conversely, if $\mathbf{AB}$ is nonsingular, so is each factor. By induction, these statements are true for any number of factors.

We have the following theorem:

Theorem. *If* $\mathbf{A}$, $\mathbf{B}$, $\mathbf{C}$, *etc., are* $n \times n$ *square matrices, all of which are nonsingular, then the inverse of the product* $(\mathbf{ABC} \cdots)$ *is the product of the inverses in reverse order.*

For, let

$$\mathbf{X} = (\mathbf{ABC} \cdots)^{-1} \tag{77}$$

This means that

$$(\mathbf{ABC} \cdots)\mathbf{X} = \mathbf{I} \tag{78}$$

Premultiplying, first by $\mathbf{A}^{-1}$, then by $\mathbf{B}^{-1}$, then by $\mathbf{C}^{-1}$, etc., we find that

$$\mathbf{X} = \cdots \mathbf{C}^{-1}\mathbf{B}^{-1}\mathbf{A}^{-1} \tag{79}$$

16. RANK OF A MATRIX

Suppose we have an $n \times n$ matrix $\mathbf{A}$. We say that its *rank* is k if there exists in $\mathbf{A}$ a nonzero minor of size $k \times k$, but no larger one. That is, we are able to strike out $(n - k)$ rows and columns of $\mathbf{A}$ in such a way that the resulting $k \times k$ matrix is nonsingular, and so has a nonzero determinant; and we are not able to obtain a nonsingular matrix by striking out any smaller number of rows and columns.

A nonsingular matrix which is $n \times n$ has rank n. If the rank of $\mathbf{A}$ is less than n, then it is singular, and the quantity $(n - k)$ is a measure of the degree of singularity involved.

17. GAUSS'S ALGORITHM[3]

Section 15 and, in particular, Eq. (73), gives a way whereby the inverse of any nonsingular matrix can be obtained. It is not, however, a practical method for inverting a matrix of any reasonable size, since it then requires the calculation of a large number of determinants.

A better method, and one suitable for either hand or machine calculation, is given by Gauss's algorithm. To be precise, this algorithm does not give, directly, the inverse of $\mathbf{A}$, although the inverse can be obtained from it. What it does, instead, is solve the equation

$$\mathbf{Ax} = \mathbf{y} \tag{80}$$

for $\mathbf{x}$, given any suitable $\mathbf{y}$.

We consider the set of equations given in Eq. (23). If $a_{11} = 0$, then there must be some equation in which the coefficient of $x_1 \neq 0$. We relabel the equations to bring this equation to the first position. Hence, we can assume that $a_{11} \neq 0$ without loss of generality.

We use the first equation to eliminate x_1 from all other equations. In particular, to eliminate the x_1 term from the ith equation $(i \neq 1)$, we subtract from the ith equation (a_{i1}/a_{11}) times the first equation. We are left with the system of equations

$$a_{11}x_1 + a_{12}x_2 + a_{13}x_3 + \cdots + a_{1n}x_n = y_1$$
$$b_{22}x_2 + b_{23}x_3 + \cdots + b_{2n}x_n = y_2'$$
$$\vdots$$
$$b_{n2}x_2 + b_{n3}x_3 + \cdots + b_{nn}x_n = y_n' \tag{81}$$

where the b's are the new coefficients so found and the y_i' are given by

$$y_i' = y_i - a_{i1}y_1/a_{11}$$

---

[3] An *algorithm* is a procedure whereby a desired result can be obtained in a finite number of computable steps. The term is usually restricted, however, to procedures that are practical for at least computer calculation.

We can now repeat the process. If all of the b_{n2} vanish, so that x_2 does not occur in any but the first equation, then we can relabel the x's so that at least some equation has a nonvanishing x_2 term, and we can relabel the equations so that this equation is in the second row. Hence, unless all of the b's are zero, we can always relabel things so that $b_{22} \neq 0$. We can then use the second equation to remove x_2 from all the later equations.

We continue the process to exhaustion. If the process does not terminate at some intermediate step, we end with the set of equations

$$
\begin{aligned}
a_{11}x_1 + a_{12}x_2 + a_{13}x_3 + \cdots + a_{1n}x_n &= y_1 \\
b_{22}x_2 + b_{23}x_3 + \cdots + b_{2n}x_n &= y_2' \\
c_{33}x_3 + \cdots + c_{3n}x_n &= y_3'' \\
&\vdots \\
f_{nn}x_n &= y_n^{(n-1)}
\end{aligned}
\tag{82}
$$

In matrix terms, we can write this as

$$
\begin{pmatrix}
a_{11} & a_{12} & a_{13} & \cdots & a_{1n} \\
0 & b_{22} & b_{23} & \cdots & b_{2n} \\
0 & 0 & c_{33} & \cdots & c_{3n} \\
\vdots & \vdots & \vdots & & \vdots \\
0 & 0 & 0 & \cdots & f_{nn}
\end{pmatrix}
\begin{pmatrix}
x_1 \\
x_2 \\
x_3 \\
\vdots \\
x_n
\end{pmatrix}
=
\begin{pmatrix}
y_1 \\
y_2' \\
y_3'' \\
\vdots \\
y_n^{(n-1)}
\end{pmatrix}
\tag{83}
$$

where the coefficients of the matrix are known, and the coefficients in the vector on the right-hand side are also known. Further, the coefficients on the main diagonal are nonzero.

A matrix of this form—i.e., in which all the coefficients below the main diagonal are zero—is called *upper triangular*. It is quite an important form since, as we have shown, here, any matrix can be put into this form. (Gauss's algorithm can be interpreted as the selection of an appropriate set of axes, and therefore as a change of the basis for the representation. We shall return to this point later.)

Equation (83) allows us to solve for **x**, given any **y**. We take the last row, and observe that

$$
x_n = y_n^{(n-1)}/f_{nn}
$$

which we can do since $f_{nn} \neq 0$. We then take the next to the last row, and use the x_n obtained to solve for x_{n-1}, and so on, up the whole set of equations. We find that the only requirement that must be satisfied to let us do this is that all the elements on the main diagonal shall be nonzero. Since we know they are nonzero, we have obtained a solution for any $\mathbf{y}$.

We can use this algorithm to find explicitly $\mathbf{A}^{-1}$. Suppose we define $\mathbf{y}_1$ as the vector all of whose components except the ith are zero and whose ith component is one. Let us use Gauss's algorithm to calculate $\mathbf{x}_i$ as the solution of

$$\mathbf{A}\mathbf{x}_i = \mathbf{y}_i \tag{84}$$

for all i from 1 to n. It is easy to see that $\mathbf{A}^{-1}$ is the matrix whose ith column is $\mathbf{x}_i$.

In the above, we slipped over one important point. It may happen that the process terminates before it has been repeated the full number of times. We then end up with an equation, for example, of the form

$$\begin{pmatrix} a_{11} & a_{12} & a_{13} & a_{14} \\ 0 & b_{22} & b_{23} & b_{24} \\ 0 & 0 & 0 & 0 \\ 0 & 0 & 0 & 0 \end{pmatrix} \begin{pmatrix} x_1 \\ x_2 \\ x_3 \\ x_4 \end{pmatrix} = \begin{pmatrix} y_1 \\ y_2' \\ y_3'' \\ y_4''' \end{pmatrix} \tag{85}$$

The matrix is still upper triangular but the terms on the main diagonal become zero after a while, and when they do, all the terms in that row and all following rows vanish. Evidently, then, we cannot solve for the vector $\mathbf{x}$ for an arbitrary $\mathbf{y}$. Specifically, in the case given in Eq. (85), for a solution to exist, we must have $y_3'' = y_4''' = 0$.

It is easy to see that the separate steps of the algorithm do not change the value of the determinant of the matrix. It is also easy to see that the determinant of any upper triangular matrix is simply the product of the elements on the main diagonal. Hence, if $\mathbf{A}$ is nonsingular, and so has a nonzero determinant, it follows that Gauss's algorithm cannot terminate prematurely.

The case of Eq. (85) is therefore seen to be the situation when $\mathbf{A}$ is singular. In this case, Eq. (85) has a solution for $\mathbf{x}$ only if $\mathbf{y}$ is in an appropriate subspace. We shall return to this problem in greater detail in Chapter XII.

There are modifications and developments of Gauss's algorithm and other procedures of somewhat similar nature that have been developed for the efficient calculation of inverses of large matrices. The design of such programs is an important discipline in its own right, and is beyond the scope of this book. Our purpose here is to show that such procedures are possible, and to show some of the properties of the end result. It can be said that Gauss's algorithm is not usually the most efficient method known for such calculations. It is, however, an important theoretical tool, and we shall have occasion to refer to its form in later chapters.

18. 2-PORT NETWORKS

We will close this chapter with a brief discussion of 2-port ladder networks. This is a matter of considerable practical interest because of the importance of such systems. It may be said that it is never necessary to use matrix algebra for their analysis. They are simple enough to be handled by ordinary algebra.

It should also be said that matrix algebra will not, in general, reduce the labor of calculation. The same number of multiplications, and so forth, must be performed. But matrix algebra does provide a systematization and standardization of procedure that can be quite useful in avoiding wasted motion and, perhaps, reducing error.

We consider, first, a general ladder network as shown in Fig. 5. We

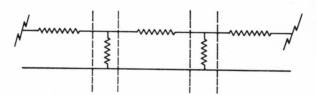

FIG. 5.   Partition of a ladder network.

note that it can be broken up into units that are connected in precisely the manner of Fig. 2.

It is convenient, therefore, to have a list of the basic units that may be used to construct the ladder. Such a list may be easily constructed from knowledge of the behavior of the units. For example, a series resistance has the equations

$$E_i = E_o + RI_o$$
$$I_i = I_o$$

which we may write as

$$\begin{pmatrix} E \\ I \end{pmatrix}_i = \begin{pmatrix} 1 & R \\ 0 & 1 \end{pmatrix} \begin{pmatrix} E \\ I \end{pmatrix}_o$$

In similar manner we find all of the elements of Table I.

TABLE I

TRANSMISSION MATRIX OF BASIC 2-PORT ELEMENTS ON $\binom{E}{I} e^{j\omega t}$ BASIS

Element	Matrix
Series impedance	$\begin{pmatrix} 1 & Z \\ 0 & 1 \end{pmatrix}$
Shunt admittance	$\begin{pmatrix} 1 & 0 \\ Y & 1 \end{pmatrix}$
Transmission line Characteristic impedance Z Electrical length φ	$\begin{pmatrix} \cos\varphi & jZ\sin\varphi \\ \dfrac{j}{Z}\sin\varphi & \cos\varphi \end{pmatrix}$
Waveguide below cutoff Characteristic impedance jX Electrical length $j\Gamma$	$\begin{pmatrix} \cosh\Gamma & jX\sinh\Gamma \\ \dfrac{-j}{X}\sinh\Gamma & \cosh\Gamma \end{pmatrix}$
Transformer	$\begin{pmatrix} \dfrac{L_1}{M} & \dfrac{j\omega(L_1L_2 - M^2)}{M} \\ \dfrac{-j}{\omega M} & \dfrac{L_2}{M} \end{pmatrix}$

Three properties of these matrices may be noted as being convenient for checking results of the calculations using the matrices.

1. The determinant of the transmission matrix of any passive reciprocal ladder network is unity. This is true of the elementary matrices listed in Table I, and by Eq. (76) is therefore true of any ladder network composed of such elements. This fact can also be deduced

directly from reciprocity. In a nonreciprocal network, the determinant still has unit magnitude, but in general is complex.

2. The transmission matrix of any symmetrical network (i.e., one that can be changed end for end without changing the system) has identical elements on the main diagonal. For, if

$$\begin{pmatrix} E_1 \\ I_1 \end{pmatrix} = \begin{pmatrix} A & B \\ C & D \end{pmatrix} \begin{pmatrix} E_2 \\ I_2 \end{pmatrix}$$

or

$$E_1 = AE_2 + BI_2$$
$$I_1 = CE_2 + DI_2$$

then, since the determinant $(AD - BC)$ is unity,

$$E_2 = DE_1 - BI_1$$
$$I_2 = -CE_1 + AI_1$$

or

$$\begin{pmatrix} E_2 \\ I_2 \end{pmatrix} = \begin{pmatrix} D & -B \\ -C & A \end{pmatrix} \begin{pmatrix} E_1 \\ I_1 \end{pmatrix}$$

However, this is not quite equivalent to changing the circuit end for end. To make it equivalent, we must change the signs of I_1 and I_2 (see Fig. 1):

$$\begin{pmatrix} E_2 \\ -I_2 \end{pmatrix} = \begin{pmatrix} D & B \\ C & A \end{pmatrix} \begin{pmatrix} E_1 \\ -I_1 \end{pmatrix}$$

For this to be identical to the original matrix, we must have $A = D$.

3. If the network is passive lossless, the diagonal terms are real and all other terms are pure imaginary. This is true of the matrices of the elements listed in Table I. It is easy to show that if it is true of **A** and **B**, then it is true of **AB**. It can also be proven directly from comparison of the real power flow ($\frac{1}{2}\{EI^* + E^*I\}$) at the input and output, combined with the fact that the determinant is unity.

19. EXAMPLE

As a simple example, let us consider the transformations that can be made with a single T section, consisting of a series impedance Z_1 followed by a shunt admittance Y, followed by a series impedance Z_2. Then from Table I:

$$\begin{pmatrix} E \\ I \end{pmatrix}_i = \begin{pmatrix} 1 & Z_1 \\ 0 & 1 \end{pmatrix} \times \begin{pmatrix} 1 & 0 \\ Y & 1 \end{pmatrix} \times \begin{pmatrix} 1 & Z_2 \\ 0 & 1 \end{pmatrix} \times \begin{pmatrix} E \\ I \end{pmatrix}_o$$

$$= \begin{pmatrix} 1 & Z_1 \\ 0 & 1 \end{pmatrix} \times \begin{pmatrix} 1 & Z_2 \\ Y & 1 + YZ_2 \end{pmatrix} \times \begin{pmatrix} E \\ I \end{pmatrix}_o$$

$$= \begin{pmatrix} 1 + YZ_1 & Z_1 + Z_2 + YZ_1Z_2 \\ Y & 1 + YZ_2 \end{pmatrix} \times \begin{pmatrix} E \\ -I \end{pmatrix}_o$$

The determinant of the matrix can be easily seen to be unity. If $Z_1 = Z_2$, the T section is symmetrical and the diagonal terms are equal. Finally, if the section is lossless, then Z_1, Z_2, and Y are pure imaginary quantities. In this case the diagonal terms are real and the contradiagonal terms are pure imaginary.

Exercises

1. Which of the following sets of vectors are linearly independent over the field of real numbers?

(a)   col(1, 2, 3);   col(4, 8, 11)
(b)   col(4, −2, −6);   col(6, −3, 9)
(c)   col(1, −3, 2);   col(5, −2, −3);   col(3, −4, 1)
(d)   col(5, 4, 3);   col(3, 3, 2);   col(8, 1, 3)
(e)   col(4, −5, 2, 6);   col(2, −2, 0, 3);   col(0, −1, 2, 0)
(f)   col(3, 4, −1, 2);   col(2, 1, −4, −2);   col(−1, 0, −1, 2)

2. Let E_n be an n-dimensional euclidean space with cartesian axes. Which of the following sets of vectors are subspaces?

(a)   All vectors whose components are integers.
(b)   All vectors in the xy-plane.
(c)   All vectors lying along either the x-axis or the y-axis.
(d)   All vectors whose end points lie on a straight line through the origin.
(e)   All vectors whose end points lie on a straight line that does not pass through the origin.
(f)   All vectors whose components, $x_1, x_2, ..., x_n$, satisfy the relation:

$$x_1 + x_2 + \cdots + x_n = 0$$

(g)   All vectors whose components satisfy the relation:

$$x_1 + x_2 + \cdots + x_n = 1$$

3. Which of the following sets of vectors form subspaces over the field of complex numbers?

(a) All n-dimensional vectors whose even-numbered components vanish.

(b) All n-dimensional vectors whose even-numbered components are equal.

(c) All n-dimensional vectors whose even-numbered components are equal to unity.

(d) All n-dimensional vectors of the form

$$\mathbf{x} = \mathrm{col}(a, b, c, a, b, c, a, \ldots)$$

where a, b, c, are arbitrary complex numbers.

(e) The same as (d) except a, b, c are arbitrary real numbers.

4. By the *sum* of two sets of vectors S_1 and S_2, we mean the set of all vectors which are the sum of a vector in S_1 and a vector in S_2. By the *union* of S_1 and S_2, we mean the set of all vectors that are in either S_1 or S_2, or possibly in both. By the *intersection* of S_1 and S_2, we mean the set of all vectors that are simultaneously in both S_1 and S_2.

If S_1 and S_2 are subspaces over a given field, which of these new sets—sum, union, and intersection—are subspaces?

5. Let

$$\mathbf{A} = \begin{pmatrix} 1+j & 2j \\ 3j & 1-j \end{pmatrix}, \qquad \mathbf{B} = \begin{pmatrix} 1-j & -j \\ j & 1+j \end{pmatrix}$$

Find $\mathbf{AB}$ and $\mathbf{BA}$. Verify that $|\mathbf{AB}|$ and $|\mathbf{BA}|$ are the product of $|\mathbf{A}|$ and $|\mathbf{B}|$.

6. Find all matrices constructed from the field of complex numbers that commute with

$$\mathbf{A} = \begin{pmatrix} 0 & 1 \\ 1 & 0 \end{pmatrix}$$

7. Find all matrices that commute with

$$\mathbf{A} = \begin{pmatrix} 0 & 0 & 1 \\ 0 & 1 & 0 \\ 1 & 0 & 0 \end{pmatrix}$$

8. Find the general expressions for the nth power of

$$\mathbf{A} = \begin{pmatrix} a & 1 \\ 0 & a \end{pmatrix} \quad \text{and} \quad \mathbf{A} = \begin{pmatrix} a & 1 & 0 \\ 0 & a & 1 \\ 0 & 0 & a \end{pmatrix}$$

Prove their validity by induction.

9.   Find the inverses of

(a)
$$\mathbf{A} = \begin{pmatrix} 1 & -1 & 1 & -1 \\ 0 & -1 & 2 & -3 \\ 0 & 0 & 1 & -3 \\ 0 & 0 & 0 & -1 \end{pmatrix}$$

(b)
$$\mathbf{A} = \begin{pmatrix} 2 & 2 & 3 \\ 1 & -1 & 0 \\ -1 & 2 & 1 \end{pmatrix}$$

(c)
$$\mathbf{A} = \begin{pmatrix} a & 1 & 0 & 0 \\ 0 & a & 1 & 0 \\ 0 & 0 & a & 1 \\ 0 & 0 & 0 & a \end{pmatrix}$$

10.   Verify Eq. (64) for the star product.

11.   Determine the transmission matrix of the symmetric 2-port network:

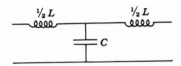

12.   Show that the form given by

$$\mathbf{A} = \begin{pmatrix} a & b \\ -b & a \end{pmatrix}$$

is preserved under matrix multiplication. That is, show that if **A** and **B** are of this form, so is (**AB**). Show that matrices of this form, with a and b real, can be used as a representation of the complex numbers, $(a + jb)$.

(This constancy of form is described by saying that the set of all matrices of this type form a *semigroup* under matrix multiplication, or that they *have the group property*. If we exclude the case where a and b are both zero, and restrict ourselves to real a and b, then they form a *group*, since every member of the set has an inverse in the set, and the set contains the identity when $a = 1$, $b = 0$.)

13.   Show that the set of matrices of the form

$$\mathbf{A} = \begin{pmatrix} a + jb & c + jd \\ -c + jd & a - jb \end{pmatrix}$$

are a semigroup under matrix multiplication. Show that, in general, **AB** $\neq$ **BA** for matrices of this type.

14. Show by example that we can have matrices $\mathbf{A}$ and $\mathbf{B}$ such that $\mathbf{A}^n$ and $\mathbf{B}^n$, with n a positive integer, converge to a limit as n goes to infinity, while $(\mathbf{AB})^n$ diverges.

15. Use Gauss's Algorithm to find that the inverse of

$$\mathbf{A} = \begin{pmatrix} a & b \\ c & d \end{pmatrix}$$

is

$$\mathbf{A}^{-1} = \frac{1}{\Delta} \begin{pmatrix} d & -b \\ -c & a \end{pmatrix}$$

where

$$\Delta = ad - bc$$

assuming Δ and a are not zero. Verify the result, both as a left inverse and as a right inverse.

16. Let P_n be the $(n + 1)$-dimensional space of all polynomials in the variable x, of degree less than or equal to n. Let D be the differentiation operator, d/dx. Find the matrix representation of D on the basis 1, $x, x^2, \ldots, x^n$.

17. Let $\mathbf{A}, \mathbf{B}, \mathbf{C}$, and $\mathbf{D}$ be $n \times n$ matrices. Let $(\mathbf{A} + \mathbf{B})$ and $(\mathbf{A} - \mathbf{B})$ be nonsingular. Show that there exist matrices $\mathbf{X}$ and $\mathbf{Y}$ such that

$$\mathbf{AX} + \mathbf{BY} = \mathbf{C}$$

$$\mathbf{BX} + \mathbf{AY} = \mathbf{D}$$

Find explicit expressions for $\mathbf{X}$ and $\mathbf{Y}$.

18. Consider a $2n \times 2n$ matrix $\mathbf{M}$, which can be partitioned into

$$\mathbf{M} = \begin{pmatrix} \mathbf{A} & \mathbf{B} \\ \mathbf{C} & \mathbf{D} \end{pmatrix}$$

where $\mathbf{A}, \mathbf{B}, \mathbf{C}$, and $\mathbf{D}$ are $n \times n$ matrices, all of which are nonsingular. Obtain the inverse of $\mathbf{M}$ as

$$\mathbf{M}^{-1} = \begin{pmatrix} (\mathbf{A} - \mathbf{BD}^{-1}\mathbf{C})^{-1} & (\mathbf{C} - \mathbf{DB}^{-1}\mathbf{A})^{-1} \\ (\mathbf{B} - \mathbf{AC}^{-1}\mathbf{D})^{-1} & (\mathbf{D} - \mathbf{CA}^{-1}\mathbf{B})^{-1} \end{pmatrix}$$

providing the inverses exist.

19. Let $\mathbf{M}$ be a $2n \times 2n$ matrix partitioned into $n \times n$ matrices:

$$\mathbf{M} = \begin{pmatrix} \mathbf{A} & \mathbf{B} \\ \mathbf{C} & \mathbf{D} \end{pmatrix}$$

where $\mathbf{D}$ is nonsingular and $\mathbf{D}$ and $\mathbf{C}$ commute. Show that

$$|\mathbf{M}| = |\mathbf{AD} - \mathbf{BC}|$$

(*Hint*: Postmultiply by

$$\begin{pmatrix} \mathbf{I} & \mathbf{0} \\ \mathbf{X} & \mathbf{I} \end{pmatrix}$$

where $\mathbf{X}$ is suitably chosen.)

CHAPTER II

The Inner Product

In defining an abstract vector, we noted that there was no *a priori* meaning given to the concept of length or to the concept of the angle between two vectors. In a vector such as that indicated in Eq. (3) of the previous chapter, what is its length, if the first component is 2 volts and the second 3 amp? Obviously, we do not know until we find some way to define what the question means.

Yet, the concepts of length and direction are useful. It is only when length has been defined that we can justify even such a simple concept as saying that a vector is "small," or that we know what we mean by a neighborhood of a point (so that our space becomes a *topological space*). It is only when we have defined direction that we can ask whether two vectors are orthogonal—i.e., perpendicular. These are very important concepts for the practical analysis of problems.

In this chapter, we shall develop the concept of measure in a linear vector space.

1. UNITARY INNER PRODUCT

We have defined a vector as the column matrix of its components which may be complex numbers:

$$\mathbf{x} = \begin{pmatrix} x_1 \\ x_2 \\ \vdots \\ x_n \end{pmatrix} \tag{1}$$

If this were a vector in ordinary 3-space expressed in terms of cartesian coordinates, we would have as its length the square root of the sum of the squares of its components. It is this concept that we wish to generalize in a useful way.

That $\mathbf{x}$ may have more than 3 components presents no problems. We would simply add the squares of all components.

A slightly more substantive problem is presented by the fact that we are allowing the components to be complex numbers. If we simply added their squares, the result would, in general, be a complex number, which seems a violation of what we want in a quantity that is to be identified as the "square of the length."

To avoid this difficulty, we therefore add not the squares of the components but the squares of their magnitudes:

$$\| \mathbf{x} \| = \left\{ \sum_i x_i{}^* x_i \right\}^{1/2} \tag{2}$$

where by $\| \mathbf{x} \|$ we mean the "length of $\mathbf{x}$", and the asterisk denotes the complex conjugate.

The question is not whether Eq. (2) is "right," since there is no right or wrong until we define our terms, but whether it is reasonable in terms of what we intuitively expect of a length, and whether it is useful for a particular problem.

That it is reasonable follows from consideration of what we expect of a length. In particular, we see that, according to Eq. (2), $\| \mathbf{x} \|$ is always a nonnegative real number. It is, furthermore, zero only if all x_i are zero so that the vector is a null vector. It is small, i.e., $< \epsilon$, only if all components are small, i.e., all x_i are such that $| x_i |$ is at least $< \epsilon$. Finally, if we double all the components, or multiply them by any scalar α, we double the length, or multiply it by α. So Eq. (2) does fit what we expect of a length.

As to whether or not it is useful depends on the problem.

Equation (2) suggests that if we have two vectors, $\mathbf{x}$ and $\mathbf{y}$, in the same linear vector space,

$$\mathbf{x} = \begin{pmatrix} x_1 \\ x_2 \\ \cdot \\ \cdot \\ \cdot \\ x_n \end{pmatrix} \qquad \mathbf{y} = \begin{pmatrix} y_1 \\ y_2 \\ \cdot \\ \cdot \\ \cdot \\ y_3 \end{pmatrix}$$

we should consider the form[1]

$$\langle \mathbf{x}, \mathbf{y} \rangle = \sum_i x_i{}^* y_i \tag{3}$$

so that, when $\mathbf{y} = \mathbf{x}$, we get the square of the length defined by Eq. (2).

$$\| \mathbf{x} \| = \langle \mathbf{x}, \mathbf{x} \rangle^{1/2} \tag{4}$$

We call the form of Eq. (3) the *inner product* of $\mathbf{x}$ and $\mathbf{y}$.

[1] Many authors use $\sum x_i y_i{}^*$. We prefer the form given above since it somewhat simplifies symbology that we shall introduce in the next section. The distinction is trivial, however, providing one is careful to note which form is being used.

We shall use the symbols $\langle \rangle$ generally to indicate an inner product, although not necessarily the specific relation of Eq. (3) since we shall soon introduce a more general inner product relation.

To consider the meaning of this, let us consider two vectors $\mathbf{x}$ and $\mathbf{y}$, of length x and y, in ordinary 2-space, where $\mathbf{x}$ is at an angle α to the #1 axis and $\mathbf{y}$ at an angle β, as in Fig. 1. Then

$$x_1 = x \cos \alpha, \qquad y_1 = y \cos \beta$$
$$x_2 = x \sin \alpha, \qquad y_2 = y \sin \beta \tag{5}$$

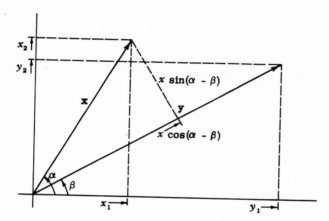

FIG. 1.   The unitary inner product of two real vectors.

and

$$\langle \mathbf{x}, \mathbf{y} \rangle = x_1 y_1 + x_2 y_2 = xy(\cos \alpha \cos \beta + \sin \alpha \sin \beta)$$
$$= xy \cos(\alpha - \beta) \tag{6}$$

Hence, in this case, $\langle \mathbf{x}, \mathbf{y} \rangle$ can be interpreted as the projection of $\mathbf{x}$ on $\mathbf{y}$, times $\mathbf{y}^*$, or, alternatively, the projection of $\mathbf{y}$ on $\mathbf{x}$, times $\mathbf{x}^*$. In terms of vector analysis, it is the dot product of $\mathbf{x}$ and $\mathbf{y}$.

We generalize what we mean by "projection of one vector on another" so that we can take over this geometric concept.

We say that Eq. (3) defines the *unitary inner product relation* and that this definition defines the space as the *unitary space* or *U-space* or U_n. We also note that Eq. (3) permits us to define the angle φ, between $\mathbf{x}$ and $\mathbf{y}$ by the relation

$$\cos \varphi = \frac{\langle \mathbf{x}, \mathbf{y} \rangle}{\langle \mathbf{x}, \mathbf{x} \rangle^{1/2} \langle \mathbf{y}, \mathbf{y} \rangle^{1/2}} \tag{7}$$

as a generalization of Eq. (6).

This does not lead to φ being always real, since $\langle x, y \rangle$ may not be real. However, since we are dealing with complex vectors, it is perhaps not surprising that complex angles arise. We shall see, however, that if $\mathbf{x}$ and $\mathbf{y}$ are real vectors, then φ is a real angle, as we might reasonably demand.

As an alternative definition, we can set

$$\cos^2 \varphi' = \frac{|\langle \mathbf{x}, \mathbf{y} \rangle|^2}{\langle \mathbf{x}, \mathbf{x} \rangle \langle \mathbf{y}, \mathbf{y} \rangle} \tag{8}$$

This is sometimes done, and results in an angle that is always real. Which equation is used, Eq. (7) or (8), is a matter of convenience in the particular application.

Before proceeding further, let us observe some important properties of the inner product relation of Eq. (3). We have, in particular, the following:

$$\langle \mathbf{x}, \mathbf{x} \rangle \geqslant 0 \tag{9}$$

the equality holding only if $\mathbf{x}$ is the null vector. Also we have

$$\langle \mathbf{x}, \mathbf{y} \rangle = \langle \mathbf{y}, \mathbf{x} \rangle^* \tag{10}$$

Scalar multiplication of the second factor simply multiplies the product:

$$\langle \mathbf{x}, a\mathbf{y} \rangle = a \langle \mathbf{x}, \mathbf{y} \rangle$$

The inner product of $\mathbf{x}$ and the sum of $\mathbf{u}$ and $\mathbf{v}$ are the sum of the inner products of $\mathbf{x}$ and $\mathbf{u}$ and $\mathbf{v}$, as we would expect of a generalization of the dot product:

$$\langle \mathbf{x}, \mathbf{u} + \mathbf{v} \rangle = \langle \mathbf{x}, \mathbf{u} \rangle + \langle \mathbf{x}, \mathbf{v} \rangle$$

These last two properties can be combined into the single equation

$$\langle \mathbf{x}, a\mathbf{u} + b\mathbf{v} \rangle = a \langle \mathbf{x}, \mathbf{u} \rangle + b \langle \mathbf{x}, \mathbf{v} \rangle \tag{11}$$

which we describe by saying that the inner product is *linear in the second factor*.

Note that the combination of Eqs. (10) and (11) gives us the equation

$$\langle a\mathbf{u} + b\mathbf{v}, \mathbf{x} \rangle = a^* \langle \mathbf{u}, \mathbf{x} \rangle + b^* \langle \mathbf{v}, \mathbf{x} \rangle$$

This relation is described by saying that the inner product is *antilinear* in the first factor. It is sometimes loosely called linear. However, the appearance of the complex conjugates of the scalar factors is significant.

We shall, in Chapter XIV, have occasion to consider a product relation that is truly linear in both factors. This we shall call a *scalar product* to avoid ambiguity in the term *inner product*.

From these properties, we can now obtain the very important *Cauchy-Schwartz inequality*:

Theorem. *Given the inner product relation of Eq.* (3), *then for any* **x** *and* **y**

$$|\langle \mathbf{x}, \mathbf{y} \rangle|^2 \leqslant \langle \mathbf{x}, \mathbf{x} \rangle \langle \mathbf{y}, \mathbf{y} \rangle \tag{12}$$

If either **x** or **y** is the null vector, then Eq. (12) is clearly true since it reduces to zero equals zero. Assume neither is null, so that

$$\langle \mathbf{x}, \mathbf{x} \rangle \neq 0, \qquad \langle \mathbf{y}, \mathbf{y} \rangle \neq 0$$

Then the theorem can be proven by considering the inner product with itself of $(a\mathbf{x} + b\mathbf{y})$:

$$\langle (a\mathbf{x} + b\mathbf{y}), (a\mathbf{x} + b\mathbf{y}) \rangle = |a|^2 \langle \mathbf{x}, \mathbf{x} \rangle + |b|^2 \langle \mathbf{y}, \mathbf{y} \rangle$$
$$+ ab^* \langle \mathbf{y}, \mathbf{x} \rangle + a^* b \langle \mathbf{x}, \mathbf{y} \rangle \geqslant 0 \tag{13}$$

which is real and nonnegative by Eq. (9). If, now, we set

$$a = \langle \mathbf{y}, \mathbf{y} \rangle, \qquad b = -\langle \mathbf{x}, \mathbf{y} \rangle^* = -\langle \mathbf{y}, \mathbf{x} \rangle$$
$$b^* = -\langle \mathbf{x}, \mathbf{y} \rangle \quad = -\langle \mathbf{y}, \mathbf{x} \rangle^*$$

then Eq. (15) becomes

$$\langle \mathbf{y}, \mathbf{y} \rangle^2 \langle \mathbf{x}, \mathbf{x} \rangle + |\langle \mathbf{x}, \mathbf{y} \rangle|^2 \langle \mathbf{y}, \mathbf{y} \rangle - \langle \mathbf{y}, \mathbf{y} \rangle |\langle \mathbf{x}, \mathbf{y}|^2 - \langle \mathbf{y}, \mathbf{y} \rangle |\langle \mathbf{x}, \mathbf{y} \rangle|^2 \geqslant 0 \tag{14}$$

Since $\langle \mathbf{y}, \mathbf{y} \rangle \neq 0$, and is real and positive, it can be factored out without changing the inequality, and Eq. (12) follows.

From this we can obtain the *Triangle inequality*, so-called because it is a generalization of the statement that any one side of a triangle is not greater than the sum of the other two sides.

Theorem. *Given the inner product relation of Eq.* (3), *then for any* **x** *and* **y**

$$\langle (\mathbf{x} + \mathbf{y}), (\mathbf{x} + \mathbf{y}) \rangle^{1/2} \leqslant \langle \mathbf{x}, \mathbf{x} \rangle^{1/2} + \langle \mathbf{y}, \mathbf{y} \rangle^{1/2} \tag{15}$$

To prove this, consider Eq. (13) with $a = b = 1$:

$$\langle (\mathbf{x} + \mathbf{y}), (\mathbf{x} + \mathbf{y}) \rangle = \langle \mathbf{x}, \mathbf{x} \rangle + \langle \mathbf{y}, \mathbf{y} \rangle + \langle \mathbf{x}, \mathbf{y} \rangle + \langle \mathbf{x}, \mathbf{y} \rangle^*$$
$$\leqslant \langle \mathbf{x}, \mathbf{x} \rangle + \langle \mathbf{y}, \mathbf{y} \rangle + 2|\langle \mathbf{x}, \mathbf{y} \rangle|$$
$$\leqslant \langle \mathbf{x}, \mathbf{x} \rangle + \langle \mathbf{y}, \mathbf{y} \rangle + 2\langle \mathbf{x}, \mathbf{x} \rangle^{1/2} \langle \mathbf{y}, \mathbf{y} \rangle^{1/2} \tag{16}$$

from Eq. (12). Hence

$$\langle(\mathbf{x}+\mathbf{y}),(\mathbf{x}+\mathbf{y})\rangle \leqslant \{\langle\mathbf{x},\mathbf{x}\rangle^{1/2}+\langle\mathbf{y},\mathbf{y}\rangle^{1/2}\}^2 \tag{17}$$

and the theorem follows.

From the Cauchy-Schwartz inequality, it follows, in either Eq. (7) or (8), that $|\cos\varphi|$ is always less than, or at most equal to, unity. Hence it is reasonable to call φ or φ' an angle.

2. ALTERNATIVE REPRESENTATION OF UNITARY INNER PRODUCT

We can simplify our symbology if we make use of the alternative representation of a vector that we have in Eq. (2) of Chapter I as a row vector:

$$\mathbf{x}^T = (x_1 \quad x_2 \quad \cdots \quad x_n) \tag{18}$$

where the superscript T indicates the transpose.

Using this symbol, then, we can write Eq. (3) as

$$\langle\mathbf{x},\mathbf{y}\rangle = \sum x_i{}^*y_i = \mathbf{x}^{*T}\mathbf{y} \tag{19}$$

involving the usual matrix multiplication.

To simplify this further, we will use a dagger ($\dagger$) to indicate the complex conjugate transpose of the vector:

$$\mathbf{x}^\dagger = \mathbf{x}^{*T} = (x_1{}^* \quad x_2{}^* \quad \cdots \quad x_n{}^*) \tag{20}$$

This is an operation that is of sufficient importance so that it has been given its own name. We call $\mathbf{x}^\dagger$ the *hermitian conjugate* of $\mathbf{x}$. It is also applied to matrices. If

$$\mathbf{A} = \begin{pmatrix} a_{11} & a_{12} & a_{13} & \cdots \\ a_{21} & a_{22} & \cdots & \\ a_{31} & \cdots & & \end{pmatrix} \tag{21}$$

then

$$\mathbf{A}^\dagger = \mathbf{A}^{*T} = \begin{pmatrix} a_{11}^* & a_{21}^* & a_{31}^* & \cdots \\ a_{12}^* & a_{22}^* & \cdots & \\ a_{13}^* & \cdots & & \end{pmatrix} \tag{22}$$

$\mathbf{A}^\dagger$ is, then, the *hermitian conjugate* of $\mathbf{A}$. We shall have considerable use for this operation later. Using this symbol, Eq. (3) or (19) becomes

$$\langle\mathbf{x},\mathbf{y}\rangle = \mathbf{x}^\dagger\mathbf{y} \tag{23}$$

We shall use both the bracket symbol and $\mathbf{x}^\dagger\mathbf{y}$, depending on whether or not we wish to emphasize that the expression of Eq. (23) is an inner product.

3. GENERAL (PROPER) INNER PRODUCT

We can now summarize the basic properties that we have used to test whether or not the unitary inner product was "reasonable," and then see if there is a more general form that also has these properties.

So that $\langle \mathbf{x}, \mathbf{x} \rangle$ shall be interpretable as the square of a length, we required that

(A) $\langle \mathbf{x}, \mathbf{x} \rangle$ real and nonnegative for all $\mathbf{x}$
(B) $\langle \mathbf{x}, \mathbf{x} \rangle = 0$ if and only if $\mathbf{x} = \mathbf{0}$

So that $\langle \mathbf{x}, \mathbf{y} \rangle$ shall condense to the above as $\mathbf{y}$ becomes $\mathbf{x}$, we require

(C) $\langle \mathbf{x}, \mathbf{y} \rangle = \langle \mathbf{y}, \mathbf{x} \rangle^*$

Finally, so that the operation shall be linear, we require that

(D) $\langle \mathbf{x}, \alpha\mathbf{y} + \beta\mathbf{z} \rangle = \alpha\langle \mathbf{x}, \mathbf{y} \rangle + \beta\langle \mathbf{x}, \mathbf{z} \rangle$ (but see footnote, page 44).

These are the four properties that we demand so that the relation shall be interpretable in a reasonable fashion as an inner product. They carry over directly from Eqs. (9)–(11).

The relation of Eq. (3) is not the only one that fits these postulates. In fact, consider the form

$$\langle \mathbf{x}, \mathbf{y} \rangle = \mathbf{x}^\dagger\mathbf{K}\mathbf{y} \tag{24}$$

where $\mathbf{K}$ is a matrix.

Property (D) follows automatically from the properties of multiplication of a matrix times a vector (cf. Chapter I, Section 8).

For property (C), we want

$$\mathbf{x}^\dagger\mathbf{K}\mathbf{y} = (\mathbf{y}^\dagger\mathbf{K}\mathbf{x})^* \tag{25}$$

or, if the coefficients of $\mathbf{K}$ are k_{ij} ,

$$\sum x_i^* k_{ij} y_j = \left\{ \sum_{ij} y_i^* k_{ij} x_j \right\}^*$$

$$= \sum_{ij} y_i k_{ij}^* x_j^* \tag{26}$$

or, reversing the i, j symbols on the right,

$$\sum_{ij} x_i{}^* k_{ij} y_j = \sum x_i{}^* k_{ji}^* y_j \tag{27}$$

Since this must be true for all **x** and **y**, evidently we must have

$$k_{ij} = k_{ji}^* \tag{28}$$

or

$$\mathbf{K} = \mathbf{K}^\dagger \tag{29}$$

This property is sufficiently important to be given a name:

Definition.   *A square matrix* **K** *such that it equals its hermitian conjugate* ($\mathbf{K} = \mathbf{K}^\dagger$) *is called* **hermitian**.

It is evident that the hermitian nature of **K** is sufficient to assure that $\langle \mathbf{x}, \mathbf{x} \rangle$ is real. It is also necessary if this is to be true for all **x**. We shall have a good deal more to say later about hermitian matrices.

Properties (A) and (B) may or may not hold. We label these properties by the definition:

Definition.   *A square hermitian matrix* **K** *is* **positive definite** *if, for* **all x** *except the null vector,*

$$\mathbf{x}^\dagger \mathbf{K} \mathbf{x} > 0 \tag{30}$$

It is **positive semidefinite** *or* **nonnegative definite** *if, for* **all x** *except the null vector,*

$$\mathbf{x}^\dagger \mathbf{K} \mathbf{x} \geqslant 0 \tag{31}$$

Similarly for *negative definite* and *negative semidefinite* or *nonpositive definite*. If none of these criteria apply for *all* **x**, then **K** is said to be *indefinite*.

Particular note should be made of the fact that the definitions specify what happens for any **x** (of the proper dimensionality, of course).

We shall later develop tests for positive definitness. For the moment, we will simply note that if Eq. (24) is to be a (proper) inner product relation, it is necessary and sufficient that **K** be hermitian and positive definite.

We have inserted in the above the word "proper." Usually, no other kind is considered. However, we shall find it of great value, later, to relax the definition and permit the **K** of Eq. (24) to have a somewhat wider scope. (Specifically, we shall allow $\mathbf{K}$ to be indefinite, thus violating properties (A) and (B).) It is in anticipation of this development that we use the term *proper* in violation of normal usage.

The unitary inner product of the previous section, Eq. (23), is a special case of this more general form of proper inner product, obtained by setting $\mathbf{K} = \mathbf{I}$, the identity matrix.

We call $\mathbf{K}$ the *metric* of the space. We can, of course, define several different metrics on a space, each generating its own inner product relation.

The derivation of the Cauchy-Schwartz and the Triangle inequalities that we gave in the preceding section for the unitary inner product did not depend on the particular definition of the unitary inner product, but rather on the properties that we stated abstractly in Eqs. (9), (10), and (11), which became properties (A)–(D) of the general proper inner product. Hence the inequalities apply with any proper inner product (but not, we add, with an improper inner product).

A linear vector space with an inner product relation having properties (A)–(D) is a *Hilbert space*. The term is more general than we need since it also includes spaces with infinite dimensionality under some additional constraints to ensure convergence.

An expression of the form

$$s(\mathbf{x}) = \mathbf{x}^\dagger \mathbf{S} \mathbf{x} = \sum_{ij} x_i^* x_j S_{ij} \tag{32}$$

is called a *quadratic form* in the variables x_i. It describes a scalar function of the variables, the dependence being the sum of terms which are quadratic in the variables involved. If $\mathbf{S}$ is hermitian ($\mathbf{S}^\dagger = \mathbf{S}$) so that $s(\mathbf{x})$ is real for any set of values of the complex variables x_i, then it is a *hermitian quadratic form*. An inner product relation defines the square of the length of a vector as a hermitian quadratic form. Such forms, however, are used for other purposes as well, some of which we will discuss later.

4. EUCLIDEAN INNER PRODUCT

In defining the unitary inner product and its generalization with a hermitian metric, we have implicitly assumed that we were dealing with the field of complex numbers. This will usually be true in the physical problems that concern us here, but there are exceptions—for example, in stress-strain theory.

If we are dealing with the field of real numbers, the obvious way to define the equivalent of Eq. (3) is

$$\langle \mathbf{x}, \mathbf{y} \rangle = \sum_i x_i y_i = \mathbf{x}^T \mathbf{y} \tag{33}$$

This form is called the *euclidean inner product relation*, and a linear vector space over which this inner product relation has been defined is a *euclidean space*, or *E-space*, or E_n.

The generalization of this that is the equivalent of Eq. (24) is

$$\langle \mathbf{x}, \mathbf{y} \rangle = \mathbf{x}^T \mathbf{S} \mathbf{y} \tag{34}$$

where $\mathbf{S}$ is a real symmetric positive definite matrix. By *symmetric*, we mean that $\mathbf{S}^T = \mathbf{S}$, so that if $\mathbf{S} = (s_{ij})$, then $s_{ij} = s_{ji}$.

If S is the linear vector space of n-dimensional vectors with real components over the field of real numbers, and $\mathbf{x}$ and $\mathbf{y}$ are any vectors in S, then the inner product relation of Eq. (34) has the following properties:

(A') $\quad \langle \mathbf{x}, \mathbf{x} \rangle$ is real and nonnegative for all $\mathbf{x}$.
(B') $\quad \langle \mathbf{x}, \mathbf{x} \rangle = 0$ if and only if $\mathbf{x} = \mathbf{0}$.
(C') $\quad \langle \mathbf{x}, \mathbf{y} \rangle = \langle \mathbf{y}, \mathbf{x} \rangle$ so that the relation is symmetric in the factors.
(D') $\quad \langle \mathbf{x}, a\mathbf{y} + b\mathbf{z} \rangle = a\langle \mathbf{x}, \mathbf{y} \rangle + b\langle \mathbf{x}, \mathbf{z} \rangle$.

The combination of (C') and (D') shows that the relation is linear in both factors.

One may ask why we bother to define this type of relation as a new thing. After all, the relation of Eq. (3) reduces to that of Eq. (33), and Eq. (24) to that of Eq. (34) if we constrain the components of $\mathbf{x}$, $\mathbf{y}$, etc., to be real.

There are two reasons for introducing a seperate definition. Firstly, there is an important conceptual difference. We have pointed out that the inner product relation of Eq. (3) or (24) is antilinear in the first factor, while that of Eq. (33) or (34) is linear in both. If, for example, we wish to develop the consequences of an inner product relation from the postulates (A)–(D), or from (A')–(D') this distinction makes an important difference.

More practically, we have pointed out that there are, in fact, two fields involved—the field from which the components of the vectors are obtained, and the field over which we form the linear vector space. The discussion so far has assumed that the same field is being used in both roles. This is usually the case, but not always. We can, for example, have vectors whose components are complex, but in a linear vector space that is closed for linear combinations with real coefficients. If so, the two types of inner product relations may give quite different answers.

As a simple example, consider the linear vector space of all vectors of the form

$$\mathbf{x} = \begin{pmatrix} a + jb \\ a - jb \end{pmatrix}$$

where a and b are real and the magnitude of a is constrained to be greater than that of b. [The constraint is necessary to make the relation of Eq. (33) positive definite.]

The inner products of Eqs. (3) and (33) then give us

$$x^\dagger y = 2(a_1 a_2 + b_1 b_2)$$

$$x^T y = 2(a_1 a_2 - b_1 b_2)$$

so that they are not the same. (We could find a $\mathbf{K}$ that would give the same answer as $\mathbf{x}^T \mathbf{y}$, but the point is that we have to start from scratch to find the equivalent $\mathbf{K}$.)

Thus the two types of inner product relations can lead to substantive differences, even though they do not in the commonest situation when only a single field is used in both roles.

5. SKEW AXES

The use of a $\mathbf{K}$ other than the identity can be interpreted as the representation of a vector in terms of skew axes.

Consider, for example, a two-dimensional vector $\mathbf{x}$ in ordinary (euclidean) space, as in Fig. 2. If we consider axes that make an angle φ with each other, then on these axes the components of the vector are x_1 and x_2, which we will assume to be real. On a cartesian basis, however, the components are a and b, where

$$a = x_1 + x_2 \cos \varphi$$

$$b = x_2 \sin \varphi$$

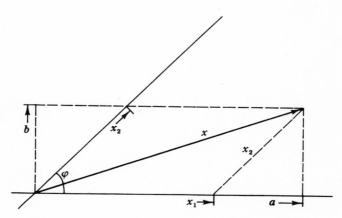

FIG. 2.   Skew axes in two-dimensional euclidean space.

The length of $\mathbf{x}$, l is then given by

$$l^2 = a^2 + b^2 = x_1^2 + 2x_1x_2 \cos \varphi + x_2^2$$

$$= (x_1 \quad x_2)\begin{pmatrix} 1 & \cos \varphi \\ \cos \varphi & 1 \end{pmatrix}\begin{pmatrix} x_1 \\ x_2 \end{pmatrix} \tag{35}$$

so that we can describe the metric of the skew axes as

$$\mathbf{K} = \begin{pmatrix} 1 & \cos \varphi \\ \cos \varphi & 1 \end{pmatrix} \tag{36}$$

There is an ambiguity here as to how one should divide the cross product term between the two corresponding terms of the $\mathbf{K}$. The ambiguity is resolved by the requirement that $\mathbf{K}$ should be hermitian if the field is complex, or symmetric if it is real.

Thus the use of skew axes leads to an inner product relation that is different from the unitary one.

It can be shown that any (proper) inner product can be considered as the result of imposing skew axes on a euclidean or unitary space. We shall later discuss how the metric, among other things, transforms as we change coordinate axes. It is always possible, by proper choice of the axes, to transform any (proper) inner product relation to the unitary one.

If this is so, then we might wonder why we bother with the more general inner product relation. Indeed, for mathematical purposes it serves only a limited purpose. However, for application purposes, skewed axes can be very useful. It may very well happen that other aspects of the system being investigated are made much simpler by using appropriately skewed axes. We may, in other words, be able to trade complexity in the representation for simplicity in the problem. This may be a useful thing to do.

More importantly, we often have no measure at all given to us *a priori*. We have emphasized that in vectors such as Eq. (3) of Chapter I, giving the state at one port of a network, we have no *a priori* measure defined. We have the axes established, but we have no way of knowing whether they are skewed or not. We have freedom to choose whatever metric is convenient to us. When we do so, we will very likely find that the convenient metric happens not to be one that makes the defined axes cartesian. We must be able to handle all sorts of odd metrics which may be appropriate to the problem even if not the simplest, mathematically.

As an example, consider a 2-port network described on an *E-I* basis, as in Eq. (3), Chapter I. If we wish to consider, instead of all such networks, only those networks that are lossless, then we might naturally consider a metric such that the square of the length of a vector describes the net real power flow through the port. Then we can describe the lossless property by saying that the length of the response vector must equal the length of the driving vector, or that the operator describing the behavior of the network is, in some appropriate sense, a *rotational* one.

The metric that does this is

$$\mathbf{K} = \frac{1}{2} \begin{pmatrix} 0 & 1 \\ 1 & 0 \end{pmatrix} \tag{37}$$

so that

$$\langle \mathbf{x}, \mathbf{x} \rangle = \mathbf{x}^\dagger \mathbf{K} \mathbf{x} = \tfrac{1}{2}(E^*I + EI^*) \tag{38}$$

This happens to be an improper inner product since, as we shall see later, the $\mathbf{K}$ that is used here is not positive definite. This fact introduces some complications which we will discuss in Chapter IX. It is introduced here only as an illustration of the way in which the physical problem can lead to the use of a particular metric.

As a more complex example, consider a transmission line whose inductance, or capacity or both, per unit length varies with time at a frequency f_p. We are, in other words, considering a paramteric line, linearized by assuming that the pump signal is so much stronger than the signal frequency that the network is unaffected by the presence of the signal frequency. If the input signal is at f_0, the circuit will generate *parametric harmonics* at $f_n = f_0 + nf_p$, where $n = 0, \pm1, \pm2, \dots$. We must be careful to retain the correct sign on the various f_n.

The linearized Manley-Rowe relation applies providing the line is nondissipative. It requires that the reduced power S, given by

$$S = \sum_n (E_n{}^*I_n + E_nI_n{}^*)/f_n \tag{39}$$

shall be constant, where E_n and I_n are the complex amplitudes of the components of voltage and current at f_n. We can express this by defining the subvectors

$$\mathbf{e} = \mathrm{col}(\dots E_{-1}, E_0, E_1, \dots)$$
$$\mathbf{i} = \mathrm{col}(\dots I_{-1}, I_0, I_1, \dots) \tag{40}$$

and the matrix

$$\mathbf{P} = \mathrm{diag}(\dots 1/f_{-1}, 1/f_0, 1/f_1, \dots) \tag{41}$$

We now define the vector

$$\mathbf{x} = \begin{pmatrix} \mathbf{e} \\ \mathbf{i} \end{pmatrix} \tag{42}$$

and the metric

$$\mathbf{K} = \begin{pmatrix} \mathbf{0} & \mathbf{P} \\ \mathbf{P} & \mathbf{0} \end{pmatrix} \tag{43}$$

The linearized Manley-Rowe relation of Eq. (39) is then expressed by the invariance, with z, of

$$S = \mathbf{x}^{\dagger}\mathbf{K}\mathbf{x} = (\mathbf{e}^{\dagger}, \mathbf{i}^{\dagger}) \begin{pmatrix} \mathbf{0} & \mathbf{P} \\ \mathbf{P} & \mathbf{0} \end{pmatrix} \begin{pmatrix} \mathbf{e} \\ \mathbf{i} \end{pmatrix} \tag{44}$$

The vectors, and $\mathbf{K}$, are, in this case, infinitely dimensional. However, if the initial excitation is at a single frequency and the line is not unduly long, only the components in the parametric harmonics of lower order are significant. Hence we can approximate the infinitely dimensional case by a finitely dimensional one.

What is essentially the same mathematical problem, leading to the same metric, arises in certain quantum mechanical problems where we require the conservation of the number of photons involved, even though the photons may have different energies, and hence different frequencies.

6. ORTHOGONALITY

One of the principal uses of a metric is that of defining what we mean by orthogonality.

Definition. *Given an inner product relation defined by the metric* $\mathbf{K}$, *two vectors* $\mathbf{x}$ *and* $\mathbf{y}$ *are* **orthogonal**, *or precisely,* **K-orthogonal**, *when*

$$\langle \mathbf{x}, \mathbf{y} \rangle = \mathbf{x}^{\dagger}\mathbf{K}\mathbf{y} = 0$$

By Eq. (7) or (8) this condition makes $\cos \varphi = 0$, so that $\varphi = 90°$. Hence this definition is a generalization of the geometric concept of perpendicularity.

For sets of vectors, we make the following definition:

Definition. *Given an inner product relation defined by the metric* $\mathbf{K}$, *the set of vectors* $\mathbf{u}_i$ *is said to be* **orthogonal**, *or better,* **K-orthogonal**, *when*

$$\langle \mathbf{u}_i, \mathbf{u}_j \rangle = \mathbf{u}_i^{\dagger}\mathbf{K}\mathbf{u}_j = 0 \qquad if \quad i \neq j \tag{45}$$

so that each pair of vectors is K-orthogonal.

Clearly, if we are using n-dimensional vectors, we cannot have more than n vectors in an orthogonal set. In fact, given a k-dimensional subspace there cannot be more than k vectors in an orthogonal set that is contained within the subspace.

The value of the property of orthogonality is that it leads to great simplification of many problems. For example, suppose we have a complete set of linearly independent vectors $\mathbf{u}_i$. We shall not consider here where these vectors come from except to say that the problem often suggests a set of vectors that are the "natural" basis for analysis. Then, by the definition of completeness, any vector $\mathbf{x}$ can be expressed as a linear combination of these vectors:

$$\mathbf{x} = \sum_i a_i \mathbf{u}_i \tag{46}$$

Since $\mathbf{x}$ has n components, this leads to n equations in the n unknowns a_i. In principle we can always solve for the a_i. (The linear independence of the set $\mathbf{u}_i$ assures that the determinant of the components of the set does not vanish. Hence, Eq. (46) is always soluble.) But this can be a monstrous task if n is large.

Suppose we have a $\mathbf{K}$ in terms of which the set $\mathbf{u}_i$ are orthogonal. If we multiply Eq. (46) by $\mathbf{u}_k{}^\dagger\mathbf{K}$, where k takes each value $1, \dots, n$ in turn, we obtain the n equations

$$\mathbf{u}_k{}^\dagger\mathbf{K}\mathbf{x} = \sum_i a_i \mathbf{u}_k{}^\dagger\mathbf{K}\mathbf{u}_i \tag{47}$$

If the set were not K-orthogonal, Eq. (47) would be just as difficult to solve, in general, as Eq. (46). If it is K-orthogonal, however, the only nonvanishing term on the right is that for which $i = k$. Hence, we have, explicitly, that

$$a_k = (\mathbf{u}_k{}^\dagger\mathbf{K}\mathbf{x})/(\mathbf{u}_k{}^\dagger\mathbf{K}\mathbf{u}_k) \tag{48}$$

and Eq. (46) becomes

$$\mathbf{x} = \sum_i \frac{(\mathbf{u}_i{}^\dagger\mathbf{K}\mathbf{x})\mathbf{u}_i}{(\mathbf{u}_i{}^\dagger\mathbf{K}\mathbf{u}_i)} \tag{49}$$

where the scalar terms in parentheses can be calculated directly.

This is one example of the immense power of orthogonality to simplify calculation. We shall encounter many more as we progress. It is, in fact, probably not an overstatement to say that orthogonality is the single most important property for the practical employment of matrix algebra.

For theoretic purposes, it is not needed. Equation (46) can, in principle, be solved without further manipulation. But for the practical solution of problems, orthogonality is almost a necessity.

7. NORMALIZATION

In the previous section we considered a set of vectors $\mathbf{u}_i$ in terms of which an arbitrary vector $\mathbf{x}$ was expressed. We saw that K-orthogonality was of great practical importance in accomplishing this.

We can achieve a further simplification of the results by adjusting properly the length of the individual vectors.

Suppose we replace $\mathbf{u}_i$ by $\mathbf{v}_i$, connected by the nonzero scalar factor α_i:

$$\mathbf{v}_i = \alpha_i \mathbf{u}_i \tag{50}$$

Then

$$\mathbf{v}_i{}^\dagger \mathbf{K} \mathbf{v}_j = \alpha_i{}^* \alpha_j \mathbf{u}_i{}^\dagger \mathbf{K} \mathbf{u}_j$$
$$= 0 \qquad\qquad \neq j$$
$$= |\alpha_i|^2 \mathbf{u}_i{}^\dagger \mathbf{K} \mathbf{u}_i, \qquad i = j \tag{51}$$

Hence, we have not changed the K-orthogonality relations. If, now, we set

$$\alpha_i = 1/(\mathbf{u}_i{}^\dagger \mathbf{K} \mathbf{u}_i)^{1/2} \tag{52}$$

which we can do since $\mathbf{u}_i{}^\dagger \mathbf{K} \mathbf{u}_i \neq 0$ and is positive (property (B)), then

$$\mathbf{v}_i{}^\dagger \mathbf{K} \mathbf{v}_j = \delta_{ij} \tag{53}$$

where δ_{ij} is the Kronecker delta, and equals 1 if $i = j$, 0 if $i \neq j$.

The set $\mathbf{v}_i$ is then said to be *normalized*—more properly, *K-normalized*. Since it is also K-orthogonal we call it *orthonormal* or *K-orthonormal*.

To put the matter formally:

Definition. *Given an inner product relation defined by the metric* $\mathbf{K}$, *a vector* $\mathbf{x}$ *is* K-**normalized** *if*

$$\mathbf{x}^\dagger \mathbf{K} \mathbf{x} = 1 \tag{54}$$

and:

Definition. *Given an inner product relation defined by the metric* $\mathbf{K}$, *a set of vectors* $\mathbf{u}_i$ *is* K-**orthonormal** *if*

$$\mathbf{u}_i{}^\dagger \mathbf{K} \mathbf{u}_j = \delta_{ij} \tag{55}$$

If the set $\mathbf{u}_i$ is K-orthonormal, then Eq. (49) expressing $\mathbf{x}$ as an expansion over this set becomes

$$\mathbf{x} = \sum_i (\mathbf{u}_i{}^\dagger \mathbf{Kx})\mathbf{u}_i \qquad (56)$$

We should note two things about such an orthonormal set. First, by properties (A) and (B), $\mathbf{u}_i{}^\dagger \mathbf{Ku}_i$ is always real and positive. Hence α_i *can* always be taken as real.

However, we should also note that α_i *need not* be taken as real. Specifically, we can multiply it by $\exp(j\varphi_i)$, where φ_i is any real number, without changing the K-orthonormality of the resultant set $\mathbf{u}_i$. Hence K-normalization is not unique, but defines the set of vectors only within arbitrary phase constants.

This ambiguity is usually of no importance, but occasionally can be used to advantage for other purposes.

8. GRAM-SCHMIDT PROCESS

We have not said anything about the source of the set $\mathbf{u}_i$. This depends, of course, on the particular problem involved, and cannot be answered in general. Certain types of problems will be discussed later, and we shall see that there are often vectors that are inherently reasonable candidates for this role.

Often, however, the set is not completely determined by the problem. We may only be able to say that we want to use vectors that are in some subspace, but nothing more. We are then faced with the problem of determining a particular set within this subspace that is K-orthonormal.

To determine such a particular set, we use what is known as the *Gram-Schmidt process.*

Suppose we are given, or have found, a set of linearly independent vectors $\mathbf{u}_1$, $\mathbf{u}_2$ ..., $\mathbf{u}_k$ that span the k-dimensional subspace. We want to obtain from these a set, $\mathbf{v}_i$, that are K-orthogonal and also span the subspace.

The process of orthogonalization and normalization can be combined, but it is not necessary or usually convenient to do so.

We choose any one of the known vectors, say $\mathbf{u}_1$, and identify it with $\mathbf{v}_1$:

$$\mathbf{v}_1 = \mathbf{u}_1 \qquad (57)$$

We then take any other vector, say $\mathbf{u}_2$, which is linearly independent of $\mathbf{u}_1$ and form the vector

$$\mathbf{v}_2 = \mathbf{u}_2 + a_{11}\mathbf{u} \qquad (58)$$

This vector is still linearly independent of u_1 providing a_{11} is finite. We want to so chose a_{11} that v_2 will be K-orthogonal to v_1,

$$\langle v_1 v_2 \rangle = \langle u_1 u_2 \rangle + a_{11}\langle u_1 u_1 \rangle = 0 \tag{59}$$

This requires that we take

$$a_{11} = -\frac{\langle u_1 u_2 \rangle}{\langle u_1 u_1 \rangle} \tag{60}$$

so that

$$v_2 = u_2 - \frac{\langle u_1 u_2 \rangle}{\langle u_1 u_1 \rangle} u_1 \tag{61}$$

To continue the process, we take a third vector, say u_3, and form the vector

$$v_3 = u_3 + a_{22}u_2 + a_{21}u_1 \tag{62}$$

We require that a_{22} and a_{21} be chosen so that v_3 is K-orthogonal to both v_1 and v_2. However, v_2 is composed of u_2 and v_1. Since we will require that v_1 and v_3 be orthogonal, it is enough, and more convenient, to require that v_3 and u_2 be orthogonal. Hence we have

$$\langle v_1 v_3 \rangle = \langle u_1 u_3 \rangle + a_{22}\langle u_1 u_2 \rangle + a_{21}\langle u_1 u_1 \rangle = 0 \tag{63}$$

$$\langle u_2 v_3 \rangle = \langle u_2 u_3 \rangle + a_{22}\langle u_2 u_2 \rangle + a_{21}\langle u_2 u_1 \rangle = 0 \tag{64}$$

If, then, we set

$$D_2 = \begin{vmatrix} \langle u_1 u_1 \rangle & \langle u_1 u_2 \rangle \\ \langle u_2 u_1 \rangle & \langle u_2 u_2 \rangle \end{vmatrix} \tag{65}$$

we find that the coefficients in Eq. (62) are

$$a_{21} = (\langle u_1 u_2 \rangle \langle u_2 u_3 \rangle - \langle u_2 u_2 \rangle \langle u_1 u_3 \rangle)/D_2 \tag{66}$$

$$a_{22} = (\langle u_2 u_1 \rangle \langle u_1 u_3 \rangle - \langle u_1 u_1 \rangle \langle u_2 u_3 \rangle)/D_2 \tag{67}$$

The process can then be continued by setting

$$v_4 = u_4 + a_{33}u_3 + a_{32}u_2 + a_{31}u_1 \tag{68}$$

and setting a_{33}, a_{32}, a_{31} so that v_4 is K-orthogonal to v_3, v_2, and v_1.

We shall not carry the process further. We shall note only that the process is possible as long as the determinants

$$D_1 = \langle \mathbf{u}_1\mathbf{u}_1 \rangle \tag{69}$$

$$D_2 = \begin{vmatrix} \langle \mathbf{u}_1\mathbf{u}_1 \rangle & \langle \mathbf{u}_1\mathbf{u}_2 \rangle \\ \langle \mathbf{u}_2\mathbf{u}_1 \rangle & \langle \mathbf{u}_2\mathbf{u}_2 \rangle \end{vmatrix} \tag{70}$$

$$D_3 = \begin{vmatrix} \langle \mathbf{u}_1\mathbf{u}_1 \rangle & \langle \mathbf{u}_1\mathbf{u}_2 \rangle & \langle \mathbf{u}_1\mathbf{u}_3 \rangle \\ \langle \mathbf{u}_2\mathbf{u}_1 \rangle & \langle \mathbf{u}_2\mathbf{u}_2 \rangle & \langle \mathbf{u}_2\mathbf{u}_3 \rangle \\ \langle \mathbf{u}_3\mathbf{u}_1 \rangle & \langle \mathbf{u}_3\mathbf{u}_2 \rangle & \langle \mathbf{u}_3\mathbf{u}_3 \rangle \end{vmatrix} \tag{71}$$

etc., are nonzero. These determinants are called the *Gramians* and it can be shown that when they are formed from a linearly independent set of vectors they do not vanish. They are, in fact, always positive.

What is of principle importance here is that it is possible, given a set of linearly independent vectors that span a subspace, to form linear combinations of these vectors that are K-orthogonal and that still span the subspace. These can then be K-normalized to form a K-orthonormal set of vectors that can be used as a basis for whatever we wish to do. The process is not unique. If we take the original vectors in a different order, we get a different set of vectors. There are other ways of modifying the process, but it always is quite possible to *orthogonalize* a set of vectors by this process.

9. THE NORM OF A VECTOR

We will conclude this chapter with a brief mention of a different relation which embodies the idea of length in a more general way:

Definition. *If* $\mathbf{x}$ *is any vector in a given space, and if there exists a real scalar function of* $\mathbf{x}$, $\| \mathbf{x} \|$, *such that*

(A) $\| \mathbf{x} \| \geqslant 0$,   all $\mathbf{x}$
(B) $\| \alpha\mathbf{x} \| = | \alpha | \| \mathbf{x} \|$
(C) $\| \mathbf{x} + \mathbf{y} \| \leqslant \| \mathbf{x} \| + \| \mathbf{y} \|$ (Minkowski's inequality)

then $\| \mathbf{x} \|$ *is said to be the* **norm** *of* $\mathbf{x}$.

One example is $\langle \mathbf{x}, \mathbf{x} \rangle^{1/2}$ where $\langle \, \rangle$ indicates any (proper) inner product.

This is not, however, the only type of norm that is possible or useful. Another example that is useful in certain types of problems is the sum of the magnitudes of the components. A third example which we will use, briefly, in the theory of Markoff matrices, is the algebraic sum of the components. This is not a valid norm for all vectors, since property (A) does not hold generally, but is valid for the particular kind of vectors that will be of interest to us there. Other examples could be cited also.

The definition of a norm permits use of the concept of *neighborhood*. We have great flexibility in its choice, and we can choose the definition that bests fits the problem. It is, therefore, of great value in the study of many problems and in establishing various important theorems.

We will not speak of the norm further in any general way. This would lead to the study of the topology of *normed vector spaces* and to the theory of *Banach spaces*.[1] But we will use various norms as they may be appropriate to other purposes.

Exercises

1.   We can express a vector $\vec{u}$ in ordinary (euclidean) space as

$$\vec{u} = \mathbf{u} = \begin{pmatrix} u_x \\ u_y \\ u_z \end{pmatrix}$$

What is the metric $\mathbf{K}$ that expresses the dot product of two vectors?

2.   Consider the matrix

$$\mathbf{A} = \begin{pmatrix} ab & c & ad \\ -bc & a & -cd \\ -d & 0 & b \end{pmatrix}$$

where a, b, c, and d are real and connected by

$$a^2 + c^2 = 1$$
$$b^2 + d^2 = 1$$

Show that, if $\mathbf{v} = \mathbf{Au}$, where $\mathbf{u}$ and $\mathbf{v}$ are vectors with coefficients in the real number field, then

$$\mathbf{v}^T\mathbf{v} = \mathbf{u}^T\mathbf{u}$$

What is the geometric significance of this result?

---

[1] A normed vector space is a *Banach space* if it is complete—i.e., contains the limit of all sequences of vectors within it. Since a finitely dimensioned space, such as we are considering here, is always complete, a finite normed vector space is necessarily a Banach space.

3. For

$$\mathbf{K} = \begin{pmatrix} 2 & 1 & 0 \\ 1 & 2 & 1 \\ 0 & 1 & 2 \end{pmatrix}$$

show that

$$\mathbf{u}_1 = \begin{pmatrix} 1 \\ 0 \\ -1 \end{pmatrix}, \quad \mathbf{u}_2 = \begin{pmatrix} 1 \\ \sqrt{2} \\ 1 \end{pmatrix}, \quad \mathbf{u}_3 = \begin{pmatrix} 1 \\ -\sqrt{2} \\ 1 \end{pmatrix}$$

are K-orthogonal. Expand $\mathbf{y} = \mathrm{col}(a, b, c)$ in terms of these vectors.

4. Consider the vectors

$$\mathbf{u}_1 = \begin{pmatrix} 1 \\ 0 \\ j \\ 0 \end{pmatrix}, \quad \mathbf{u}_2 = \begin{pmatrix} 0 \\ 1 \\ j \\ 0 \end{pmatrix}, \quad \mathbf{u}_3 = \begin{pmatrix} 0 \\ 0 \\ 1 \\ 1 \end{pmatrix}$$

Starting with $\mathbf{u}_1 = \mathbf{v}_1$, obtain vectors $\mathbf{v}_1$, $\mathbf{v}_2$, $\mathbf{v}_3$ which are pairwise orthogonal for the unitary inner product ($\mathbf{K} = \mathbf{I}$), and which span the subspace spanned by $\mathbf{u}_1$, $\mathbf{u}_2$, $\mathbf{u}_3$. Normalize $\mathbf{v}_1$, $\mathbf{v}_2$, $\mathbf{v}_3$ for this inner product.

5. Show, by finding specific vectors, that the $\mathbf{K}$ of Eq. (37) is indefinite —i.e., neither positive definite nor negative definite.

6. Show that

$$\mathbf{K} = \begin{pmatrix} 2 & 1 \\ 1 & 2 \end{pmatrix}$$

is positive definite.

7. Find vectors which, together with the following sets, form an orthogonal basis, with respect to the unitary inner product, for the whole space:

(a) $\mathrm{col}(2, 2, 1)$; $\mathrm{col}(-2, 1, 2)$
(b) $\mathrm{col}(1, 1, 1, 1)$; $\mathrm{col}(1, -1, 1, -1)$
(c) $\mathrm{col}(1, 1, 1, 1)$; $\mathrm{col}(1, 1, 3, -5)$

8. In euclidean 3-space, the three diagonals through the center of a cube are orthogonal. Prove the corresponding statement about an n-dimensional cube in euclidean n-space.

9. Consider euclidean n-space in which a set of cartesian coordinates is established. Find n points with nonnegative coordinates such that the distance between every pair of points, and from every point to the origin, is unity. (The points, together with the origin, are said to form the vertices of a *regular simplex* whose side is of unit length.)

10. If S is a subspace of the space P, then U is said to be the *orthogonal complement* of S with respect to a given inner product relation (or *K-orthogonal complement*, if we wish to be specific) if any vector in U is K-orthogonal to every vector in S, and U contains all such vectors in P. Show that U is a subspace. Show that, if the inner product relation is proper, U and S are disjoint—i.e., contain no vector in common.

11. Find the orthogonal complement (see Exercise 10) with respect to the unitary inner product, of the subspaces spanned by the following sets of vectors:

(a)   col(1, 1, 2)
(b)   col(2, 1, −1);   col(2, 2, −1)
(c)   col(2, j, 1, j);   col(j, 1, 2, j)
(d)   col(1 + j, 1 − j, 1);   col(2, −2j, 1 − j)

12. Let

$$\mathbf{K} = \begin{pmatrix} 2 & 1 & 0 \\ 1 & 2 & 1 \\ 0 & 1 & 2 \end{pmatrix}$$

be a metric.

With respect to the inner product so defined, find the K-orthogonal complement of the following sets of vectors:

(a)   col(1, 1, 0)
(b)   col(1, −2, 1)
(c)   col(1 − j, 2j, −1);   col(3, −2, 3)

13. A *functional* $f(\mathbf{x})$ defined over a given linear vector space, S, is a scalar-valued function of the vector. It is a *linear* functional if, for any scalars, a and b, and any vectors, $\mathbf{u}$ and $\mathbf{v}$ in S, $f(a\mathbf{u} + b\mathbf{v}) = af(\mathbf{u}) + bf(\mathbf{v})$. Show that, under a given proper inner product, any linear functional can be expressed as

$$f(\mathbf{x}) = \langle \mathbf{w}, \mathbf{x} \rangle$$

where $\mathbf{w}$ is a vector in S.

Outline of proof:

Let S_1 be the subspace of all vectors in S such that $f(\mathbf{x}) = 0$. (Why is it a subspace?) If $S_1 = S$, let $\mathbf{w}$ be the null vector. If S_1 is a proper subspace, let $\mathbf{w}$ be a vector in the orthogonal complement of S_1, normalized so that $\langle \mathbf{w}, \mathbf{w} \rangle = f(\mathbf{w})$. (Does such a vector always exist?) For any vector, $\mathbf{x}$, in S, consider

$$\mathbf{x}' = \mathbf{x} - \frac{f(\mathbf{x})}{f(\mathbf{w})} \mathbf{w}$$

Then $\mathbf{x}'$ is in S_1 (why?), and $\langle \mathbf{w}, \mathbf{x}' \rangle = 0$. From this it follows immediately that $\langle \mathbf{w}, \mathbf{x} \rangle = f(\mathbf{x})$.

How does this proof depend on the inner product being proper?

CHAPTER III

Eigenvalues and Eigenvectors

We are now ready to begin the study of the possible behavior of a matrix. The concept that we shall take as central for this purpose is the eigenvalues and their associated eigenvectors and chains of generalized eigenvectors. In this chapter, we will develop this concept itself, both analytically and by appeal to physical intuition. The rigorous development, we will defer to later chapters, particularly Chapter VIII.

1. BASIC CONCEPT

We consider the equation

$$y = Ax \tag{1}$$

and say that A is an operation that maps the space of possible x onto the space of possible y. If A is an $n \times n$ matrix, then we can consider the linear vector space S of n-dimensional vectors, and say that A maps S onto or into itself.

Now many things can happen. If we consider all x in S, then the situation can be quite complicated. However, among all of S, there may be, and in fact will be, certain vectors that behave in a particularly simple way. These vectors are simply stretched or compressed, or their phase is changed. That is, the effect of A on them simply multiplies them by some scalar. If x_i is such a vector, then

$$Ax_i = \lambda_i x_i \tag{2}$$

where λ_i is a scalar quantity.

A vector x_i that satisfies Eq. (2) is an *eigenvector* of A, and the corresponding scalar λ_i is an *eigenvalue*.

Other terms are also used. Some authors call the vectors *proper vectors* or *characteristic vectors* and the scalars *proper values* or *characteristic values*. The terms *eigenvectors* and *eigenvalues* seem to be winning out, however, in spite of their confused etymology (eigenvalue is a semitranslation of the German word "eigenwerte"), and we shall use them here.

We can easily illustrate what is happening here from strain theory. Suppose we put a block of material under a pure compression along the y-axis. Then it expands along the x-axis as shown in Fig. 1. (We will

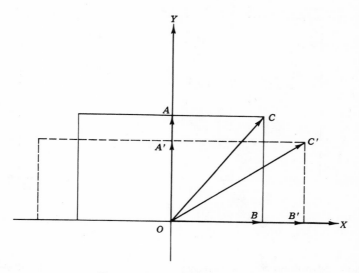

FIG. 1.   Pure compression strain.

consider only two dimensions for simplicity.) The solid outline is the shape before compression, and the dotted outline the shape after compression. The vector *OA* becomes *OA'*, *OB* becomes *OB'* and *OC* becomes *OC'*.

The vector *OC* is transformed by a combination of a change in length, perhaps, and a rotation. *OA* and *OB*, however, only have their lengths affected, *OA* in this case being shortened and *OB* lengthened. *OA* and *OB* are then eigenvectors. The ratios *OA'/OA* and *OB'/OB* are the corresponding eigenvalues.

This was a particularly simple situation since only a pure compression was involved. In Fig. 2, we consider a combination of compression and shear. Again, points *A*, *B*, *C*, and *D* move to points *A'*, *B'*, *C'* and *D'*, with *O* being fixed as the point of reference. *OB* remains an eigenvector with eigenvalue *OB'/OB*. *OA* is no longer an eigenvector since it is rotated as well as compressed. We do find, however, some other one particular direction, in this case *OD*, such that the vector has only its magnitude changed. The eigenvectors, then, are *OB* and *OD*.

In this case, the eigenvectors are not perpendicular to each other.

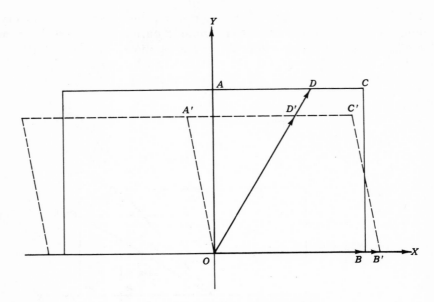

FIG. 2.   Compression plus sheer strain.

In the terminology of strain theory, the principal axes of the deformation are skewed.

The identification of the eigenvectors is important not only for the description of the situation, but because it simplifies the calculation of the effect on any other vector. Suppose, in Fig. 1 or 2, we designate the eigenvectors as $\mathbf{u}_1$ and $\mathbf{u}_2$, and the corresponding eigenvalues as λ_1 and λ_2. Let $\mathbf{v}$ be any other vector, such as OC. Then we can write

$$\mathbf{v} = a\mathbf{u}_1 + b\mathbf{u}_2 \tag{3}$$

where a and b are constants. In the case of Fig. 1, if $\mathbf{u}_1$ is the unit vector along the x-axis, and $\mathbf{u}_2$ the unit vector along the y-axis, then a is the x component of $\mathbf{v}$, and b the y-component. In the case of Fig. 2, we can take $\mathbf{u}_1$ and $\mathbf{u}_2$ as unit vectors along the skewed axes of OB and OD.

We will assume the effect of the deformation is uniform through the material so that the problem is linear. Then the effect on $\mathbf{v}$ is to move it to

$$\mathbf{v}' = \lambda_1 a\mathbf{u}_1 + \lambda_2 b\mathbf{u}_2 \tag{4}$$

and we can easily calculate the position of OC' for any OC.

The vector OC, in other words, is resolved into its components along the eigenvectors. The effect of the deformation on OC can then be considered as the combination of its effects on these components. Since the components are themselves eigenvectors, its effect on them is a simple multiplication by their respective eigenvalues.

The ability to so resolve an arbitrary vector into components that are eigenvectors depends on the existence of a sufficient number of eigenvectors to span the space. That this may not be true is indicated in Fig. 3, where we consider a pure shear deformation. OB remains an

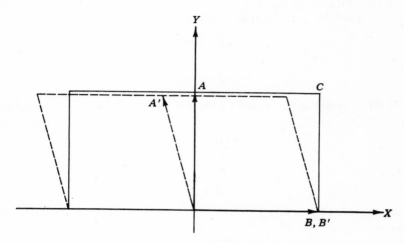

FIG. 3.   Pure sheer strain.

eigenvector, in this case with eigenvalue one. Neither OA nor any OC is an eigenvector. Any vector that is not along the x-axis is subject to some rotation. We shall later investigate how we may obtain a sufficient number of vectors to handle such a problem. This does, however, illustrate the possibility that a matrix may not have enough eigenvectors to span the whole space on which it operates.

2. CHARACTERISTIC OR ITERATIVE IMPEDANCE

As another preliminary example, consider a 2-port network, as in Fig. 4, described as a transmission matrix on an E-I basis, using the complex amplitude.

If the network is a transmission line, it may be described by its characteristic impedance. More generally, a 2-port network usually has an iterative impedance Z_c such that if port #2 is terminated in Z_c,

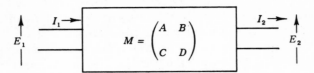

FIG. 4. Two-port network on an E-I basis.

then the impedance looking into port #1 is Z_c. To put this formally, Z_c is defined by the condition that if

$$E_2 = Z_c I_2 \qquad (5)$$

then

$$E_1 = Z_c I_1 \qquad (6)$$

If the network is described on an E-I basis and $\mathbf{M}$ is its transmission, or $ABCD$, matrix, then

$$\binom{E_1}{I_1} = \mathbf{M}\binom{E_2}{I_2} \qquad (7)$$

If we let

$$\mathbf{u} = \binom{Z_c}{1} \qquad (8)$$

and substitute Eqs. (5) and (6) in Eq. (7), we find that

$$\mathbf{M}\binom{E_2}{I_2} = I_2\mathbf{M}\mathbf{u} = \binom{E_1}{I_1} = I_1\mathbf{u}$$

or

$$\mathbf{M}\mathbf{u} = (I_1/I_2)\mathbf{u} \qquad (9)$$

Hence $\mathbf{u}$ is an eigenvector of $\mathbf{M}$ with eigenvalue (I_1/I_2). If E_1, I_1, etc., are complex amplitudes, this ratio may be complex. If its magnitude is unity, as it must be if the network is lossless, then it is the phase delay through the network.

Thus the characteristic impedance of a transmission line, or the iterative impedance of a 2-port network is simply an indirect way of defining the appropriate eigenvector, Eq. (8), of the transmission matrix. The phase delay with this termination is the eigenvalue.

3. FORMAL DEVELOPMENT

With these preliminary examples out of the way we will now proceed to the more formal, and general, definition and development of the underlying concepts.

Definition. *Given an* $n \times n$ *square matrix* **A**, *the* n*-dimensional vector* **x** *is an* **eigenvector** *with* **eigenvalue** λ *if and only if*

$$\mathbf{Ax} = \lambda\mathbf{x} \tag{10}$$

In expanded form, if

$$\mathbf{x} = \begin{pmatrix} x_1 \\ x_2 \\ \vdots \\ x_n \end{pmatrix}_\lambda, \qquad \mathbf{A} = \begin{pmatrix} a_{11} & a_{12} & \cdots & \\ a_{21} & a_{22} & \cdots & \\ \vdots & & & \\ a_{n1} & a_{n2} & \cdots & a_{nn} \end{pmatrix} \tag{11}$$

then **x** is an eigenvector of **A** with eigenvalue λ if

$$a_{11}x_1 + a_{12}x_2 + \cdots + a_{1n}x_n = \lambda x_1$$

$$a_{21}x_1 + a_{22}x_2 + \cdots + a_{2n}x_n = \lambda x_2$$

$$\cdots$$

$$a_{n1}x_1 + a_{n2}x_2 + \cdots + a_{nn}x_n = \lambda x_n \tag{12}$$

In specifying an eigenvector as the column matrix of its components, we will find it convenient to write the corresponding eigenvalue outside the parentheses at the lower right corner, as we have done in Eq. (11). We shall adopt this as a convention when we need to be specific.

We have the following theorem which will provide the foundation for much of what we do:

Theorem 1. *Given a linear vector space* S *over a field* F *that is algebraically complete, and a square matrix* **A** *whose components are in* F, *which maps* S *onto or into itself, then there exists in* S *at least one vector that is an eigenvector of* **A** *with eigenvalue* λ *in* F.

The requirement that the field be *algebraically complete* means that it contains the roots of all polynomial with coefficients in the field. The field of real numbers is not algebraically complete. It does not, for example, contain the roots of $(x^2 + 1)$. The field of complex numbers is, however, algebraically complete.

This restriction of the field is necessary. A rotation in euclidean 2-space, for example, does not have any eigenvector with real coefficients. All of its eigenvectors are complex.

We should also note that the theorem does not require that S shall be the whole space. It only requires that, if **x** is any vector in S, then (**Ax**) shall be a vector in S. This is a condition that we shall use extensively later, and will describe by saying that S is *invariant for* **A**. Obviously, the whole space is invariant for any square matrix of corresponding dimensionality.

We also note that the theorem does not say that there is more than one eigenvector in S. There may, in fact, be only one. All we can say in general is that there is at least one.

We shall not prove this theorem.[1] It depends ultimately on *Brouwer's fix point theorem* from the theory of topologic spaces. Its rigorous derivation would carry us too far afield. We will, instead, only argue its plausibility from the procedure that we can use for the actual determination of the eigenvalues and eigenvectors.

4. DETERMINATION OF THE EIGENVALUES

To determine the eigenvalues of a matrix **A** as given in Eq. (11), we rewrite Eq. (12) to the form

$$(a_{11} - \lambda)x_1 + a_{12}x_2 + \cdots + a_{1n}x_n \qquad = .0$$

$$a_{21}x_1 + (a_{22} - \lambda)x_2 + \cdots + a_{2n}x_n = 0$$

$$\cdots$$

$$a_{n1}x_1 + a_{n2}x_2 + \cdots + (a_{nn} - \lambda)x_n = 0 \qquad (13)$$

These form a set of n linear homogeneous equations in the n unknowns x_1, x_2, ..., x_n. From elementary theory, we know that this has a nontrivial solution (i.e., excluding the solution $x_1 = x_2 = \cdots = x_n = 0$) if, but only if, the determinant of the coefficients vanishes.

$$\begin{vmatrix} a_{11} - \lambda & a_{12} & \cdots & a_{1n} \\ a_{21} & a_{22} - \lambda & \cdots & a_{2n} \\ \vdots & & & \vdots \\ a_{n1} & a_{n2} & \cdots & a_{nn} - \lambda \end{vmatrix} = 0 \qquad (14)$$

We can write this formally as

$$|\mathbf{A} - \lambda\mathbf{I}| = 0 \qquad (15)$$

Equation (14) or (15) is a polynomial in λ of degree n. It is called the *characteristic equation* of **A**.

The coefficients of the characteristic equation of **A** are obtained from the coefficients of **A** by a finite number of multiplications and additions.

---

[1] The theorem can be stated much more broadly than we have done. It applies, for example, to any bounded continuous operator linear or not, on a finite-dimensional space. Under certain circumstances it applies to infinitely dimensioned spaces.

Hence, if the coefficients of $\mathbf{A}$ are in the field F, so are the coefficients of its characteristic equation. If, then, F is a field that is algebraically complete, all the roots of Eq. (14) or (15) are in F. Under these circumstances, we know that this polynomial has at least one root. Therefore $\mathbf{A}$ has at least one eigenvalue in F.

More generally, if F is algebraically complete, we can always factor the characteristic polynomial:

$$| \mathbf{A} - \lambda \mathbf{I} | = \alpha(\lambda - \lambda_1)^{n_1}(\lambda - \lambda_2)^{n_2} \cdots (\lambda - \lambda_k)^{n_k} \qquad (16)$$

where λ_1, λ_2, ..., λ_k are the eigenvalues of $\mathbf{A}$, and n_1, ..., n_k are positive integers, and α some nonzero scalar in F.

If we factor the characteristic equation as in Eq. (16), we say that the *multiplicity* of the eigenvalue λ_i is n_i.

Since the characteristic equation is a polynomial of degree n, the sum of the multiplicities of the distinct eigenvalues is clearly n.

Given, then, an eigenvalue that is a root of the characteristic equation, we can substitute it in Eq. (13) and obtain one or more linearly independent sets of values x_1, ..., x_n that are solutions. These are, then, eigenvectors.

In Eq. (13), if, for a given λ_i, we know that x_1, ..., x_n is a solution, then αx_1, αx_2, ..., αx_n will also be a solution for any α. In other words, if $\mathbf{x}_i$ is a solution to Eq. (2) for a given λ_i, so is $\alpha \mathbf{x}_i$. It might be better, therefore, if it were not so awkward, to speak of a "1-dimensional eigen linear vector space" rather than an eigenvector. We do, in fact, generally speak of $\mathbf{x}_i$ and $\alpha \mathbf{x}_i$ as being the same eigenvector.

5. SINGULARITY

We have defined a singular matrix as one for which the determinant vanishes. We can observe that this condition is equivalent to saying that the characteristic equation, Eq. (15), is satisfied by $\lambda = 0$.

Hence a necessary and sufficient condition for $\mathbf{A}$ to be singular is that it have as one of its eigenvalues the value zero.

Conversely, a necessary and sufficient condition for the nonsingularity of $\mathbf{A}$ is that none of its eigenvalues are zero. The two conditions are equivalent.

If $\mathbf{A}$ is singular, then the fact that zero is an eigenvalue of $\mathbf{A}$ means that there must exist at least one eigenvector for this eigenvalue, or that there must exist at least one vector $\mathbf{x}$ such that

$$\mathbf{Ax} = 0$$

We say, in this case, that $\mathbf{x}$ is *annihilated* by $\mathbf{A}$.

6. LINEAR INDEPENDENCE

We now must consider two questions. We must ask what happens if there are two or more solutions to Eq. (13) for the same value of λ. And we must ask what relation exists between eigenvectors having different eigenvalues.

Theorem 2. *If x_i are a set of vectors all of which are eigenvectors of* **A** *with the same eigenvalue λ, then any linear combination of the x_i is an eigenvector of* **A** *with eigenvalue λ.*

This follows immediately from the linearity of **A**. Let

$$y = \sum_i a_i x_i \tag{17}$$

where, for all the x_i being considered,

$$A x_i = \lambda x_i$$

Then

$$A y = \sum_i a_i A x_i = \sum_i a_i \lambda x_i = \lambda y \tag{18}$$

It follows that if we have a set of k linearly independent eigenvectors of **A** with the same eigenvalue, then the k-dimensional subspace spanned by these vectors is a subspace any vector of which is an eigenvector of **A** with this same eigenvalue.

If there exist k linearly independent eigenvectors of **A** with the same eigenvalue, we say that **A** has a k-*fold degeneracy* for this eigenvalue. The presence of degeneracy creates an ambiguity in the specification of the eigenvectors. We can choose any set of k linearly independent vectors in the appropriate subspace. When we make such a choice, we say that we *resolve the degeneracy*.

We should note that this theorem allows us to resolve a degeneracy in a matrix, **A**, so as to obtain a set of orthogonal eigenvectors that span the degeneracy. We can take any set of k linearly independent eigenvectors with the given eigenvalue. We can employ the Gram-Schmidt process (Chapter II, Section 8) to develop from them k mutually orthogonal vectors that span the same space. These vectors will then also be eigenvectors of **A** with the given eigenvalue.

We shall later have occasion to examine in detail certain classes of matrices (normal, hermitian, and unitary) which we know have a complete set of eigenvectors, and for which we know that any pair of eigenvectors with discrete eigenvalues are orthogonal. These matrices can be degenerate. Hence we do not know, *a priori*, that any complete set of eigenvectors *are* orthogonal. But, from this theorem, and using the Gram-Schmidt process to resolve any degeneracies that may be present, we do know that we *can* obtain a complete set of orthogonal eigenvectors.

The Gram-Schmidt process does not help us with more general classes of matrices, however. True, from the eigenvectors we can obtain a set of mutually orthogonal vectors, but these will not, in general, be eigenvectors. We can use it, however, to resolve the degeneracies if we can find an inner product relation which does make orthogonal the eigenvectors with distinct eigenvalues.

The other theorem we wish is the following:

Theorem 3. *Eigenvectors of* $\mathbf{A}$ *having distinct eigenvalues are linearly independent.*

We prove this by assuming the contrary and showing it false.

Suppose there exists a set of nonzero constants c_1, ..., c_k such that

$$c_1\mathbf{x}_1 + c_2\mathbf{x}_2 + \cdots + c_k\mathbf{x}_k = 0, \qquad c_i \neq 0, \quad i = 1, ..., k. \tag{19}$$

where

$$\mathbf{A}\mathbf{x}_i = \lambda_i\mathbf{x}_i$$

and

$$\lambda_i \neq \lambda_j \quad \text{if} \quad i \neq j$$

Note that we have not said that the set $\mathbf{x}_1$, ..., $\mathbf{x}_k$ are all the eigenvectors of $\mathbf{A}$. Also, we have not specified how any degeneracy of $\mathbf{A}$ has been resolved. Thus Eq. (19) includes any possible situation.

Suppose, now, we operate on Eq. (19) with $(\mathbf{A} - \lambda_1\mathbf{I})$. Then, since

$$(\mathbf{A} - \lambda_1\mathbf{I})\mathbf{x}_1 = \mathbf{A}\mathbf{x}_1 - \lambda\mathbf{x}_1 = 0$$

$$(\mathbf{A} - \lambda_1\mathbf{I})\mathbf{x}_i = \mathbf{A}\mathbf{x}_i - \lambda_1\mathbf{x}_i = (\lambda_i - \lambda_1)\mathbf{x}_i \neq 0 \quad \text{if} \quad i \neq 1$$

we obtain

$$c_2(\lambda_2 - \lambda_1)\mathbf{x}_2 + \cdots + c_k(\lambda_k - \lambda_1)\mathbf{x}_k = 0 \tag{20}$$

Operating now with $(\mathbf{A} - \lambda_2\mathbf{I})$, we are left with

$$c_3(\lambda_3 - \lambda_1)(\lambda_3 - \lambda_2)\mathbf{x}_3 + \cdots + c_k(\lambda_k - \lambda_1)(\lambda_k - \lambda_2)\mathbf{x}_k = 0 \tag{21}$$

Continuing, we eventually are left with only the single term

$$c_k \left\{ \prod_{i=1}^{k-1} (\lambda_k - \lambda_i) \right\} \mathbf{x}_k = 0 \tag{22}$$

The factors in the product are nonzero, since the eigenvalues are distinct. The vector $\mathbf{x}_k$ is nonnull. Hence, c_k must vanish. But this is contrary to the assumption. Hence, it is not possible to write an equation like Eq. (19), and the theorem is proven.

7. SEMISIMPLICITY

We can now consider the number of linearly independent eigenvectors that a matrix may have.

Suppose $\mathbf{A}$ is $n \times n$ and suppose it has n distinct eigenvalues. The development given shows that there is at least one eigenvector for each eigenvalue. However, eigenvectors with distinct eigenvalues are linearly independent, and in an n-dimensional space, there can be only n linearly independent vectors. Hence, there can be only one eigenvector (within a scalar factor) for each eigenvalue.

If $\mathbf{A}$ is $n \times n$ and λ_i is a root of multiplicity n_i, then there may be as many as n_i linearly independent eigenvectors with this eigenvalue. There may not be that many, of course. We can only assert that there is at least one and not more than n_i.

An eigenvalue of multiplicity n_i may generate up to an n_i-fold degeneracy, no more.

These statements will be proven more rigorously in Chapter VIII. For the moment, we shall only assert that they are true, and hope that the development so far has made them plausible.

If $\mathbf{A}$ has a total of n linearly independent eigenvectors, regardless of degeneracy, then $\mathbf{A}$ is said to be *semisimple*.

The name arises because the operation of scalar multiplication is said to be simple. Multiplication of a vector by a semisimple matrix is not simple, but an arbitrary vector can be expanded on the eigenvectors, on each of which a semisimple matrix operates simply. Hence, multiplication by such a matrix is the next best thing, and so that operation is called semisimple.

The question immediately arises as to how one knows whether a given matrix is semisimple or not. Unfortunately there is no easy answer in general, although we shall see that there are identifiable classes of matrices that are always semisimple. But in general one must either study the eigenvectors themselves, or determine some of the other properties of the matrix that may not be easily calculated if the matrix is large.

8. NONSEMISIMPLE MATRICES

We have pointed out that a matrix may not have a complete set of eigenvectors.

Suppose **A** has eigenvalue λ_i with multiplicity $m_i > 1$. Then it has at least one eigenvector with this eigenvalue. The degeneracy of the eigenvectors associated with this eigenvalue may, however, be less than m_i. The problem, then, is to find some other vectors which are somehow associated with λ_i, and which are linearly independent of the eigenvectors.

The eigenvector, $\mathbf{x}_i$, is a vector that satisfies the equation

$$(\mathbf{A} - \lambda_i \mathbf{I})\mathbf{x}_i = 0$$

so that $\mathbf{x}_i$ is annihilated by $(\mathbf{A} - \lambda_i \mathbf{I})$.

If, now, we do not have enough vectors that are annihilated by $(\mathbf{A} - \lambda_i \mathbf{I})$, it is perhaps not unreasonable to consider those vectors that are annihilated by $(\mathbf{A} - \lambda_i \mathbf{I})^2$, $(\mathbf{A} - \lambda_i \mathbf{I})^3$, etc., until we get enough vectors.

We shall show in Chapter VIII that this procedure is successful. We can define a *chain* of length k of *generalized eigenvectors* by the relations

$$(\mathbf{A} - \lambda_i \mathbf{I})\mathbf{x}_{i,1} = 0$$
$$(\mathbf{A} - \lambda_i \mathbf{I})\mathbf{x}_{i,2} = \mathbf{x}_{i,1}$$
$$(\mathbf{A} - \lambda_i \mathbf{I})\mathbf{x}_{i,3} = \mathbf{x}_{i,2} \tag{23}$$
$$(\mathbf{A} - \lambda_i \mathbf{I})\mathbf{x}_{i,k} = \mathbf{x}_{i,k-1}$$

or, substituting successively,

$$(\mathbf{A} - \lambda_i \mathbf{I})\mathbf{x}_{i,1} = 0$$
$$(\mathbf{A} - \lambda_i \mathbf{I})^2\mathbf{x}_{i,2} = 0$$
$$\vdots \tag{24}$$
$$(\mathbf{A} - \lambda_i \mathbf{I})^k\mathbf{x}_{i,k} = 0$$

Then $\mathbf{x}_{i,1}$ is the eigenvector; $\mathbf{x}_{i,2}$ is a *generalized eigenvector of rank* 2; and so on until $\mathbf{x}_{i,k}$ is a *generalized eigenvector of rank* k.

Actually, the proper procedure for handling the most general case is to start from the generalized eigenvector of highest rank. Specifically, we consider the subspace of all vectors that are anihilated by some power of $(\mathbf{A} - \lambda_i \mathbf{I})$. That this is a subspace can be readily verified. (See Chapter I, Section 3.) We call this subspace the eigensubspace for the eigenvalue λ_i. We now ask, for what value of k does there exist a vector, $\mathbf{x}_{i,k}$ in the subspace such that

$$(\mathbf{A} - \lambda_i \mathbf{I})^{k-1}\mathbf{x}_{i,k} \neq 0$$

and

$$(\mathbf{A} - \lambda_i \mathbf{I})^k\mathbf{x}_{i,k} = 0 \tag{25}$$

and such that there is no vector in the subspace that is not anihiliated at least by $(\mathbf{A} - \lambda_i\mathbf{I})^k$. This gives us a vector that is a generalized eigenvector of rank k, where k is length of the longest chain associated with this eigenvalue. We then define the rest of the chain by

$$\mathbf{x}_{i,k-1} = (\mathbf{A} - \lambda_i\mathbf{I})\mathbf{x}_{ik}$$
$$\vdots$$
$$\mathbf{x}_{i,1} = (\mathbf{A} - \lambda_i\mathbf{I})^{k-1}\mathbf{x}_{i,k} \tag{26}$$

Then $\mathbf{x}_{i,1}$ is an eigenvector.

We consider now the subspace, if any, that is annihilated by some power of $(\mathbf{A} - \lambda_i\mathbf{I})$ but is linearly independent of the chain already found. We use the same process on this subspace to form another chain. We continue the process as long as necessary until there remain no vectors that are linearly independent of the chains already found and which are annihilated by some power of $(\mathbf{A} - \lambda_i\mathbf{I})$.

If, then, we consider eigenvectors that are not part of a longer chain as being chains of length one, then we find that the sum of the lengths of all the chains associated with a given eigenvalue is always exactly equal to the multiplicity of the eigenvalue.

We can prove, and will do so in Chapter VIII, that the totality of the eigenvectors and generalized eigenvectors of a matrix form a complete set of linearly independent vectors, providing all degeneracies are properly resolved.

9. DEGENERACY IN A CHAIN

We should observe that there is a great deal of degeneracy in a chain. Suppose we have that

$$(\mathbf{A} - \lambda\mathbf{I})\mathbf{x}_1 = 0$$
$$(\mathbf{A} - \lambda\mathbf{I})\mathbf{x}_2 = \mathbf{x}$$
$$\vdots$$
$$(\mathbf{A} - \lambda\mathbf{I})\mathbf{x}_k = \mathbf{x}_{k-1} \tag{27}$$

where we have changed the symbology slightly from that used before. Then

$$\mathbf{y}_1 = \mathbf{x}_1$$
$$\mathbf{y}_2 = \mathbf{x}_2 + a\mathbf{x}_1$$
$$\mathbf{y}_3 = \mathbf{x}_3 + a\mathbf{x}_2 + b\mathbf{x}_1$$
$$\vdots$$
$$\mathbf{y}_k = \mathbf{x}_k + a\mathbf{x}_{k-1} + b\mathbf{x}_{k-2} + \cdots + f\mathbf{x}_1 \tag{28}$$

where a, b, ..., f are any scalars, is also a chain, as may be readily verified.

We note that the subspace spanned by the vectors $\mathbf{y}_1$, $\mathbf{y}_2$, ..., $\mathbf{y}_k$ is the same as that spanned by $\mathbf{x}_1$, $\mathbf{x}_2$, ..., $\mathbf{x}_k$. We have not changed the subspace, only the detailed structure of the individual members of the chain.

In the set of equations (28), we observe that only the member of highest rank contains all the arbitrary constants. Once this member is chosen, the whole chain is determined. This, then, is the reason why we said that the proper way to generate a chain is from the member of highest rank. Had we started from the eigenvector, we would have had to make arbitrary choices at each step along the way.

10. EXAMPLES

It is perhaps well to illustrate the foregoing before proceeding. Consider the matrix

$$\mathbf{A} = \begin{pmatrix} 1 & 1 & 0 \\ 0 & 1 & 1 \\ 0 & 0 & 1 \end{pmatrix} \tag{29}$$

Its characteristic equation, Eq. (15), is

$$(1 - \lambda)^3 = 0$$

so that it has only the eigenvalue 1 with multiplicity 3. If it had a complete set of eigenvectors with this eigenvalue it would necessarily be the identity. This is true since, if so, any vector in the space would be a linear combination of these vectors, and therefore an eigenvector with unit eigenvalue. Hence $\mathbf{A}$ would map every vector onto itself, and would therefore be the identity.

That it is not the identity tells us that it is not semisimple.

The operators of Eq. (26) are

$$\mathbf{A} - \mathbf{I} = \begin{pmatrix} 0 & 1 & 0 \\ 0 & 0 & 1 \\ 0 & 0 & 0 \end{pmatrix}$$

$$(\mathbf{A} - \mathbf{I})^2 = \begin{pmatrix} 0 & 0 & 1 \\ 0 & 0 & 0 \\ 0 & 0 & 0 \end{pmatrix} \tag{30}$$

$$(\mathbf{A} - \mathbf{I})^3 = 0$$

The vector

$$\mathbf{x}_3 = \begin{pmatrix} a \\ b \\ c \end{pmatrix}_1 \tag{31}$$

is annihilated by $(\mathbf{A} - \mathbf{I})^3$ which is the null matrix, and is not annihilated by $(\mathbf{A} - \mathbf{I})^2$ if $c \neq 0$. We therefore know that this a generalized eigenvector of rank 3. The rest of the chain is then found immediately:

$$\mathbf{x}_2 = (\mathbf{A} - \mathbf{I})\mathbf{x}_3 = \begin{pmatrix} b \\ c \\ 0 \end{pmatrix}_1$$

$$\mathbf{x}_1 = (\mathbf{A} - \mathbf{I})\mathbf{x}_2 = \begin{pmatrix} c \\ 0 \\ 0 \end{pmatrix}_1$$

(32)

As a second example, consider

$$\mathbf{A} = \begin{pmatrix} 0 & 1 & 0 & j \\ 1 & 0 & -j & 0 \\ 0 & -j & 0 & 1 \\ j & 0 & 1 & 0 \end{pmatrix}$$

(33)

The characteristic equation, Eq. (15), is

$$\lambda^4 = 0$$

so that the matrix has only the eigenvalue 0 with multiplicity 4. Again $\mathbf{A}$ cannot be semisimple since, if it were, it would be the null matrix. With this value of λ, the operators of Eq. (26) are

$$(\mathbf{A} - \lambda\mathbf{I})^2 = \mathbf{A}^2 = 0$$

so that $\mathbf{A}$ must have a chain of length 2. It could have two such chains, or it could have only one plus two eigenvectors.

For a general vector, we find that

$$\mathbf{A} \begin{pmatrix} a \\ b \\ c \\ d \end{pmatrix} = \begin{pmatrix} b + jd \\ a - jc \\ -j(b + jd) \\ j(a - jc) \end{pmatrix}_0$$

so that the vector is not annihilated providing either $b \neq -jd$ or $a \neq jc$. Since there are two conditions, it is evident that there are two chains of length 2. Since there is degeneracy between them, we can take any vector that satisfies either or both of these conditions. We can take, for example,

$$\mathbf{x}_2 = \begin{pmatrix} 0 \\ b \\ 0 \\ d \end{pmatrix}_0 \qquad \mathbf{x}_4 = \begin{pmatrix} a \\ 0 \\ c \\ 0 \end{pmatrix}_0$$

$$d \neq jb \qquad\qquad a \neq jc$$

(34)

and find the rest of the chains $(\mathbf{x}_2, \mathbf{x}_1)$ and $(\mathbf{x}_4, \mathbf{x}_3)$ to be

$$\mathbf{x}_1 = \mathbf{A}\mathbf{x}_2 = \begin{pmatrix} b + jd \\ 0 \\ -j(b + jd) \\ 0 \end{pmatrix}_0 \qquad \mathbf{x}_3 = \begin{pmatrix} 0 \\ a - jc \\ 0 \\ j(a - jc) \end{pmatrix}_0 \qquad (35)$$

Or we could start with

$$\mathbf{y}_2 = (\alpha \mathbf{x}_2 + \beta \mathbf{x}_4)$$

and obtain

$$\mathbf{y}_1 = (\alpha \mathbf{x}_1 + \beta \mathbf{x}_3)$$

11. π-SECTION OF A FILTER

As a final example, illustrating how the necessity for considering generalized eigenvectors can arise in a practical problem, consider the circuit of Fig. 5 which shows one section of a high pass filter. We

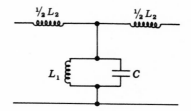

FIG. 5.   Pass band filter section.

assume that the elements are ideal lumped lossless elements. If we replace L_2 by $L_2\,dx$, $1/L_1$ by dx/L_1, and C by $C\,dx$, this becomes the equivalent circuit of an infinitismal section of a waveguide for a single TE mode.

By the methods given at the end of Chapter I, we find that the transmission matrix of this circuit on an E-I basis is given by

$$\mathbf{M} = \begin{pmatrix} \{1 + \tfrac{1}{2}L_2/L_1 - \tfrac{1}{2}\omega^2 L_2 C\} & j\{\omega L_2 + \tfrac{1}{4}\omega L_2^2/L_1 - \tfrac{1}{4}\omega^3 L_2^2 C\} \\ j\{-1/\omega L_1 + \omega C\} & \{1 + \tfrac{1}{2}L_2/L_1 - \tfrac{1}{2}\omega^2 L_2 C\} \end{pmatrix}$$

$$= \begin{pmatrix} \cos\varphi & jZ \sin\varphi \\ \dfrac{j}{Z} \sin\varphi & \cos\varphi \end{pmatrix} \qquad (36)$$

where

$$\cos \varphi = 1 + \frac{1}{2}\frac{L_2}{L_1} - \frac{1}{2}\omega^2 L_2 C$$

$$= 1 + \frac{1}{2}\frac{L_2}{L_1}\left(1 - \frac{\omega^2}{\omega_c{}^2}\right)$$

$$Z^2 = \frac{L_2}{C}\frac{\omega^2(\omega_\infty{}^2 - \omega^2)}{(\omega^2 - \omega_c{}^2)(\omega_\infty{}^2 - \omega_c{}^2)}$$

$$\omega_c{}^2 = 1/L_1 C$$

$$\omega_\infty{}^2 = \omega_c{}^2 + 4/L_2 C$$

The expressions for ω_c and ω_∞ are the lower and upper cutoffs, respectively. For $\omega_c < \omega < \omega_\infty$, φ and Z are real, thus defining the passband. For $\omega < \omega_c$ or $\omega > \omega_\infty$, Z and φ become purely imaginary and we have the stop bands. For the waveguide, $\omega_\infty = \infty$ so that there is no finite upper cutoff.

We observe that at ω_c, Z becomes ∞, and at ω_∞ it becomes zero. The eigenvectors of $\mathbf{M}$, Eq. (36), are

$$\mathbf{x} = \begin{pmatrix} \pm Z \\ 1 \end{pmatrix}_{e^{\pm j\varphi}} \qquad \text{or} \qquad \begin{pmatrix} 1 \\ \pm 1/Z \end{pmatrix}_{e^{\pm j\varphi}} \tag{37}$$

When Z does not equal zero or infinity, there are two linearly independent eigenvectors. At either cutoff, however, the two eigenvectors become the same, and we must go to the concept of the generalized eigenvector to develop a complete system of vectors.

At $\omega = \omega_c$, $\mathbf{M}$ becomes

$$\mathbf{M}(\omega_c) = \begin{pmatrix} 1 & j\omega_c L_2 \\ 0 & 1 \end{pmatrix} \tag{38}$$

so that the circuit looks the same as a pure series inductance equal to L_2. A suitable chain is given by

$$\mathbf{x}_2 = \begin{pmatrix} 0 \\ 1 \end{pmatrix}_1, \qquad \mathbf{x}_1 = (\mathbf{A} - \mathbf{I})\mathbf{x}_2 = \begin{pmatrix} j\omega_c L_2 \\ 0 \end{pmatrix} \tag{39}$$

At $\omega = \omega_\infty$, $\mathbf{M}$ becomes

$$\mathbf{M}(\omega_\infty) = \begin{pmatrix} -1 & 0 \\ 4j/\omega_\infty L_2 & -1 \end{pmatrix} \tag{40}$$

which does not have quite as simple an interpretation. (It can be interpreted as being equivalent to an ideal inverting transformer, to give the minus signs, and a pure shunt admittance.)

A suitable chain is given by

$$\mathbf{x}_2 = \begin{pmatrix} 1 \\ 0 \end{pmatrix}_{-1}, \qquad \mathbf{x}_1 = (\mathbf{A} + \mathbf{I})\mathbf{x}_2 = \begin{pmatrix} 0 \\ 4j/\omega_\infty L_2 \end{pmatrix} \tag{41}$$

The matrix, then, is semisimple inside either the passband or the stopbands. As we go from the passband to a stopband, however, there is an abrupt change of regime from purely real to purely imaginary, signaled by the change of φ, the effective electrical length, and the iterated impedance Z from pure real to pure imaginary values. It is at the boundary between the two regimes that semisimplicity disappears and generalized eigenvectors must be used.

As a general observation, semisimplicity seems to be the practical rule except at the limit of some regime or approximation. Had we retained the loss factors that are present in any physical embodiment of Fig. 5, the problem would not have arisen.

12. STRUCTURE OF THE CHARACTERISTIC EQUATION

The characteristic equation, as given by Eq. (15), is a polynomial in λ of degree n, such that the coefficient of λ^n is $(-1)^n$. We can, however, be more specific by using the fact that its roots are λ_1, λ_2, ..., λ_n, where any multiplicity of the roots is accounted for by writing the same root the appropriate number of times. Specifically we can write the characteristic equation as

$$| \mathbf{A} - \lambda \mathbf{I} | = \prod_{i=1}^{n} (\lambda_i - \lambda) \tag{42}$$

multiplicities being included.

If we expand Eq. (42), we see that it can be written as

$$| \mathbf{A} - \lambda \mathbf{I} | = \prod_{i=1}^{n} \lambda_i - \sum_{j=1}^{n} \left(\prod_{i=1}^{n} \lambda_i \right) \lambda / \lambda_j + \cdots$$

$$+ \left(\sum_{i=1}^{n} \lambda_i \right) (-1)^{n-1} \lambda^{n-1} + (-1)^n \lambda^n \tag{43}$$

The coefficient of λ^m, where $0 \leqslant m < n$, is $(-1)^m$ times the sum of all possible products of $(n - m)$ of the eigenvalues, multiplicities included.

For example, if $\mathbf{A}$ is a 4×4 matrix, and

$$| \mathbf{A} - \lambda \mathbf{I} | = a_4 - a_3 \lambda + a_2 \lambda^2 - a_1 \lambda^3 + \lambda^4$$

then

$$a_4 = \lambda_1 \lambda_2 \lambda_3 \lambda_4$$
$$a_3 = \lambda_1 \lambda_2 \lambda_3 + \lambda_1 \lambda_2 \lambda_4 + \lambda_1 \lambda_3 \lambda_4 + \lambda_2 \lambda_3 \lambda_4$$
$$a_2 = \lambda_1 \lambda_2 + \lambda_1 \lambda_3 + \lambda_1 \lambda_4 + \lambda_2 \lambda_3 + \lambda_2 \lambda_4 + \lambda_3 \lambda_4$$
$$a_1 = \lambda_1 + \lambda_2 + \lambda_3 + \lambda_4$$

We can obtain another description of these coefficients. Let us write, generally,

$$| \mathbf{A} - \lambda \mathbf{I} | = p(\lambda) = a_n - a_{n-1}\lambda + \cdots + (-1)^{n-1}a_1\lambda^{n-1} + (-1)^n\lambda^n$$

$$= \sum_{m=0}^{n} (-1)^{n-m} a_m \lambda^{n-m} \tag{44}$$

where $a_0 = 1$.

Evidently, then, we can write

$$a_{n-m} = \frac{(-1)^m}{m!} \left(\frac{d^m p}{d\lambda^m} \right)_{\lambda=0} \tag{45}$$

so that a_{n-m} is obtained from the mth derivative of $p(\lambda) = | \mathbf{A} - \lambda \mathbf{I} |$, evaluated at $\lambda = 0$. The coefficient a_n is $p(0)$ itself, or the determinant of $\mathbf{A}$.

Applying the rules for the derivative of a determinant, we find that these coefficients have a special form. If, for example, $\mathbf{A}$ is 4×4, we find that

$$\frac{dp}{d\lambda} = \begin{vmatrix} -1 & 0 & 0 & 0 \\ A_{21} & A_{22} - \lambda & A_{23} & A_{24} \\ A_{31} & A_{32} & A_{33} - \lambda & A_{34} \\ A_{41} & A_{42} & A_{43} & A_{44} - \lambda \end{vmatrix}$$

$$+ \begin{vmatrix} A_{11} - \lambda & A_{12} & A_{13} & A_{14} \\ 0 & -1 & 0 & 0 \\ A_{31} & A_{32} & A_{33} - \lambda & A_{34} \\ A_{41} & A_{42} & A_{43} & A_{44} - \lambda \end{vmatrix}$$

$$+ \begin{vmatrix} A_{11} - \lambda & A_{12} & A_{13} & A_{14} \\ A_{21} & A_{22} - \lambda & A_{23} & A_{24} \\ 0 & 0 & -1 & 0 \\ A_{41} & A_{42} & A_{43} & A_{44} - \lambda \end{vmatrix} \tag{46}$$

$$+ \begin{vmatrix} A_{11} - \lambda & A_{12} & A_{13} & A_{14} \\ A_{21} & A_{22} - \lambda & A_{23} & A_{24} \\ A_{31} & A_{32} & A_{33} - \lambda & A_{34} \\ 0 & 0 & 0 & -1 \end{vmatrix}$$

and, at $\lambda = 0$,

$$\frac{dp}{d\lambda}\bigg|_{\lambda=0} = - \begin{vmatrix} A_{22} & A_{23} & A_{24} \\ A_{32} & A_{33} & A_{34} \\ A_{42} & A_{43} & A_{44} \end{vmatrix} - \begin{vmatrix} A_{11} & A_{13} & A_{14} \\ A_{31} & A_{33} & A_{34} \\ A_{41} & A_{43} & A_{44} \end{vmatrix}$$

$$- \begin{vmatrix} A_{11} & A_{12} & A_{14} \\ A_{21} & A_{22} & A_{24} \\ A_{41} & A_{42} & A_{44} \end{vmatrix} - \begin{vmatrix} A_{11} & A_{12} & A_{13} \\ A_{21} & A_{22} & A_{23} \\ A_{31} & A_{32} & A_{33} \end{vmatrix} \tag{47}$$

The first determinant is the minor obtained from **A** by striking out the first row and first column, the second by striking out the second row and column, etc.

A minor obtained from a determinant by striking out rows and columns symmetrically is called a *principal minor* of **A**.

Equation (47), with Eq. (45), says that a_3 is the sum of the 3-rowed principal minors of **A**.

Continuing, we find that

$$\frac{d^2p}{d\lambda^2}\bigg|_{\lambda=0} = 2\begin{vmatrix} A_{33} & A_{34} \\ A_{43} & A_{44} \end{vmatrix} + 2\begin{vmatrix} A_{22} & A_{24} \\ A_{42} & A_{44} \end{vmatrix} + 2\begin{vmatrix} A_{11} & A_{14} \\ A_{41} & A_{44} \end{vmatrix}$$

$$+ 2\begin{vmatrix} A_{22} & A_{23} \\ A_{32} & A_{33} \end{vmatrix} + 2\begin{vmatrix} A_{11} & A_{13} \\ A_{31} & A_{33} \end{vmatrix} + 2\begin{vmatrix} A_{11} & A_{12} \\ A_{21} & A_{22} \end{vmatrix} \tag{48}$$

The factor 2 results from the fact that each terms is obtained in two ways. The first determinant in Eq. (48) is obtained, for example, in the derivative of both the first and second determinants in Eq. (46). The same is true of all the other terms in Eq. (48).

We find, then, that a_2 is simply the sum of all the 2-rowed principal minors of **A**.

In general, if the characteristic equation of an $n \times n$ matrix **A** is written in the form of Eq. (44), the coefficient a_m is the sum of all the m-rowed principal minors of **A**.

Thus we have two developments of the coefficients a_m. One is an internal one, expressing it as the sum of all possible products of m of the eigenvalues, multiplicities included. The other, and external description, is as the sum of the m-rowed principal minors of **A**.

The importance of these coefficients lies in the fact, which we shall show in Chapter V, that the characteristic equation, and hence these coefficients, are independent of the coordinate system. Thus they form a set of *scalar invariants* of the matrix **A**, which, in an appropriate sense, characterize the mapping which **A** describes.

13. RANK OF A MATRIX

We have defined the rank of a matrix as the size of the largest nonzero minor contained in the matrix. Suppose **A** is an $n \times n$ matrix of rank k. Then all the minors, and hence all the principal minors of rank greater than k, are zero. Hence, in Eq. (44), all the coefficients a_m with m greater than k vanish. The characteristic equation, then, is divisible by λ^{n-k}, or zero is an eigenvalue of **A** with multiplicity at least $(n - k)$.

On the other hand, the rank is not synonymous with the number of nonzero eigenvalues. Consider, for example, the matrix

$$\mathbf{A} = \begin{pmatrix} 0 & a & b & c \\ 0 & 0 & d & e \\ 0 & 0 & 0 & f \\ 0 & 0 & 0 & 0 \end{pmatrix}$$

The only eigenvalue of $\mathbf{A}$ is zero but, if a, d, and f are not zero, its rank is 3. What has happened here is that there is only a single eigenvector, which is the end of a chain of length four, with zero eigenvalue. The difference between the dimensionality of the matrix and the rank is the number of linearly independent eigenvectors with zero eigenvalue, and does not count generalized eigenvectors.

A better way of stating this is that the difference of the dimensionality and the rank is the dimensionality of what we shall call the *null space* of the matrix—i.e., the space containing all vectors that are annihilated by the matrix.

14. THE TRACE OF A MATRIX

Two of the coefficients of the characteristic equation are of particular importance. One, a_n, we have already seen. It is simply the determinant of $\mathbf{A}$ (and is also the only n-rowed principal minor of $\mathbf{A}$). The other is the coefficient a_1, or the coefficient, times $(-1)^{n-1}$, of λ^{n-1}.

This coefficient is, we have seen, the algebraic sum of the eigenvalues of $\mathbf{A}$, multiplicities included. It is also the sum of the 1-rowed principal minors of $\mathbf{A}$, which are simply the elements on the main diagonal of $\mathbf{A}$. This coefficient is of sufficient importance to be given a special name. It is called the *trace* of $\mathbf{A}$, written tr $\mathbf{A}$:

$$\text{tr } \mathbf{A} = \sum_i A_{ii} = \sum_i \lambda_i \tag{49}$$

It is also sometimes called the *spur* of $\mathbf{A}$ (from the German word meaning track or trail) and written sp $\mathbf{A}$.

Its importance is partly in the ease with which it can be calculated. It provides, then, a scalar that characterizes $\mathbf{A}$ at least to a limited extent, and which is independent of the coordinate system being used.

A somewhat more profound reason for its importance is that it is a scalar function that is linear in $\mathbf{A}$, so that

$$\text{tr } \alpha\mathbf{A} = \alpha \text{ tr } \mathbf{A} \tag{50}$$

where α is a scalar. This property we describe by saying that it is a *linear functional* of $\mathbf{A}$. We shall see later that this is a significant property, and will discuss some of its uses.

15. RECIPROCAL VECTORS

Our work so far has been based on the representation of a vector as a column matrix. We have emphasized, however, that we could just as well have taken the row matrix as our standard representation. We shall, therefore, take the time here to consider what are the analogous results in the space of row matrices—which is sometimes called the *adjoint vector space* or *dual space*.

To do this, it is convenient to start with a slightly different concept, the vector set that is *reciprocal* to a given set under the unitary inner product, since in this way we avoid some of the problems of degeneracy and the like. We assume that we have a set of vectors, $\mathbf{u}_i$, which are complete and linearly independent. We ask if we can find a set $\mathbf{w}_i$ such that

$$\mathbf{w}_i{}^\dagger \mathbf{u}_j = \delta_{ij} \tag{51}$$

where δ_{ij} is the Kronecker delta. If so, we shall call this set the set of *reciprocal vectors* to the set $\mathbf{u}_i$. It implies the unitary inner product relation. We could consider a more general inner product relation, but there seems to be no great advantage in doing so.

Such a set can always be found. Consider, for example, $\mathbf{w}_1$. We require that

$$\mathbf{w}_1{}^\dagger \mathbf{u}_1 = 1$$

$$\mathbf{w}_1{}^\dagger \mathbf{u}_i = 0, \qquad i \neq 1$$

Let the components of $\mathbf{w}_1$ be w_{1i} and $\mathbf{u}_i$ be u_{ij}. Then these equations require that

$$\sum_j w_{1j}^* u_{1j} = 1$$

$$\sum_j w_{1j}^* u_{ij} = 0, \qquad i \neq 1$$

These equations are a set of n linear inhomogeneous equations in the n unknowns w_{1j}^*. The left-hand side is nonsingular since the $\mathbf{u}_i$ are linearly independent. Therefore, they can be solved for the w_{1j}^*, or for the vector $\mathbf{w}_1$.

In similar fashion, we can solve for the other $\mathbf{w}_i$.

We may describe this process by saying that the set $\mathbf{u}_i$ ($i \neq 1$) spans an $(n - 1)$-dimensional subspace. We can find a direction which is orthogonal to this entire subspace. The inner product with $\mathbf{u}_1$ of any vector with this direction is nonzero. Hence we can fix the sign and magnitude of $\mathbf{w}_1$, taken along this direction, so that $\mathbf{w}_1{}^t\mathbf{u}_1 = 1$.

The set $\mathbf{w}_i$ so found must be linearly independent. For suppose they were not. Then there would exist a nontrivial set of scalars c_i such that

$$\sum_i c_i \mathbf{w}_i = 0$$

Multiplying Eq. (51) by $c_i{}^*$ and adding over all i for a fixed j, we obtain

$$\sum_i c_i{}^* \mathbf{w}_i{}^t \mathbf{u}_j = c_i{}^* \delta_{ij} = c_j{}^*$$

This can be written as

$$c_j{}^* = \left(\sum_i c_i \mathbf{w}_i\right)^t \mathbf{u}_j = 0$$

by assumption. But this must be true for any j, so that all the scalars must vanish, contrary to assumption. Hence the set $\mathbf{w}_i$ must be linearly independent.

If we use the set $\mathbf{u}_i$ as a basis for the whole space, the set $\mathbf{w}_i$ is the *reciprocal basis*.

16. RECIPROCAL EIGENVECTORS

If the set $\mathbf{u}_i$ are a complete set of eigenvectors for a semisimple matrix $\mathbf{A}$, we may now ask what role is played by the set of reciprocal vectors, $\mathbf{w}_i$?

We consider the set of unitary inner products of $\mathbf{w}_i$ with $\mathbf{A}\mathbf{u}_j$:

$$\mathbf{w}_i{}^\dagger (\mathbf{A}\mathbf{u}_j) = \mathbf{w}_i{}^\dagger (\lambda_j \mathbf{u}_j) = \lambda_j \delta_{ij} = \lambda_i \delta_{ij}$$

However, this inner product can also be written as $(\mathbf{w}_i{}^\dagger \mathbf{A})\mathbf{u}_j$. With Eq. (51), then,

$$(\mathbf{w}_i{}^\dagger \mathbf{A})\mathbf{u}_j = (\lambda_i \mathbf{w}_i{}^\dagger)\mathbf{u}_j$$

or

$$(\mathbf{w}_i{}^\dagger \mathbf{A} - \lambda_i \mathbf{w}_i{}^\dagger)\mathbf{u}_j = 0$$

Since this must be true for any $\mathbf{u}_j$ in the complete set, the left-hand vector must be the null vector, and

$$\mathbf{w}_i{}^\dagger \mathbf{A} = \lambda_i \mathbf{w}_i{}^\dagger \tag{52}$$

We call $\mathbf{w}_i{}^\dagger$ a *left-hand* or *reciprocal eigenvector* of $\mathbf{A}$, with the same eigenvalue as the corresponding $\mathbf{u}_i$.

We can also take the hermitian conjugate of Eq. (52) and write

$$\mathbf{A}^\dagger \mathbf{w}_i = \lambda_i{}^* \mathbf{w}_i \tag{53}$$

so that the set $\mathbf{w}_i$ are the eigenvectors of $\mathbf{A}^\dagger$, the hermitian conjugate of $\mathbf{A}$. The eigenvalues are the complex conjugates of the corresponding eigenvalues of $\mathbf{A}$. In the next chapter, we shall see that we can describe this by saying that the $\mathbf{w}_i$ are the eigenvectors of the matrix that is "adjoint to $\mathbf{A}$ under the unitary inner product."

We recall that the set $\mathbf{u}_i$ are not completely fixed. We can multiply each $\mathbf{u}_i$ by any scalar, except zero, and it remains an eigenvector. Further, if $\mathbf{A}$ is degenerate, we can resolve its degeneracies in any way we like. These changes will all affect the particular set $\mathbf{w}_i$ that is obtained, but will not affect the validity of Eq. (52). It is to avoid these ambiguities that we have approached the problem of finding the left-hand eigenvectors through the concept of a reciprocal set of vectors.

17. RECIPROCAL GENERALIZED EIGENVECTORS

There remains the question of what happens when $\mathbf{A}$ is not semisimple. Suppose, to be specific, we have a chain of length p with eigenvalue λ:

$$\mathbf{A}\mathbf{u}_1 = \lambda \mathbf{u}_1$$
$$\mathbf{A}\mathbf{u}_2 = \lambda \mathbf{u}_2 + \mathbf{u}_1$$
$$\cdots$$
$$\mathbf{A}\mathbf{u}_p = \lambda \mathbf{u}_p + \mathbf{u}_{p-1} \tag{54}$$

Any other eigenvectors and chains that $\mathbf{A}$ may have do not affect the argument.

We determine the set $\mathbf{w}_i$ that is reciprocal to all the vectors of the set $\mathbf{u}_i$. The nonzero inner products of $\mathbf{w}_i$ ($1 \leqslant i \leqslant p$) with $\mathbf{A}\mathbf{u}_i$ are

$$\mathbf{w}_1{}^\dagger \mathbf{A}\mathbf{u}_1 = \lambda, \qquad \mathbf{w}_1{}^\dagger \mathbf{A}\mathbf{u}_2 = 1$$
$$\mathbf{w}_2{}^\dagger \mathbf{A}\mathbf{u}_2 = \lambda, \qquad \mathbf{w}_2{}^\dagger \mathbf{A}\mathbf{u}_3 = 1$$
$$\cdots \qquad\qquad \cdots$$
$$\mathbf{w}_{p-1}{}^\dagger \mathbf{A}\mathbf{u}_{p-1} = \lambda, \qquad \mathbf{w}_{p-1}{}^\dagger \mathbf{A}\mathbf{u}_p = 1$$
$$\mathbf{w}_p{}^\dagger \mathbf{A}\mathbf{u}_p = \lambda \tag{55}$$

The vectors that satisfy these relations are

$$\mathbf{w}_p{}^\dagger \mathbf{A} = \lambda \mathbf{w}_p{}^\dagger$$
$$\mathbf{w}_{p-1}^\dagger \mathbf{A} = \lambda \mathbf{w}_{p-1}^\dagger + \mathbf{w}_p{}^\dagger$$
$$\cdots$$
$$\mathbf{w}_1{}^\dagger \mathbf{A} = \lambda \mathbf{w}_1{}^\dagger + \mathbf{w}_2{}^\dagger \tag{56}$$

or, taking the hermitian conjugate,

$$\mathbf{A}^\dagger \mathbf{w}_p = \lambda^* \mathbf{w}_p$$
$$\mathbf{A}^\dagger \mathbf{w}_{p-1} = \lambda^* \mathbf{w}_{p-1} + \mathbf{w}_p$$
$$\cdots$$
$$\mathbf{A}^\dagger \mathbf{w}_1 = \lambda^* \mathbf{w}_1 + \mathbf{w}_2 \tag{57}$$

The set $\mathbf{w}_1$, ..., $\mathbf{w}_p$ are a chain of length p of the matrix $\mathbf{A}^\dagger$, *but in the reverse order* from that of the chain $\mathbf{u}_1$, ..., $\mathbf{u}_p$. If $\mathbf{u}_i$ is a generalized eigenvector of the matrix $\mathbf{A}$ with rank k in a chain of length p, then $\mathbf{w}_i$ is a generalized eigenvector of $\mathbf{A}^\dagger$, also in a chain of length p, but with rank $(p - k)$. This reversal of the order of the generalized eigenvectors in the chains is a property of considerable importance which we will use later (for example, in Chapter XII).

As an example, consider the matrix of Eq. (33) and the chains of vectors:

$$\mathbf{x}_1 = \begin{pmatrix} 1 \\ 0 \\ -j \\ 0 \end{pmatrix}, \qquad \mathbf{x}_2 = \begin{pmatrix} 0 \\ 1 \\ 0 \\ 0 \end{pmatrix}$$

$$\mathbf{x}_3 = \begin{pmatrix} 0 \\ 1 \\ 0 \\ j \end{pmatrix}, \qquad \mathbf{x}_4 = \begin{pmatrix} 1 \\ 0 \\ 0 \\ 0 \end{pmatrix}$$

so that

$$\mathbf{A}\mathbf{x}_1 = 0, \qquad \mathbf{A}\mathbf{x}_3 = 0$$
$$\mathbf{A}\mathbf{x}_2 = \mathbf{x}_1, \qquad \mathbf{A}\mathbf{x}_4 = \mathbf{x}_3$$

We can find the reciprocal vectors to be

$$\mathbf{w}_1 = \begin{pmatrix} 0 \\ 0 \\ -j \\ 0 \end{pmatrix}, \qquad \mathbf{w}_2 = \begin{pmatrix} 0 \\ 1 \\ 0 \\ -j \end{pmatrix}$$

$$\mathbf{w}_3 = \begin{pmatrix} 0 \\ 0 \\ 0 \\ j \end{pmatrix}, \qquad \mathbf{w}_4 = \begin{pmatrix} 1 \\ 0 \\ j \\ 0 \end{pmatrix}$$

so that

$$\mathbf{w}_i{}^\dagger \mathbf{x}_j = \delta_{ij}$$

We observe now that

$$\mathbf{A}^\dagger \mathbf{w}_1 = \mathbf{w}_2, \qquad \mathbf{A}^\dagger \mathbf{w}_3 = \mathbf{w}_4$$
$$\mathbf{A}^\dagger \mathbf{w}_2 = \mathbf{0}, \qquad \mathbf{A}^\dagger \mathbf{w}_4 = \mathbf{0}$$

so that $\mathbf{w}_1$, $\mathbf{w}_2$, $\mathbf{w}_3$, and $\mathbf{w}_4$ are chains of generalized eigenvectors of $\mathbf{A}^\dagger$, but labeled in reverse order in each chain.

18. VARIATIONAL DESCRIPTION OF THE EIGENVECTORS AND EIGENVALUES

As the final topic of this chapter, we shall show that the eigenvalues and eigenvectors can be given a variational significance. This will give us additional insight into the meaning of the eigenvectors. It is also a useful property, on occasion, for the development of approximate methods.

We consider the scalar-valued function of the vector $\mathbf{x}$ defined by

$$p(x) = (\mathbf{x}^\dagger \mathbf{A} \mathbf{x})/(\mathbf{x}^\dagger \mathbf{x}) \tag{58}$$

This is indeed a scalar since both $(\mathbf{x}^\dagger \mathbf{A} \mathbf{x})$ and $(\mathbf{x}^\dagger \mathbf{x})$ are scalars. Further, since $(\mathbf{x}^\dagger \mathbf{x})$ is positive definite, the function is well defined as long as we exclude some finite neighborhood of $\mathbf{x} = \mathbf{0}$. The function $p(\mathbf{x})$ is known as the *Raleigh quotient*.

We now ask: Is it possible to find an $\mathbf{x}$ such that $p(\mathbf{x})$ has a stationary value? By this we mean, an $\mathbf{x}$ such that $p(\mathbf{x} + \delta \mathbf{x}) = p(\mathbf{x})$ to the first order for any small variation, $\delta \mathbf{x}$.

The answer in general is negative. There is no such $\mathbf{x}$. However, for certain types of matrices, they do exist. When they exist, the appropriate vectors are eigenvectors, and the corresponding values of $p(\mathbf{x})$ are the corresponding eigenvalues.

The commonest class of matrices to which this method is applied is that of hermitian matrices, for which $\mathbf{A}^\dagger = \mathbf{A}$ or the class of symmetric matrices. This method will give all the eigenvectors and eigenvalues of a hermitian matrix. However, this is not a necessary condition. A broader condition for the success of the method is that the matrix shall be what we shall call "normal," which requires only that it commute with its hermitian conjugate.

Partly as an exercise in matrix manipulation, and partly for its own sake, we shall consider the problem generally, without any *a priori* condition on **A**. We ask, then, for the condition that will allow us to set

$$p(\mathbf{x} + \delta\mathbf{x}) = \frac{(\mathbf{x} + \delta\mathbf{x})^\dagger\mathbf{A}(\mathbf{x} + \delta\mathbf{x})}{(\mathbf{x} + \delta\mathbf{x})^\dagger(\mathbf{x} + \delta\mathbf{x})} = p(\mathbf{x}) \tag{59}$$

at least to the first order in $\delta\mathbf{x}$, for any small $\delta\mathbf{x}$. Equating Eq. (59) to (58), cross multiplying, and retaining only the terms that are first order in $\delta\mathbf{x}$ or $\delta\mathbf{x}^\dagger$, we obtain

$$(\mathbf{x}^\dagger\mathbf{x})\{(\delta\mathbf{x})^\dagger\mathbf{A}\mathbf{x} + \mathbf{x}^\dagger\mathbf{A}(\delta\mathbf{x})\} = (\mathbf{x}^\dagger\mathbf{A}\mathbf{x})\{(\delta\mathbf{x})^\dagger\mathbf{x} + \mathbf{x}^\dagger(\delta\mathbf{x})\}$$

or

$$(\delta\mathbf{x})^\dagger\{\mathbf{A}\mathbf{x} - p(\mathbf{x})\mathbf{x}\} + \{\mathbf{x}^\dagger\mathbf{A} - p(\mathbf{x})\mathbf{x}^\dagger\}\,\delta\mathbf{x} = 0 \tag{60}$$

Equation (60) must be true for all $\delta\mathbf{x}$ that do not make $\mathbf{x} + \delta\mathbf{x}$ the null vector. In particular, if it is true for $\delta\mathbf{x}$, it must be true for $j\,\delta\mathbf{x}$. Substituting this in Eq. (60) and removing the factor j, we get

$$(\delta\mathbf{x})^\dagger\{\mathbf{A}\mathbf{x} - p(\mathbf{x})\mathbf{x}\} - \{\mathbf{x}^\dagger\mathbf{A} - p(\mathbf{x})\mathbf{x}^\dagger\}\,\delta\mathbf{x} = 0 \tag{61}$$

Comparing Eqs. (60) and (61) we find we must have

$$(\delta\mathbf{x})^\dagger\{\mathbf{A}\mathbf{x} - p(\mathbf{x})\mathbf{x}\} = 0$$
$$\{\mathbf{x}^\dagger\mathbf{A} - p(\mathbf{x})\mathbf{x}^\dagger\}\,\delta\mathbf{x} = 0$$

Each of these must be true for all $\delta\mathbf{x}$. Therefore, the vectors in the brackets must be the null vectors:

$$\mathbf{A}\mathbf{x} - p(\mathbf{x})\mathbf{x} = 0 \tag{62}$$

$$\mathbf{x}^\dagger\mathbf{A} - p(\mathbf{x})\mathbf{x}^\dagger = 0 \tag{63}$$

Equation (63) can be put into more usual form by taking its hermitian conjugate, giving

$$\mathbf{A}^\dagger\mathbf{x} - p^*(\mathbf{x})\mathbf{x} = 0 \tag{64}$$

Equations (62) and (64) are eigenvector equations. Equation (62) tells us that $\mathbf{x}$ is an eigenvector of **A** with eigenvalue $p(\mathbf{x})$, while Eq. (64) says it is an eigenvector of $\mathbf{A}^\dagger$ with eigenvalue $p^*(\mathbf{x})$.

The necessary and sufficient condition for the existence of stationary values of $p(\mathbf{x})$ is, then, that **A** and $\mathbf{A}^\dagger$ shall have an eigenvector in common. The necessary and sufficient condition that this method shall give all the eigenvectors of $\mathbf{A}$ is that all eigenvectors of $\mathbf{A}$ shall also be eigenvectors of $\mathbf{A}^{\dagger}$. We shall show, in the next chapter, that this is true of normal matrices, and so of hermitian matrices which are a subset of the set of normal matrices. We can also show that this condition is necessary if the method is to give *all* the eigenvectors.

If $\mathbf{A}$ is hermitian, we can observe that the quadratic form $\mathbf{x}^{\dagger}\mathbf{A}\mathbf{x}$ is real for any $\mathbf{x}$. It follows that the Raleigh quotient is real. Hence the eigenvalues found by this method are all real. We shall find, in the next chapter, that all the eigenvalues of a hermitian matrix are real.

If, instead of the Raleigh quotient of Eq. (58), we use

$$p(\mathbf{x}) = (\mathbf{x}^{\dagger}\mathbf{K}\mathbf{A}\mathbf{x})/(\mathbf{x}^{\dagger}\mathbf{K}\mathbf{x}) \tag{65}$$

where $\mathbf{K}$ is positive definite and hermitian ($\mathbf{K}^{\dagger} = \mathbf{K}$), we obtain much the same results. Equation (62) is the same after factoring out the nonsingular $\mathbf{K}$. Instead of Eq. (64), we obtain

$$(\mathbf{K}^{-1}\mathbf{A}^{\dagger}\mathbf{K})\mathbf{x} - p^{*}(\mathbf{x})\mathbf{x} = \mathbf{0} \tag{66}$$

Hence the condition, in this case, is that the eigenvectors of $\mathbf{A}$ shall also be eigenvectors of $(\mathbf{K}^{-1}\mathbf{A}^{\dagger}\mathbf{K})$. In the next chapter, we shall see that this matrix is what we shall call the "K-adjoint" of $\mathbf{A}$, and that this requirement is equivalent to the requirement that $\mathbf{A}$ be what we shall call "K-normal."

We observe that Eq. (65) is essentially similar to Eq. (58) except that the inner product involved is more general. We can, in fact, write either of them as

$$p(\mathbf{x}) = \frac{\langle \mathbf{x}, \mathbf{A}\mathbf{x} \rangle}{\langle \mathbf{x}, \mathbf{x} \rangle} \tag{67}$$

This requires positive definiteness to assure that the denominator is well behaved—i.e., the inner product relation must be proper.

We could use an improper inner product by considering the variation of the scalar function of two vectors

$$p(\mathbf{x}, \mathbf{y}) = \frac{\langle \mathbf{y}, \mathbf{A}\mathbf{x} \rangle}{\langle \mathbf{y}, \mathbf{x} \rangle} \tag{68}$$

with the constraint that, having chosen an $\mathbf{x} \neq 0$, we must choose $\mathbf{y}$ so that $| \langle \mathbf{y}, \mathbf{x} \rangle |$ shall be greater than some positive real ϵ. We find again that $\mathbf{x}$ is an eigenvector of $\mathbf{A}$ and $p(\mathbf{x}, \mathbf{y})$ the eigenvalue. The equivalent of Eq. (66) now involves $\mathbf{y}$, not $\mathbf{x}$, which allows some more involved inferences. We shall not pursue this matter further here, since we will consider it in detail from another point of view later (Chapter IX).

As a approximation method, we can consider the Raleigh quotient where $\mathbf{x}$ is constrained to some subspace of the whole space. The determination of the vectors in this subspace for which $p(\mathbf{x})$ is stationary then gives a best approximation, in the subspace, to the eigenvectors, which may not be in the subspace at all. Suppose, for example, $\mathbf{A}_0$ is a matrix whose eigenvectors and eigenvalues are known, and suppose we·wish to know approximately at least the eigenvectors and values of $\mathbf{A} = \mathbf{A}_0 + \epsilon \mathbf{A}_1$, where ϵ is a small perturbation parameter. We can use this technique to study the approximate effect of the perturbation. If, for example, $\mathbf{x}_1$ and $\mathbf{x}_2$ are degenerate eigenvectors of $\mathbf{A}_0$, it may happen that the perturbation resolves the degeneracy, and $\mathbf{A}$ has eigenvectors $\mathbf{y}_1$ and $\mathbf{y}_2$ that are not degenerate, but are close to the subspace spanned by $\mathbf{x}_1$ and $\mathbf{x}_2$. We can use the variational method to determine the best approximation to $\mathbf{y}_1$ and $\mathbf{y}_2$ in this subspace, which may be a very good approximation indeed. (We will later see how to study this problem in other ways as well.)

Exercises

1. Find the eigenvalues and eigenvectors of

$$\mathbf{A} = \begin{pmatrix} a & b & 0 \\ c & a & b \\ 0 & c & a \end{pmatrix}$$

2. Find the eigenvalues and eigenvectors of

$$\mathbf{A} = \begin{pmatrix} \tfrac{1}{2}(1-j) & 0 & \tfrac{1}{2}(1-j) & 0 \\ 0 & \tfrac{1}{2}(-1+j) & 0 & \tfrac{1}{2}(-1+j) \\ \tfrac{1}{2}(-1+j) & 0 & \tfrac{1}{2}(1-j) & 0 \\ 0 & \tfrac{1}{2}(1-j) & 0 & \tfrac{1}{2}(-1+j) \end{pmatrix}$$

3. Find the eigenvalues and chains of generalized eigenvectors of

$$\mathbf{A} = \begin{pmatrix} 2 & \tfrac{1}{2} & 0 & \tfrac{1}{2} \\ \tfrac{1}{2} & 0 & \tfrac{1}{2}j & 2 \\ 0 & \tfrac{1}{2}j & 2 & \tfrac{1}{2}j \\ \tfrac{1}{2} & 2 & \tfrac{1}{2}j & 0 \end{pmatrix}$$

Show the degeneracy of the chain explicitly.

4. Consider the matrix

$$\mathbf{A} = \begin{pmatrix} \cos\theta & \sin\theta \\ -\sin\theta & \cos\theta \end{pmatrix}$$

where θ is real and not zero or a multiple of π. This matrix describes a rotation in euclidean 2-space. Find its eigenvalues and eigenvectors. Observe that its eigenvalues are complex, and that its eigenvectors, however normalized, have at least one complex coefficient. It follows that in the field of real numbers, $\mathbf{A}$ has no eigenvalues or eigenvectors. This is a consequence of the fact that the field of real numbers is not algebraically complete. What is the physical significance of this? Would you expect the same thing to be true of a rotation in euclidean 3-space?

5. Consider the matrix

$$\mathbf{A} = \begin{pmatrix} j & \frac{1}{2} & -\frac{1}{2}j & 0 \\ \frac{1}{2} & 0 & 1 & \frac{1}{2}j \\ \frac{1}{2}j & -1 & 0 & -\frac{1}{2} \\ 0 & \frac{1}{2}j & \frac{1}{2} & j \end{pmatrix}$$

Verify that

$$\mathbf{x}_1 = \begin{pmatrix} 1 \\ 0 \\ 0 \\ j \end{pmatrix}, \quad \mathbf{x}_2 = \begin{pmatrix} 0 \\ 1 \\ j \\ 0 \end{pmatrix}, \quad \mathbf{x}_3 = \begin{pmatrix} 1 \\ 0 \\ 0 \\ -j \end{pmatrix}, \quad \mathbf{x}_4 = \begin{pmatrix} 0 \\ j \\ 1 \\ 0 \end{pmatrix}$$

are eigenvectors and generalized eigenvectors of $\mathbf{A}$. Find the reciprocal set and verify that they are eigenvectors of $\mathbf{A}^\dagger$. Observe the reversal of order.

6. Consider the vectors in euclidean 3-space:

$$\mathbf{x}_1 = \begin{pmatrix} 1 \\ 1 \\ 0 \end{pmatrix}, \quad \mathbf{x}_2 = \begin{pmatrix} 0 \\ 1 \\ 0 \end{pmatrix}, \quad \mathbf{x}_3 = \begin{pmatrix} 0 \\ 1 \\ 1 \end{pmatrix}$$

Obtain the reciprocal vectors under the euclidean inner product.

7. Find the eigenvalues of a matrix of the form

$$\mathbf{A} = \begin{pmatrix} 0 & 0 & \cdots & 0 & \alpha_1 \\ 0 & 0 & \cdots & \alpha_2 & 0 \\ & \cdots & & & \\ 0 & \alpha_{n-1} & \cdots & 0 & 0 \\ \alpha_n & 0 & \cdots & 0 & 0 \end{pmatrix}$$

What are the corresponding eigenvectors if the α_i are all nonzero? What happens if, say, $\alpha_1 = 0$, $\alpha_n \neq 0$?

8. If **A** is an $n \times n$ matrix such that $\mathbf{AX} = \mathbf{XA}$ for **X** any $n \times n$ matrix with coefficients in the field of complex numbers, prove that **A** must be a scalar times the identity. (This is a specific case of what is called "Schur's lemma," which is quite important in group theory.)

9. Suppose **A** and **B** are $n \times n$ hermitian matrices, both of which are positive definite. Let λ_n be the largest eigenvalue of **A**. Show that the largest eigenvalue of $(\mathbf{A} + \mathbf{B})$ is larger than λ_n . (Hint: Use the variational expression for the eigenvalues.)

10. What is the characteristic equation of a matrix of the form

$$
\mathbf{A} = \begin{pmatrix}
0 & 1 & 0 & 0 & \cdots & 0 \\
0 & 0 & 1 & 0 & \cdots & 0 \\
0 & 0 & 0 & 1 & \cdots & 0 \\
\cdots \\
0 & 0 & 0 & 0 & \cdots & 1 \\
-a_{n-1} & -a_{n-2} & -a_{n-3} & -a_{n-4} & \cdots & -a_0
\end{pmatrix}
$$

Hence conclude that every polynomial of degree n is the characteristic equation of some $n \times n$ matrix.

(The form involved, here, is the block used in the so-called *rational canonical form*. That is, it can be shown that every matrix can be put into quasidiagonal form, where the submatrices on the diagonal have the form given.)

11. Show that if s is a scalar variable, then, to the first order in s,

$$| \mathbf{I} + s\mathbf{A} | = \mathbf{I} + s \operatorname{tr} \mathbf{A} + \cdots$$

Show that if s is a scalar variable, then, to the first order in s,

$$| \mathbf{A} + s\mathbf{B} | = | \mathbf{A} |\{1 + s \operatorname{tr}(\mathbf{A}^{-1}\mathbf{B}) + \cdots\}$$

Suppose **A** is an $n \times n$ matrix such that

$$\operatorname{tr}(\mathbf{AX}) = 0$$

for any **X**. Show that **A** must be the null matrix.

12. If $\rho(\mathbf{A})$ is the rank of **A**, show that, for any $n \times n$ matrix, **A**, there exists a **B** such that $\mathbf{AB} = 0$ and

$$\rho(\mathbf{A}) + \rho(\mathbf{B}) = n$$

CHAPTER IV

Hermitian, Unitary, and Normal Matrices

We shall now consider certain special classes of matrices. In some applications, e.g., quantum mechanics, these classes are important in their own right. In quantum mechanics, one of the postulates is that an observable quantity is necessarily represented by a hermitian operator. Hence such operators have a very special importance.

In other situations, such as coupled mode theory, this is not so. However, even in this case, it is sometimes possible to change the coordinate axes to ones in terms of which the operator assumes a designated form. If so, even when it is inconvenient to make the transformation to that form, we still gain knowledge of some of its properties by studying the form.

These classes are also important from a mathematical standpoint. One of the key questions of matrix algebra is to determine the structure of a matrix—i.e., whether it is semisimple or not. There is no systematic way of doing this in general except by finding explicitly the eigenvectors and chains. This is an unsatisfactory situation, but is a problem that has not been solved. In the case of these special classes, however, this is not true. We will show that any matrix that is of any of these types is necessarily semisimple. In fact, we can go further and show that the eigenvectors are always orthogonal under the unitary inner product relation. Since the type can be determined easily and directly from the matrix itself, this is a rather remarkable accomplishment. Further, it is a very useful one since orthogonality is an extremely powerful tool for making tractable problem that would other wise be too formidable for practical solution.

Finally, it may be observed that the analysis of these types of matrices involves methods that penetrate quite deeply into the nature of the transformation represented by the matrix. Thus they provide a good illustration and point of reference for these methods of analysis.

1. ADJOINT RELATION

To define the classes of matrices that we are considering, we will use the concept of an adjoint matrix.

97

The term *adjoint*, meaning literally "joined to," indicates only an operator that is somehow derived from the given one.

We shall use the term in a very precise way. This way is a specialization of its use in the more general theory of abstract linear vector spaces (including infinitely dimensioned matrices and integral equations). It is derived from, and dependent on, the concept of an inner product relation.

Stated broadly, the inner product relation, $\langle \mathbf{x}, \mathbf{y} \rangle$, is a way of combining two vectors so as to obtain a scalar quantity, a *functional*, that can be regarded as a generalization of the dot product of vector analysis.

If we allow the operator $\mathbf{A}$ to transform one of these vectors, say $\mathbf{y}$, to $\mathbf{Ay}$, then we have changed the scalar function involved. But this change could also have been obtained by allowing some other operator, $\mathbf{A}^{\#}$, to operate on the other component $\mathbf{x}$ of the inner product.

Our ultimate interest is generally in how various scalar quantities are transformed. We want to know the amplification or decay factor, or something of the sort. That which can be read off a meter or measured with a yard stick is necessarily a scalar quantity, and it is such things that we generally want to know.

If there are two processes by which the same change can be induced in a given scalar quantity, and which are equivalent in the sense of yielding the same answer regardless of initial or boundary conditions, then it may be worthwhile to investigate the relation between these processes.

We are, therefore, lead to define the adjointness relation with respect to a given inner product by the following:

Definition.   *Given a linear vector space with an inner product relation defined. If* $\mathbf{A}$ *is a matrix operator in this space, then* $\mathbf{A}^{\#}$ *is its* **adjoint** *if*

$$\langle \mathbf{x}, \mathbf{Ay} \rangle = \langle \mathbf{A}^{\#}\mathbf{x}, \mathbf{y} \rangle \tag{1}$$

for **all** $\mathbf{x}$ *and* $\mathbf{y}$ *in the space.*

It can be shown that any linear operator in any linear vector space with any proper inner product relation has an adjoint and that this adjoint is unique.

We shall not attempt such a general proof. For the types of inner product relations that we will consider, however, the existence and uniqueness of the adjoint are not difficult to see.

We are, for example, particularly interested (in this chapter) in the unitary inner product, defined as

$$\langle \mathbf{x}, \mathbf{y} \rangle = \mathbf{x}^{\dagger}\mathbf{y} \tag{2}$$

If, for a given $\mathbf{A}$, we seek $\mathbf{A}^{\#}$ according to Eq. (1), with this definition of the inner product we see that we require, for all $\mathbf{x}$ and $\mathbf{y}$,

$$(\mathbf{A}^{\#}\mathbf{x})^{\dagger}\mathbf{y} = \mathbf{x}^{\dagger}\mathbf{A}^{\#\dagger}\mathbf{y} = \mathbf{x}^{\dagger}\mathbf{A}\mathbf{y} \tag{3}$$

This will be true providing the operators are equal, or

$$\mathbf{A}^{\#} = \mathbf{A}^{\dagger} \tag{4}$$

Furthermore, if the operators are not equal, then there must be some $\mathbf{y}$ for which $\mathbf{A}\mathbf{y}$ is different from $(\mathbf{A}^{\#\dagger}\mathbf{y})$, and some $\mathbf{x}$ for which this difference is significant. Hence the adjoint is unique.

We will later consider a more general inner product relation using the metric $\mathbf{K}$:

$$\langle \mathbf{x}, \mathbf{y} \rangle = \mathbf{x}^{\dagger}\mathbf{K}\mathbf{y} \tag{5}$$

where $\mathbf{K}$ is nonsingular, hermitian, and, for the present, positive definite. We require, in this case, that for all $\mathbf{x}$ and $\mathbf{y}$

$$(\mathbf{A}^{\#}\mathbf{x})^{\dagger}\mathbf{K}\mathbf{y} = \mathbf{x}^{\dagger}\mathbf{A}^{\#\dagger}\mathbf{K}\mathbf{y} = \mathbf{x}^{\dagger}\mathbf{K}\mathbf{A}\mathbf{y} \tag{6}$$

Again the operators must be equal, so that the unique solution is

$$\mathbf{A}^{\#} = \mathbf{K}^{-1}\mathbf{A}^{\dagger}\mathbf{K} \tag{7}$$

It is these adjoint operators with which we shall be dealing. That consideration of them is a useful thing will become evident. The argument we have given above is intended to make plausible what may otherwise seem a wholly arbitrary act. The final proof of utility is developed only by making use of the concept.

2. RULE OF COMBINATION

We will need to know what is the adjoint, under a given inner product relation, of the product of two operators.

This we can find by considering the inner product of $\mathbf{x}$ and $(\mathbf{AB}\mathbf{y})$:

$$\langle \mathbf{x}, \mathbf{AB}\mathbf{y} \rangle = \langle (\mathbf{AB})^{\#}\mathbf{x}, \mathbf{y} \rangle$$
$$= \langle \mathbf{A}^{\#}\mathbf{x}, \mathbf{B}\mathbf{y} \rangle = \langle \mathbf{B}^{\#}\mathbf{A}^{\#}\mathbf{x}, \mathbf{y} \rangle \tag{8}$$

We see that

$$(\mathbf{AB})^{\#} = \mathbf{B}^{\#}\mathbf{A}^{\#} \tag{9}$$

so that the adjoint of a product is the product of the adjoints in reverse order.

Since the hermitian conjugate $\mathbf{A}^\dagger$ is the adjoint under the unitary inner product, this provides a simple proof of the rule of combination under hermitian conjugation:

$$(\mathbf{AB})^\dagger = \mathbf{B}^\dagger\mathbf{A}^\dagger \tag{10}$$

We shall shortly have occasion to use these relations.

3. THE BASIC TYPES

With the unitary inner product relation of Eq. (2), the adjoint of a matrix $\mathbf{A}$, as given by Eq. (4), is the hermitian conjugate.

We are lead to ask how this adjoint operator compares with the original operator, and we find it convenient to define various classes of matrices for which this relation between $\mathbf{A}$ and its adjoint has useful simplicities.

Definition. *If $\mathbf{A}$ is equal to its adjoint under the unitary inner product, then $\mathbf{A}$ is* **hermitian**:

$$\mathbf{A} = \mathbf{A}^\dagger \tag{11}$$

It is also convenient to give a name to the opposite situation:

Definition. *If $\mathbf{A}$ is the negative of its adjoint under the unitary inner product relation, $\mathbf{A}$ is* **skew-hermitian**:

$$\mathbf{A}^\dagger = -\mathbf{A} \tag{12}$$

The next simplest possible relation, perhaps, is given by:

Definition. *If the adjoint to A under the unitary inner product is equal to the reciprocal of $\mathbf{A}$, then $\mathbf{A}$ is* **unitary**:

$$\mathbf{A}^\dagger = \mathbf{A}^{-1} \quad \text{or} \quad \mathbf{AA}^\dagger = \mathbf{I} = \mathbf{A}^\dagger\mathbf{A} \tag{13}$$

This, of course, implies that a unitary matrix is nonsingular.

The final relation that concerns us is commutativity:

Definition. *If $\mathbf{A}$ commutes with its adjoint under the unitary inner product, $\mathbf{A}$ is* **normal**:

$$\mathbf{AA}^\dagger = \mathbf{A}^\dagger\mathbf{A} \tag{14}$$

Since $\mathbf{A}$ necessarily commutes both with itself and with its reciprocal, it follows that any hermitian or unitary matrix is normal. The converse, however, is not true.

If we are dealing with vectors and matrices formed from the field of real numbers, then the unitary inner product is replaced by the euclidean inner product:

$$\langle \mathbf{x}, \mathbf{y} \rangle = \mathbf{x}^T \mathbf{y} \tag{15}$$

where $(^T)$ means simply the transpose. The adjoint of $\mathbf{A}$ is $\mathbf{A}^T$. We then call matrices that are self-adjoint *symmetric* since terms that are symmetrically placed across the main diagonal are equal ($a_{ij} = a_{ji}$). Symmetric matrices correspond to hermitian matrices.

A matrix $\mathbf{A}$ such that its transpose equals $(-\mathbf{A})$ is *skew-symmetric*.

A matrix such that $\mathbf{A}^T$ is $\mathbf{A}^{-1}$—corresponding to a unitary matrix—is called *orthogonal*.

If $\mathbf{A}$ commutes with $\mathbf{A}^T$, however, it is still called *normal*.

We can summarize these definitions in Table I.

TABLE I

TYPES OF MATRICES

	complex numbers	Real numbers
Inner product, $\langle \mathbf{xy} \rangle$:	$\mathbf{x}^\dagger \mathbf{y}$	$\mathbf{x}^T \mathbf{y}$
Adjoint to $\mathbf{A}$, $\mathbf{A}^\#$:	$\mathbf{A}^\dagger$	$\mathbf{A}^T$

Type of matrix	Name	
$\mathbf{A}^\# = \mathbf{A}$	Hermitian	Symmetric
$\mathbf{A}^\# = \mathbf{A}^{-1}$	Unitary	Orthogonal
$\mathbf{A}\mathbf{A}^\# = \mathbf{A}^\#\mathbf{A}$	Normal	Normal
$\mathbf{A}^\# = -\mathbf{A}$	Skew-hermitian	Skew-symmetric

It is a matter of great importance, although we shall not use it immediately, that the class of $n \times n$ unitary matrices form a group.[1]

Firstly, the identity is in the set. Secondly, we have already observed that $\mathbf{A}$ must be nonsingular if $\mathbf{A}$ is unitary. It then follows immediately that if $\mathbf{A}$ is unitary, so is $\mathbf{A}^{-1}$. Finally, if $\mathbf{A}$ and $\mathbf{B}$ are both unitary, then so is $\mathbf{AB}$, since

$$(\mathbf{AB})^\dagger = \mathbf{B}^\dagger\mathbf{A}^\dagger = \mathbf{B}^{-1}\mathbf{A}^{-1} = (\mathbf{AB})^{-1} \tag{16}$$

[1] A set of elements $\{A, B, C, ...\}$ form a product *group* if the operation of multiplication is defined and if (a) the product of any two elements of the set is in the set (the *group property*), (b) every element in the set has an inverse in the set, and (c) the identity is in the set.

In similar manner it is evident that orthogonal $n \times n$ matrices are a group.

The significance of these observations lies in the interpretation of an $n \times n$ unitary (orthogonal) matrix as a rotation in n-dimensional unitary (euclidean) space. That such matrices form a group means that any sequence of rotations can be expressed as a single rotation.

As a rigorous statement, the preceding paragraph should be turned around. It is because these types form groups that they can be interpreted as rotations. However, we shall not pursue these thoughts here.

4. DECOMPOSITION INTO HERMITIAN COMPONENTS

We can resolve an arbitrary matrix into hermitian components. Consider a matrix $\mathbf{A}$ that is not, in general, hermitian. Define the matrices $\mathbf{A}_1$ and $\mathbf{A}_2$:

$$\mathbf{A}_1 = \tfrac{1}{2}(\mathbf{A} + \mathbf{A}^\dagger) \tag{17}$$

$$\mathbf{A}_2 = -j\tfrac{1}{2}(\mathbf{A} - \mathbf{A}^\dagger) \tag{18}$$

then

$$\mathbf{A} = \mathbf{A}_1 + j\mathbf{A}_2 \tag{19}$$

Furthermore, both $\mathbf{A}_1$ and $\mathbf{A}_2$ are hermitian since

$$\mathbf{A}_1{}^\dagger = \tfrac{1}{2}(\mathbf{A} + \mathbf{A}^\dagger)^\dagger = \tfrac{1}{2}(\mathbf{A}^\dagger + \mathbf{A}) = \mathbf{A}_1$$
$$\mathbf{A}_2{}^\dagger = +j\tfrac{1}{2}(\mathbf{A} - \mathbf{A}^\dagger)^\dagger = \tfrac{1}{2}j(\mathbf{A}^\dagger - \mathbf{A}) = \mathbf{A}_2 \tag{20}$$

We observe the analogy between the $\mathbf{A}_1$ and $j\mathbf{A}_2$ components of $\mathbf{A}$ and the real and imaginary components of a number. This is more than an analogy. It is, in fact, a direct generalization of the resolution of a complex number, and reduces to it if $\mathbf{A}$ is a 1×1 matrix.

5. POLAR DECOMPOSITION

There is a second way of decomposing an arbitrary matrix. Given any matrix $\mathbf{A}$, we can find hermitian matrices $\mathbf{H}_1$ and $\mathbf{H}_2$ and unitary matrices $\mathbf{U}_1$ and $\mathbf{U}_2$, such that

$$\mathbf{A} = \mathbf{H}_1\mathbf{U}_1 = \mathbf{U}_2\mathbf{H}_2 \tag{21}$$

We shall not completely prove this decomposition at this point. We shall simply observe that

$$\mathbf{A}^\dagger = \mathbf{U}_1{}^\dagger\mathbf{H}_1{}^\dagger = \mathbf{U}_1^{-1}\mathbf{H}_1$$

$$= \mathbf{H}_2{}^\dagger\mathbf{U}_2{}^\dagger = \mathbf{H}_2\mathbf{U}_2^{-1} \tag{22}$$

Hence we require $\mathbf{H}_1$ and $\mathbf{H}_2$ to be such that

$$\mathbf{H}_1{}^2 = \mathbf{H}_1\mathbf{U}_1\mathbf{U}_1^{-1}\mathbf{H}_1 = \mathbf{AA}^\dagger \tag{23}$$

$$\mathbf{H}_2{}^2 = \mathbf{H}_2\mathbf{U}_2^{-1}\mathbf{U}_2\mathbf{H}_2 = \mathbf{A}^\dagger\mathbf{A} \tag{24}$$

The right-hand side of these equations are hermitian, regardless of $\mathbf{A}$, since

$$(\mathbf{AA}^\dagger)^\dagger = \mathbf{AA}^\dagger$$
$$(\mathbf{A}^\dagger\mathbf{A})^\dagger = \mathbf{A}^\dagger\mathbf{A} \tag{25}$$

We shall see later (Chapter VI, Section 5) that this fact necessarily implies the existence of hermitian $\mathbf{H}_1$ and $\mathbf{H}_2$. If, further, $\mathbf{A}$ is nonsingular, then so are $\mathbf{H}_1$ and $\mathbf{H}_2$ and we can set

$$\mathbf{U}_1 = \mathbf{H}_1^{-1}\mathbf{A} \tag{26}$$

$$\mathbf{U}_2 = \mathbf{AH}_2^{-1} \tag{27}$$

and find that $\mathbf{U}_1$ and $\mathbf{U}_2$ are unitary; since

$$\mathbf{U}_1\mathbf{U}_1{}^\dagger = \mathbf{H}_1^{-1}\mathbf{AA}^\dagger\mathbf{H}_1^{-1} = \mathbf{H}_1^{-1}\mathbf{H}_1{}^2\mathbf{H}_1^{-1} = \mathbf{I}$$
$$\mathbf{U}_2{}^\dagger\mathbf{U}_2 = \mathbf{H}_2^{-1}\mathbf{A}^\dagger\mathbf{AH}_2^{-1} = \mathbf{H}_2^{-1}\mathbf{H}_2{}^2\mathbf{H}_2^{-1} = \mathbf{I} \tag{28}$$

The case when $\mathbf{A}$ may be singular requires a little more elaborate treatment. $\mathbf{H}_1$ and $\mathbf{H}_2$ are still determined as above, but are then singular, so that we cannot obtain $\mathbf{U}_1$ and $\mathbf{U}_2$ as above. We will simply assert that it is still possible to solve Eq. (26) or (27) for $\mathbf{U}_1$ or $\mathbf{U}_2$, although the solution is then not unique.

This decomposition is called a polar one because we will find that any unitary matrix $\mathbf{U}$ can be written as $\exp(j\mathbf{F})$ where $\mathbf{F}$ is hermitian. (We have not yet defined the exponential of a matrix, but we will come to it shortly.) Hence Eq. (21) can be made to look like the polar representation of a complex number. Again, this is not simply an analogy, but is a direct generalization of the process in the theory of complex numbers.

It should be noted that, in general, $\mathbf{H}_1 \neq \mathbf{H}_2$ and $\mathbf{U}_1 \neq \mathbf{U}_2$ so that we have, in general, two distinct polar decompositions—a right-hand one and a left-hand one.

6. STRUCTURE OF NORMAL MATRICES

So far we have defined the types of matrices that concern us here. In the two types of decompositions of a general matrix, we have given some indication of their use. We must now consider what we can say about their structure.

The most important of their properties concern their eigenvectors. Specifically, we shall show that any normal, hermitian, or unitary matrix is semisimple, and that their eigenvectors can be chosen to be orthogonal by pairs.

It is enough to prove this for normal matrices since this class includes the other classes. Further, we can prove it as easily for the general proper inner product as for the unitary inner product. We shall later discuss the significance of this generality.

Before tackling the structure problem itself, we need to develop a few concepts and preliminary theorems.

Definition. *Given an inner product relation and a subspace U, the* **orthogonal complement** *of U is the maximal subspace V, such that if* **x** *is any vector in V, then for all vectors* **y** *in U*

$$\langle \mathbf{x}, \mathbf{y} \rangle = 0 \tag{29}$$

That is, V is the totality of all vectors, each of which is orthogonal to all vectors in U. That V is a subspace is evident since, if **u** and **v** are in V, then $(a\mathbf{u} + b\mathbf{v})$ is also in V.

We now need the following:

Theorem 1. *If the inner product relation is proper, a subspace U and its orthogonal complement V are disjoint—i.e. have no vector in common, except the null vector.*

Note that this theorem applies only to a proper inner product. It need not be true, and in general is not true, if the inner product relation is improper.

Suppose U is spanned by $\mathbf{x}_1$, $\mathbf{x}_2$, ..., $\mathbf{x}_k$. Then any linear combination of these vectors is in U. Suppose some such combination

$$\mathbf{y} = \sum c_i \mathbf{x}_i \tag{30}$$

is not only in U but also in V. Then

$$\langle \mathbf{y}, \mathbf{y} \rangle = \langle \mathbf{y}, \sum c_i \mathbf{x}_i \rangle = \sum c_i \langle \mathbf{y}, \mathbf{x}_i \rangle = 0 \tag{31}$$

since, by assumption, all the $\langle \mathbf{y}, \mathbf{x}_i \rangle$ vanish. Since the inner product is proper, $\langle \mathbf{y}, \mathbf{y} \rangle$ can equal zero only if **y** is the null vector. Hence U and V are disjoint.

We shall also need the following:

Theorem 2. *If U is a proper subspace and V its orthogonal complement under a proper inner product, then V is nonvoid.*

This is a special case of the "Projection theorem" that we shall prove in Chapter XII. The point of this theorem is that since U is a proper subspace, there must exist at least one vector that is not wholly in U. We can resolve this vector into two components, one in U, which is its *projection on U*, and the other orthogonal to all vectors in U, and so in V. Hence, if there exists any vector in the whole space which is not wholly in U, then V is nonempty.

We recall the definition of invariance. A subspace U is *invariant* for a matrix $\mathbf{A}$ if whenever $\mathbf{x}$ is in U so is $(\mathbf{Ax})$. With this definition, we have the following:

Theorem 3. *If U is invariant for $\mathbf{A}$, then V, its orthogonal complement under a given inner product, is invariant for $\mathbf{A}^{\#}$, the adjoint to $\mathbf{A}$ under the given inner product.*

Suppose $\mathbf{x}$ is any vector in U, and $\mathbf{y}$ any vector in V. Since U is invariant for $\mathbf{A}$, $\mathbf{Ax}$ is in U and, by the definition of adjointness,

$$\langle \mathbf{y}, \mathbf{Ax} \rangle = \langle \mathbf{A}^{\#}\mathbf{y}, \mathbf{x} \rangle = 0 \tag{32}$$

Hence $\mathbf{A}^{\#}\mathbf{y}$ is orthogonal to any vector in U, and so is in V. Therefore V is invariant for $\mathbf{A}^{\#}$.

We are now ready to consider the problem that we wish to study:

Theorem 4. *If, under a given proper inner product relation, $\mathbf{A}$ commutes with its adjoint $\mathbf{A}^{\#}$, then $\mathbf{A}$ is semisimple and we can so choose its eigenvectors that they are orthogonal by pairs under the given inner product relation.*

We will prove this by developing a process by which, in principle, such a set can be found, and by showing that this set will contain n linearly independent eigenvectors.

The difficulty in proving the theorem comes from the fact that $\mathbf{A}$ may have degeneracy. If so, the degeneracy must be properly resolved to obtain the required orthogonality relations. We can only assert that an orthogonal set of eigenvectors exists, not that any set is necessarily orthogonal.

By Theorem 1, Chapter III, $\mathbf{A}$ has at least one eigenvector. Suppose it is $\mathbf{x}_1$:

$$\mathbf{Ax}_1 = \lambda_1 \mathbf{x}_1 \tag{33}$$

By repeatedly applying $\mathbf{A}^\#$ to this vector, we construct what is called a *cyclic subspace of* $\mathbf{A}^\#$. (We shall have much to say about cyclic subspaces in Chapter VIII.) We let

$$\mathbf{y}_1 = \mathbf{x}_1$$
$$\mathbf{y}_2 = \mathbf{A}^\#\mathbf{x}_1$$
$$\cdots$$
$$\mathbf{y}_k = \mathbf{A}^\#\mathbf{y}_{k-1} = (\mathbf{A}^\#)^{k-1}\mathbf{x}_1 \tag{34}$$

Of these vectors, only a finite number, say $\mathbf{y}_1, ..., \mathbf{y}_k$, can be linearly independent. If $\mathbf{y}_{k+1}$ is linearly dependent on $\mathbf{y}_1, ..., \mathbf{y}_k$, then so will all higher $\mathbf{y}_i$. If

$$\mathbf{y}_{k+1} = \sum_1^k a_i\mathbf{y}_i$$

then

$$\mathbf{y}_{k+2} = \mathbf{A}^\#\mathbf{y}_{k+1} = \sum_i^k a_i\mathbf{A}^\#\mathbf{y}_i = \sum_1^k a_i\mathbf{y}_{i+1} = \sum_2^k a_{i-1}\mathbf{y}_i + a_k\mathbf{y}_{k+1}$$
$$= \sum_2^k a_{i-1}\mathbf{y}_i + a_k \sum_1^k a_i\mathbf{y}_i \tag{35}$$

By induction, this is true for all higher $\mathbf{y}_i$.

If, now, S_1 is the linear envelope of $\mathbf{y}_1, ..., \mathbf{y}_k$, it is a subspace that is invariant for $\mathbf{A}^\#$ Therefore, by Theorem 1, Chapter III, it contains at least one eigenvector of $\mathbf{A}^\#$, say $\mathbf{u}_1$:

$$\mathbf{A}^\#\mathbf{u}_1 = \mu_1\mathbf{u}_1 \tag{36}$$

Since $\mathbf{A}$ is normal, all vectors in S_1, and, in particular, $\mathbf{u}_1$, are eigenvectors of $\mathbf{A}$ with eigenvalue λ_1. This follows directly from the commutivity of $\mathbf{A}$ and $\mathbf{A}^\#$:

$$\mathbf{A}(\mathbf{A}^\#)^p\mathbf{x}_1 = \mathbf{A}\mathbf{A}^\#(\mathbf{A}^\#)^{p-1}\mathbf{x}_1 = \mathbf{A}^\#\mathbf{A}(\mathbf{A}^\#)^{p-1}\mathbf{x}_1$$
$$= \cdots = (\mathbf{A}^\#)^p\mathbf{A}\mathbf{x}_1 = \lambda_1(\mathbf{A}^\#)^p\mathbf{x}_1 \tag{37}$$

Hence, because $\mathbf{x}_1$ is an eigenvector of $\mathbf{A}$ with eigenvalue λ_1, and $\mathbf{A}$ commutes with $\mathbf{A}^\#$, $(\mathbf{A}^\#)^p\mathbf{x}_1$ is also an eigenvector of $\mathbf{A}$ with this same eigenvalue for p any positive integer. Hence, by Theorem 2, Chapter III, any vector in S_1 is an eigenvector of $\mathbf{A}$.

The vector $\mathbf{u}_1$ is a simultaneous eigenvector of $\mathbf{A}$ and $\mathbf{A}^\#$.

Let U_1 be the subspace spanned by $\mathbf{u}_1$, and V_1 be its orthogonal complement. U_1 is invariant for both $\mathbf{A}$ and $\mathbf{A}^\#$. Hence, by Theorem 3,

V_1 is invariant for both $\mathbf{A}^{\#}$ and $\mathbf{A}$. Also, by Theorem 2, it is nonempty.

Being invariant for $\mathbf{A}$, V_1 contains at least one eigenvector of $\mathbf{A}$, say $\mathbf{x}_2$. Using $\mathbf{x}_2$, we construct the corresponding cyclic subspace of $\mathbf{A}^{\#}$. Since V_1 is invariant for $\mathbf{A}^{\#}$, this subspace is wholly within V_1, and so orthogonal to $\mathbf{u}_1$. It contains at least one eigenvector of $\mathbf{A}^{\#}$, say $\mathbf{u}_2$. The vector $\mathbf{u}_2$ is also an eigenvector of $\mathbf{A}$, since $\mathbf{x}_2$ was.

The vector $\mathbf{u}_2$ is a simultaneous eigenvector of both $\mathbf{A}$ and $\mathbf{A}^{\#}$ which is orthogonal to $\mathbf{u}_1$.

We continue the process by forming the subspace U_2, spanned by $\mathbf{u}_1$ and $\mathbf{u}_2$, and considering its orthogonal complement, V_2.

At each step, we have a k-dimensional subspace U_k, spanned by the orthogonal vectors $\mathbf{u}_1, ..., \mathbf{u}_k$ which are simultaneous eigenvectors of both $\mathbf{A}$ and $\mathbf{A}^{\#}$. By the same arguments as above, we know that we can find in V_k an eigenvector of $\mathbf{A}$, that we can use this vector to generate a cyclic subspace in V_k with $\mathbf{A}^{\#}$, and that we can find in this cyclic subspace a simultaneous eigenvector of both $\mathbf{A}$ and $\mathbf{A}^{\#}$, say $\mathbf{u}_{k+1}$ which, being in V_k, is therefore orthogonal to all the preceding eigenvectors, $\mathbf{u}_1, ..., \mathbf{u}_k$.

We can continue the process as long as U_k is a proper subspace—i.e. as long as it is not the whole space. But it is not the whole space until it contains n vectors. Therefore, we are able to generate a total of n vectors that are simultaneous eigenvectors of both $\mathbf{A}$ and $\mathbf{A}^{\#}$. We find that $\mathbf{A}$, and also $\mathbf{A}^{\#}$, are necessarily semisimple, and the theorem is proven.

7. THE CONVERSE THEOREM

The converse is also true—i.e., the statement about the eigenvectors is sufficient to assure the commutativity of the matrix with its adjoint:

Theorem 5. *If the matrix $\mathbf{A}$ has a complete set of eigenvectors $\mathbf{u}_1, \mathbf{u}_2, ..., \mathbf{u}_n$ which are orthogonal by pairs:*

$$\langle \mathbf{u}_i, \mathbf{u}_j \rangle = 0, \quad i \neq j \tag{38}$$

then $\mathbf{A}$ is normal and

$$\mathbf{A}\mathbf{A}^{\#} = \mathbf{A}^{\#}\mathbf{A} \tag{39}$$

We prove this by proving, first, that the $\mathbf{u}_i$ are also eigenvectors of $\mathbf{A}^{\#}$. We form the vectors

$$\mathbf{y}_i = \mathbf{A}^{\#}\mathbf{u}_i - \lambda_i^{*}\mathbf{u}_i \tag{40}$$

We want to show that the vectors $\mathbf{y}_i$ are all null vectors. To do this, we form the inner product of $\mathbf{y}_i$ with each $\mathbf{u}_j$ in turn:

$$
\begin{aligned}
\langle \mathbf{u}_j, \mathbf{y}_i \rangle &= \langle \mathbf{u}_j, \mathbf{A}^\#\mathbf{u}_i \rangle - \lambda_i^* \langle \mathbf{u}_j, \mathbf{u}_i \rangle \\
&= \langle \mathbf{A}\mathbf{u}_j, \mathbf{u}_i \rangle - \lambda_i^* \langle \mathbf{u}_j, \mathbf{u}_i \rangle \\
&= \lambda_j^* \langle \mathbf{u}_j, \mathbf{u}_i \rangle - \lambda_i^* \langle \mathbf{u}_j, \mathbf{u}_i \rangle \\
&= (\lambda_j^* - \lambda_i^*) \langle \mathbf{u}_j, \mathbf{u}_i \rangle = 0
\end{aligned}
\tag{41}
$$

When $i = j$ the expression vanishes by the factor $(\lambda_j^* - \lambda_i^*)$. Otherwise it vanishes because of the orthogonality.

The set $\mathbf{u}_i$ is assumed complete. This expression, Eq. (41), then says that the projection of $\mathbf{y}_i$ on each of the complete set of vectors $\mathbf{u}_j$ vanishes. Hence $\mathbf{y}_i$ must be the null vector for all i, and

$$
\mathbf{A}^\#\mathbf{u}_i = \lambda_i^*\mathbf{u}_i
\tag{42}
$$

so that the $\mathbf{u}_i$ are eigenvectors of $\mathbf{A}^\#$ with eigenvalues λ_i^*.

From this, the normality follows immediately, for consider any vector $\mathbf{x}$. It can be expanded in terms of the $\mathbf{u}_i$, since they are assumed to be a complete set:

$$
\mathbf{x} = \sum_i a_i \mathbf{u}_i
\tag{43}
$$

Then

$$
\begin{aligned}
\mathbf{A}^\#\mathbf{A}\mathbf{x} &= \mathbf{A}^\#\mathbf{A} \sum_i a_i \mathbf{u}_i \\
&= \mathbf{A}^\# \sum_i a_i \lambda_i \mathbf{u}_i \\
&= \sum_i a_i \lambda_i \lambda_i^* \mathbf{u}_i \\
&= \mathbf{A} \sum_i a_i \lambda_i^* \mathbf{u}_i \\
&= \mathbf{A}\mathbf{A}^\# \sum_i a_i \mathbf{u}_i = \mathbf{A}\mathbf{A}^\#\mathbf{x}
\end{aligned}
\tag{44}
$$

Since this is true for any $\mathbf{x}$ it follows that

$$
\mathbf{A}^\#\mathbf{A} = \mathbf{A}\mathbf{A}^\#
\tag{45}
$$

and $\mathbf{A}$ is normal.

We have both *exterior* and *interior* definitions of normality. By an *exterior* definition, we mean one that depends on the form of the operator —in this case that it be such that it commutes with its adjoint, the hermitian conjugate. By an *interior* definition, we mean one that describes it in terms of its structure—in this case, semisimplicity with orthogonal eigenvectors. In general, an exterior definition provides a useful test whereby a given matrix can be categorized as belonging to the class or not. The interior definition, however, is closer to the properties that are common to the class of operators, and so is more useful in determining the consequences of a given operator being of the given type.

8. HERMITIAN MATRICES

We have seen that hermitian matrices are also normal. Hence we know immediately that they are semisimple and that their eigenvectors can be chosen to be orthogonal under the unitary inner product. We must now ask what additional interior property distinguishes them. The answer is provided by the following:

Theorem 6. *If* **A** *is self-adjoint, its eigenvalues are real.*

Consider the set of eigenvectors $\mathbf{x}_1$, $\mathbf{x}_2$, ..., $\mathbf{x}_n$ which we know to be complete:

$$\mathbf{A}\mathbf{x}_i = \lambda_i\mathbf{x}_i \tag{46}$$

We form the inner product and use the self-adjointness:

$$\langle \mathbf{x}_i, \mathbf{A}\mathbf{x}_j \rangle = \lambda_j\langle \mathbf{x}_i, \mathbf{x}_j \rangle = \langle \mathbf{A}^{\#}\mathbf{x}_i, \mathbf{x}_j \rangle = \langle \mathbf{A}\mathbf{x}_i, \mathbf{x}_j \rangle$$
$$= \lambda_i{}^*\langle \mathbf{x}_i, \mathbf{x}_j \rangle = 0 \tag{47}$$

We find that

$$(\lambda_i{}^* - \lambda_j)\langle \mathbf{x}_i, \mathbf{x}_j \rangle = 0 \tag{48}$$

If $i = j$, the positive definiteness of the inner product prevents its vanishing. Hence we must have

$$\lambda_i{}^* = \lambda_i \tag{49}$$

so that λ_i is real.

We can also notice that Eq. (48) tells us immediately that eigenvectors with different eigenalues are necessarily orthogonal. The whole difficulty of proving Theorem 4 lies in (a) proving completeness and (b) taking account of the possibility of degeneracy.

The converse theorem can also be proven—i.e., that if **A** has a complete set of orthogonal eigenvectors with real eigenvalues, then **A** is self-adjoint. We shall not prove this since it can very easily be proven with the dyad expansion that we shall consider later.

9. UNITARY MATRICES

Analogously, for the other subclass of the class of normal matrices we have the following:

Theorem 7. *If* $\mathbf{A}$ *is a matrix such that its adjoint equals its reciprocal, then its eigenvalues have unit modulus.*

Again we consider the set of eigenvectors $\mathbf{x}_1$, $\mathbf{x}_2$, ..., $\mathbf{x}_n$ which we know to be complete, this time forming the inner product:

$$\langle \mathbf{Ax}_i , \mathbf{Ax}_j \rangle = \lambda_i{}^*\lambda_j \langle \mathbf{x}_i , \mathbf{x}_j \rangle$$
$$= \langle \mathbf{x}_i , \mathbf{A}^\# \mathbf{Ax}_j \rangle = \langle \mathbf{x}_i , \mathbf{Ix}_j \rangle$$
$$= \langle \mathbf{x}_i , \mathbf{x}_j \rangle \tag{50}$$

We find that

$$(\lambda_i{}^*\lambda_j - 1)\langle \mathbf{x}_i , \mathbf{x}_j \rangle = 0 \tag{51}$$

Setting $i = j$, we find that since $\langle \mathbf{x}_i \mathbf{x}_i \rangle \neq 0$ by the positive definiteness of the inner product, $|\lambda_i|^2 = 1$, as required.

We note again that eigenvectors with distinct eigenvalues are necessarily orthogonal. It is only in the degenerate case that orthogonality may be difficult to achieve.

10. GENERAL (PROPER) INNER PRODUCT

The preceding sections have been written in terms of the unitary inner product. The proofs of the theorems, however, depended only on the positive definiteness of the inner product and on the use of the appropriate definition of adjointness and of orthogonality.

We have seen before that it is quite possible to use as the inner product the relation

$$\langle \mathbf{x}, \mathbf{y} \rangle = \mathbf{x}^\dagger \mathbf{K} \mathbf{y} \tag{52}$$

providing $\mathbf{K}$ is hermitian and positive definite so that $\langle \mathbf{x}, \mathbf{x} \rangle$ is real and positive for any $\mathbf{x}$ except the null vector. In this case, $\mathbf{x}$ and $\mathbf{y}$ are said to be *K-orthogonal*, if

$$\langle \mathbf{x}, \mathbf{y} \rangle = \mathbf{x}^\dagger \mathbf{K} \mathbf{y} = 0 \tag{53}$$

The adjoint relation requires that for any $\mathbf{x}$ and $\mathbf{y}$

$$\langle \mathbf{x}, \mathbf{Ay} \rangle = \langle \mathbf{A}^\# \mathbf{x}, \mathbf{y} \rangle \tag{54}$$

or that

$$x^\dagger KAy = (A^\# x)^\dagger Ky = x^\dagger A^{\#\dagger} Ky \tag{55}$$

For this to hold for any x and y we must have

$$KA = A^{\#\dagger}K \tag{56}$$

so that the *K-adjoint* of A is

$$A^\# = K^{-1}A^\dagger K \tag{57}$$

since K is hermitian.

With this reinterpretation of orthogonality and the adjoint operator the definitions and theorems given carry over directly:

Definition.   *A matrix A is K-**normal** if it commutes with its K-adjoint*:

$$AK^{-1}A^\dagger K = K^{-1}A^\dagger KA \tag{58}$$

Definition.   *A matrix A is K-**hermitian** if it equals its K-adjoint*:

$$A = K^{-1}A^\dagger K \tag{59}$$

or

$$KA = A^\dagger K$$

Definition.   *A matrix A is K-**skew-hermitian** if A equals the negative of its K-adjoint*:

$$A = -K^{-1}AK \tag{60}$$

Definition.   *A matrix A is K-**unitary** if its K-adjoint equals its reciprocal*:

$$K^{-1}A^\dagger K = A^{-1} \tag{61}$$

or

$$A^\dagger KA = K \tag{62}$$

Theorem 8.   *A K-normal matrix A has a complete set of eigenvectors that can be chosen to be K-orthogonal in pairs, and conversely.*

Theorem 9.   *The eigenvalues of a K-hermitian matrix are real, and those of a K-unitary matrix are of unit magnitude.*

We emphasize that these theorems depend on the inner product relation being proper—i.e., positive definite. We shall later consider how these theorems must be modified if this is not so.

The factor that we have introduced here is the possibility of using skew axes.

As a simple example, suppose we wish to consider a deformation which is a combination of compression and shear. The stress axes—the eigenvectors—will not then be perpendicular to each other and the stress matrix will not be hermitian, or even normal. If, however, we use a **K** such that with the resultant inner product, these stress axes are K-orthogonal, then the stress matrix will be K-hermitian, since the eigenvalues are real. This may lead to considerable simplification of the problem. The nature of these simplifications will be seen later.

We will here add only that the principal purpose of using any specially selected inner product relation is, as we have said before, to obtain orthogonality. While orthogonality is usually not necessary in principle, it is practically always convenient and may be the only thing that reduces the complexity of a problem to a tractable level.

In the definition of K-normal, K-hermitian, and K-unitary operators, we have a device whereby we can make the eigenvectors of an arbitrary matrix orthogonal.

Exercises

1. Consider the metric

$$\mathbf{K} = \begin{pmatrix} a & 0 \\ 0 & b \end{pmatrix}$$

where a and b are real, nonzero, positive constants. For a given a and b, what is the form of the general K-hermitian matrix? Verify that the eigenvalues are always real. Find the eigenvectors in the general case and verify that they are K-orthogonal.

2. Show that Z being a real nonzero constant, and θ real, the matrix

$$\mathbf{M} = \begin{pmatrix} \cos\theta & jZ\sin\theta \\ (j/Z)\sin\theta & \cos\theta \end{pmatrix}$$

is K-unitary for

$$\mathbf{K} = \begin{pmatrix} 1/Z & 0 \\ 0 & Z \end{pmatrix}$$

If **M** is the transmission matrix of a transmission line with characteristic impedance Z, what is the physical significance of this metric? Find the eigenvectors and show that they are K-orthogonal.

3. Show that an arbitrary $n \times n$ matrix **A** can be resolved into $(\mathbf{A}_1 + j\mathbf{A}_2)$ where $\mathbf{A}_1$ and $\mathbf{A}_2$ are both K-hermitian.

4. Show that for an arbitrary matrix $\mathbf{A}$, the matrices $\mathbf{AA}^\dagger$ and $\mathbf{A}^\dagger\mathbf{A}$ are hermitian. Observe that this statement is meaningful and valid even if $\mathbf{A}$ is rectangular.

What are the corresponding forms that are K-hermitian? Assume, in this case, that $\mathbf{A}$ is square. (This is not strictly necessary but, if $\mathbf{A}$ is rectangular, the interpretation of $\mathbf{K}$ requires considerable modification.)

5. Find a normal matrix that is neither hermitian nor unitary. Find its eigenvectors and show that they are orthogonal under the unitary inner product (or, if degenerate, can be so chosen.)

6. If $\mathbf{A}$ is an arbitrary $n \times n$ matrix and α and β are complex numbers, show that $(\alpha\mathbf{A} + \beta\mathbf{A}^\dagger)$ is normal.

7. If $\mathbf{A}$ is a matrix such that

$$\| \mathbf{Ax} \| = \| \mathbf{A}^\dagger\mathbf{x} \|$$

for all $\mathbf{x}$, where

$$\| \mathbf{x} \| = \langle \mathbf{x}, \mathbf{x} \rangle^{1/2}$$

under the unitary inner product, show that $\mathbf{A}$ is normal. What is the analogous theorem for an arbitrary inner product?

8. Prove:

    (a) If $\mathbf{A}$ is normal and idempotent $(\mathbf{A}^2 = \mathbf{A})$, then $\mathbf{A}$ is hermitian;
    (b) If $\mathbf{A}$ is normal and nilpotent $(\mathbf{A}^2 = 0)$, then $\mathbf{A}$ is the null matrix.

9. If $\mathbf{A}$ is hermitian, show that $\mathbf{A}$ and $\mathbf{A}^\dagger$ have the same characteristic equation.

10. Show by example that the product of two hermitian matrices need not be hermitian.

11. If $\mathbf{A}$ and $\mathbf{B}$ are self-adjoint under a given inner product, show that $(\mathbf{AB} + \mathbf{BA})$ is self-adjoint and $(\mathbf{AB} - \mathbf{BA})$ is skew-self-adjoint. Show that the same is true if $\mathbf{A}$ and $\mathbf{B}$ are skew-self-adjoint. What happens if one is self-adjoint and the other skew-self-adjoint?

12. Show that if $\mathbf{A}$ is self-adjoint under a proper inner product relation, and $\mathbf{x}$ is a vector such that $\mathbf{A}^2\mathbf{x} = 0$, then $\mathbf{Ax} = 0$.

13. Let $\mathbf{A}$ and $\mathbf{B}$ be hermitian matrices. Let $\mathbf{B}$ be positive definite. Show that the solutions of

$$\mathbf{A} - \lambda\mathbf{B} \,| = 0$$

are given by the stationary values of

$$p = \frac{x^\dagger A x}{x^\dagger B x}$$

What is the significance of the vectors for which p is stationary?

14. A matrix T such that $T^2 = I$ is said to be an *involution*. Show that, if T satisfies any two of the following three conditions, it satisfies the third:

(a) T is hermitian
(b) T is unitary
(c) T is an involution.

15. Show that $A^\dagger$ can be expressed as a polynomial in A if and only if A is normal.

16. (a) If A is skew-hermitian, show that

$$U = (A + I)(A - I)^{-1}$$

is unitary.

(b) If U is unitary and $(U - I)$ is nonsingular, show that

$$A = (U - I)^{-1}(U + I)$$

is skew-hermitian.

(The matrices A and U are the *Cayley transforms* of each other. This transformation is the analogue of $w = (z + 1)/(z - 1)$.)

(*Hint*: $(A + I)$ and $(A - I)^{-1}$ commute. Why? So do $(U - I)^{-1}$ and $(U + I)$. Why?)

CHAPTER V

Change of Basis, Diagonalization, and the Jordan Canonical Form

In this chapter we shall consider the process of diagonalization, if this be possible, or in general, of reduction to the *Jordan canonical form*.

This is a process that is of great importance in simplifying various relations and processes. It is often easy to prove a given theorem for diagonal matrices where it would be very difficult to prove it directly for a more general type. If we can show that the property established by the theorem is unaffected by the type of transformation that will diagonalize the more general type, this provides a simple method of general proof.

For a process that is used so often in the theoretical study of matrices, it is remarkable how rarely one actually goes through the process of diagonalization. For most purposes it is enough to know that it can be done, without actually bothering to do it. This in no way argues against the importance of the process.

Before actually tackling the process, we need to know what is meant by transformation of a matrix. There are several transformations that can be considered. Of these the one of immediate importance is called a *similarity transformation*. It results from a *change of basis*.

1. CHANGE OF BASIS AND SIMILARITY TRANSFORMATIONS

We have said that the vector that we write as a column matrix is a *representation of the abstract vector*. If the system being described is a network, for example, the vector describes what is happening at the port or collection of ports that we choose to call the input, or output.

The abstract vector is the actual physical state at these ports. As such, it cannot be written down until we have specified some convention for doing so. We must define what is indicated by each number in the column array, and in what units. We must, in other words, specify the particular coordinate axes that we are going to use. Only when this has been done can we write down a vector in a meaningful way. The vector that is so written is called a representation of the abstract vector.

In so specifying the coordinate axes, we are, in effect, defining the unit vectors along the coordinate axes. That is, we are defining what is meant by a vector all of whose components except the ith are zero, and whose ith component is unity. The specification of what such a set of unit vectors mean is a specification of the *basis* of the representation.

A matrix is a representation of an abstract operator that maps a linear vector space onto or into either itself or another space. It, too, depends on the basis. It is only when a basis has been chosen that we can represent the abstract vectors by column arrays. And it is only then that we can represent the abstract operator as the square (or rectangular) array that we call a matrix.

Given such a representation, we can ask what will happen if we choose to use a different set of basis vectors. Is it possible that a given operation can be expressed in some particularly simple way if we choose some particular basis? It is the search for such a simplification that concerns us here.

Let us consider a single abstract vector represented on two different bases as $\mathbf{x}$ and $\mathbf{u}$. Because the relation between these representations is linear and homogeneous, it can be expressed as a matrix, $\mathbf{S}$. That is, we can write

$$\mathbf{x} = \mathbf{Su}. \tag{1}$$

If $\mathbf{u}$ is any one of the unit vectors on the new basis, then $\mathbf{x}$ is the representation of that vector on the old. Since the unit vector along the ith axis is a vector all of whose components are zero except the ith, which is unity, it follows that $\mathbf{S}$ is the matrix whose ith column is the ith unit vector of the new representation, expressed on the basis of the old. This defines $\mathbf{S}$. Equation (1), with this $\mathbf{S}$, is the law of transformation for any vector when the basis is transformed in the given way.

If the new basis is to be a satisfactory basis, then the new basis vectors must all be linearly independent. Otherwise, they are not a basis for the space. It follows that $\mathbf{S}$ must be nonsingular. Therefore it has an inverse, and we can write

$$\mathbf{u} = \mathbf{S}^{-1}\mathbf{x} \tag{2}$$

as the law of transformation of vectors in going from the new basis to the old.

Suppose that we have a mapping of the whole space onto or into itself, according to the equation

$$\mathbf{y} = \mathbf{Ax}. \tag{3}$$

This is expressed by the matrix **A** which is a representation of an abstract operator. It is contingent on the particular basis chosen. Supposing, however, we change the basis according to Eq. (1). The abstract operation is the same. How, then, does the representation of the transformation change?

We know how the vectors transform. It is, therefore, a simple matter to find out how the matrix transforms. If we set

$$\mathbf{x} = \mathbf{Su}, \qquad \mathbf{y} = \mathbf{Sv} \tag{4}$$

and substitute these in Eq. (3), and then premultiply by $\mathbf{S}^{-1}$, which we know exists, we find that

$$\mathbf{v} = (\mathbf{S}^{-1}\mathbf{AS})\mathbf{u} = \mathbf{A}'\mathbf{u} \tag{5}$$

Hence the same abstract relation will be maintained, and only its representation changed, if we transform **A** to **A**′ where

$$\mathbf{A}' = \mathbf{S}^{-1}\mathbf{AS} \tag{6}$$

This is the law of transformation of an operator **A** that is involved in the relation indicated in Eq. (3) when we change the basis of the representation.

The transformation of Eq. (6), when **S** is nonsingular, is called a *similarity transformation*.

Two matrices that are related by an equation of the form of Eq. (6) where **S** is nonsingular are said to be *similar*. They can be considered to be representations on different bases of the same abstract operator.

While a relation such as Eq. (6) allows a good deal of flexibility in that, for a given **A**, **A**′ can take on quite a range of values, it is by no means unlimited. We shall see later that the eigenvalues and structure are invariant under any similarity transformation; that is, if there is some **S** such that Eq. (6) holds, then **A** and **A**′ have the same eigenvalues and structure. Although we shall prove this later, we can perhaps see that it is true by observing that the eigenvalues and structure are properties of the abstract transformation, and so should be expected to be independent of the basis.

A similarity transformation is sometimes also known as a *collineatory transformation*.

2. EQUIVALENCE TRANSFORMATIONS

The similarity transformation was the result of considering **x** and **y**, in Eq. (3), to be vectors in the same vector space, and changing the basis of this space.

We can equally well consider $\mathbf{x}$ and $\mathbf{y}$ to be in different spaces. In fact we must do so if they have different dimensionality—in which case $\mathbf{A}$ is rectangular rather than square—or are otherwise incompatible.

In this case, we can change the bases of the two spaces in different ways. If we do so by letting

$$\mathbf{x} = \mathbf{Su}, \qquad \mathbf{u} = \mathbf{S}^{-1}\mathbf{x}$$
$$\mathbf{y} = \mathbf{Tv}, \qquad \mathbf{v} = \mathbf{T}^{-1}\mathbf{y} \tag{7}$$

then we find we must set

$$\mathbf{A}' = \mathbf{T}^{-1}\mathbf{AS} \tag{8}$$

to obtain Eq. (5).

A transformation of the form of Eq. (8), where both $\mathbf{S}$ and $\mathbf{T}$ are nonsingular, is called an *equivalence transformation*. Two matrices that are so related are called *equivalent*.[1]

We will not have much occasion to use equivalent transformations, although they are of importance for example in the theory that develops certain techniques of calculation. We include them here primarily for completeness.

3. CONGRUENT AND CONJUNCTIVE TRANSFORMATIONS

Two other types of transformations are of importance to us. If $\mathbf{A}$ and $\mathbf{B}$ are related by

$$\mathbf{B} = \mathbf{S}^T\mathbf{AS} \tag{9}$$

where (^{T}) indicates the transpose, $\mathbf{A}$ and $\mathbf{B}$ are said to be *congruent*.

If they are related by

$$\mathbf{B} = \mathbf{S}^\dagger\mathbf{AS} \tag{10}$$

where ($\dagger$) indicates the hermitian conjugate, or complex conjugate transpose, they are said to be *conjunctive*.

While these transformations are equivalence ones, their significance for our purposes arises in a rather different context.

---

[1] There is some variation in the literature on names for the various types of transformations and on their definitions. We are here following the usage of G. A. Korn and T. M. Korn, "Mathematical Handbook for Scientists and Engineers," McGraw-Hill, New York, 1961.

Suppose we consider **x** and **y**, of Eq. (1), as being in the same vector space, and suppose an inner product relation is established in this space by a metric **K** so that

$$\langle \mathbf{x}, \mathbf{y} \rangle = \mathbf{x}^\dagger \mathbf{K} \mathbf{y} \tag{11}$$

is the "dot product" of **x** and **y**, or the magnitude of the projection of **x** on **y**, times the complex conjugate of the magnitude of **y**.

Suppose now we change the basis of the space by Eqs. (2) and (6), and suppose we require that this inner product function be invariant. That is, we are requiring that the inner product relation, or the dot product, be a property of the abstract vectors, and not of the particular representations being employed. This is a reasonable requirement since the inner product relation was originally developed to give meaning to the concept of length. Since we want the length to be a property of the abstract vector, we require the inner product to be independent of the basis.

If we substitute Eqs. (2) and (6) in Eq. (11) we find

$$\langle \mathbf{x}, \mathbf{y} \rangle = (\mathbf{S}\mathbf{u})^\dagger \mathbf{K} (\mathbf{S}\mathbf{v}) = \mathbf{u}^\dagger \mathbf{S}^\dagger \mathbf{K} \mathbf{S} \mathbf{v} \tag{12}$$

We wish to so define $\langle \mathbf{u}, \mathbf{v} \rangle$ that it will be equal to $\langle \mathbf{x}, \mathbf{y} \rangle$ for all **x** and **y**. To accomplish this, we define

$$\langle \mathbf{u}, \mathbf{v} \rangle = \mathbf{u}^\dagger \mathbf{K}' \mathbf{v} \tag{13}$$

and see that we must set

$$\mathbf{K}' = \mathbf{S}^\dagger \mathbf{K} \mathbf{S} \tag{14}$$

Hence, to preserve the inner product under a change of basis, the metric, **K**, must change by a conjunctive transformation.

If we were limiting ourselves to vectors and matrices constructed from the field of real numbers, rather than the field of complex numbers, we would have found that the metric would have to be changed by a congruent transformation.

This illustrates the fact that what transformation is used on a given matrix is determined by the use of the matrix. Under a change of basis, **A** transforms by a similarity transformation if it is a transmission matrix in an equation such as Eq. (3) but transforms conjunctively if it is a metric being used in an equation like Eq. (11).

4. EXAMPLE

As a simple example which will illustrate the principles involved here without excessive calculation, consider the transmission matrix of a 2-port network which we will assume to be constructed symmetrically from lossless and reciprocal elements, and which is operating in a passband. As we have indicated in Chapter III, Eq. (36), the matrix of such a network can be written on an E-I basis as

$$\mathbf{M} = \begin{pmatrix} \cos\varphi & jZ\sin\varphi \\ (j/Z)\sin\varphi & \cos\varphi \end{pmatrix} \qquad (15)$$

where Z and φ are both real.

The eigenvectors of this matrix were given in Chapter III, Eq. (37). With these, we construct the matrix

$$\mathbf{S} = \begin{pmatrix} Z & -Z \\ 1 & 1 \end{pmatrix} \qquad (16)$$

so that we are transforming to the eigenvectors as basis.

We find that

$$\mathbf{S}^{-1} = \frac{1}{2}\begin{pmatrix} 1/Z & 1 \\ -1/Z & 1 \end{pmatrix} \qquad (17)$$

On this basis, the transmission matrix becomes

$$\mathbf{M}' = \mathbf{S}^{-1}\mathbf{MS} = \begin{pmatrix} \cos\varphi + j\sin\varphi & 0 \\ 0 & \cos\varphi - j\sin\varphi \end{pmatrix}$$
$$= \operatorname{diag}(e^{j\varphi},\, e^{-j\varphi}) \qquad (18)$$

Hence, on this basis, $\mathbf{M}$ is transformed to a particularly simple form, the diagonal form.

We have also observed in Chapter II, Section 5, that we can express the conservation of real power flow in a lossless 2-port network by the metric

$$\mathbf{K} = \frac{1}{2}\begin{pmatrix} 0 & 1 \\ 1 & 0 \end{pmatrix} \qquad (19)$$

That is, for this $\mathbf{K}$, the $\mathbf{M}$ of Eq. (15) is K-unitary:

$$\mathbf{M}^{\dagger}\mathbf{KM} = \mathbf{K} \qquad (20)$$

as may be readily verified.

The transformation of the metric that occurs as we change the basis is to $\mathbf{K}'$, as in Eq. (14):

$$\mathbf{K}' = \mathbf{S}^{\dagger}\mathbf{KS} = Z\begin{pmatrix} 1 & 0 \\ 0 & -1 \end{pmatrix} \qquad (21)$$

which is also particularly simple, being Z times what we shall call a *parity* matrix. (The factor Z could be removed by a more careful normalization of the eigenvectors.)

A basis on which the appropriate metric is diagonalized with ± 1 everywhere along the main diagonal is sometimes described as one which puts the system *on a wave basis*. The fact that, in this case, $\mathbf{M}$ is also diagonal on this basis simply means that the waves involved are not coupled.

Thus, by changing the basis, we can drastically affect the form of the representation of the physical process. We shall shortly show that we can use this process, in general, to simplify the form of any representation.

5. GAUGE INVARIANCE

If we are using matrix analysis to study a physical problem, the possibilities are limited by the fact that the physical system does not know what basis we are using. The actual physical state is described by the abstract vector, and the transformation induced by the system by the abstract operator. We introduce a basis so that we can obtain a representation of the vector or operator that we can write down and manipulate as we will. The basis, then, is a matter of our convenience, and has no meaning in terms of the physical processes actually occuring.

What this means is that the properties that we seek, if they are to be properties of the system and not of the particular representation, must be unaffected by the particular choice of basis. They must be *invariant* under any admissable change of basis.

This is the *principle of gauge invariance*. It is useful for determining those properties that are properties of the system, and for checking the results of theoretic analysis.

6. INVARIANCE OF THE EIGENVALUES UNDER A CHANGE OF BASIS

We shall show that the eigenvalues and structure of a given matrix $\mathbf{A}$ are not affected by a similarity transformation. This would be expected since the behavior that defines an eigenvector certainly appears to be a property of the abstract vector, and not of its representation.

Consider an eigenvector $\mathbf{x}$ with eigenvalue λ:

$$\mathbf{Ax} = \lambda \mathbf{x} \tag{22}$$

If we change the basis according to Eq. (4), then we have seen that $\mathbf{A}$ is transformed according to Eq. (6). Substituting Eq. (4) and premultiplying by $\mathbf{S}^{-1}$, we find

$$\mathbf{A}'\mathbf{u} = \lambda\mathbf{u} \tag{23}$$

Hence $\mathbf{u} = \mathbf{S}\mathbf{x}$ is an eigenvector of $\mathbf{A}'$ with eigenvalue λ. The eigenvector appears to be different, although in fact it is only being represented on different axes. But the eigenvalue is the same.

We next observe that any degeneracy of the eigenvectors associated with the eigenvalue λ is unchanged. If two or more vectors are related by a linear equation, then, using Eq. (4) and the fact that $\mathbf{S}$ is nonsingular, the new representations are related by the same equation. If, therefore, there are k linearly independent eigenvectors with eigenvalue λ on one basis, this is still true after a change of basis.

If now $\mathbf{x}_1$ is an eigenvector with eigenvalue λ of $\mathbf{A}$, and $\mathbf{x}_2$ the generalized eigenvector of rank 2 associated with $\mathbf{x}_1$:

$$\mathbf{A}\mathbf{x}_2 = \lambda\mathbf{x}_2 + \mathbf{x}_1 \tag{24}$$

then, if we change the basis according to Eq. (4),

$$\mathbf{x}_1 = \mathbf{S}\mathbf{u}_1, \qquad \mathbf{x}_2 = \mathbf{S}\mathbf{u}_2$$

we find that

$$\mathbf{A}'\mathbf{u}_2 = \lambda\mathbf{u}_2 + \mathbf{u}_1 \tag{25}$$

We have seen already that since $\mathbf{x}_1$ is an eigenvector of $\mathbf{A}$, $\mathbf{u}_1$ is an eigenvector of $\mathbf{A}'$ with the same eigenvalue. Hence Eq. (25) says that $\mathbf{u}_2$ is now a generalized eigenvector of rank 2 of $\mathbf{A}'$ associated with the eigenvector $\mathbf{u}_1$.

By induction, a whole chain of generalized eigenvectors of $\mathbf{A}$ goes into a chain of the same length and eigenvalue of $\mathbf{A}'$.

7. INVARIANCE OF THE TRACE

Since the eigenvalues and structure of a matrix are invariant under a change of basis, it follows that the characteristic equation is also invariant under a change of basis. This establishes the invariance of the scalars discussed in Chapter III, Section 12, including, in particular, the determinant and the trace.

Because of the importance of the latter, it is perhaps worthwhile to establish its invariance directly, as well. We have that

$$\operatorname{tr}\mathbf{A} = \sum A_{ii} \tag{26}$$

Under a similarity transformation with **S**, we generate the matrix **B** such that

$$B_{ij} = \sum_{kh} (S^{-1})_{ik} A_{kh} S_{hj} \tag{27}$$

where **S**$^{-1}$ is defined so that

$$\sum_{j} (S^{-1})_{ij} S_{jk} = \delta_{ik} \tag{28}$$

The trace of **B** is then

$$\text{tr } \mathbf{B} = \sum_{i} B_{ii} = \sum_{ikh} (S^{-1})_{ik} A_{kh} S_{hi}$$

$$= \sum_{kh} A_{kh} \delta_{kh} = \sum_{k} A_{kk} = \text{tr } \mathbf{A} \tag{29}$$

Hence the trace is preserved through a similarity transformation.

Similar methods can be used to prove the invariance of the other scalar invariants, using their definition as the sum of the k-rowed principal minors, although the method becomes cumbersome as k becomes more than 2 or 3.

8. VARIATION OF THE EIGENVALUES UNDER A CONJUNCTIVE TRANSFORMATION

A conjunctive (or congruent) transformation does permit manipulation of the eigenvalues. We shall here simply state the significant results since we have not yet established the necessary background.

We use a conjunctive transformation to change the metric, **K**, that gives measure to the vector space. For this purpose, **K** is required to be hermitian so that $\langle \mathbf{x}, \mathbf{x} \rangle$ will be real for all **x**. We showed, in Chapter IV, that a hermitian matrix is necessarily semisimple and always has real eigenvalues.

Further, if **K** is hermitian, then so is **K**′, since

$$\mathbf{K}' = \mathbf{S}^{\dagger}\mathbf{K}\mathbf{S} \tag{30}$$

is also hermitian. This is true because, as we have shown, the hermitian conjugate of the product of matrices is the product of the hermitian conjugates of the matrices, but taken in reverse order so that

$$\mathbf{K}'^{\dagger} = (\mathbf{S}^{\dagger}\mathbf{K}\mathbf{S})^{\dagger} = \mathbf{S}^{\dagger}\mathbf{K}^{\dagger}(\mathbf{S}^{\dagger})^{\dagger}$$

$$= \mathbf{S}^{\dagger}\mathbf{K}\mathbf{S} = \mathbf{K}' \tag{31}$$

Hence the eigenvalues of **K**′ are also necessarily real.

It can be shown that by suitable choice of $\mathbf{S}$, we can change the magnitude of the nonzero eigenvalues of $\mathbf{K}$ at will (except that if $\mathbf{S}$ is specified to be nonsingular, we cannot reduce any of them to zero), but we cannot change their signs. This theorem is called *Sylvester's law of inertia*.

If we have a hermitian matrix, its *signature* is the difference of the number of positive and negative eigenvalues, counting multiplicities. Hence the signature is invariant.

We can also show that it is possible to so choose the basis that $\mathbf{K}'$ is diagonal (i.e., with zeros everywhere except on the main diagonal) with ± 1's along the diagonal. Such a $\mathbf{K}$ is known as a *parity matrix* and, in some applications, the basis that accomplishes this reduction is known as a *wave basis*.

9. DIAGONALIZATION

Returning now to our original problem of finding a simple representation of an abstract operator, consider a matrix, $\mathbf{A}$. We will initially consider a matrix $\mathbf{A}$ that is semisimple—i.e., which has a complete set of eigenvectors. Suppose these eigenvectors are $\mathbf{x}_1$, ..., $\mathbf{x}_n$ with eigenvalues λ_1, ..., λ_n :

$$\mathbf{A}\mathbf{x}_i = \lambda_i \mathbf{x}_i \qquad (32)$$

We are not asserting that all the λ_j are distinct, but are permitting $\mathbf{A}$ to be degenerate. We are assuming that the set $\mathbf{x}_i$ do form a complete set so that it spans the whole space.

It is perhaps reasonable to ask what happens if we change the basis by a similarity transformation to the set of eigenvectors. At least these are the only vectors that suggest themselves as playing a special role for the given operator.

Consider

$$\mathbf{S} = (\mathbf{x}_1 \quad \mathbf{x}_2 \quad \cdots \quad \mathbf{x}_n) \qquad (33)$$

That is, $\mathbf{S}$ is the matrix whose columns are the eigenvectors of $\mathbf{A}$, expressed as column matrices.

$\mathbf{S}$ is then a square matrix. Further, if we multiply $\mathbf{S}$ by a vector all of whose components are zero except the kth which is unity, we get just $\mathbf{x}_k$. That is, a unit vector along the kth axis of the new coordinate system generates the kth eigenvector of $\mathbf{A}$ on the old basis. Hence a similarity transformation using this $\mathbf{S}$ does change the basis to the set $\mathbf{x}_1$, ..., $\mathbf{x}_n$.

$\mathbf{S}$ is nonsingular since the set of eigenvectors is assumed to be linearly independent. Therefore an inverse exists. However, the question is, what is it?

In Chapter III, Section 15, we defined the reciprocal vector set to a given complete set, $\mathbf{x}_i$. These were the complete set $\mathbf{w}_i$ such that

$$\mathbf{w}_i{}^\dagger \mathbf{x}_j = \delta_{ij} \tag{34}$$

We also showed that if the $\mathbf{x}_i$ are linearly independent, so are the resultant $\mathbf{w}_i$.

We will see now that the reciprocal vectors give us the inverse of $\mathbf{S}$. Specifically, if $\mathbf{S}$ is defined as in Eq. (33), then $\mathbf{S}^{-1}$ is given by

$$\mathbf{S}^{-1} = \begin{pmatrix} \mathbf{w}_1{}^\dagger \\ \mathbf{w}_2{}^\dagger \\ \vdots \\ \mathbf{w}_n{}^\dagger \end{pmatrix} \tag{35}$$

so that $\mathbf{S}^{-1}$ is the matrix whose rows are the hermitian conjugates of the reciprocal vectors expressed as column vectors.

This is true since

$$\mathbf{S}^{-1}\mathbf{S} = \begin{pmatrix} \mathbf{w}_1{}^\dagger \mathbf{x}_1 & \mathbf{w}_1{}^\dagger \mathbf{x}_2 & \cdots \\ \mathbf{w}_2{}^\dagger \mathbf{x}_2 & \mathbf{w}_2{}^\dagger \mathbf{x}_2 & \\ \mathbf{w}_3{}^\dagger \mathbf{x}_1 & \mathbf{w}_3 \mathbf{x}_2 & \\ \vdots & \vdots & \end{pmatrix} = \mathbf{I} \tag{36}$$

Now, evidently, if we postmultiply $\mathbf{A}$ by $\mathbf{S}$, we have

$$\mathbf{AS} = \mathbf{A}(\mathbf{x}_1 \quad \mathbf{x}_2 \quad \cdots \quad \mathbf{x}_n) = (\lambda_1 \mathbf{x}_1 \quad \lambda_2 \mathbf{x}_2 \quad \cdots \quad \lambda_n \mathbf{x}_n) \tag{37}$$

and, if we premultiply this by $\mathbf{S}^{-1}$, we find

$$\mathbf{S}^{-1}\mathbf{AS} = \begin{pmatrix} \mathbf{w}_1{}^\dagger \\ \mathbf{w}_2{}^\dagger \\ \vdots \\ \mathbf{w}_n{}^\dagger \end{pmatrix} \times (\lambda_1 \mathbf{x}_1 \quad \lambda_2 \mathbf{x}_2 \quad \cdots \quad \lambda_n \mathbf{x}_n)$$

$$= \begin{pmatrix} \lambda_1 \mathbf{w}_1{}^\dagger \mathbf{x}_1 & \lambda_2 \mathbf{w}_1{}^\dagger \mathbf{x}_2 & \cdots \\ \lambda_1 \mathbf{w}_2{}^\dagger \mathbf{x}_1 & \lambda_2 \mathbf{w}_2{}^\dagger \mathbf{x}_2 & \\ \vdots & \vdots & \end{pmatrix}$$

$$= \begin{pmatrix} \lambda_1 & 0 & 0 & \\ 0 & \lambda_2 & 0 & \\ 0 & 0 & \lambda_3 & \cdots \\ & & \vdots & & \lambda_n \end{pmatrix}$$

$$= \mathrm{diag}(\lambda_1, \lambda_2, \lambda_3, ..., \lambda_n) \tag{38}$$

By the change of basis to the eigenvectors of $\mathbf{A}$, the matrix $\mathbf{A}$ has been *reduced to diagonal form.* Further, the elements on the diagonal are the eigenvalues of $\mathbf{A}$. Hence we have achieved our purpose since we have thus found a basis in terms of which $\mathbf{A}$ has assumed a particularly simple form.

The transformation is not unique. In Eq. (33) we could have taken the eigenvectors in any order. The eigenvalues would then have appeared in $\mathbf{S^{-1}AS}$ in the corresponding order, but the matrix is still diagonal.

Also, if we multiply an eigenvector by any nonzero scalar, it is still an eigenvector. Hence we could multiply the columns of $\mathbf{S}$ in Eq. (33) by any set of nonzero scalars. The reciprocal eigenvectors, and hence $\mathbf{S^{-1}}$ from Eq. (35), will then be changed correspondingly. In this case the transformed matrix is unchanged, and only $\mathbf{S}$ is affected.

Finally, if there is degeneracy in $\mathbf{A}$, we can use any vectors that span the subspace of the degeneracy. If, for example, $\lambda_1 = \lambda_2$, we can use in the $\mathbf{S}$ of Eq. (33) any two linearly independent linear combinations of $\mathbf{x}_1$ and $\mathbf{x}_2$ in place of $\mathbf{x}_1$ and $\mathbf{x}_2$. The corresponding reciprocal eigenvectors, $\mathbf{w}_1$ and $\mathbf{w}_2$, will then have to be chosen appropriately to the chosen vectors, but the same diagonal matrix, Eq. (38), will result.

The important result is that if a matrix $\mathbf{A}$ is semisimple, then we can always change the basis in such a way that the matrix becomes diagonal with the eigenvalues of the original matrix along the diagonal.

10. DIAGONALIZATION OF NORMAL MATRICES

We have seen that the class of normal matrices, which includes hermitian and unitary matrices, is of particular importance. It is, therefore, worthwhile to see if they can be diagonalized in some particularly convenient way.

We saw, in Chapter IV, that normal matrices are always semisimple, and that eigenvectors with distinct eigenvalues are always orthogonal. By the Gram-Schmidt process, we can resolve any degeneracies into orthogonal eigenvectors. Finally, we can normalize all the eigenvectors so that their inner product with themselves is unity. We can in summary, always obtain a complete set of eigenvectors $\mathbf{x}_i$ such that

$$\mathbf{x}_i^\dagger \mathbf{x}_j = \delta_{ij} \tag{39}$$

It is then reasonable to ask if these particular vectors have a preferred role. If we construct the $\mathbf{S}$ matrix of Eq. (33) from these particular vectors, does it have any special properties?

If we compare Eq. (39) with Eq. (34), we find that the $\mathbf{x}_i$ so defined are their own reciprocal set. The inverse matrix $\mathbf{S^{-1}}$, given by Eq. (35), is then the same as would be obtained by taking the hermitian conjugate of $\mathbf{S}$:

$$\mathbf{S}^{-1} = \mathbf{S}^\dagger$$

Hence $\mathbf{S}$ is unitary.

If $\mathbf{A}$ is normal we can always find an $\mathbf{S}$ that will diagonalize it by a similarity transformation, where $\mathbf{S}$ is unitary:

$$\mathbf{A} = \mathbf{S}\,\mathrm{diag}(\lambda_1, \lambda_2, ...)\mathbf{S}^{-1}$$
$$= \mathbf{S}\,\mathrm{diag}(\lambda_1, \lambda_2, ...)\mathbf{S}^\dagger \tag{40}$$

The similarity transformation then becomes a conjunctive one. It is also sometimes a *unitary transformation.*

We can generalize these results to any proper inner product, since the orthogonality conditions are unaffected by this generalization. It is always possible, if K is positive definite, to diagonalize any K-normal, K-hermitian, or K-unitary matrix, by a similarity transformation with an $\mathbf{S}$ that is K-unitary. The $\mathbf{S}$ that does this is constructed from eigenvectors that are K-orthogonal by pairs, and normalized to unity under the K-inner product.

11. CONJUNCTIVE TRANSFORMATION OF A HERMITIAN MATRIX

We can now use the preceding results to show how we can modify the metric $\mathbf{K}$ by a change of basis. We have seen that under a change of basis a metric changes conjunctively. We shall show that the change of basis can be chosen to reduce the metric to a parity matrix.

The theorem of the preceding section shows that a hermitian $\mathbf{K}$ can be diagonalized to $\mathbf{K}'$ by a transformation which is both a similarity transformation, and a conjunctive one, since $\mathbf{S}$ is unitary. Now let $\mathbf{D}$ be the diagonal matrix whose ith term on the main diagonal is $1/\sqrt{|\lambda_i|}$, where λ_i is the ith eigenvalue of $\mathbf{K}$ or $\mathbf{K}'$ ordered according to their sequence in $\mathbf{K}'$. Then $\mathbf{D}^\dagger = \mathbf{D}$. We use this $\mathbf{D}$ to conjunctively transform $\mathbf{K}'$ to to $\mathbf{K}''$:

$$\mathbf{K}'' = \mathbf{D}^\dagger \mathbf{K}' \mathbf{D} = \mathrm{diag}(\mathrm{sgn}\,\lambda_1, \mathrm{sgn}\,\lambda_2, ...)$$

where

$$\mathrm{sgn}\,\lambda_i = 1 \quad \text{if} \quad \lambda_i > 0$$
$$= -1 \quad \text{if} \quad \lambda_i < 0$$

$\mathbf{K}''$ is, then, a *parity matrix.*

If we write $\mathbf{K}''$ in terms of $\mathbf{K}$, we have

$$\mathbf{K}'' = \mathbf{D}^\dagger \mathbf{S}^\dagger \mathbf{K} \mathbf{S} \mathbf{D} = (\mathbf{S}\mathbf{D})^\dagger \mathbf{K}(\mathbf{S}\mathbf{D}) \tag{41}$$

Hence $\mathbf{K}''$ is obtained from $\mathbf{K}$ by a conjunctive transformation with the matrix $(\mathbf{S}\mathbf{D})$—which, it should be noted, is, in general, no longer unitary.

It is, therefore, always possible to find a matrix which will conjunctively transform any nonsingular hermitian matrix into a parity matrix. In particular, it is always possible to change the basis for the representation of a system so as to put the metric into the form of a parity matrix.

We can make a further conjunctive transformation of Eq. (41) with a *permutation matrix*—i.e., a matrix with only a single nonzero term in each row and each column, that term being unity. Such a transformation will permute the terms on the main diagonal, allowing us to arrange the sequence of signs in the parity matrix in any order desired.

Finally, we will note that if we allow $\mathbf{K}$ to be singular, essentially the same procedure can be carried out, except that the terms in the $\mathbf{D}$ matrix corresponding to the zero-valued eigenvalues must be taken as any finite value. We end up with a matrix that looks like a parity matrix except that some of the terms on the main diagonal are zero instead of ± 1... .

12. EXAMPLE

As an example of this process, consider the Manley-Rowe metric. In Chapter II, Section 5, we considered the case of parametric interaction in a nondissipative structure. We showed that the linearized Manley-Rowe relations, on the basis of the complex voltage and current amplitudes at the various parametric harmonics, could be expressed as the metric

$$\mathbf{K} = \begin{pmatrix} 0 & \mathbf{P} \\ \mathbf{P} & 0 \end{pmatrix} \tag{42}$$

where

$$\mathbf{P} = \mathrm{diag}(..., 1/f_{-1}, 1/f_0, 1/f_1, ...) \tag{43}$$

Suppose, now, we define the matrix

$$\mathbf{Z} = \mathrm{diag}(..., Z_{-1}, Z_0, Z_1, ...) \tag{44}$$

where Z_i can be interpreted as the characteristic impedance of a transmission line at the frequency f_i.

We let

$$\mathbf{S} = \begin{pmatrix} \mathbf{Z} & -\mathbf{Z} \\ \mathbf{I} & \mathbf{I} \end{pmatrix} \tag{45}$$

and find that

$$\mathbf{K}' = \mathbf{S^\dagger K S} = \begin{pmatrix} \mathbf{ZP + PZ} & \mathbf{ZP - PZ} \\ \mathbf{-ZP + PZ} & \mathbf{-ZP - PZ} \end{pmatrix}$$

However, $\mathbf{P}$ and $\mathbf{Z}$ are both diagonal matrices. Hence they commute. Therefore, we are left only with

$$\mathbf{K}' = 2 \begin{pmatrix} \mathbf{PZ} & 0 \\ 0 & \mathbf{-PZ} \end{pmatrix} \tag{46}$$

and $\mathbf{K}'$ is diagonal.

By a further change of basis using a diagonal matrix—which amounts to a renormalization of the waves involved—we can obtain a $\mathbf{K}''$ with only ± 1 on the main diagonal. Thus we obtain a pure parity matrix.

The signs are still somewhat mixed up since $f_n = f_0 + nf_p$ is negative for n sufficiently large negative. We can, if we like, sort them out with a suitable permutation matrix and obtain

$$\mathbf{K}''' = \begin{pmatrix} \mathbf{I} & 0 \\ 0 & \mathbf{-I} \end{pmatrix}$$

where the two identity matrices have the same dimensionality. This metric, then, has zero signature.

We can note a further possibility. Suppose, on this basis,

$$\mathbf{H}''' = \begin{pmatrix} \mathbf{I} & 0 \\ 0 & \mathbf{I} \end{pmatrix} = \mathbf{I}$$

is also a suitable metric. If the vector, on this basis, is

$$\mathbf{x} = \begin{pmatrix} \mathbf{u} \\ \mathbf{v} \end{pmatrix} = \begin{pmatrix} \text{col}(\cdots \ u_i \ \cdots) \\ \text{col}(\cdots \ v_i \ \cdots) \end{pmatrix}$$

then the metric $\mathbf{K}'''$ asserts the invariance of

$$s_1 = \mathbf{u^\dagger u} - \mathbf{v^\dagger v} = \sum_i |u_i|^2 - \sum_i |v_i|^2$$

while $\mathbf{H}'''$ asserts the invariance of

$$s_2 = \mathbf{u^\dagger u} + \mathbf{v^\dagger v} = \sum_i |u_i|^2 + \sum_i |v_i|^2$$

Hence the simultaneous assertion of both asserts the seperate invariance of

$$s_1' = \mathbf{u^\dagger u} = \sum_i |u_i|^2$$

and

$$s_2' = \sum \mathbf{v}^\dagger \mathbf{v} = \sum | v_i |^2$$

If, as mentioned before, the Z_i are characteristic impedances of the line at the referenced frequency, then the set of u_i can be interpreted as the amplitudes of the forward waves in the line, and the set of v_i as the backward waves. Thus the simultaneous assertion of both $\mathbf{K}'''$ and $\mathbf{H}'''$ as metrics of the system implies that these two sets of waves are independent of each other. We can therefore use $\mathbf{K}'''$ and $\mathbf{H}'''$ to specify what we may call an *ideal parametric line*, i.e., a line without dissipation or internal reflection. That is, we can use these two metrics to study whether it is physically possible, and if so what is required, to make such a line. (It turns out that it is indeed possible, at least theoretically, and that what is required is that the distributed capacity and inductance of the line both vary parametrically in such a way as to maintain constant characteristic impedance.)

13. POSITIVE DEFINITE HERMITIAN FORMS

In Chapter II, we specified that for an inner product relation to be proper, it had to be positive definite. This requires that the scalar function of $\mathbf{x}$ given by

$$s(\mathbf{x}) = \mathbf{x}^\dagger \mathbf{K} \mathbf{x} \qquad (47)$$

be real and positive for all nonnull vectors in the space. We did not, at that time, give any test for positive definiteness other than the definition itself. With the diagonalization process given, we can now improve on this situation.

For $s(\mathbf{x})$ to be real for all $\mathbf{x}$ whose components are in the field of complex numbers, $\mathbf{K}$ must be hermitian. Hence the diagonalization process of the preceding two sections apply, and we can write

$$s(\mathbf{x}) = \mathbf{x}^\dagger \mathbf{S}^{\dagger-1} \mathbf{K}' \mathbf{S}^{-1} \mathbf{x} = (\mathbf{S}^{-1}\mathbf{x})^\dagger \mathbf{K}'(\mathbf{S}^{-1}\mathbf{x}) \qquad (48)$$

where $\mathbf{S}$ is nonsingular and $\mathbf{K}'$ is real diagonal. The transformation $\mathbf{y} = \mathbf{S}^{-1}\mathbf{x}$ is evidently a mapping of the whole space onto itself. It is, therefore, enough to consider the value of s for all possible vectors, $\mathbf{y}$.

Let $\mathbf{y}_i$ be the vector all of whose components are zero excepts the ith, which is unity. For this vector,

$$s(\mathbf{y}_i) = \lambda_i \qquad (49)$$

where λ_i is the eigenvalue of $\mathbf{K}$ that appears in the ith position of $\mathbf{K}'$.

Evidently, a necessary condition for $\mathbf{K}$ to be positive definite is that all of the λ_i be positive. If any are negative, the s for the corresponding

y_i is negative. If any are zero, then the corresponding s is zero for the nonnull vector y_i.

A necessary condition that K shall be positive semidefinite is that none of the λ_i be negative.

That these conditions are also sufficient is seen by considering the general vector y whose h component is y_i. For this vector

$$s(y) = \sum_i \lambda_i |\, y_i\, |^2 = \sum_i \{\lambda_i^{1/2} |\, y_i\, |\}^2 \tag{50}$$

so that, if all of the λ_i are positive, s is the sum of squares, and hence cannot be negative for any y, or zero for any y but the null vector.

14. LAGRANGE'S METHOD

We will give here another method for the diagonalization of a hermitian quadratic form, and its expression as the sum or difference of a sequence of squares—i.e., of reducing K to parity form.

We consider again the hermitian quadratic form

$$s(x) = x^\dagger K x = \sum_{ij} x_i^* x_j k_{ij} \tag{51}$$

where, since K is hermitian

$$k_{ij} = k_{ji}^*, \qquad k_{ii} \text{ real}$$

Suppose, first, that $k_{11} \neq 0$. Define the quadratic form s_1 by the equation

$$s(x) = s_1(x) + \frac{1}{k_{11}} \left|\, \sum_i k_{1i} x_i\, \right|^2 \tag{52}$$

We assert that $s_1(x)$ is a hermitian quadratic form which does not contain the variable x_1.

That it is hermitian is obvious, since it is the difference of two hermitian forms. To show that it does not contain x_1, we expand the sum and isolate the terms that contain x_1:

$$\frac{1}{k_{11}} \left|\, \sum_i k_{1i} x_i\, \right|^2 = \frac{1}{k_{11}} \left\{ \sum_i k_{1i} x_i \right\} \left\{ \sum_j k_{1j} x_j \right\}^*$$

$$= \frac{1}{k_{11}} \sum_{ij} k_{1i} k_{j1} x_i x_j^*$$

$$= k_{11} |\, x_1\, |^2 + \sum_{j \neq 1} k_{j1} x_1 x_j^* + \sum_{i \neq 1} k_{1i} x_i x_1^* + \frac{1}{k_{11}} \sum_{\substack{i \neq 1 \\ j \neq 1}} k_{1i} k_{j1} x_i x_j^* \tag{53}$$

The terms containing x_1 and $x_1{}^*$ are precisely the terms of $s(\mathbf{x})$ containing x_1 and $x_1{}^*$. Hence $s_1(\mathbf{x})$ does not contain x_1 or $x_1{}^*$.

If $k_{11} = 0$, but some other diagonal term, say k_{rr} is nonzero, then we can, by the same method, construct an $s_1(\mathbf{x})$ that does not contain x_r or $x_r{}^*$.

We can repeat this process as long as s_i contains at least one nonzero diagonal term. If we can continue the process until no residual form exists at all, then we have reduced $s(\mathbf{x})$ to the sum or difference of a sequence of squares, depending on whether the k_{ii} at the corresponding step is positive or negative. If, now, we set

$$y_1 = \frac{1}{\sqrt{|k_{11}|}} \sum_i k_{1i}x_i \qquad (54)$$

and let y_2, y_3, etc., be the square root of the magnitude of the terms isolated in the successive steps, then the y_i are linearly independent. The function y_1, for example, includes the variable x_1 which is absent from all successive y_i. These vectors, augmented if necessary by additional linearly independent vectors, form a basis in terms of which $\mathbf{K}$ is reduced to parity form, or to the modified parity form with some zeros on the diagonal if $\mathbf{K}$ is singular.

The process given so far depends on there being, at each step, at least one nonzero diagonal term. Suppose, instead, that all $k_{ii} = 0$ but, for example, $k_{12} \neq 0$. Then $k_{21} = k_{12}^* \neq 0$. Define s_{12} by the equation

$$s(\mathbf{x}) = s_{12}(\mathbf{x}) + \frac{1}{2}\left|\sum_i \left\{\frac{k_{1i}}{k_{12}}\,x_i + k_{2i}x_i\right\}\right|^2 - \frac{1}{2}\left|\sum_i \left\{\frac{k_{1i}}{k_{12}} - k_{2i}x_i\right\}\right|^2 \qquad (55)$$

We now assert that $s_{12}(\mathbf{x})$ is a hermitian quadratic form that does not contain either x_1 or x_2. That it is hermitian is obvious. We expand the sum:

$$\frac{1}{2}\left|\sum_i \left(\frac{k_{1i}}{k_{12}}\,x_i + k_{2i}x_i\right)\right|^2 - \frac{1}{2}\left|\sum_i \left(\frac{k_{1i}}{k_{12}}\,x_i - k_{2i}x_i\right)\right|^2$$

$$= \sum_{i,j}\left(\frac{k_{1i}k_{j2}}{k_{12}} + \frac{k_{2i}k_{j1}}{k_{21}}\right)x_ix_j{}^*$$

$$= \sum_{j \neq 1} k_{j1}x_1x_j{}^* + \sum_{j \neq 2} k_{j2}x_2x_j{}^*$$

$$+ \sum_{i \neq 1} k_{1i}x_ix_1{}^* + \sum_{i \neq 2} k_{2i}x_ix_2{}^*$$

$$+ \sum_{i,j \neq 1,2}\left(\frac{k_{1i}k_{j2}}{k_{12}} + \frac{k_{2i}k_{j1}}{k_{21}}\right)x_ix_j{}^* \qquad (56)$$

since $k_{11} = k_{22} = 0$.

This expansion contains all the terms of $s(\mathbf{x})$ that contain either x_1 or x_2. Hence s_{12} does not contain x_1 or x_2. We have isolated the terms in x_1 and x_2 as the difference of two squares.

The vectors

$$\sum_i (k_{1i}/k_{12})x_i \quad \text{and} \quad \sum_i k_{2i}x_i \tag{57}$$

are linearly independent since the first contains a nonzero term in x_2 but not x_1, and the second in x_1 but not x_2. Hence their sum and difference:

$$y_1 = \sum_i \left(\frac{k_{1i}}{k_{12}} + k_{2i} \right) x_i$$

$$y_2 = \sum_i \left(\frac{k_{1i}}{k_{12}} - k_{2i} \right) x_i \tag{58}$$

are linearly independent.

By these processes, the quadratic form $s(\mathbf{x})$ can be reduced to the algebraic sum of a sequence of signed square terms, each of which is linearly independent of the others. The terms involved provide a basis for the reduction of a nonsingular $\mathbf{K}$ to parity form.

15. CANONICAL FORM OF A NONSEMISIMPLE MATRIX

We consider now a matrix that is not semisimple. As we have seen, we obtain a complete set of vectors in this case by forming chains of generalized eigenvectors:

$$\mathbf{A}\mathbf{x}_i = \lambda_1 \mathbf{x}_1$$

$$\mathbf{A}\mathbf{x}_2 = \lambda_1 \mathbf{x}_2 + \mathbf{x}_1 \tag{59}$$

$$\mathbf{A}\mathbf{x}_3 = \lambda_1 \mathbf{x}_3 + \mathbf{x}_2$$

so that $\mathbf{x}_1$ is an eigenvector, $\mathbf{x}_2$ a generalized eigenvector of rank two, $\mathbf{x}_3$ of rank 3, and so on. In addition, we may have other eigenvectors or chains of generalized eigenvectors.

These vectors form a complete set of linearly independent vectors. Therefore, by the same argument as before, we can form a complete set of reciprocal vectors $\mathbf{w}_1, ..., \mathbf{w}_n$ such that

$$\mathbf{w}_i{}^\dagger \mathbf{x}_j = \delta_{ij} \tag{60}$$

Then, as before, if we set

$$\mathbf{S} = (\mathbf{x}_1, \mathbf{x}_2, ..., \mathbf{x}_n) \tag{61}$$

the reciprocal matrix is

$$\mathbf{S}^{-1} = \begin{pmatrix} \mathbf{w_1}^\dagger \\ \mathbf{w_2}^\dagger \\ \vdots \\ \mathbf{w_n}^\dagger \end{pmatrix} \tag{62}$$

We find, however, that

$$\mathbf{AS} = (\lambda_1\mathbf{x_1}, \lambda_1\mathbf{x_2} + \mathbf{x_1}, \lambda_1\mathbf{x_3} + \mathbf{x_2}, \ldots) \tag{63}$$

so that

$$\mathbf{S}^{-1}\mathbf{AS} = \begin{pmatrix} \lambda_1\mathbf{w_1}^\dagger\mathbf{x_1} & \mathbf{w_1}^\dagger(\lambda_1\mathbf{x_2}+\mathbf{x_1}) & \mathbf{w_1}^\dagger(\lambda_1\mathbf{x_3}+\mathbf{x_2}) & \cdots \\ \lambda_1\mathbf{w_2}^\dagger\mathbf{x_1} & \mathbf{w_2}^\dagger(\lambda_1\mathbf{x_2}+\mathbf{x_1}) & \mathbf{w_2}^\dagger(\lambda_1\mathbf{x_3}+\mathbf{x_2}) \\ \lambda_1\mathbf{w_3}^\dagger\mathbf{x_1} & \mathbf{w_3}^\dagger(\lambda_1\mathbf{x_2}+\mathbf{x_1}) & \mathbf{w_3}^\dagger(\lambda_1\mathbf{x_3}+\mathbf{x_2}) \\ \vdots & & & \end{pmatrix}$$

$$= \begin{pmatrix} \lambda_1 & 1 & 0 & \cdots \\ 0 & \lambda_1 & 1 \\ 0 & 0 & \lambda_1 \\ \vdots & & & \end{pmatrix} \tag{64}$$

We can generalize this statement by saying that if the chains of generalized eigenvectors are arranged in $\mathbf{S}$ in order of ascending rank, then

$$\mathbf{S}^{-1}\mathbf{AS} = \begin{pmatrix} \mathbf{J}_{k_1}(\lambda_1) & 0 & 0 & \\ 0 & \mathbf{J}_{k_2}(\lambda_2) & 0 & \\ 0 & 0 & \mathbf{J}_{k_3}(\lambda_3) & \\ & & & \ddots \end{pmatrix} \tag{65}$$

where $\mathbf{J}_{k_i}(\lambda_i)$ is a $k_i \times k_i$ matrix, k_i being the length of the chain involved, with λ_i along the diagonal, 1 along the first super diagonal, and zeros elsewhere. For example,

$$\mathbf{J}_1(\lambda) = \lambda$$

$$\mathbf{J}_2(\lambda) = \begin{pmatrix} \lambda & 1 \\ 0 & \lambda \end{pmatrix} \tag{66}$$

$$\mathbf{J}_3(\lambda) = \begin{pmatrix} \lambda & 1 & 0 \\ 0 & \lambda & 1 \\ 0 & 0 & \lambda \end{pmatrix}$$

etc.

Again we should note that the transformation to the form of Eq. (65) is not unique. The chains in **S** of Eq. (61) may be taken in any order with consequent adjustment of the order of the blocks in Eq. (65) but without loss of canonical form. Any degeneracies between chains can be resolved arbitrarily. Further, any chain of length greater than one is automatically degenerate. So the transformation to the canonical form is not unique. The important fact, however, is that it is always possible.

We shall also note that the diagonal form of Eq. (38) is included in the canonical form of Eq. (65) in which all the k_i are unity. This is true since an isolated eigenvector can be considered as a chain of length one.

The zeros of Eq. (65) are rectangular null matrices of appropriate dimensionality to fill out the array around the matrices on the diagonal.

The matrix $J_{k_i}(\lambda_i)$ is called the *upper Jordan block of order* k_i. If the units are, instead, on the first infradiagonal—i.e., the diagonal next below the main diagonal—the form is called a *lower Jordan block*. This will result in Eq. (65) if the order of the chains are reversed in the **S** matrix of Eq. (63).

The form of Eq. (64) or (65) is the *Jordan canonical form* of the matrix **A**. (Properly, it is the upper Jordan canonical form, but the specification of the upper form is usually to be understood unless otherwise stated.)

We shall give a more rigorous derivation of these results in Chapter VIII.

16. EXAMPLE

As a specific example of reduction to canonical form, consider the matrix:

$$\mathbf{A} = \begin{pmatrix} 0 & 1 & -2j & 0 \\ 0 & 0 & 0 & -2j \\ 2j & 0 & 0 & 1 \\ 0 & 2j & 0 & 0 \end{pmatrix} \tag{67}$$

The characteristic equation is

$$|\mathbf{A} - \lambda\mathbf{I}| = (\lambda^2 - 4)^2 = 0 \tag{68}$$

so that the eigenvalues are ± 2, each with multiplicity 2.

Consider, first, the eigenvalue 2. We look for vectors $\mathbf{x} = \text{col}(a, b, c, d)$ such that $\mathbf{Ax} = 2\mathbf{x}$. This gives us the set of simultaneous equations:

$$b - 2jc = 2a$$
$$-2jd = 2b$$
$$2ja + d = 2c$$
$$2jb = 2d$$

The second and fourth equations are the same, within a factor of j. If we substitute $d = jb$ into the third, we get

$$2a + b = -2jc$$

For this to be consistent with the first, we must have $b = 0$. Hence, there is only the single eigenvector with eigenvalue 2:

$$\mathbf{x}_1 = \begin{pmatrix} 1 \\ 0 \\ j \\ 0 \end{pmatrix}_2$$

which we have arbitrarily normalized by setting $a = 1$.

Since the eigenvalue has multiplicity 2, there must be a generalized eigenvector. We look for a vector, $\mathbf{x}_2 = \text{col}(a,\ b,\ c,\ d)$, such that $\mathbf{Ax}_2 = 2\mathbf{x}_2 + \mathbf{x}_1$. This requires that

$$\begin{aligned} b - 2jc &= 2a + 1 \\ -2jd &= 2b \\ 2ja + d &= 2c + j \\ 2jb &= 2d \end{aligned}$$

Again, the second and fourth are the same. Substituting $d = jb$ in the third, we obtain

$$2a + b = -2jc + 1$$

This, with the first equation, requires that

$$\begin{aligned} b &= 1 \\ c &= ja \end{aligned}$$

But the last, $c = ja$, is the condition for $\mathbf{x}_1$. This simply reflects the fact that we can add to $\mathbf{x}_2$ any factor times $\mathbf{x}_1$ without affecting its role in the chain. The simplest choice, then, is to let

$$\mathbf{x}_2 = \begin{pmatrix} 0 \\ 1 \\ 0 \\ j \end{pmatrix}_2$$

In similar fashion, we find, for the eigenvalue -2, the chain

$$\mathbf{x}_3 = \begin{pmatrix} 1 \\ 0 \\ -j \\ 0 \end{pmatrix}_{-2}, \qquad \mathbf{x}_4 = \begin{pmatrix} 0 \\ 1 \\ 0 \\ -j \end{pmatrix}_{-2}$$

We therefore can set, in Eq. (61),

$$\mathbf{S} = (\mathbf{x}_1, \mathbf{x}_2, \mathbf{x}_3, \mathbf{x}_4) = \begin{pmatrix} 1 & 0 & 1 & 0 \\ 0 & 1 & 0 & 1 \\ j & 0 & -j & 0 \\ 0 & j & 0 & -j \end{pmatrix}$$

We can find, also, that

$$\mathbf{S}^{-1} = \frac{1}{2} \begin{pmatrix} 1 & 0 & -j & 0 \\ 0 & 1 & 0 & -j \\ 1 & 0 & j & 0 \\ 0 & 1 & 0 & j \end{pmatrix}$$

Finally, we find that

$$\mathbf{A}' = \mathbf{S}^{-1}\mathbf{A}\mathbf{S} = \begin{pmatrix} 2 & 1 & 0 & 0 \\ 0 & 2 & 0 & 0 \\ 0 & 0 & -2 & 1 \\ 0 & 0 & 0 & -2 \end{pmatrix} \tag{69}$$

which we recognize as the Jordan canonical form.

The particular transformation that we have used is not unique. We could have normalized $\mathbf{x}_1$ and $\mathbf{x}_3$ in any way we liked, with the corresponding renormalizations of $\mathbf{x}_2$ and $\mathbf{x}_4$. And we could have added to $\mathbf{x}_2$ any factor times $\mathbf{x}_1$, and to $\mathbf{x}_4$ any factor times $\mathbf{x}_3$. These choices affect $\mathbf{S}$, and so $\mathbf{S}^{-1}$, but would not have affected $\mathbf{A}'$. The significant thing that we have illustrated here is that it is possible to find a basis in terms of which $\mathbf{A}$ takes the canonical form.

17. POWERS AND POLYNOMIALS OF A MATRIX

We shall now use the Jordan canonical form to develop some of the properties of a power of a matrix, and so of a polynomial function of a matrix. This is the first step in developing the notion of a function of a matrix. It also lays the foundation for certain important theorems that follow.

We start by noting an important property of the similarity transformation which we can state in general terms as:

Theorem 1. *If we are given two matrices* $\mathbf{A}$ *and* $\mathbf{B}$, *and change the basis of both by a given similarity transformation to* $\mathbf{A}'$ *and* $\mathbf{B}'$, *then* $(\mathbf{A}'\mathbf{B}')$ *is the transformation of* $(\mathbf{AB})$.

This is to be expected since the product **AB**, being the successive application of the two operators, should be a property of the abstract operators, and should not depend on the representations involved.

The theorem can also be stated by saying a similarity transformation generates an *isomorphism*.[2]

The theorem follows immediately from the definition of a similarity transformation. If we are given

$$\mathbf{A'} = \mathbf{SAS}^{-1}$$
$$\mathbf{B'} = \mathbf{SBS}^{-1} \tag{70}$$

then

$$\begin{aligned}
\mathbf{A'B'} &= (\mathbf{SAS}^{-1})(\mathbf{SBS}^{-1}) \\
&= \mathbf{SA}(\mathbf{S}^{-1}\mathbf{S})\mathbf{BS}^{-1} \\
&= \mathbf{S}(\mathbf{AB})\mathbf{S}^{-1}
\end{aligned} \tag{71}$$

so that **A'B'** is the transform of **AB**.

In particular, suppose we have a given matrix **A**, and suppose it is transformed into Jordan canonical form **D** by **S**:

$$\mathbf{D} = \mathbf{S}^{-1}\mathbf{AS}$$
$$\mathbf{A} = \mathbf{SDS}^{-1} \tag{72}$$

Then we have

$$\mathbf{A}^2 = \mathbf{SDS}^{-1}\mathbf{SDS}^{-1} = \mathbf{SD}^2\mathbf{S}^{-1} \tag{73}$$

or, by induction,

$$\mathbf{A}^k = \mathbf{SD}^k\mathbf{S}^{-1} \tag{74}$$

If **A** is semisimple, then **D** is a diagonal matrix, $\mathrm{diag}(\lambda_1, \lambda_2, ..., \lambda_n)$, and, evidently,

$$\mathbf{D}^2 = \mathrm{diag}(\lambda_1^2, \lambda_2^2, ..., \lambda_n^2)$$

---

[2] Given a space S consisting of elements a, b, c, etc., and an operation whereby two elements of S combine to form a third, $c = (a, b)$, and a second space S' of elements a', b', c' with an operation whereby two elements of S' combine to form a third, $c' = (a'\,b')$, then the relation of S to S' is *homomorphic* if there exists a correspondence which relates to each element of S an element of S' such that if a is related to a' and b to b', then (a, b) is related to (a', b'). If the correspondence is one-to-one, the relation is *isomorphic*.

In particular, if the matrices **A**, **B**, **C**, etc., are related in a one-to-one fashion to the matrices **A'**, **B'**, **C'** such that, under matrix multiplication,

$$\mathbf{A'B'} = (\mathbf{AB})'$$

then the relation is an isomorphism.

or, generally,

$$\mathbf{D}^k = \mathrm{diag}(\lambda_1{}^k, \lambda_2{}^k, ..., \lambda_n{}^k) \tag{75}$$

It is then convenient to define the zeroth power of $\mathbf{D}$ as

$$\begin{aligned} \mathbf{D}^0 &= \mathrm{diag}(\lambda_1{}^0, \lambda_2{}^0, ..., \lambda_n{}^0) \\ &= \mathrm{diag}(1, 1, ..., 1) = \mathbf{I} \end{aligned} \tag{76}$$

Then

$$\mathbf{A}^0 = \mathbf{SD}^0\mathbf{S}^{-1} = \mathbf{SIS}^{-1} = \mathbf{SS}^{-1} = \mathbf{I} \tag{77}$$

Suppose now we have a polynomial of degree m:

$$p(x) = a_0 + a_1 x + \cdots + a_m x^m \tag{78}$$

We can, evidently, define the equivalent polynomial of $\mathbf{A}$ as

$$p(\mathbf{A}) = a_0\mathbf{I} + a_1\mathbf{A} + a_2\mathbf{A}^2 + \cdots + a_m\mathbf{A}^m \tag{79}$$

If we change the basis with $\mathbf{S}$, we find

$$\begin{aligned} p(\mathbf{D}) = \mathbf{S}^{-1}p(\mathbf{A})\mathbf{S} &= a_0\mathbf{S}^{-1}\mathbf{S} + a_1\mathbf{S}^{-1}\mathbf{A}\mathbf{S} + a_2\mathbf{S}^{-1}\mathbf{A}^2\mathbf{S} + \cdots + a_m\mathbf{S}^{-1}\mathbf{A}^m\mathbf{S} \\ &= a_0\mathbf{I} + a_1\mathbf{D} + a_2\mathbf{D}^2 + \cdots + a_m\mathbf{D}^m \end{aligned} \tag{80}$$

and, if $\mathbf{A}$ is semisimple,

$$p(\mathbf{D}) = \begin{pmatrix} a_0 + a_1\lambda_1 + \cdots + a_m\lambda_1{}^m & 0 & \cdots \\ 0 & a_0 + a_1\lambda_2 + \cdots + a_m\lambda_2{}^m & \cdots \\ \cdots & & \end{pmatrix}$$

$$= \mathrm{diag}(p(\lambda_1), p(\lambda_2), ..., p(\lambda_i), ..., p(\lambda_m)) \tag{81}$$

Hence we have that

$$p(\mathbf{A}) = \mathbf{S}\{\mathrm{diag}(p(\lambda_1), p(\lambda_2), ..., p(\lambda_m))\}\mathbf{S}^{-1} \tag{82}$$

If $\mathbf{A}$ is not semisimple, the results are more complicated since the power of a Jordan block is not a Jordan block. We find that it is, in fact,

$$\mathbf{J}^m = \begin{pmatrix} \lambda^m & \binom{m}{1}\lambda^{m-1} & \binom{m}{2}\lambda^{m-2} & \cdots \\ 0 & \lambda^m & \binom{m}{1}\lambda^{m-1} & \cdots \\ 0 & 0 & \lambda^m & \cdots \\ \text{etc.} & & & \end{pmatrix} \tag{83}$$

where

$$\binom{n}{k} = \frac{n!}{k!(n-k)!}$$

i.e., the binomial coefficient. This is easily proven by induction. We write the ij term of $\mathbf{J}$ as

$$J_{ij} = \lambda\delta_{ij} + \delta_{i+1,j}$$

Suppose that the ij term of $\mathbf{J}^m$ is

$$(\mathbf{J}^m)_{ij} = \binom{m}{j-i}\lambda^{m-j+i} \qquad \text{if } i \leqslant j \leqslant n \qquad (84)$$
$$= 0 \qquad\qquad\qquad \text{otherwise}$$

This is true for $m = 1$.

Then, if this is true for m, we see that

$$(\mathbf{J}^{m+1})_{ij} = \sum_k (\lambda\delta_{ik} + \delta_{i+1,k})\binom{m}{j-k}\lambda^{m-j+k}$$

$$= \left\{ \binom{m}{j-i} + \binom{m}{j-i-1} \right\}\lambda^{m-j+i+1}$$

$$= \binom{m+1}{j-i}\lambda^{(m+1)-j+i} \qquad (85)$$

and it is therefore true for $(m+1)$.

We should investigate in detail what happens at the edge of the nonzero range of i and j, but this is straightforward.

It should be noted that $\mathbf{J}^m$ has the same dimensionality as the original $\mathbf{J}$. Therefore, if we are taking the mth power of a $p \times p$ Jordan block, with $m > (p-1)$ we use only the binomial coefficients up to $\binom{m}{p-1}$.

If we consider the polynomial $p(x)$ of order m,

$$p(x) = a_m x^m + a_{m-1}x^{m-1} + \cdots + a_0 \qquad (86)$$

it is not difficult to see that

$$p\{\mathbf{J}(\lambda)\} = \begin{pmatrix} p(\lambda) & \dfrac{p'(\lambda)}{1!} & \dfrac{p''(\lambda)}{2!} & \dfrac{p'''(\lambda)}{3!} & \cdots \\ 0 & p(\lambda) & \dfrac{p'(\lambda)}{1!} & \dfrac{p''(\lambda)}{2!} & \cdots \\ 0 & 0 & p(\lambda) & \dfrac{p'(\lambda)}{1!} & \\ \text{etc.} & & & & \end{pmatrix} \qquad (87)$$

where

$$p'(x) = dp/dx$$
$$p''(x) = d^2p/dx^2$$

In particular, it should be noted that if $\mathbf{J}(\lambda)$ is $k \times k$, then the highest derivative that appears in Eq. (87) is the $(k-1)$st.

18. THE CAYLEY-HAMILTON THEOREM

From the results of the previous section, we can obtain an immediate proof of the Cayley-Hamilton theorem:

Theorem 2. *Any matrix satisfies its own characteristic equation. That is, we consider the characteristic equation of* $\mathbf{A}$:

$$| \mathbf{A} - \lambda \mathbf{I} | = p(\lambda) = 0 \tag{88}$$

where $p(\lambda)$ *is the characteristic polynomial in* λ *of* $\mathbf{A}$. *Then it follows that*

$$p(\mathbf{A}) = 0 \tag{89}$$

If $\mathbf{A}$ is semisimple, then this follows directly from Eq. (82). For, by definition, the eigenvalues are the roots of the characteristic polynomial and

$$p(\lambda_1) = p(\lambda_2) = \cdots = p(\lambda_n) = 0 \tag{90}$$

Hence $p(\mathbf{A})$ is the null matrix.

Suppose $\mathbf{A}$ contains a chain of length k with eigenvalue λ_i. Then λ_i must be a root of the characteristic polynomial with at least multiplicity k. (It may have higher multiplicity if there are, in addition to the chain, other eigenvectors or chains with the same eigenvalue—i.e., if there is degeneracy beyond that implied by the chain itself.) Hence $p(\lambda)$ must contain at least the factor $(\lambda - \lambda_i)^k$

$$p(\lambda) = (\lambda - \lambda_i)^k g(\lambda) \tag{91}$$

where $g(\lambda)$ is a polynomial in λ.

Now a chain of length k is represented in the Jordan canonical form by a Jordan block of dimensionality $k \times k$. Hence, from the last statement of the previous section, $p\{\mathbf{J}_k(\lambda_i)\}$ includes only $p(\lambda_i)$, $p'(\lambda_i), \ldots, p^{k-1}(\lambda_i)$—i.e., up to the $(k-1)$st derivative of $p(\lambda)$, evaluated at $\lambda = \lambda_i$. But the $(k-1)$st derivative of Eq. (91) still contains $\lambda - \lambda_i$ as a factor. Hence all the terms of Eq. (87) vanish.

Hence even when $\mathbf{A}$ is not semisimple, it still obeys the Cayley-Hamilton theorem.

We have proven the theorem for a matrix in canonical form. However, this establishes it in general. For suppose $\mathbf{A}$ were such that Eq. (89) were false. Then Eq. (80) states that it would be false for $\mathbf{D}$, the related canonical form. But this is false. Hence it must be true that any matrix regardless of its form, satisfies its own characteristic equation.

The significance of this theorem is that it states that if $\mathbf{A}$ is an $n \times n$ matrix, then $\mathbf{A}^n$ and, by induction, all higher powers, can always be expressed as a linear combination of the first $n - 1$ powers of $\mathbf{A}$, including $\mathbf{A}^0 = \mathbf{I}$. Since the whole class of $n \times n$ matrices include n^2 linearly independent forms, this represents a rather remarkable restriction of the matrices that can be written as functions of a given matrix.

19. THE MINIMUM POLYNOMIAL

While the Cayley-Hamilton theorem imposes an upper limit on the number of linearly independent forms that can be reached by taking powers of a given matrix $\mathbf{A}$, it may not be the best we can do.

If we have a polynomial, $p(x)$,

$$p(x) = a_0 + a_1 x + \cdots + a_m x^m \tag{92}$$

where a_0, a_1, ..., a_m are scalar constants, and if

$$p(\mathbf{A}) = a_0 \mathbf{I} + a_1 \mathbf{A} + \cdots + a_m \mathbf{A}^m = \mathbf{0} \tag{93}$$

we say that $p(x)$ *annihilates* $\mathbf{A}$.

The Cayley-Hamilton theorem states that the characteristic polynomial is one such annihilating polynomial. But evidently there is a class of such polynomials.

In this class of annihilating polynomials, there is one of lowest degree and such that the coefficient of the highest order of x, a_m, is unity. This polynomial is called the *minimum polynomial of* $\mathbf{A}$.

The minimum polynomial of $\mathbf{A}$ is a factor of all annihilating polynomials of $\mathbf{A}$. For let $\varphi(x)$ be the minimum polynomial, and let $\psi(x)$ be any other annihilating polynomial. Since the degree of $\psi(x)$ is at least as large as that of $\varphi(x)$, we can write

$$\psi(x) = \theta(x)\varphi(x) + r(x) \tag{94}$$

where $\theta(x)$ is a scalar factor or polynomial in x and $r(x)$ is a polynomial of degree less than that of $\varphi(x)$. (The remainder theorem of scalar algebra.) However, $\psi(x)$ is an annihilating polynomial for $\mathbf{A}$:

$$\psi(\mathbf{A}) = \theta(\mathbf{A})\varphi(\mathbf{A}) + r(\mathbf{A}) = \mathbf{0} \tag{95}$$

Since $\varphi(\mathbf{A})$ vanishes, so must $r(\mathbf{A})$. Hence $r(\mathbf{A})$ is an annihilating polynomial which is of degree less than the minimum polynomial, contrary to assumption. Hence $r(x)$ must vanish identically and $\varphi(x)$ be a divisor of $\psi(x)$.

The characteristic polynomial of $\mathbf{A}$ is the polynomial whose roots are the eigenvalues of $\mathbf{A}$, each with the multiplicity of the root:

$$p(\lambda) = \prod_{i=1}^{m} (\lambda - \lambda_i)^{k_i} \tag{96}$$

where k_i is the multiplicity of the root.

If $\mathbf{A}$ is semisimple, then Eq. (82) shows that $\mathbf{A}$ will be annihilated not only by Eq. (96) but also by

$$\varphi(\lambda) = \prod{}' (\lambda - \lambda_i) \tag{97}$$

where the prime on the product symbol indicates that the product is over all *distinct* factors.

Furthermore, Eq. (82) makes it evident that there is no polynomial function of λ of lower degree which will reduce to zero all the terms on the diagonal.

Hence Eq. (97) is the minimum polynomial of a semisimple matrix. Its degree is equal to the number of *distinct* eigenvalues of $\mathbf{A}$.

If $\mathbf{A}$ is not semisimple, then Eq. (97) is not sufficient. If there is a chain of length m_1 with eigenvalue λ_1, then Eq. (87) shows that $p(\mathbf{A})$ contains terms up to and including the $(m_1 - 1)$st derivative of the polynomial. Hence $\varphi(\lambda)$ must contain the factor $(\lambda - \lambda_1)^{m_1}$. The minimum polynomial must be given by

$$\varphi(\lambda) = \prod{}' (\lambda - \lambda_i)^{m_{i,\max}} \tag{98}$$

where, again, the prime indicates the product over factors with distinct λ_i, and $m_{i,\max}$ is the length of the longest chain with eigenvalue λ_i.

A necessary and sufficient condition that $\mathbf{A}$ be semisimple is that it be annihilated by a polynomial, Eq. (97), all of whose roots are simple.

20. EXAMPLES

As an example of a minimum polynomial, consider the matrix of Chapter III, Eq. (33). We discovered there that its only eigenvalue is zero, with multiplicity 4. The characteristic polynomial is $\lambda^4 = 0$, but we can observe that $\mathbf{A}^2 = \mathbf{0}$. It is, in other words, annihilated by the polynomial $\varphi(\lambda) = \lambda^2$. Hence, we can deduce immediately that it contains at least one chain of length 2, and no longer chain. It might have a chain of length 2 and two simple eigenvectors, or it might have two chains, each of length 2. We found, in Chapter III, that the latter case is true.

As a second example, consider the matrix of Eq. (67) of this chapter. The characteristic equation is given in Eq. (68). By trial, we can find that no factor in this equation can be eliminated and still leave the polynomial an annihilating one. Hence both eigenvalues must be associated with chains of length 2. We can also easily verify that **A** is, in fact, annihilated by its characteristic equation, or that

$$\mathbf{A}^4 - 8\mathbf{A}^2 + 16\mathbf{I} = 0$$

as it should, by the Cayley-Hamilton theorem.

21. SUMMARY

What we have done here is to find a particular set of axes in terms of which a matrix used as a transmission operator assumes a particularly simple form.

We started by considering the matrix as describing the properties of an operator that transforms one state vector into another. This operator is *abstract* in the sense that, although it exists, it cannot be specified until we have specified some particular set of coordinate axes. Only after the axes—i.e., the *basis*—has been chosen does the abstract operator become identifiable as a particular matrix.

Viewed in this light, we are lead to ask what happens if we change the coordinate axes. If we are given a matrix that is used as a transmission operator—i.e., as in Eq. (3)—we can regard it as a *representation* of the abstract operator on some particular basis. We can then ask what would be the representation of the same abstract operator on some different basis, whose relation to the original basis is known. We have seen that the answer to this question is the similarity transformation in which the matrix is postmultiplied by the matrix **S** that connects the two bases and premultiplied by its inverse.

The concept of a change of basis is a very important one in our work. It allows us, for example, to translate a given problem into one that may be simpler or more convenient for other reasons. In particular, it often allows us to prove theorems using highly specialized forms of matrices. It is for this reason, primarily, that we have gone to the work of setting up the Jordan canonical form of a matrix, which, in the case of a matrix of simple structure, is the diagonal form. We have, for example, been able to prove without too much trouble the Cayley-Hamilton theorem using this form. Since the statement of this theorem is independent of the basis, it follows that it must be true for any matrix.

This gives us a powerful method of analysis which we will have much occasion to use.

Exercises

1. Show that the matrix

$$\mathbf{A} = \begin{pmatrix} 0 & 0 & -j & 0 \\ 0 & 0 & 0 & j \\ j & 0 & 0 & 0 \\ 0 & -j & 0 & 0 \end{pmatrix}$$

obeys the Cayley-Hamilton theorem. What is its minimum polynomial?

2. Show that the matrix

$$\mathbf{A} = \begin{pmatrix} \frac{3}{2} & 0 & j & 0 \\ 0 & -\frac{1}{2} & 0 & j \\ j & 0 & \frac{1}{2} & 0 \\ 0 & j & 0 & -\frac{3}{2} \end{pmatrix}$$

obeys the Cayley-Hamilton theorem. What is its minimum polynomial?

3. Put the matrix of Exercise 5, Chapter III into Jordan canonical form.

4. An $n \times n$ matrix of the form

$$\begin{pmatrix} \cdot & \cdot & & & & \\ & \cdot & & & & \\ & & 0 & 1 & 0 & 0 \\ & & 0 & 0 & 1 & 0 \\ & & 0 & 0 & 0 & 1 \\ \cdots & & -d & -c & -b & -a \end{pmatrix}$$

is sometimes said to be in *rational canonical form*. (The full rational canonical form is quasi diagonal with blocks on the diagonal of the form given.) What is the characteristic equation of this form? Prove the results by induction on the dimensionality. We can conclude from this that given any polynomial of degree n, we can find an $n \times n$ matrix for which the polynomial is the characteristic equation. (By working with the complete form, we can show that given any polynomial of degree less than n, we can find an $n \times n$ matrix for which the given polynomial is the minimum polynomial.)

5. Use the Cayley-Hamilton theorem to express $\mathbf{A}^{-1}$ as a polynomial in $\mathbf{A}$, assuming $\mathbf{A}$ to be nonsingular. Do the same using the minimum polynomial.

6. Let $\mathbf{X}$ be a matrix of the form

$$\mathbf{X} = \begin{pmatrix} a & jb \\ jc & d \end{pmatrix}$$

where a, b, c, and d are real, and the determinant of $\mathbf{X}$, $(ad + bc)$, is unity. Use the Cayley-Hamilton theorem to obtain a recursion formula for $\mathbf{X}^n$, n being a positive integer. Show that the solution to this formula is

$$\mathbf{X}^n = \mathbf{X}\,\frac{\sin n\theta}{\sin \theta} - \mathbf{I}\,\frac{\sin(n - 1)\theta}{\sin \theta}$$

where θ is defined as

$$\theta = \cos^{-1} \tfrac{1}{2}(a + d)$$

(If we let $w = \tfrac{1}{2}(a + d)$, we can write this as

$$\mathbf{X}^n = \mathbf{X}U_n(w) - \mathbf{I}U_{n-1}(w)$$

where $U_n(w)$ is the *Chebbyscheff polynomial* of the first kind in the variable w and of order n. It is not obvious that

$$U_n(w) = \sin n(\cos^{-1} w)/\sin \cos^{-1} w$$

is a polynomial in w, but it is.)

(This formula has direct application in the study of delay lines and other periodic or iterated 2-port networks. Such lines can often be regarded as the result of cascading identical 2-ports in series. The formula permits us to calculate, directly, the transmission matrix of any finite number of such elements from the matrix of a single element.)

7. Express the following as the sum or difference of the squares of magnitudes using Lagrange's method:

(a) $\quad | x_1 |^2 + | x_2 |^2 + | x_3 |^2 - j(x_1{}^*x_2 - x_2{}^*x_1)$
$\qquad + (x_1{}^*x_3 + x_3{}^*x_1) + 3j(x_2{}^*x_3 - x_3{}^*x_2)$

(b) $\quad | x_1 |^2 + 3| x_2 |^2 + 2| x_3 |^2 + 2j(x_1{}^*x_2 - x_2{}^*x_1)$
$\qquad + j(x_1{}^*x_3 - x_3{}^*x_1) + (x_2{}^*x_3 + x_3{}^*x_2)$

(c) $\quad | x_1 |^2 + 2(x_1{}^*x_2 + x_2{}^*x_1) + 2j(x_2{}^*x_3 - x_3{}^*x_2)$

(d) $\quad | x_3 |^2 + 3(x_1{}^*x_2 + x_2{}^*x_1) + (x_1{}^*x_3 + x_3{}^*x_1) + (x_2{}^*x_3 + x_3{}^*x_2)$

(e) $\quad 4(x_1{}^*x_2 + x_2{}^*x_1) - 4j(x_2{}^*x_3 - x_3{}^*x_2)$

8. If $\mathbf{A}$ is similar to $\mathbf{B}$, (i.e., $\mathbf{A}$ is related to $\mathbf{B}$ by a similarity transformation) prove that $\mathbf{A}^\dagger$ is similar to $\mathbf{B}^\dagger$, $\mathbf{T}^{-1}\mathbf{A}\mathbf{T}$ to $\mathbf{T}^{-1}\mathbf{B}\mathbf{T}$ ($\mathbf{T}$ nonsingular), and $\mathbf{T}^{-1}\mathbf{A}^\dagger\mathbf{T}$ to $\mathbf{T}^{-1}\mathbf{B}^\dagger\mathbf{T}$.

9. Show that $\mathbf{AB}$ and $\mathbf{BA}$ are similar—i.e., related by a similarity transformation—if either $\mathbf{A}$ or $\mathbf{B}$ is nonsingular. Show by example that they need not be similar if both $\mathbf{A}$ and $\mathbf{B}$ are singular.

CHAPTER VI

Functions of a Matrix

In the previous chapter, we considered polynomials of a matrix. We found it possible to define these in a meaningful way, using the properties of the Jordan canonical form.

In this chapter, we shall be concerned with more general kinds of functions. We shall ask ourselves if, or when, we can take a function, $f(x)$, and apply it to a matrix, forming $f(\mathbf{A})$ as a meaningful entity.

There are many reasons for wanting to make this identification. For one, we certainly want to be make contact, if we can, with the general theory of functions. This branch of mathematics has so much substance to it that it would be very surprising if a connection to it did not prove to be rewarding.

More immediately, perhaps, we often find that the initial analysis of a physical problem generates a set of differential equations. When this happens, if the problem is linear, we find that we can write the equations as a differential equation involving a vector as the unknown and one or more matrices as the coefficients of the equation. If the equation is of a sufficiently simple type, we can use our knowledge of ordinary differential theory to write down a formal solution. We are then faced with two problems. Firstly, what does the formal solution mean? Secondly, is it really the right answer? It is to these problems that we shall address ourselves in this chapter.

1. DIFFERENTIAL EQUATIONS

We will here be concerned primarily with a vector differential equation of the form:

$$\frac{d\mathbf{x}}{dz} = -j\mathbf{R}\mathbf{x} \tag{1}$$

where $\mathbf{x}$ is a column vector whose coefficients are functions of the scalar variable z. (It, of course, makes no mathematical difference if the scalar variable is time t instead of a space variable z.)

147

By the derivative of a vector, we mean the vector whose coefficients are the derivatives of the coefficients of the vector:

$$\frac{d\mathbf{x}}{dz} = \begin{pmatrix} dx_1/dz \\ dx_2/dz \\ \vdots \\ dx_n/dz \end{pmatrix} \tag{2}$$

If $\mathbf{x}$ is an n-dimensional vector, $\mathbf{R}$ is an $n \times n$ matrix. If $\mathbf{R}$ is constant, we say that the system is *uniform*. If its coefficients are themselves functions of z, then we call the system *nonuniform*. We call $\mathbf{R}$ the *system matrix*.

The scalar factor $(-j)$ is pulled out as a matter of slight convenience. In some of the later chapters, such as Chapter XIII, we shall retain it in the system matrix, which we shall then symbolize by $\mathbf{S}$. This, however, should cause no confusion.

As an example of the source of such an equation, consider the equations of a lossless transmission line, expressed in terms of the complex amplitudes at frequency ω:

$$\frac{dE}{dz} = -j\omega L I$$

$$\frac{dI}{dz} = -j\omega C E$$

where L and C are the inductance and capacity per unit length. If the line is uniform, L and C are independent of z.

The solution of this problem is, of course, easily obtained by ordinary means. We have no need for the rather sophisticated techniques that are our concern here. Nevertheless, this problem will provide a good illustration of these techniques, precisely because it is a problem that is not obscured by intrinsic difficulty. The techniques are ones that are useful and useable in problems that are far more difficult.

We can write these equations in the form of Eq. (1) if we define the 2-dimensional vector whose components are E and I:

$$\mathbf{x} = \begin{pmatrix} E \\ I \end{pmatrix}$$

If we define $\mathbf{R}$ to be the 2×2 matrix

$$\mathbf{R} = \begin{pmatrix} 0 & \omega L \\ \omega C & 0 \end{pmatrix} = \begin{pmatrix} 0 & \beta Z \\ \beta/Z & 0 \end{pmatrix} \tag{3}$$

where $\beta = \omega\sqrt{LC}$, $Z = \sqrt{L/C}$, then $d\mathbf{x}/dz$ does obey Eq. (1).

Looking now at Eq. (1), with $\mathbf{R}$ constant, we might expect its solution to be

$$\mathbf{x}(z) = e^{-j\mathbf{R}z}\mathbf{x}(0) \tag{4}$$

where $\mathbf{x}(0)$ is the boundary condition at $z = 0$. This, at least, would be the solution were Eq. (1) a scalar equation.

The problem, then, is to give a meaning to such forms as $\exp(-j\mathbf{R}z)$ that will permit the solution of Eq. (1) as Eq. (4). If we can do so, we will have a solution to a large class of problems of considerable practical importance. Whether or not this solution is easily calculable is another question. However, we will at least have a formal solution whose properties can be studied.

2. REDUCTION OF DEGREE

Before tackling the central question, let us observe that Eq. (1) has a very broad range of applicability. If we let $\mathbf{R}$ be a function of z, then Eq. (1) includes all linear differential equations in the single independent variable z, of whatever finite order. If $\mathbf{R}$ is constant, it includes all linear differential equations with constant coefficients.

The reason for this is that we can always trade dimensionality for order. Suppose, for example, we have the second-order vector differential equation

$$\frac{d^2\mathbf{u}}{dz^2} = \mathbf{A}\frac{d\mathbf{u}}{dz} + \mathbf{B}\mathbf{u} \tag{5}$$

where $\mathbf{A}$ and $\mathbf{B}$ are matrices. If we define the vector $\mathbf{v}$

$$\frac{d\mathbf{u}}{dz} = \mathbf{v} \tag{6}$$

then Eq. (5) can be written

$$\frac{d\mathbf{v}}{dz} = \mathbf{A}\mathbf{v} + \mathbf{B}\mathbf{u} \tag{7}$$

We can then define the vector

$$\mathbf{x} = \begin{pmatrix} \mathbf{u} \\ \mathbf{v} \end{pmatrix} \tag{8}$$

and combine Eqs. (6) and (7) into the first-order equation

$$\frac{d\mathbf{x}}{dz} = \frac{d}{dz}\begin{pmatrix} \mathbf{u} \\ \mathbf{v} \end{pmatrix} = \begin{pmatrix} \mathbf{0} & \mathbf{I} \\ \mathbf{B} & \mathbf{A} \end{pmatrix}\mathbf{x} \tag{9}$$

We can, in this way, always reduce the order of the equation by increasing the dimensionality, and so put any linear differential equation with constant coefficients into the form of Eq. (1).

3. SERIES EXPANSION

With these preliminary remarks, let us now return to the main purpose of this chapter, the development of the concept of a function of a matrix.

The easiest way to extend the concept of a polynomial of a matrix that was developed in the previous chapter is to consider a power series of a matrix. Suppose we have a function $f(x)$ defined as a power series in x:

$$f(x) = \sum_{n=0}^{\infty} a_n x^n \tag{10}$$

It is then an obvious step to define the corresponding function of the matrix $\mathbf{A}$ as the same power series:

$$f(\mathbf{A}) = \sum_{n=0}^{\infty} a_n \mathbf{A}^n \tag{11}$$

We should observe that the minimum polynomial of $\mathbf{A}$ expresses $\mathbf{A}^m$ in terms of the lower powers, where m is the degree of the minimum polynomial. Hence all higher powers can be so expressed, and Eq. (11), if meaningful at all, can be reduced to a polynomial in $\mathbf{A}$ of degree less than m. We shall study this property more explicitly later in the chapter.

The immediate question is whether or when, Eq. (11) is meaningful. In particular, we must ask if, or when, the series converges. To study this question let us express $\mathbf{A}$ as a similarity transformation on its Jordan canonical form $\mathbf{J}$:

$$\mathbf{A} = \mathbf{SJS}^{-1} \tag{12}$$

Then, for any finite N, if we define f_N as the sum of the first $(N+1)$ terms of Eq. (11),

$$f_N(\mathbf{A}) = \sum_{n=0}^{N} a_n (\mathbf{SJS}^{-1})^n$$

$$= \mathbf{S} \left(\sum_{n=0}^{N} a_n \mathbf{J}^n \right) \mathbf{S}^{-1} \tag{13}$$

Suppose, first, that **A** is semisimple. Then

$$\mathbf{J} = \text{diag}(\lambda_1, \lambda_2, ...)$$

and

$$\mathbf{J}^n = \text{diag}(\lambda_1{}^n, \lambda_2{}^n, ...)$$

so that

$$f_N(\mathbf{A}) = \mathbf{S}\left\{\text{diag}\left(\sum a_n\lambda_1{}^n, \quad \sum a_n\lambda_2{}^n, ...\right)\right\}\mathbf{S}^{-1}$$

$$= \mathbf{S}\{\text{diag}(f_N(\lambda_1), f_N(\lambda_2), ...)\}\mathbf{S}^{-1} \tag{14}$$

the sums being taken up to N.

We can then take the limit of $f_N(\mathbf{A})$ as N goes to infinity providing all of the λ_i are in the region of convergence of Eq. (10).

If **A** is not semisimple, then

$$\mathbf{J} = \text{quasidiag}\{\mathbf{J}_{m_1}(\lambda_1), \mathbf{J}_{m_2}(\lambda_2), ...\}$$

where $\mathbf{J}_{m_i}(\lambda_i)$ is the $m_i \times m_i$ Jordan block. Then we see that

$$\mathbf{J}^n = \text{quasidiag}\{\mathbf{J}_{m_1}^n(\lambda_1), \mathbf{J}_{m_2}^n(\lambda_2), ...\} \tag{15}$$

where $\mathbf{J}_{m_1}^n(\lambda_1)$ is the nth power of $\mathbf{J}_{m_1}$, which is given by Eq. (83) of Chapter V.

If we substitute Eq. (15) in Eq. (13), we see that Eq. (11) is meaningful providing the various series converge. In fact, using Eq. (87) of Chapter V, we see that what is required is that

$$f_N(\lambda_i) = \sum_{n=0}^{N} a_n\lambda_i{}^n$$

shall converge to a limit as $N \to \infty$, and that

$$\left(\frac{d^k}{d\lambda^k} f_N(\lambda)\right)_{\lambda=\lambda_i}$$

shall also converge in the limit for any k less than the length of the longest chain of λ_i.

As usual, we are primarily concerned with functions $f(x)$ that are analytic in some region. From the theory of analytic functions, we know that all derivatives of $f(x)$ are analytic at any interior point of the region in which $f(x)$ is analytic. In particular, if Eq. (10) converges in any given range, then all its derivatives will converge inside that range.

Hence, even if A is not semisimple, Eq. (11) will be meaningful if all of the eigenvalues of A are interior points of the region for which Eq. (10) converges.

Instead of the expansion of Eq. (10), we could clearly have expanded about some value x_0 and reached the same conclusion. It is therefore enough if $f(x)$ is analytic in a circle about some x_0 that includes as interior points all the eigenvalues of A.

By a fairly obvious extension of this argument, using the process of analytic continuation, we find that it is enough if $f(x)$ is analytic in some simply connected region that includes as interior points all the eigenvalues of A.

We shall call such a function *admissable for* A.

For a function $f(x)$ that is admissable for A, we therefore define $f(A)$ by the following:

If A is semisimple, and diagonalized by S according to Eq. (12), then

$$f(A) = S\{\text{diag}(f(\lambda_1), f(\lambda_2), ...)\}S^{-1} \tag{16}$$

If A is not semisimple but is put into Jordan canonical form by Eq. (12), then

$$f(A) = S\{\text{quasidiag}(f\{J_{m_1}(\lambda_1)\}, f\{J_{m_2}(\lambda_2)\}, ...)\}S^{-1} \tag{17}$$

where $f\{J_{m_i}(\lambda_i)\}$ is the $m_i \times m_i$ matrix

$$f\{J_{m_i}(\lambda_i)\} = \begin{pmatrix} f(\lambda_i) & \dfrac{f'(\lambda_i)}{1!} & \dfrac{f''(\lambda_i)}{2!} & \cdots \\ 0 & f(\lambda_i) & \dfrac{f'(\lambda_i)}{1!} & \cdots \\ 0 & 0 & f(\lambda_i) & \cdots \\ \text{etc.} & & & \end{pmatrix} \tag{18}$$

as in Eq. (87) of Chapter V.

We have not, at this point, proven that the function so defined is appropriate to the problem we originally set ourselves—i.e., making Eq. (4) be a formal solution to Eq. (1). We will return to this point shortly, and will here simply assert that it is appropriate.

4. TRANSMISSION LINE

To illustrate the use of the series expansion of a function to define the function of a matrix, we shall complete the solution of the transmission line equations.

It will be convenient to use the second form of $\mathbf{R}$ in Eq. (3). We find that

$$\mathbf{R}^2 = \begin{pmatrix} \beta^2 & 0 \\ 0 & \beta^2 \end{pmatrix} = \beta^2 \mathbf{I} \tag{19}$$

Hence the series expansion of the exponential in Eq. (4) is

$$
\begin{aligned}
e^{-j\mathbf{R}z} &= \mathbf{I} - j\mathbf{R}z - \frac{1}{2!}\,\mathbf{R}^2 z^2 + j\,\frac{1}{3!}\,\mathbf{R}^3 z^3 + \cdots \\
&= \mathbf{I} - j\mathbf{R}z - \frac{1}{2!}\,\beta^2 z^2 \mathbf{I} + j\,\frac{1}{3!}\,\beta^2 z^3 \mathbf{R} + \cdots \\
&= \mathbf{I}\left(1 - \frac{1}{2!}\,\beta^2 z^2 + \frac{1}{4!}\,\beta^4 z^4 - \cdots\right) \\
&\quad - j\,\frac{\mathbf{R}}{\beta}\left(\beta z - \frac{1}{3!}\,\beta^3 z^3 + \frac{1}{5!}\,\beta^5 z^5 - \cdots\right) \\
&= \mathbf{I}\cos\beta z - j\,\frac{1}{\beta}\,\mathbf{R}\sin\beta z \\
&= \begin{pmatrix} \cos\beta z & -jZ\sin\beta z \\ -\dfrac{j}{Z}\sin\beta z & \cos\beta z \end{pmatrix}
\end{aligned}
\tag{20}
$$

when we substitute for $\mathbf{I}$ and $\mathbf{R}$.

Hence we obtain the solution

$$E(z) = E(0)\cos\beta z - jZI(0)\sin\beta z$$

$$I(z) = -j\,\frac{E(0)}{Z}\sin\beta z + I(0)\cos\beta z \tag{21}$$

The minus signs on the off-diagonal terms are perhaps confusing. However, we are expressing the values at z in terms of the values at $z = 0$ so that the load is considered as being at $z = 0$. To express the electrical length in terms that are positive if the load is to the right, we must take z negative and set

$$\theta = -\beta z \tag{22}$$

The solution will then take its usual form.

5. SQUARE ROOT FUNCTION

As a second example, let us now complete the development of the polar decomposition of an arbitrary nonsingular matrix that we started in Chapter IV, Section 5. The problem that we were left with there was to solve

$$\mathbf{H}_1{}^2 = \mathbf{A}\mathbf{A}^\dagger \tag{23}$$

or

$$\mathbf{H}_2{}^2 = \mathbf{A}^\dagger\mathbf{A} \tag{24}$$

for a hermitian $\mathbf{H}_1$ or $\mathbf{H}_2$, so that we need to obtain the square root of $\mathbf{H}_1{}^2$ or $\mathbf{H}_2{}^2$.

We found there that $\mathbf{H}_1{}^2$ and $\mathbf{H}_2{}^2$ are hermitian. Hence they are semisimple and their eigenvalues are real. Further, since $\mathbf{A}$ is nonsingular their eigenvalues are nonzero, and we can exclude the branch point of the square root function at $x = 0$.

Further, we can see that $\mathbf{H}_1{}^2$ and $\mathbf{H}_2{}^2$ are positive definite since, for any nonnull $\mathbf{x}$,

$$\mathbf{x}^\dagger\mathbf{H}_1{}^2\mathbf{x} = \mathbf{x}^\dagger\mathbf{A}\mathbf{A}^\dagger\mathbf{x} = (\mathbf{A}^\dagger\mathbf{x})^\dagger(\mathbf{A}^\dagger\mathbf{x}) = \mathbf{y}^\dagger\mathbf{y} \tag{25}$$

which is real and positive, and $\mathbf{y}$ is nonnull as long as $\mathbf{x}$ is. Hence the eigenvalues are positive. We can designate the eigenvalues of $\mathbf{H}_1{}^2$ as $\lambda_1{}^2, \lambda_2{}^2, ...$, where $\lambda_1, \lambda_2, ...$ are real, and write $\mathbf{H}_1{}^2$ as

$$\mathbf{H}_1{}^2 = \mathbf{S}\{\text{diag}(\lambda_1{}^2, \lambda_2{}^2, ...)\}\mathbf{S}^{-1} \tag{26}$$

We are then able to take as $\mathbf{H}_1$

$$\mathbf{H}_1 = \mathbf{S}\{\text{diag}(\lambda_1, \lambda_2, ...)\}\mathbf{S}^{-1} \tag{27}$$

and, because $\mathbf{S}$ can be taken as unitary and $\lambda_1, \lambda_2, ...$ real, we find that $\mathbf{H}_1$ is hermitian.

We can, as a matter of fact, go further. So far, we have an arbitrary choice possible for the signs of $\lambda_1, \lambda_2, ...$. We can specify that these shall be taken as positive. If so, $\mathbf{H}_1$ is positive definite. This is an application of a theorem that can be proven generally that a positive definite hermitian matrix has a unique square root that is also positive definite hermitian.

We are then able to determine $\mathbf{H}_1$ uniquely. By similar methods, we can determine $\mathbf{H}_2$ uniquely. Providing $\mathbf{A}$ is nonsingular, $\mathbf{U}_1$ and $\mathbf{U}_2$ are uniquely determined by Eqs. (26) and (27) of Chapter IV, and the two polar decompositions are completely and uniquely determined.

If $\mathbf{A}$ is singular, then $\mathbf{H}_1$ and $\mathbf{H}_2$ are still uniquely determined as above, except that now we can only require that they be positive semidefinite instead of definite. The unitary components $\mathbf{U}_1$ and $\mathbf{U}_2$ can now not be determined by Eqs. (26) and (27) of Chapter IV. They are, in fact, no longer uniquely determined. The solution of Eqs. (21) of Chapter IV, where $\mathbf{A}$ and $\mathbf{H}_1$ and $\mathbf{H}_2$ are known but may be nonsingular, will be discussed in more detail in Chapter XII.

6. UNITARY MATRICES AS EXPONENTIALS

As a third example, we shall show that if $\mathbf{U}$ is a unitary matrix, it can be expressed as

$$\mathbf{U} = e^{j\mathbf{H}} \tag{28}$$

where $\mathbf{H}$ is a hermitian matrix. Thus we complete the analogy of hermitian matrices to real numbers, and unitary matrices to the numbers with unit modulus, i.e., numbers expressible as $\exp(j\alpha)$ where α is real.

We have shown (Chapter IV) that a unitary matrix is always semi-simple with eigenvalues that are of unit modulus, and so expressible as $\exp(j\lambda_i)$ where all λ_i are real. Hence we can write any $\mathbf{U}$ as

$$\mathbf{U} = \mathbf{S}\{\operatorname{diag}(e^{j\lambda_1}, e^{j\lambda_2}, ...)\}\mathbf{S}^{-1} \tag{29}$$

and can take as $\mathbf{H}$

$$\mathbf{H} = \mathbf{S}\{\operatorname{diag}(\lambda_1, \lambda_2, ...)\}\mathbf{S}^{-1} \tag{30}$$

Then $\mathbf{H}$ is such that Eq. (28) holds.

Further, we have found, in Chapter V, Section 10, that $\mathbf{S}$ can be taken to be unitary, so that $\mathbf{S}^{-1} = \mathbf{S}^\dagger$. Hence

$$\mathbf{H}^\dagger = \mathbf{S}^{\dagger-1}\{\operatorname{diag}(\lambda_1, \lambda_2, ...)\}\mathbf{S}^\dagger$$

$$= \mathbf{S}\{\operatorname{diag}(\lambda_1, \lambda_2, ...)\}\mathbf{S}^{-1} = \mathbf{H}$$

and $\mathbf{H}$ is hermitian.

Since each λ_i can be changed by any multiple of 2π without affecting Eq. (29), the $\mathbf{H}$ so determined is not unique.

Note that we can obtain the same results using any proper inner product. A $\mathbf{K}$-unitary matrix, with $\mathbf{K}$ positive definite, can always be expressed as the exponential of j times a $\mathbf{K}$-hermitian matrix.

7. EIGENVECTORS

We must now consider what are the important properties of $f(\mathbf{A})$, and, in particular, how it is related to $\mathbf{A}$. This aspect is important both in its own right and in preparation for asking if Eq. (4) is really the solution of Eq. (1).

We have seen, in Eq. (16) or (17) with (18) that if λ_i is an eigenvalue of $\mathbf{A}$, then $f(\lambda_i)$ is an eigenvalue of $f(\mathbf{A})$. The question immediately arises as to how the eigenvectors are related. In answer to this we have the following:

Theorem 1. *If $f(x)$ is an admissable function of a matrix $\mathbf{A}$, and $\mathbf{x}_i$ is an eigenvector of $\mathbf{A}$ with eigenvalue λ_i , then $\mathbf{x}_i$ is also an eigenvector of $f(\mathbf{A})$, but with eigenvalue $f(\lambda_i)$.*

This follows immediately from Eq. (16) if $\mathbf{A}$ is semisimple, or from Eqs. (17) and (18) if $\mathbf{A}$ is not. We should note, however, that if $\mathbf{A}$ is not semisimple, then the chains of $f(\mathbf{A})$ are, in general, different from those of $\mathbf{A}$, since Eq. (18) is not the Jordan block. The same invariant subspaces are involved, but their organization into chains of generalized eigenvectors is, in general, different.

The converse of Theorem 1 for semisimple matrices is valid:

Theorem 2. *If $\mathbf{A}$ and $\mathbf{B}$ are semisimple, and any eigenvector of $\mathbf{A}$, regardless of how any degeneracies in $\mathbf{A}$ are resolved, is also an eigenvector of $\mathbf{B}$, then $\mathbf{B}$ can be expressed as an admissable function of $\mathbf{A}$.*

Evidently any degeneracies of $\mathbf{A}$ must also occur in $\mathbf{B}$, although not vice versa. That is, if $\mathbf{x}_1$ and $\mathbf{x}_2$ are eigenvectors of $\mathbf{A}$ with the same eigenvalue, then they must also be eigenvectors of $\mathbf{B}$ with the same eigenvalue. This follows since $\alpha \mathbf{x}_1 + \beta \mathbf{x}_2$ is also an eigenvector of $\mathbf{A}$, and so must also be an eigenvector of $\mathbf{B}$ for any α and β.

Suppose that the distinct eigenvalues of $\mathbf{A}$ are λ_i . Suppose further that $\mathbf{x}_i$ is any eigenvector of $\mathbf{A}$ with eigenvalue λ_i . It is then an eigenvector of $\mathbf{B}$. Suppose its eigenvalue for $\mathbf{B}$ is μ_i . Then, corresponding to each discrete λ_i we have a particular μ_i , not all of which may be distinct.

The function

$$p(\lambda) = \sum_i \mu_i \prod_{j \neq i} \frac{(\lambda - \lambda_j)}{(\lambda_i - \lambda_j)} \tag{31}$$

is a polynomial that takes the specified values μ_i at the points $\lambda = \lambda_i$. The summation is over the indices i that lead to distinct λ_i , and the product over the same set excluding $j = i$.

Being a polynomial, it is an admissable function for all $\mathbf{A}$. We assert that

$$\mathbf{B} = p(\mathbf{A}) = \sum_i \mu_i \prod_{j \neq i} \frac{(\mathbf{A} - \lambda_j \mathbf{I})}{(\lambda_i - \lambda_j)} \tag{32}$$

Consider any eigenvector $\mathbf{x}_k$ of $\mathbf{A}$. Then if $k \neq i$, there is some factor in the product that is zero. Hence the summation reduces to the single term with $i = k$, and

$$p(\mathbf{A})\mathbf{x}_k = \mu_k \prod_{j \neq k} \frac{(\mathbf{A} - \lambda_j \mathbf{I})}{(\lambda_k - \lambda_j)} \, \mathbf{x}_k = \mu_k \mathbf{x}_k \tag{33}$$

Hence $\mathbf{B}$ has the desired eigenvectors and eigenvalues. Since the linear envelope of all possible $\mathbf{x}_k$ is the whole space, $\mathbf{A}$ being semisimple, $p(\mathbf{A})$ must be identical to $\mathbf{B}$.

The polynomial given by Eq. (31) is the *Lagrange-Sylvester interpolation polynomial* for the polynomial of lowest degree that assumes a set of specified values at a specified finite set of points.

The corresponding theorem for $\mathbf{A}$ not semisimple is much more involved. In the first place, as we have pointed out, the chains of generalized eigenvectors of $\mathbf{A}$ do not go directly into properly organized chains of $\mathbf{B}$. Hence it is difficult to state explicit and simple conditions that will tell us if $\mathbf{B}$ is expressible as a function of $\mathbf{A}$, except to say that any change of basis that puts $\mathbf{A}$ into canonical form must put $\mathbf{B}$ into the form of Eqs. (17) and (18).

Secondly, to develop a function with the desired properties, we need to specify not only the values of $p(\lambda_i)$, but also $p'(\lambda_i) = (dp(\lambda)/d\lambda)_{\lambda = \lambda_i}$, $p''(\lambda_i)$, ..., $p^{m_i - 1}(\lambda_i)$. It is possible to develop a form of the Lagrange-Sylvester interpolation polynomial involving higher powers of the factors that meet these conditions, but the results are rather involved.

Since the question seems to be largely of academic interest with few practical applications, we shall not take the time to study this question in detail.

8. SPECTRUM OF A MATRIX

We will digress for a moment from our main line of effort to introduce the following concept, which has great importance in the theory of general linear operators.

Definition. *If $\mathbf{A}$ is a semisimple operator whose distinct eigenvalues are $\lambda_1, \lambda_2, ..., \lambda_k$, and if the values of a function $f(\lambda)$ are specified for $\lambda = \lambda_1, \lambda = \lambda_2, ..., \lambda = \lambda_k$, then $f(\lambda)$ is said to be* **defined on the spectrum of $\mathbf{A}$**.

Note that we are not saying that $\mathbf{A}$ is nondegenerate. But we are only listing those eigenvalues of $\mathbf{A}$ that are distinct.

We extend this definition to the general $\mathbf{A}$ that may be nonsemisimple in the following:

Definition. *If* **A** *is an operator whose distinct eigenvalues are* λ_i, λ_2, ..., λ_k, *and if* m_i *is the length of the longest chain with eigenvalue* λ_i, *then if* $f(\lambda)$ *is a function such that for all* λ_i, *the set*

$$f(\lambda_i)$$

$$f'(\lambda_i) = \frac{df(\lambda)}{d\lambda}\bigg|_{\lambda=\lambda_i}$$

$$...$$

$$f^{(m_i-1)}(\lambda_i) = \frac{d^{m_i-1}f(\lambda)}{d\lambda^{m_i-1}}\bigg|_{\lambda=\lambda_i} \tag{34}$$

have specified values, then $f(\lambda)$ *is said to be* **defined on the spectrum of A**.

The significance of this concept lies in the fact that if $f(\lambda)$ and $g(\lambda)$ are two functions that may be quite different in total but which do take the same values on the spectrum of **A**, then

$$f(\mathbf{A}) = g(\mathbf{A}) \tag{35}$$

For the purpose of determining $f(\mathbf{A})$, the only significant properties of $f(\lambda)$ are its values on the spectrum of **A**.

We have given a polynomial, Eq. (31), which assumes any designated values on the spectrum of a semisimple **A**. We asserted the existence of an analogous polynomial for **A** not semisimple. These polynomials are unique in the following sense:

Theorem 3. *Given a matrix* **A** *whose minimum polynomial is of rank* $m = \Sigma m_i$, *there exists a unique polynomial of rank less than m which assumes a specified nontrivial set of values on the spectrum of* **A**. *This polynomial is the Lagrange-Sylvester interpolation polynomial.*

Since there are a finite number of conditions to be met, it is obvious that we can find a polynomial, say $\psi(\lambda)$, that assumes a given set of values on the spectrum of **A**.

Since the minimum polynomial, $\varphi(\lambda)$, of **A** reduces **A** to the null matrix, $\varphi(\lambda)$ is a polynomial that is zero on the spectrum of **A**.

If $\psi(\lambda)$ is of degree greater than m, the degree of $\varphi(\lambda)$, we can write

$$\psi(\lambda) = \chi(\lambda)\varphi(\lambda) + r(\lambda) \tag{36}$$

where $\chi(\lambda)$ is a polynomial and $r(\lambda)$ is the remainder polynomial and is of degree less than m.

Since $\varphi(\lambda)$ is zero on the entire spectrum of **A**, so is $\chi(\lambda)\varphi(\lambda)$. Hence $r(\lambda)$ is a polynomial that takes the desired values on the spectrum of **A**.

The polynomial $r(\lambda)$ is unique. For suppose there existed another polynomial, say $s(\lambda)$, that is of degree less than m and that assumes the specified values on the spectrum of $\mathbf{A}$. Then $\{r(\lambda) - s(\lambda)\}$ would be a polynomial of degree less than m which is zero on the entire spectrum of $\mathbf{A}$. Then it would be an annihilating polynomial, and $\varphi(\lambda)$ would not be the minimum polynomial.

Since the Lagrange-Sylvester interpolation polynomial is such a polynomial with a rank of less than m [this is true of Eq. (31) and is also true of the generalized from that we have not given] it is the unique polynomial indicated.

This theorem can, in fact, be used as the definition of the Lagrange-Sylvester interpolation polynomial.

9. EXAMPLE

The requirement given here that $\mathbf{B} = f(\mathbf{A})$, with $\mathbf{A}$ semisimple, must have the same eigenvectors as $\mathbf{A}$, and eigenvalues $f(\lambda_i)$, gives us another method of calculating $f(\mathbf{A})$.

As an example, let us consider again the calculation of $\exp(-j\mathbf{R}z)$ with the $\mathbf{R}$ of Eq. (3). We see that the eigenvectors of $\mathbf{R}$, with their eigenvalues, are

$$\mathbf{x}_1 = \begin{pmatrix} Z \\ 1 \end{pmatrix}_\beta, \qquad \mathbf{x}_2 = \begin{pmatrix} Z \\ -1 \end{pmatrix}_{-\beta} \tag{37}$$

If we write

$$e^{-j\mathbf{R}z} = \begin{pmatrix} A & B \\ C & D \end{pmatrix}$$

then we require $\mathbf{x}_1$ to be an eigenvector with eigenvalue $\exp(-j\beta z)$, and $\mathbf{x}_2$ with $\exp(j\beta z)$. Using Eq. (37), these conditions become

$$\begin{aligned}
AZ + B &= Ze^{-j\beta z} \\
CZ + D &= e^{-j\beta z} \\
AZ - B &= Ze^{j\beta z} \\
CZ - D &= -e^{j\beta z}
\end{aligned} \tag{38}$$

which we can solve for A, B, C, and D, finding

$$\begin{aligned}
A &= \cos \beta z \\
B &= -jZ \sin \beta z \\
C &= -(j/Z) \sin \beta z \\
D &= \cos \beta z
\end{aligned}$$

or

$$e^{\perp j\mathbf{R}z} = \begin{pmatrix} \cos \beta z & -jZ \sin \beta z \\ \dfrac{-j}{Z} \sin \beta z & \cos \beta z \end{pmatrix} \tag{39}$$

as before, Eq. (20).

Alternatively, we can use Eq. (32) to obtain the same results directly by computing

$$e^{-j\mathbf{R}z} = e^{-j\beta z} \frac{(\mathbf{R} + \beta \mathbf{I})}{2\beta} + \frac{e^{j\beta z}(\mathbf{R} - \beta \mathbf{I})}{(-2\beta)} \tag{40}$$

Thus we have developed several methods of evaluating a function of a matrix. We will find others as we proceed.

There still remains the question of whether or when the function as defined has the properties that we expect of the given function. In particular, is it true that the exponential function so defined gives us the solution to Eq. (1)?

Preparatory to considering this question we need to look at the question of commutativity.

10. COMMUTATIVITY

For reasons that will shortly become clear, we need to discover what structural relations will assure that $\mathbf{A}$ and $\mathbf{B}$ commute.

We may note immediately that if $\mathbf{A}$ and $\mathbf{B}$ are semisimple and $\mathbf{B} = f(\mathbf{A})$, then they commute, as is evident from Eq. (16) since diagonal matrices commute. In fact, we can go further and say that whenever $\mathbf{B} = f(\mathbf{A})$, $f(x)$ being an admissable function in the sense defined, $\mathbf{B}$ commutes with $\mathbf{A}$ regardless of whether or not $\mathbf{A}$ is semisimple. This is evident if $\mathbf{B}$ can be expressed as a power series in $\mathbf{A}$ since any power of $\mathbf{A}$ commutes with $\mathbf{A}$. It also follows from the more general definition involving analytic continuation of a power series definition, or from Eqs. (17) and (18).

This condition is not, however, necessary. For example, $\mathbf{I}$ commutes with all matrices of the same size, and only multiples of $\mathbf{I}$ can be written as functions of $\mathbf{I}$.

The applicable theorem for $\mathbf{A}$ and $\mathbf{B}$ semisimple is the following:

Theorem 4. *If $\mathbf{A}$ and $\mathbf{B}$ are semisimple, then they commute if and only if they have a complete set of eigenvectors in common.*

This differs from Theorem 2 in that the latter specified that *any* eigenvector of **A** was an eigenvector of **B** also. Theorem 4 only requires that there be *some* complete set of common eigenvectors.

If such a set exists, say x_i, then any vector **y** can be expanded on these vectors

$$y = \sum a_i x_i$$

If

$$Ax_i = \lambda_i x_i$$

$$Bx_i = \mu_i x_i$$

we see that

$$A(By) = A \sum_i a_i Bx_i = A \sum a_i \mu_i x_i = \sum a_i \mu_i \lambda_i x_i$$

and

$$B(Ay) = B \sum a_i \lambda_i x_i = \sum a_i \mu_i \lambda_i x_i$$

Since these are equal for all **y**, it follows that $AB = BA$ and the matrices commute.

The necessity is more difficult to prove since we may have to resolve degeneracies very carefully. We can, however, prove the necessity by successive changes of basis. We note first that if **A** and **B** commute, so do $S^{-1}AS$ and $S^{-1}BS$. Hence commutation does not depend on the basis.

Suppose now we choose a basis on which **A'**, the transformed matrix, is diagonal. We can also order the basis so as to collect together all occurrences of the same eigenvalue so that we can write

$$A' = \text{quasidiag}(\lambda_1 I_1, \lambda_2 I_2, ...) = S^{-1}AS \tag{41}$$

where the dimensions of I_i are the multiplicity of λ_i.

It is evident that **B'** must have the form

$$B' = S^{-1}BS = \text{quasidiag}(B_1, B_2, ...) \tag{42}$$

where B_i has the same dimensionality as I_i.

Let us now define **A″** and **B″** on a new basis by the transformation with

$$A'' = T^{-1}A'T = (ST)^{-1}A(ST)$$

$$B'' = T^{-1}B'T = (ST)^{-1}B(ST)$$

where $\mathbf{T}$ is of the form

$$\mathbf{T} = \text{quasidiag}(\mathbf{T}_1, \mathbf{T}_2, ...) \tag{43}$$

where, again, $\mathbf{T}_i$ has the same dimensionality as $\mathbf{I}_i$ and $\mathbf{B}_i$. We see that

$$\mathbf{A}'' = \text{quasidiag}(\lambda_1\mathbf{T}_1^{-1}\mathbf{T}_1, \lambda_2\mathbf{T}_2^{-1}\mathbf{T}_2, ...) = \mathbf{A}'$$

so that $\mathbf{A}''$ is unchanged from $\mathbf{A}'$ regardless of $\mathbf{T}_1, \mathbf{T}_2, ...$.
On the other hand,

$$\mathbf{B}'' = \text{quasidiag}(\mathbf{T}_1^{-1}\mathbf{B}_1\mathbf{T}_1, \mathbf{T}_2^{-1}\mathbf{B}_2\mathbf{T}_2, ...) \tag{44}$$

Since $\mathbf{B}$, and hence $\mathbf{B}'$, is semisimple, we can infer (and can prove with some careful analysis) that $\mathbf{B}_1, \mathbf{B}_2, ...$ are semisimple. Hence we can choose $\mathbf{T}_1, \mathbf{T}_2, ...$ to diagonalize $\mathbf{B}_1, \mathbf{B}_2, ...$, and so $\mathbf{B}''$.

We have found a basis in terms of which $\mathbf{A}$ and $\mathbf{B}$ are simultaneously diagonalized. It follows that the columns of the transformation matrix $(\mathbf{ST})$ are a linearly independent set of simultaneous eigenvectors of $\mathbf{A}$ and $\mathbf{B}$.

This proof, as given, is not wholly rigorous, and rather lacks elegance in its dependence on diagonalization. These defects can be corrected, but the development given here is sufficient for our purpose. It is, as a matter of fact, a nice example of the use of the Jordan canonical representation to obtain a quick analysis of a problem.

If $\mathbf{A}$ and $\mathbf{B}$ are not semisimple, then the question of necessary and sufficient conditions gets quite involved, due to the possibility of overlapping degeneracies both within and between chains. We shall not consider this question here, but will only point out that this question, too, can be considered using the Jordan canonical form.

11. FUNCTIONAL RELATIONS

Suppose, now, that we are considering some function $f(x)$ that is admissable for two or more matrices, say $\mathbf{A}$ and $\mathbf{B}$. Suppose, further, we have from scalar function theory, some functional relation involving $f(x)$, such as a law of composition giving $f(x + y)$ in terms of $f(x)$ and $f(y)$. We can ask if we can establish conditions under which this functional relation can be carried over into the case when the argument of the function is a matrix.

We have, for example, the functional relation of the exponential that

$$e^{x+y} = e^x e^y \tag{45}$$

Is it true, or under what conditions is it true, that

$$e^{\mathbf{A}+\mathbf{B}} = e^{\mathbf{A}} e^{\mathbf{B}} ? \tag{46}$$

We may say in general that the properties of $f(x)$ which are obtained from scalar function theory depend on the properties of x that are described by saying that x is an element in a field. The only significant difference between the algebra of matrices with matrix multiplication and the algebra of a number field is the question of commutivity.[1] It therefore follows as a general principle that a functional relation will continue to hold even though the arguments are matrices, *providing* the matrices commute. This does not say that it necessarily will not hold if they do not, but only that commutativity is enough to assure behavior essentially like that of scalar functions.

We shall give two important examples. We shall consider, first, the binomial theorem.

Theorem 5. *If* **A** *and* **B** *commute, then, for any positive integer* n

$$(\mathbf{A} + \mathbf{B})^n = \sum_{k=0}^{n} \binom{n}{k} \mathbf{A}^{n-k} \mathbf{B}^k \tag{47}$$

where

$$\binom{n}{k} = \frac{n!}{k!(n-k)!}$$

This is true for $n = 1$. Assume true for n. Then

$$(\mathbf{A} + \mathbf{B})^{n+1} = (\mathbf{A} + \mathbf{B}) \sum_{k=0}^{n} \binom{n}{k} \mathbf{A}^{n-k} \mathbf{B}^k$$

$$= \sum_{k=0}^{n} \binom{n}{k} \mathbf{A}^{n+1-k} \mathbf{B}^k + \sum_{k=0}^{n} \binom{n}{k} \mathbf{A}^{n-k} \mathbf{B}^{k+1}$$

by the commutativity of **A** and **B**.

---

[1] The correct statement is that if a set of commuting matrices form a linear vector space over a field F, then it is a homomorphic mapping of F.

Then, changing $k + 1$ in the second sum to k,

$$(\mathbf{A} + \mathbf{B})^{n+1} = \mathbf{A}^{n+1} + \sum_{k=1}^{n} \binom{n}{k} \mathbf{A}^{n+1-k}\mathbf{B}^k$$

$$+ \sum_{k=1}^{n} \binom{n}{k-1} \mathbf{A}^{n-k+1}\mathbf{B}^k + \mathbf{B}^{n+1}$$

$$= \mathbf{A}^{n+1} + \sum_{k=1}^{n} \binom{n+1}{k} \mathbf{A}^{n-k+1}\mathbf{B}^k + \mathbf{B}^{n+1}$$

$$= \sum_{k=0}^{n+1} \binom{n+1}{k} \mathbf{A}^{n+1-k}\mathbf{B}^k$$

Hence it is true for $n + 1$, and the theorem is proved by induction.

We have already seen (page 25) that this expansion fails even for $n = 2$ if $\mathbf{A}$ and $\mathbf{B}$ do not commute.

The second example that we shall consider in detail is the law of composition of exponentials, Eq. (46):

Theorem 6.   *If $\mathbf{A}$ and $\mathbf{B}$ commute, then*

$$e^{\mathbf{A}+\mathbf{B}} = e^{\mathbf{A}}e^{\mathbf{B}} \tag{48}$$

To prove this, we make a series expansion on both sides, and use the binomial theorem on the left:

$$e^{\mathbf{A}+\mathbf{B}} = \sum \frac{1}{n!} (\mathbf{A} + \mathbf{B})^n$$

$$= \sum_{n=0}^{\infty} \sum_{k=0}^{n} \frac{1}{k!(n-k)!} \mathbf{A}^{n-k}\mathbf{B}^k \tag{49}$$

and

$$e^{\mathbf{A}}e^{\mathbf{B}} = \sum_{r=0}^{\infty} \frac{1}{r!} \mathbf{A}^r \sum_{s=0}^{\infty} \frac{1}{s!} \mathbf{B}^s \tag{50}$$

If we let $k = s$, and $n = (r + s)$, n can go from 0 to ∞, but k can only go from 0 to n before r becomes negative. Hence

$$e^{\mathbf{A}}e^{\mathbf{B}} = \sum_{n=0}^{\infty} \sum_{k=0}^{n} \frac{1}{k!(n-k)!} \mathbf{A}^{n-k}\mathbf{B}^k \tag{51}$$

which is the same as Eq. (49). Hence the theorem is true.

It is not evident that Eq. (48) is necessarily false if **A** and **B** do not commute, although this is true.

We are now ready to return to our original question of whether or not Eq. (4) is a solution to Eq. (1) if **R** is constant.

12. DERIVATIVE OF $e^{-j\mathbf{R}z}$, **R** CONSTANT

If Eq. (4) is to be a solution to Eq. (1) for any boundary condition $\mathbf{x}(0)$, we must have

$$\frac{d}{dz}\left(e^{-j\mathbf{R}z}\right) = \lim_{\delta z \to 0} \frac{1}{\delta z} \{e^{-j\mathbf{R}(z+\delta z)} - e^{-j\mathbf{R}z}\}$$

$$= -j\mathbf{R}e^{-j\mathbf{R}z} \tag{52}$$

Now $(-j\mathbf{R}z)$ commutes with $(-j\mathbf{R}\delta z)$. Therefore the first exponential in the bracket can be factored by Theorem 6. Furthermore, we can expand $\exp(-j\mathbf{R}\delta z)$ in series form:

$$e^{-j\mathbf{R}\delta z} = \mathbf{I} - j\mathbf{R}\,\delta z + O(\delta z^2)$$

where $O(\delta z^2)$ means additional terms in δz^2 and higher orders.

Hence we see that

$$\frac{d}{dz}\left(e^{-j\mathbf{R}z}\right) = \lim_{\delta z \to 0} \frac{1}{\delta z} \{(e^{-j\mathbf{R}\delta z} - \mathbf{I})e^{-j\mathbf{R}z}\}$$

$$= \lim_{\delta z \to 0} \frac{1}{\delta z} \{-j\mathbf{R}\delta z + O(\delta z^2)\}e^{-j\mathbf{R}z}$$

$$= -j\mathbf{R}e^{-j\mathbf{R}z} \tag{53}$$

We have verified Eq. (52) and can therefore conclude that Eq. (4) is in fact the solution of Eq. (1) where the function $\exp(-j\mathbf{R}z)$ is defined in the manner developed.

13. **R** NOT CONSTANT

We might hope that when **R** is not constant, we could still solve Eq. (1) as

$$\mathbf{x}(z) = \exp\left(-j \int_0^z \mathbf{R}\,dz\right) \mathbf{x}(0) \tag{54}$$

This, however, is true only under some very tight restrictions on **R**. To see that this is so, let

$$\mathbf{P}(z) = -j \int_0^z \mathbf{R}\,dz \tag{55}$$

We now ask ourselves when is

$$\frac{d}{dz}\{e^{\mathbf{P}(z)}\} = \left(\frac{d\mathbf{P}}{dz}\right)e^{\mathbf{P}(z)} \text{ ?}$$

Applying the definition of the derivative, we find

$$\frac{d}{dz}e^{\mathbf{P}} = \lim_{\delta z \to 0} \frac{1}{\delta z}\{e^{\mathbf{P}(z+\delta z)} - e^{\mathbf{P}(z)}\}$$

We can now expand $\mathbf{P}(z + \delta z)$ as a Taylor series around z. This operation is justified since we accomplish it by taking the scalar Taylor expansion of the coefficients separately.

$$\mathbf{P}(z + \delta z) = \mathbf{P}(z) + \delta z \frac{d\mathbf{P}(z)}{dz} + O(\delta z^2)$$

If we can factor the exponential we obtain

$$\frac{d}{dz}e^{\mathbf{P}} = \lim_{\delta z \to 0} \frac{1}{\delta z}\{e^{d\mathbf{P}/dz\,\delta z} - \mathbf{I}\}\,e^{\mathbf{P}}$$

$$= \frac{d\mathbf{P}}{dz}e^{\mathbf{P}} \tag{56}$$

which is the form we want.

However, the factorization involved in Eq. (56) is known to be valid only if the terms commute, or if $\mathbf{P}(z)$ commutes with $d\mathbf{P}/dz$ or $\int_0^z \mathbf{R}\,dz$ commutes with $\mathbf{R}$.

Assuming semisimplicity, the necessary and sufficient condition for this is that they shall have a complete set of common eigenvectors. This, furthermore, must be true for all z. It is perhaps fairly evident that this requires that there be a set of eigenvectors that are independent of z, so that the only variations in $\mathbf{R}$ occur in its eigenvalues. (A rigorous proof of this statement, even assuming $\mathbf{R}$ semisimple, is fairly difficult. It can be done using the dyad expansion of Chapter X.) Hence the dependence of $\mathbf{R}$ on z can be only of the very restricted type that does not cause the eigenvectors to rotate.

The more general case, where $\mathbf{R}$ is allowed to vary, even under suitable restrictions of continuity, etc., cannot be solved as Eq. (54). Indeed, the practical solution of such problems (nonuniform systems) becomes an extremely difficult task.

14. DERIVATIVE OF A POWER

Closely related to the above is the question of differentiating the power of a matrix function of z, $\mathbf{U}(z)$. We can, for example, study the derivative of the exponential function by differentiating its power series. We will therefore take this opportunity to consider the derivative of $\mathbf{U}^n$, where n is an integer.

The basic theorem for this purpose is the following:

Theorem 7. *If* $\mathbf{U}$ *and* $\mathbf{V}$ *are two* $n \times n$ *matrix functions of* z, *which may be the same, then*

$$\frac{d}{dz}(\mathbf{UV}) = \frac{d\mathbf{U}}{dz}\mathbf{V} + \mathbf{U}\frac{d\mathbf{V}}{dz} \tag{57}$$

We shall, in Chapter XIII, describe this property as indicating that the operation of differentiation is a *derivation*. It is a more general property than is apparent here, however, and is one that is of great importance for the underlying theory.

We can easily prove this theorem from the definition of a derivative:

$$\frac{d}{dz}(\mathbf{UV}) = \lim_{\delta z \to 0}\left\{\frac{\mathbf{U}(z + \delta z)\mathbf{V}(z + \delta z) - \mathbf{U}(z)\mathbf{V}(z)}{\delta z}\right\} \tag{58}$$

Now, $\mathbf{U}(z + \delta z)$ and $\mathbf{V}(z + \delta z)$ can be expanded in a Taylor series:

$$\mathbf{U}(z + \delta z) = \mathbf{U}(z) + \delta z\, \mathbf{U}'(z) + \cdots$$
$$\mathbf{V}(z + \delta z) = \mathbf{V}(z) + \delta z\, \mathbf{V}'(z) + \cdots$$

where the prime indicates the derivative. Equation (58) becomes

$$\frac{d}{dz}(\mathbf{UV}) = \lim_{\delta z \to 0}\frac{1}{\delta z}\{(\mathbf{U} + \delta z\, \mathbf{U}')(\mathbf{V} + \delta z\, \mathbf{V}') - \mathbf{UV}\}$$

$$= \mathbf{UV}' + \mathbf{U}'\mathbf{V}$$

We observe that we must preserve the order of the terms carefully, unless they commute.

From this theorem, we see that

$$\frac{d}{dz}\mathbf{U}^2 = \mathbf{U}'\mathbf{U} + \mathbf{UU}' \tag{59}$$

We note that this equals $2\mathbf{UU}'$, as would be the case if $\mathbf{U}$ were a scalar function, if but *only* if, $\mathbf{U}$ commutes with $\mathbf{U}'$.

By induction, we can easily prove that if n is any positive integer,

$$\frac{d\mathbf{U}^n}{dz} = \mathbf{U}'\mathbf{U}^{n-1} + \mathbf{UU}'\mathbf{U}^{n-2} + \cdots + \mathbf{U}^{n-1}\mathbf{U}' \tag{60}$$

Since there are n terms in this expression, we see that if $\mathbf{U}$ commutes with $\mathbf{U}'$, this equals $n\mathbf{U}^{n-1}\mathbf{U}'$, again in accordance with scalar theory.

If n is a negative integer, we can most easily find the appropriate formula by differentiating the equation

$$\mathbf{U}^n\mathbf{U}^{-n} = \mathbf{I}$$

We obtain

$$\frac{d\mathbf{U}^n}{dz}\mathbf{U}^{-n} + \mathbf{U}^n\frac{d\mathbf{U}^{-n}}{dz} = 0$$

so that

$$\frac{d\mathbf{U}^{-n}}{dz} = -\mathbf{U}^{-n}\frac{d\mathbf{U}^n}{dz}\mathbf{U}^{-n}$$

$$= -\{\mathbf{U}^{-n}\mathbf{U}'\mathbf{U}^{-1} + \mathbf{U}^{-(n-1)}\mathbf{U}'\mathbf{U}^{-2} + \cdots + \mathbf{U}^{-1}\mathbf{U}'\mathbf{U}^{-n}\} \quad (61)$$

For the exponential function, we find that

$$\frac{d}{dz}e^{\mathbf{U}} = \frac{d}{dz}\left\{\mathbf{I} + \mathbf{U} + \frac{1}{2!}\mathbf{U}^2 + \cdots\right\}$$

$$= \mathbf{U}' + \frac{1}{2!}(\mathbf{U}\mathbf{U}' + \mathbf{U}'\mathbf{U}) + \frac{1}{3!}(\mathbf{U}^2\mathbf{U}' + \mathbf{U}\mathbf{U}'\mathbf{U} + \mathbf{U}'\mathbf{U}^2) + \cdots \quad (62)$$

If now $\mathbf{U}$ and $\mathbf{U}'$ commute, but not otherwise,

$$\frac{d}{dz}e^{\mathbf{U}} = \mathbf{U}' + \mathbf{U}\mathbf{U}' + \frac{1}{2!}\mathbf{U}^2\mathbf{U}' + \cdots$$

$$= \mathbf{U}'\left\{\mathbf{I} + \mathbf{U} + \frac{1}{2!}\mathbf{U}^2 + \cdots\right\}$$

$$= \mathbf{U}'e^{\mathbf{U}} \quad (63)$$

15. EXAMPLE

We will conclude by considering the transmission line equations again, and considering when Eq. (54) is applicable.

The eigenvectors of Eq. (3) are given by Eq. (37). Hence, for them to be constant, Z must be constant, and the z-dependency must be in β alone. If we define the effective electrical length, θ:

$$\theta = \int_0^z \beta\,dz$$

then

$$\int_0^z \mathbf{R}\,dz = \begin{pmatrix} 0 & \theta Z \\ \theta/Z & 0 \end{pmatrix}$$

which does in fact commute with $\mathbf{R}$. The solution by Eq. (54) is

$$\mathbf{x}(z) = \begin{pmatrix} \cos\theta & -jZ\sin\theta \\ (-j/Z)\sin\theta & \cos\theta \end{pmatrix}$$

The only difference from Eq. (20) is in the definition of the effective electrical length as θ instead of (βz).

If, on the other hand, we let Z, the local characteristic impedance of the line, be a function of z, then we have a vastly more difficult problem. In fact, exact solutions to a nonuniform line are known for only a very few types of variation.

Exercises

1. Express the following differential equations as first-order vector differential equations:

(a) $\quad a\dfrac{d^2x}{dz^2} + b\dfrac{dx}{dz} + cx = 0$

(b) $\quad \dfrac{d^2x}{dz^2} + \dfrac{1}{z}\dfrac{dx}{dz} + \left(1 - \dfrac{n^2}{z^2}\right) = 0$ \hfill (Bessel's equation)

(c) $\quad (z^2 - 1)\dfrac{d^2x}{dz^2} + 2z\dfrac{dx}{dz} - \alpha(\alpha + 1)x = 0$ \hfill (Legendre's equation)

(d) $\quad \dfrac{d^2x}{dz^2} + (b - h^2\cos^2 z)x = 0$ \hfill (Mathieu's equation)

(e) $\quad \dfrac{d}{dz}\left(p\dfrac{dx}{dz}\right) + (\overset{..}{q} + \lambda r)x = 0$ \hfill (Liouville's equation)

(f) $\quad \dfrac{d^3x}{dz^2} + p\dfrac{d^2x}{dz^2} + q\dfrac{dx}{dz} + rx = 0$

2. Evaluate $\exp(\mathbf{A}z)$ where

(a) $\quad \mathbf{A} = \begin{pmatrix} a & 1 \\ 0 & a \end{pmatrix}$ \qquad (b) $\quad \mathbf{A} = \begin{pmatrix} a & 1 & 0 \\ 0 & a & 1 \\ 0 & 0 & a \end{pmatrix}$

3. The matrix

$$\mathbf{A} = \begin{pmatrix} 4 & 0 \\ 0 & 1 \end{pmatrix}$$

has four square roots:

$$\mathbf{A}^{1/2} = \begin{pmatrix} \pm 2 & 0 \\ 0 & \pm 1 \end{pmatrix}$$

Describe the simply connected regions including the eigenvalues of **A** in which the square-root function is analytic which lead to these various results.

4. Under what conditions is the formula

$$(I + A)^{-1} = I - A + A^2 - A^3 + \cdots$$

valid? Use this formula to obtain the inverse of

$$B = \begin{pmatrix} 1 & \alpha \\ \alpha* & 1 \end{pmatrix}$$

5. If **A** is an $n \times n$ matrix such that $A^2 = A$, it is *idempotent*. If $A^2 = 0$, it is *nilpotent*. If $A^2 = I$, it is an *involution*. Determine $\exp(Az)$ if **A** is (a) idempotent, (b) nilpotent, (c) an involution.

6. By completing the square, obtain the solution to the matrix equation

$$X^2 + \tfrac{1}{2}(BX + XB) + C = 0$$

In the scalar analogue of this problem, we obtain just two solutions. Is this true here also? Use this formula to obtain all the solutions to

$$X^2 + 5X + 4I = 0$$

7. The scalar Riccati equation

$$\frac{dy}{dz} = y^2 + py + q$$

is converted to a linear second-order equation by the substitution

$$y = -\frac{1}{u}\frac{du}{dz}$$

Show that the same procedure can be used on the matrix Riccati equation

$$\frac{dY}{dz} = Y^2 + PY + Q$$

What happens if we put the factors in the wrong order?

8. Show that the solution of

$$\frac{dM}{dz} = e^{zA}M, \qquad M(0) = I$$

where $\mathbf{A}$ is a constant matrix, is

$$\mathbf{M} = \exp \left\{ \sum_{n=0}^{\infty} \frac{1}{(n+1)!} \mathbf{A}^n z^{n+1} \right\}$$

9. Let $\mathbf{X}(z)$ be a square matrix function of z that satisfies the functional relation

$$\mathbf{X}(u + v) = \mathbf{X}(u)\mathbf{X}(v)$$

for all u and v. If we assume that $\mathbf{X}(z)$ is differentiable for all z, show that

$$\frac{d\mathbf{X}(z)}{dz} = \mathbf{A}\mathbf{X}(z)$$

where $\mathbf{A}$ is a constant matrix.

(*Hint*: Differentiate the functional relation with respect to u and v *separately*.)

(*Comment*: The functional relation is known as *Polya's equation*. You are asked to prove, in effect, that the solution to it is necessarily an exponential. This is vastly more difficult to prove, however, without assuming differentiability.)

10. Show that if $\mathbf{A}$ is nonsingular, the solution to the recursion equation

$$\mathbf{X}_{n+1} = \mathbf{X}_n(2\mathbf{I} - \mathbf{A}\mathbf{X}_n)$$

is

$$\mathbf{X}_n = \mathbf{A}^{-1}\{\mathbf{I} - (\mathbf{I} - \mathbf{A}\mathbf{B})^{2^n}\}$$

where $\mathbf{X}_0 = \mathbf{B}$. Under what conditions will this converge as n goes to infinity? If it converges, what is its limit?

CHAPTER VII

The Matricant

In this chapter we shall develop a general solution to the problem of solving the equation

$$\frac{d\mathbf{x}(z)}{dz} = -j\mathbf{R}\mathbf{x}(z) \tag{1}$$

or, setting $\mathbf{S} = -j\mathbf{R}$,

$$\frac{d\mathbf{x}}{dz} = \mathbf{S}\mathbf{x} \tag{1'}$$

where $\mathbf{R}$ or $\mathbf{S}$ may be a function of z.

We hasten to add that the solution, although a general one, has only a limited range of practical application because of the difficulty of computing it. Nevertheless it is of interest, both as a demonstration of the existence of solutions and as leading to approximate methods that are sometimes useful.

As a prototype problem, we can consider a transmission line whose impedance varies with distance. $\mathbf{R}$ is a function of z, having the form, on an $E - I$ basis,

$$\mathbf{R} = \begin{pmatrix} 0 & \beta Z(z) \\ \beta/Z(z) & 0 \end{pmatrix}$$

If Z were constant, so that $\mathbf{R}$ is constant, the solution would be

$$\mathbf{x}(z) = \exp(-j\mathbf{R}z)\mathbf{x}(0) \tag{2}$$

We are, in a sense, looking for a generalization of the process of "exponentiation". (This statement can be given rigorous meaning by a group-theoretic approach, but this is beyond the scope of our work here. This analogy is also one way of arriving at Feyman's method of "summing over histories" in quantum mechanical problems, which is also outside our scope.)

1. INTEGRAL MATRIX

Consider the system described by Eq. (1). If $\mathbf{R}(z)$ is reasonably well behaved, there is a complete set of solutions to it in any finite range.

The necessary and sufficient condition for this to be true in the range $a < z < b$ is that everywhere in this range the components of $\mathbf{R}$, R_{ij} obey the Lipschitz condition:

Lipschitz Condition. $R_{ij}(z)$ *is said to obey the* **Lipschitz condition** *if for any z and z' in the given range, there exists a constant k such that*

$$| R_{ij}(z) - R_{ij}(z')| \leqslant k|\, z - z'\, | \tag{3}$$

If R_{ij} obeys the Lipschitz condition it is continuous. If it is also continuously differentiable, then it obeys the Lipschitz condition. The Lipschitz condition, then, is intermediate between continuous and continuously differentiable.

If $\mathbf{R}(z)$ obeys the Lipschitz condition at all z in a finite range, there exist a set of n linearly independent solutions to Eq. (1), where n is the dimensionality of the system. Call these solutions $\mathbf{x}_i(z)$ $(i = 1, 2, ..., n)$.

Consider the matrix $\mathbf{X}(z)$ whose ith column is $\mathbf{x}_i(z)$:

$$\mathbf{X}(z) = (\mathbf{x}_1 \quad \mathbf{x}_2 \quad \mathbf{x}_3 \quad \cdots \quad \mathbf{x}_n) \tag{4}$$

Then $\mathbf{X}(z)$ obeys the matrix differential equation

$$\frac{d\mathbf{X}(z)}{dz} = -j\mathbf{R}\mathbf{X} \tag{5}$$

where, by the derivative of a matrix, we mean the matrix whose components are the derivatives of the original matrix.

The matrix $\mathbf{X}(z)$ is called an *integral matrix* of the system.

Since the columns are linearly independent, an integral matrix is nonsingular at all z.

This can also be proven directly by considering the determinant of $\mathbf{X}$. If we differentiate $|\,\mathbf{X}\,|$ by rows, we get the sum of terms such as

$$\begin{vmatrix} X_{11} & X_{12} & \cdots \\ \vdots & & \\ \dfrac{dX_{k1}}{dz} & \dfrac{dX_{k2}}{dz} & \cdots \\ \vdots & & \end{vmatrix}$$

Using the fact that

$$\frac{dX_{ij}}{dz} = -j \sum R_{ik} X_{kj}$$

each term becomes

$$-j \begin{vmatrix} X_{11} & X_{12} & \cdots \\ \vdots & & \\ \sum_i R_{ki} X_{i1} & \sum_i R_{ki} X_{i2} & \cdots \\ \vdots & & \end{vmatrix}$$

Collecting the coefficients of R_{ki}, we obtain

$$-jR_{ki}\{X_{i1}\Delta_{k1} + X_{i2}\Delta_{k2} + \cdots\}$$

where Δ_{ki} is the minor of $|\mathbf{X}|$ obtained by removing the kth row and ith column. The bracketed terms vanish unless $i = k$ when it becomes the Laplace development of the determinant. Hence we have

$$\frac{d|\mathbf{X}|}{dz} = -j|\mathbf{X}| \sum R_{ii} = -j|\mathbf{X}| \operatorname{tr} \mathbf{R} \tag{6}$$

or

$$|\mathbf{X}| = \exp\left[-j\int_0^z (\operatorname{tr} \mathbf{R})\, dz\right] |\mathbf{X}_0| \tag{7}$$

This is known as the *Jacobi identity*. (It must not, however, be confused with the Jacobi identity of Lie algebras that will be discussed in Chapter XIII.)

The trace of any bounded matrix is finite, so that the exponential of its integral cannot vanish for any finite z. Hence, if $\mathbf{X}(z)$ exists at all, it must be everywhere nonsingular.

2. THE MATRICANT

The boundary condition on Eq. (5) can be applied at any z, say z_0 in the form of $\mathbf{X}(z_0)$. Clearly this can be taken as we wish, with the sole requirement that $\mathbf{X}(z_0)$ must be nonsingular.

In particular, we can take $\mathbf{X}(z_0) = \mathbf{I}$. If this be done, then $\mathbf{X}(z)$ becomes what is known as the *matricant* of the system, which we will write as $\mathbf{M}(z, z_0)$. Specifically, we say that:

Definition. *If* $\mathbf{R}(z)$ *is a system matrix whose coefficients everywhere obey the Lipschitz condition, then* $\mathbf{M}(z, z_0)$ *is the* **matricant of the system** *if*

$$\frac{\partial \mathbf{M}(z, z_0)}{\partial z} = -j\mathbf{R}(z)\mathbf{M}(z, z_0) \tag{8}$$

and

$$\mathbf{M}(z_0, z_0) = \mathbf{I} \tag{9}$$

It should be carefully noted that not all integral matrices of a system are matricants. There is no guarantee that a given $\mathbf{X}(z)$ becomes the identity at any z. The class of matricants for a given $\mathbf{R}(z)$ as z_0 takes all possible values is a subclass of the integral matrices of the system.

If the specific boundary condition applied at z_0 is $\mathbf{x}(z_0)$, then the response vector at z is

$$\mathbf{x}(z) = \mathbf{M}(z, z_0)\mathbf{x}(z_0) \tag{10}$$

The analogy of the matricant to a Green's function is evident. In fact, the Green's function can be regarded as the matricant extended to infinitely dimensioned Hilbert spaces.

If the system matrix $\mathbf{R}$ is constant, then from Eq. (2) it is evident that

$$\mathbf{M}(z, z_0) = \exp\{-j\mathbf{R}(z - z_0)\} \tag{11}$$

While Eq. (11) applies only to this simple case, some of the properties of the exponential carry over to the more general situation:

Theorem 1. *If* $\mathbf{M}(z, z')$ *is the matricant of a system with system matrix* $\mathbf{R}(z)$, *then*

$$\mathbf{M}(z, z')\mathbf{M}(z', z'') = \mathbf{M}(z, z'') \tag{12}$$

This is evident from the definition of the matricant. $\mathbf{M}(z', z'')$ describes what is the effect at z' due to the situation at z'', and $\mathbf{M}(z, z')$ gives the effect at z due to the situation at z'. Hence the combination should be the matricant $\mathbf{M}(z, z'')$. However, to prove this more carefully, we prove first the following:

Lemma 1. *If* $\mathbf{X}(z)$ *and* $\mathbf{Y}(z)$ *are two integral matrices of a given system, then*

$$\mathbf{Y}(z) = \mathbf{XC} \tag{13}$$

where $\mathbf{C}$ *is some constant nonsingular matrix. Conversely, if* $\mathbf{X}$ *is an integral matrix, and* $\mathbf{C}$ *any nonsingular matrix, then* $(\mathbf{XC})$ *is an integral matrix.*

Proving the converse first, if we postmultiply Eq. (5) by $\mathbf{C}$, where $\mathbf{C}$ is any nonsingular constant matrix, we find

$$\frac{d(\mathbf{XC})}{dz} = -j\mathbf{R}(\mathbf{XC})$$

Hence $\mathbf{XC}$ is an integral matrix.

On the other hand, if $\mathbf{X}$ and $\mathbf{Y}$ are two integral matrices, then since $\mathbf{Y}$ is nonsingular, we can write

$$
\begin{aligned}
\frac{d\mathbf{X}}{dz} &= \frac{d}{dz}\{\mathbf{Y}(\mathbf{Y}^{-1}\mathbf{X})\} = \frac{d\mathbf{Y}}{dz}\mathbf{Y}^{-1}\mathbf{X} + \mathbf{Y}\frac{d}{dz}(\mathbf{Y}^{-1}\mathbf{X}) \\
&= -j(\mathbf{RY})\mathbf{Y}^{-1}\mathbf{X} + \mathbf{Y}\frac{d}{dz}(\mathbf{Y}^{-1}\mathbf{X}) \\
&= -j\mathbf{RX} + \mathbf{Y}\frac{d}{dz}(\mathbf{Y}^{-1}\mathbf{X})
\end{aligned}
$$

Since $\mathbf{X}$ is also an integral matrix the left-hand side becomes $-j\mathbf{RX}$. Since $\mathbf{Y}$ is nonsingular, we are left with

$$
\frac{d}{dz}(\mathbf{Y}^{-1}\mathbf{X}) = 0
$$

or
$$
\mathbf{Y}^{-1}\mathbf{X} = \mathbf{C} \tag{14}
$$

where $\mathbf{C}$ is a constant matrix.

Since $\mathbf{X}$ and $\mathbf{Y}$ are nonsingular $\mathbf{C}$ must be also.

Hence the lemma is proved.

From the lemma, we have that there exists a constant nonsingular matrix $\mathbf{C}$ such that

$$
\mathbf{M}(z, z')\mathbf{C} = \mathbf{M}(z, z'')
$$

since $\mathbf{M}(z, z')$ and $\mathbf{M}(z, z'')$ are both integral matrices. Setting $z = z'$, $\mathbf{M}(z, z')$ becomes the identity, and

$$
\mathbf{C} = \mathbf{M}(z', z'')
$$

The theorem is proven.

From the theorem, it follows that

$$
\mathbf{M}(z', z) = \{\mathbf{M}(z, z')\}^{-1} \tag{15}
$$

Hence the inverse of any matricant of a given system is also a matricant of the system.

3. MATRICANTS OF RELATED SYSTEMS

Suppose $\mathbf{M}_0(z, z')$ is the matricant of the system

$$
\frac{d\mathbf{M}_0}{dz} = -j\mathbf{R}_0\mathbf{M}_0 \tag{16}
$$

Suppose we seek the matricant of the system whose system matrix has been changed to $(\mathbf{R}_0 + \mathbf{R}_1)$. If we call the matricant of this system $\mathbf{M}_1(z, z')$, we can seek a solution of the form

$$\mathbf{M}_1(z, z') = \mathbf{M}_0(z, z')\mathbf{P}(z, z') \qquad (17)$$

Since both $\mathbf{M}_0$ and $\mathbf{M}_1$ become the identity at $z = z'$, we must have

$$\mathbf{P}(z', z') = \mathbf{I} \qquad (18)$$

which suggests that $\mathbf{P}(z, z')$ may be a matricant of still another system. We find that this is so. Differentiating Eq. (17) with respect to z, we find that

$$\frac{\partial \mathbf{M}_1}{\partial z} = \frac{\partial \mathbf{M}_0}{\partial z}\mathbf{P} + \mathbf{M}_0\frac{\partial \mathbf{P}}{\partial z} = -j\mathbf{R}_0\mathbf{M}_0\mathbf{P} + \mathbf{M}_0\frac{\partial \mathbf{P}}{\partial z}$$
$$= -j(\mathbf{R}_0 + \mathbf{R}_1)\mathbf{M}_0\mathbf{P}$$

since $\mathbf{M}_1$ is the matricant for $(\mathbf{R}_0 + \mathbf{R}_1)$.

Hence, since $\mathbf{M}_0$ is nonsingular,

$$\frac{\partial \mathbf{P}(z, z')}{\partial z} = -j(\mathbf{M}_0^{-1}\mathbf{R}_1\mathbf{M}_0)\mathbf{P} \qquad (19)$$

and $\mathbf{P}$ is the matricant for the system whose system matrix is $(\mathbf{M}_0^{-1}\mathbf{R}_1\mathbf{M}_0)$.

This approach is particularly useful if $\mathbf{M}_0$ is known and $\mathbf{R}_1$ is small compared to $\mathbf{R}_0$, so that it may be considered a perturbation on $\mathbf{R}_0$. The change to Eq. (19) removes the effect of the unperturbed system, leaving only the perturbations for further analysis.

What has, in fact, been done here is to change the basis from the original one to a set of linearly independent solutions of the unperturbed problem. The new basis is now z-dependent, but this does not interfere unduly.

4. PEANO EXPANSION

The matricant equations, Eqs. (8) and (9), can be solved iteratively. The resulting expansion always converges and gives the matricant, so that it is a valid solution in principle.

Unfortunately, it is very often an impractical solution. While it does converge, it will often do so only very slowly. Indeed, it seems to be a general principle that when the expansion is useable, there are always other ways of obtaining the same result, often at much less effort. Nevertheless, it is important to know that such a solution does exist.

If nothing else, we can seek with confidence for whatever is the best way of obtaining the answers we want.

The expansion is obtained by setting up a sequence of matrix-valued functions which are interrelated through Eq. (8). In particular, we set

$$\mathbf{M}_0 = \mathbf{I}$$

and

$$\frac{d\mathbf{M}_i}{dz} = -j\mathbf{R}\mathbf{M}_{i-1}, \qquad \mathbf{M}_i(0) = \mathbf{I} \tag{20}$$

where we have set $z_0 = 0$ to simplify the notation.

We see that, formally,

$$\mathbf{M}_1 = \mathbf{I} - j \int_0^z \mathbf{R}(z') \, dz'$$

$$\mathbf{M}_2 = \mathbf{I} - j \int_0^z \mathbf{R}(z') \, dz' - \int_0^z dz' \, \mathbf{R}(z') \int_0^{z'} \mathbf{R}(z'') \, dz''$$

$$\mathbf{M}_3 = \mathbf{I} - j \int_0^z \mathbf{R}(z') \, dz' - \int_0^z dz' \, \mathbf{R}(z') \int_0^{z'} \mathbf{R}(z'') \, dz''$$

$$+ j \int_0^z dz' \, \mathbf{R}(z') \int_0^{z'} dz'' \, \mathbf{R}(z'') \int_0^{z''} dz''' \, \mathbf{R}(z''') \tag{21}$$

and so forth.

Alternatively, if we set $\mathbf{S} = -j\mathbf{R}$, we have

$$\mathbf{M}_0 = \mathbf{I}$$
$$\frac{d\mathbf{M}_i}{dz} = \mathbf{S}\mathbf{M}_{i-1} \tag{22}$$

and

$$\mathbf{M}_1 = \mathbf{I} + \int_0^z \mathbf{S}(z') \, dz'$$

$$\mathbf{M}_2 = \mathbf{I} + \int_0^z \mathbf{S}(z')\mathbf{M}_1(z') \, dz' \tag{23}$$

$$\vdots$$

so that in the limit we can expect the matricant to be given by the series

$$\mathbf{M}(z) = \mathbf{I} + \int_0^z \mathbf{S}(z') \, dz' + \int_0^z \mathbf{S}(z') \int_0^{z'} \mathbf{S}(z'') \, dz' \, dz''$$

$$+ \int_0^z \mathbf{S}(z') \int_0^{z'} \mathbf{S}(z'') \int_0^{z''} \mathbf{S}(z''') \, dz' \, dz'' \, dz'''$$

$$+ \cdots \tag{24}$$

We shall now prove the following:

Theorem 2. *If* $S(z)$ *is continuous and single valued for all values of the real variable* z, *then the series given by Eq. (24) is absolutely and uniformly convergent in any finite range of* z, *and is equal to the matricant with* $z_0 = 0$.

To prove this, we define the *majorant* of $S(z)$, $\psi(z)$, as the real scalar function of z such that for all z

$$\psi(z) = \max_{ij} \{| S_{ij}(z)|\} \tag{25}$$

i.e., $\psi(z)$ is the magnitude of the largest component of $S(z)$.

Since $S(z)$ is assumed continuous, so is $\psi(z)$. Further, it is everywhere nonnegative.

We also define the matrix H as the $n \times n$ matrix all of whose components are unity. H is a constant matrix which has the property that

$$H^2 = nH \tag{26}$$

We will use $\psi(z)$ and H to develop a sequence of matrices that, in a suitable sense, is everywhere not less than what we shall call the modulus of the sequence of matrices M_1, M_2, ... defined by Eq. (23). Since this derived sequence is uniformly convergent, the sequence of moduli of M_i must be uniformly convergent also.

By the modulus of any matrix M we mean the matrix all of whose components are the moduli of the corresponding components of M:

$$\operatorname{mod} M = (| M_{ij} |) \tag{27}$$

The matrix $\operatorname{mod} M$ is then *nonnegative* (not to be confused with nonnegative definite), in the sense that all of its components are real and nonnegative.

Given two real matrices A and B we shall say that A is *less than or equal to* B $(A \leqslant B)$ if for all i and j

$$A_{ij} \leqslant B_{ij}$$

(This is not a definition of the relation $\leqslant$ that is generally useful since it does not provide a well-ordered relation, but it is what we need here.)

We have, then,

$$\operatorname{mod} S \leqslant \psi(z)H. \tag{28}$$

Using this in Eq. (23), we find that

$$\operatorname{mod} M_1 \leqslant I + \int_0^z \operatorname{mod} S(z) \, dz$$

$$\leqslant I + \int_0^z \psi(z)H \, dz$$

$$= I + H\varphi \tag{29}$$

where

$$\varphi = \int_0^z \psi(z)\, dz \tag{30}$$

which is a nonnegative real function for all positive z that increases monotonically from $\varphi(0) = 0$.

$$\text{mod } \mathbf{M}_2 \leqslant \mathbf{I} + \int_0^z (\text{mod } \mathbf{S})(\text{mod } \mathbf{M}_1)\, dz$$

$$\leqslant \mathbf{I} + \int_0^z \psi \mathbf{H}(\mathbf{I} + \varphi \mathbf{H})\, dz$$

$$= \mathbf{I} + \mathbf{H} \int_0^z (\psi + n\varphi\psi)\, dz$$

from Eq. (26).

Now, integrating by parts, we see that

$$\int \varphi\psi\, dz = \varphi^2/2$$

In fact, we have generally

$$\int_0^z \varphi^n\psi\, dz = \varphi^{n+1} - \int (n\varphi^{n-1}\psi)\varphi\, dz$$

$$= \varphi^{n+1} - n \int \varphi^n\psi\, dz$$

so that

$$\int_0^z \varphi^n\psi\, dz = \frac{\varphi^{n+1}}{n+1} \tag{31}$$

Hence,

$$\text{mod } \mathbf{M}_2 \leqslant \mathbf{I} + \mathbf{H}\left(\varphi + \frac{n\varphi^2}{2!}\right) \tag{32}$$

Suppose, generally,

$$\text{mod } \mathbf{M}_r \leqslant \mathbf{I} + \mathbf{H} \sum_{i=1}^r \frac{n^{i-1}\varphi^i}{i!} \tag{33}$$

Then

$$\text{mod } \mathbf{M}_{r+1} \leqslant \mathbf{I} + \int_0^z (\text{mod } \mathbf{M}_r)(\text{mod } \mathbf{S})\, dz$$

$$\leqslant \mathbf{I} + \int_0^z \left\{ \mathbf{I} + \mathbf{H} \sum_{i=1}^r \frac{n^{i-1}\varphi^i}{i!} \right\} (\psi\mathbf{H})\, dz$$

$$\leqslant \mathbf{I} + \int_0^z \mathbf{H} \left\{ \psi + \sum_{i=1}^r \frac{n^i\varphi^i}{i!}\, \psi \right\} dz$$

$$= \mathbf{I} + \mathbf{H} \left\{ \varphi + \sum_{i=1}^r \frac{n^i\varphi^{i+1}}{(i+1)!} \right\}$$

$$= \mathbf{I} + \mathbf{H} \sum_{i=1}^{r+1} \frac{n^{i-1}\varphi^i}{i!} \tag{34}$$

so that, by induction, Eq. (33) is valid for r any positive integer.

Equation (33) says that the sequence of ij coefficients of $\mathbf{M}_i$ are absolutely bounded by the ij coefficients of the sequence of the right side of Eq. (33). In the limit, as $r \to \infty$, Eq. (33) becomes

$$\text{mod } \mathbf{M} \leqslant \mathbf{I} + \mathbf{H} \sum_{i=1}^{\infty} \frac{n^{i-1}\varphi^i}{i!}$$

$$= \mathbf{I} + \frac{1}{n} \mathbf{H}(e^{n\varphi} - 1) \tag{35}$$

Since the sequence of $\mathbf{M}_i$, or the partial sums of $\mathbf{M}$, is absolutely bounded by mod $\mathbf{M}$ of Eq. (35), the series of Eq. (24) is absolutely and uniformly convergent.

Since the series of Eq. (24) is uniformly and absolutely convergent, we can differentiate it term by term. Since each term of the resulting series is equal to $\mathbf{S}$ times the corresponding term of Eq. (24), the derivative series is also uniformly and absolutely convergent, so that we can factor $\mathbf{S}$ out, and so verify that Eq. (24) is, in fact, the matricant for $z > 0$.

If $z < 0$, we can apply the same argument with the signs of the integral changed.

Hence the theorem is proven for all finite z.

The expansion can be proven valid under more general conditions than those stated. All that is required is that $\mathbf{S}(z)$ be single valued, bounded, and integrable over a range including 0 and z as interior points. We can also extend it to z as a complex variable by suitable restriction on the path of integration. In particular, we require that (a) the coefficients of $\mathbf{S}(z)$ be single valued and analytic in a *star region* formed by nonintersecting straight lines drawn from all the singularities and branch points of the coefficients of $\mathbf{S}(z)$ to infinity, (b) the points 0 and z be within this star region, and (c) all integrals are to be taken over a continuous path that lies wholly within the star region.

The theorem provides us with additional information giving us an upper bound on the magnitude of the coefficients of the matricant:

Corollary 1. *The ij coefficient of the matricant M_{ij} is bounded by*

$$| M_{ij} | \leqslant \delta_{ij} + \frac{1}{n} (e^{n\varphi} - 1) \tag{36}$$

The proof of the theorem depends on the properties of the majorant $\psi(z)$ and the fact that $\mathbf{H}$ is nonnegative and obeys Eq. (26). We can sharpen the corollary somewhat as follows:

Corollary 2. *Given a nonnegative matrix $\mathbf{J}$ such that*

$$\mathbf{J}^2 = \alpha \mathbf{J} \tag{37}$$

where α is a positive real number, and a nonnegative function $\psi(z)$ such that

$$| S_{ij}(z)| \leqslant \psi(z) J_{ij} \tag{38}$$

the matricant of Eq. (24) is bounded by

$$| M_{ij} | \leqslant \delta_{ij} + \frac{1}{\alpha} (e^{\alpha\varphi} - 1) J_{ij} \tag{39}$$

The proof follows exactly that of the theorem itself.

5. ERROR OF APPROXIMATION

These corollaries provide upper bounds on the behavior of the matricant with z. How useful they are depends on the circumstances. Often they give bounds that are far above the actual system behavior.

On the other hand, they are sometimes useful in testing the validity of an approximation. Suppose we have a system described by Eq. (1'). Suppose also that we have obtained an approximate matricant, $\mathbf{M}_0(z)$ with $\mathbf{M}_0(0) = \mathbf{I}$. We wish to obtain at least a bound on the possible error of the approximation.

The approximate matricant is the exact solution of a system whose system operator S_0, is given by

$$S_0(z) = \frac{dM_0}{dz} M_0^{-1} \tag{40}$$

We define P by

$$P = M_0^{-1}M \tag{41}$$

so that the true matricant of the system is given by M_0P. By Eq. (19), P satisfies the equation

$$\frac{dP}{dz} = \{M_0^{-1}(S - S_0)M_0\}P, \qquad P(0) = I \tag{42}$$

We can now apply Corollary 1 or Eq. (35) to P:

$$\mathrm{mod}\ P \leqslant I + \frac{1}{n} H(e^{n\varphi} - 1) \tag{43}$$

where φ is the integral of the majorant of $\{M_0^{-1}(S - S_0)M_0\}$, or we can apply Corollary 2 if a J exists that matches $\{M_0^{-1}(S - S_0)M_0\}$ better than H.

If we find that $\mathrm{mod}\ P$ is sufficiently near I for our purposes, then we know that the approximation is suitable. If not, then we cannot be sure, either way.

6. BOUND ON THE DIFFERENCE

An upper bound can also be established on the difference of two matricants. Again, the principal use of this bound is in establishing the validity of an approximation.

Changing the notation slightly, suppose

$$\frac{dM}{dz} = SM, \qquad M(0) = I$$

$$\frac{dN}{dz} = TN, \qquad N(0) = I \tag{44}$$

Suppose we can find a constant nonnegative J such that

$$J^2 = \alpha J \tag{45}$$

and nonnegative real functions ψ and η such that

$$\begin{aligned} \mathrm{mod}\,\mathbf{S} &\leqslant \psi\mathbf{J} \\ \mathrm{mod}(\mathbf{T} - \mathbf{S}) &\leqslant \eta\mathbf{J} \end{aligned} \tag{46}$$

Define the integrals

$$\varphi = \int_0^z \psi\,dz, \qquad \kappa = \int_0^z \eta\,dz \tag{47}$$

for positive z.

We also define the partial sums

$$\mathbf{M}_1 = \mathbf{I} + \int_0^z \mathbf{S}(z)\,dz$$

$$\mathbf{M}_{p+1} = \mathbf{I} + \int_0^z \mathbf{S}(z)\mathbf{M}_p\,dz, \qquad p \geqslant 1$$

$$\mathbf{N}_1 = \mathbf{I} + \int_0^z \mathbf{T}(z)\,dz$$

$$\mathbf{N}_{p+1} = \mathbf{I} + \int_0^z \mathbf{T}(z)\mathbf{N}_p(z)\,dz, \qquad p \geqslant 1$$

We can then write

$$\mathbf{N}_1 - \mathbf{M}_1 = \int_0^z (\mathbf{T} - \mathbf{S})\,dz \tag{48}$$

$$\mathbf{N}_{p+1} - \mathbf{M}_{p+1} = \int_0^z (\mathbf{T}\mathbf{N}_p - \mathbf{S}\mathbf{M}_p)\,dz$$

$$= \int_0^z \{(\mathbf{T} - \mathbf{S})\mathbf{M}_p + \mathbf{T}(\mathbf{N}_p - \mathbf{M}_p)\}\,dz \tag{49}$$

Then

$$\mathrm{mod}(\mathbf{N}_1 - \mathbf{M}_1) \leqslant \kappa\mathbf{J} \tag{50}$$

$$\mathrm{mod}(\mathbf{N}_{p+1} - \mathbf{M}_{p+1}) \leqslant \int_0^z \{\eta\mathbf{J}\,\mathrm{mod}\,\mathbf{M}_p + (\psi + \eta)\mathbf{J}\,\mathrm{mod}(\mathbf{N}_p - \mathbf{M}_p)\}\,dz \tag{51}$$

Further, from Eq. (33), we have

$$\mathrm{mod}\,\mathbf{M}_p \leqslant \mathbf{I} + \mathbf{J}\sum_{k=1}^{p} \frac{\alpha^{k-1}}{k!}\,\varphi^k \tag{52}$$

We assert that

$$\mathrm{mod}(\mathbf{N}_p - \mathbf{M}_p) \leqslant \mathbf{J}\sum_{k=1}^{p} \frac{\alpha^{k-1}}{k!}\{(\kappa + \varphi)^k - \varphi^k\} \tag{53}$$

This is true for $p = 1$. If true for p, then from Eq. (51):

$$\mathrm{mod}(\mathbf{N}_{p+1} - \mathbf{M}_{p+1}) \leqslant \int_0^z \left\{ \eta \mathbf{J} \left(\mathbf{I} + \mathbf{J} \sum_1^p \frac{\alpha^{k-1}}{k!} \varphi^k \right) \right.$$

$$\left. + (\psi + \eta)\mathbf{J}^2 \sum_{k=1}^p \frac{\alpha^{k-1}}{k!} [(\kappa + \varphi)^k - \varphi^k] \right\} dz$$

$$\tag{54}$$

$$= \kappa \mathbf{J} + \sum_{k=1}^p \frac{\alpha^k}{k!} \mathbf{J} \int_0^z \{ \eta \varphi^k + (\psi + \eta)[(\kappa + \varphi)^k - \varphi^k] \} \, dz$$

Now the integral in Eq. (54) can be integrated by parts:

$$\int_0^z \{ \eta \varphi^k + (\psi + \eta)[(\kappa + \varphi)^k - \varphi^k] \} \, dz$$

$$= \int_0^z \{ (\psi + \eta)(\kappa + \varphi)^k - \psi \varphi^k \} \, dz$$

$$= (\kappa + \varphi)^{k+1} - \varphi^{k+1} - k \int_0^k \{ (\kappa + \varphi)^k (\psi + \eta) - \psi \varphi^k \} \, dz$$

and so is equal to

$$\frac{1}{k+1} \{ (\kappa + \varphi)^{k+1} - \varphi^{k+1} \} \tag{55}$$

Putting this in Eq. (54), we find that

$$\mathrm{mod}(\mathbf{N}_{p+1} - \mathbf{M}_{p+1}) \leqslant \kappa \mathbf{J} + \sum_{k=1}^p \frac{\alpha^k}{(k+1)!} \mathbf{J} \{ (\kappa + \varphi)^{k+1} - \varphi^{k+1} \}$$

$$= \mathbf{J} \sum_{k=1}^{p+1} \frac{\alpha^{k-1}}{k!} \{ (\kappa + \varphi)^k - \varphi^k \} \tag{56}$$

by shifting the value of k.

Hence, Eq. (53) is established by induction.

In the limit, as $p \to \infty$,

$$\mathrm{mod}(\mathbf{N} - \mathbf{M}) \leqslant \mathbf{J} \sum_{k=1}^\infty \frac{\alpha^{k-1}}{k!} \{ (\kappa + \varphi)^k - \varphi^k \}$$

$$= \frac{1}{\alpha} \mathbf{J} \{ e^{\alpha(\kappa + \varphi)} - e^{\alpha \varphi} \}$$

$$= \frac{1}{\alpha} \mathbf{J} e^{\alpha \varphi} \{ e^{\alpha \kappa} - 1 \} \tag{57}$$

This gives us an upper bound on the absolute magnitude of the difference of the matricants in terms of the integrals of the majorants of one system operator and of the difference of the two system operators.

7. APPROXIMATE EXPANSION

Since we have an expression for the expansion of the matricant, we are led to consider when we can use a limited number of its terms as an approximation to the matricant.

If $\mathbf{R}$ in Eq. (8) were constant, the expansion, Eq. (21), would be a power series in z. Each successive integration raises the power of z by one. We would expect that the first k terms of Eq. (21) would be an approximation that is valid for sufficiently small z (or for z sufficiently near z_0).

The difficulty is that the dependence on z is essentially exponential, with the term in the exponent being either pure imaginary or complex. Generally, we are interested in the situation where there may be a large phase term plus a substantial growth or decay term. Hence z, in this case, is very far from small. To obtain a terminated power series that is a good approximation to such an exponential factor requires a large number of terms. Hence this is not a good method of approximation.

We could avoid this difficulty—or at least greatly reduce its effect—if we could eliminate the rapid phase change before applying the expansion. It is precisely for this reason that the transformation of Section 3 becomes important. Equation (19) describes the system on a basis that already includes the solved part of the problem. If this solved part includes the rapidly varying phase part, we may be left with a problem for which the first two or three terms of Eq. (21) are a valid and useful approximation.

As an example, consider a transmission line with a slight linear taper of the characteristic impedence $Z = Z_0(1 + kz)$, where k is small so that $kz \ll 1$. We can then approximate $1/Z$ as $(1 - kz)/Z_0$ and write, on an $E - I$ basis,

$$\mathbf{R} = \begin{pmatrix} 0 & \beta Z_0(1 + kz) \\ \beta(1 - kz)/Z_0 & 0 \end{pmatrix}$$

and let

$$\mathbf{R}_0 = \begin{pmatrix} 0 & \beta Z_0 \\ \beta/Z_0 & 0 \end{pmatrix}$$

$$\mathbf{R}_1 = kz \begin{pmatrix} 0 & \beta Z_0 \\ -\beta/Z_0 & 0 \end{pmatrix}$$

Then we have

$$\mathbf{M}_0 = \exp(-j\mathbf{R}_0 z) = \begin{pmatrix} \cos \beta z & -jZ_0 \sin \beta z \\ -(j/Z_0) \sin \beta z & \cos \beta z \end{pmatrix}$$

so that

$$(\mathbf{M}_0^{-1}\mathbf{R}_1\mathbf{M}_0) = k\beta z \begin{pmatrix} -j \sin 2\beta z & Z \cos 2\beta z \\ -(1/Z) \cos 2\beta z & j \sin 2\beta z \end{pmatrix}$$

To the first order in k, the solution of Eq. (19), according to Eq. (21), is

$$\mathbf{P} = \mathbf{I} - jk\beta \int_0^z \begin{pmatrix} -jz \sin 2\beta z & Zz \cos 2\beta z \\ -(z/Z) \cos 2\beta z & jz \sin 2\beta z \end{pmatrix} dz$$

or

$$\mathbf{P} = \mathbf{I} - \frac{k}{4\beta} \begin{pmatrix} (\sin \alpha - \alpha \cos \alpha) & jZ(\cos \alpha + \alpha \sin \alpha - 1) \\ -(j/Z)(\cos \alpha + \alpha \sin \alpha - 1) & -(\sin \alpha - \alpha \cos \alpha) \end{pmatrix}$$

where

$$\alpha = 2\beta z$$

Then

$$\mathbf{M}(z) = \mathbf{M}_0(z)\mathbf{P}(z)$$

It will be noted that this expression does not depend on z being small, only kz. Hence it is valid for any finite z, for sufficiently small k.

8. INHOMOGENEOUS EQUATIONS

The matricant can also be used for the inhomogeneous form of Eq. (1):

$$\frac{d\mathbf{x}}{dz} = -j\mathbf{R}\mathbf{x} + \mathbf{y}(z) \tag{58}$$

where $\mathbf{y}$ may also be a function of $\mathbf{z}$.

We consider the matricant of the system $\mathbf{M}(z, z_0)$

$$\frac{d\mathbf{M}}{dz} = -j\mathbf{R}\mathbf{M}, \qquad \mathbf{M}(z_0, z_0) = \mathbf{I} \tag{59}$$

We look for a solution of the form

$$\mathbf{x}(z) = \mathbf{M}(z, z_0)\mathbf{u}(z) \tag{60}$$

Substituting this in Eq. (58), we obtain

$$\frac{d\mathbf{M}}{dz}\mathbf{u} + \mathbf{M}\frac{d\mathbf{u}}{dz} = -j\mathbf{RMu} + \mathbf{M}\frac{d\mathbf{u}}{dz} = -j\mathbf{RMu} + \mathbf{y}$$

$$\frac{d\mathbf{u}}{dz} = \mathbf{M}^{-1}\mathbf{y}$$

$$\mathbf{u} = \int_{z_0}^{z} \mathbf{M}^{-1}\mathbf{y}(z)\,dz + \mathbf{u}_0 \tag{61}$$

Substituting this back in Eq. (60), we find

$$\mathbf{x}(z) = \mathbf{M}(z, z_0)\int_{z_0}^{z} \mathbf{M}^{-1}(z', z_0)\mathbf{y}(z')\,dz' + \mathbf{M}(z, z_0)\mathbf{u}_0 \tag{62}$$

If we let $z = z_0$, we find that $\mathbf{u}_0 = \mathbf{x}(z_0)$. Hence the solution is

$$\mathbf{x}(z) = \mathbf{M}(z, z_0)\mathbf{x}(z_0) + \int_{z_0}^{z} \mathbf{K}(z, z')\mathbf{y}(z')\,dz'$$

where

$$\mathbf{K}(z, z') = \mathbf{M}(z, z_0)\mathbf{M}^{-1}(z', z_0)$$

$$= \mathbf{M}(z, z_0)\mathbf{M}(z_0, z')$$

$$= \mathbf{M}(z, z') \tag{63}$$

from Eqs. (15) and (12). The kernel $\mathbf{K}(z, z')$ is known as the *Cauchy* matrix, and is itself a matricant.

We have found the solution of the inhomogeneous equation as the sum of the solution of the homogeneous equation and the integral of the inhomogeneity with the Cauchy matrix.

9. THE MULTIPLICATIVE INTEGRAL OF VOLTERRA

We shall conclude this chapter with a brief account of a special type of integration called the *multiplicative integral of Volterra*. Its value is twofold. It gives a procedure for the numerical calculation of the matricant that is well adapted to machine computation in some cases. Also, it is conceptually interesting.

Suppose we have a system described by $\mathbf{R}(z)$ and wish to calculate the matricant from z_0 to z. We can divide the interval into a sequence of short sections

$$z_0 < z_1 < z_2 < \cdots < z_n = z$$

By the product rule for the matricant, Theorem 1, Eq. (12), the matricant of the whole interval is the product of the matricants for the subintervals

$$\mathbf{M}(z, z_0) = \mathbf{M}(z_n , z_{n-1})\mathbf{M}(z_{n-1} , z_{n-2}) \cdots \mathbf{M}(z_1 , z_0) \qquad (64)$$

Now, if each subinterval is short enough, $\mathbf{R}(z)$ is essentially constant within it. Hence we can write, approximately,

$$\mathbf{M}(z_{i+1} , z_i) = e^{-j\mathbf{R}(z_i)(\Delta z_i)} \qquad (65)$$

where

$$\Delta z_i = z_{i+1} - z_i$$

We can expand this and write, approximately,

$$\mathbf{M}(z_{i+1} , z_i) = \mathbf{I} - j\mathbf{R}(z_i)\,\Delta z_i \qquad (66)$$

Hence

$$\mathbf{M}(z, z_0) = \prod \{\mathbf{I} - j\mathbf{R}(z_i)\,\Delta z_i\} \qquad (67)$$

In the limit, as all $\Delta z_i \to 0$, this expression becomes what is called the *multiplicative integral* of $\{-j\mathbf{R}(z)\}$, symbolized as

$$\mathbf{M}(z, z_0) = \int_{z_0}^{z} \{\mathbf{I} - j\mathbf{R}(z)\,dz\} \qquad (68)$$

It is easy to see that if the various values of $\mathbf{R}(z)$ commute, this expression becomes idential to

$$\exp\left\{-j\int_{z_0}^{z} \mathbf{R}(z)\,dz\right\} \qquad (69)$$

It is the noncommutivity of $\mathbf{R}(z)$ at various values of z that causes the trouble.

We have not attempted to establish the form of the multiplicative integral rigorously. This can, however, be done.

The inverse operation to the multiplicative integral is the *multiplicative derivative*, symbolized by $D_z\mathbf{X}$, and obtained as

$$D_z\mathbf{X}(z) = \frac{d\mathbf{X}}{dz}\,\mathbf{X}^{-1} \qquad (70)$$

For suppose $\mathbf{X}(z)$ is an integral matrix of a system whose system operator is $\mathbf{R}(z)$:

$$\frac{d\mathbf{X}}{dz} = -j\mathbf{R}\mathbf{X}$$

Then by Eq. (13), the lemma of Theorem 1,

$$\mathbf{X}(z) = \mathbf{M}(z, z_0)\mathbf{X}(z_0)$$

and

$$\mathbf{M}(z, z_0) = \mathbf{X}(z)\mathbf{X}^{-1}(z_0)$$

so that

$$\int_{z_0}^{\hat{}z} \{\mathbf{I} - j\mathbf{R}(z)\, dz\} = \mathbf{X}(z)\mathbf{X}^{-1}(z_0) \tag{71}$$

and

$$D_z \int_{z_0}^{\hat{}z} \{\mathbf{I} - j\mathbf{R}(z)\, dz\} = \frac{d}{dz}\{\mathbf{X}(z)\mathbf{X}^{-1}(z_0)\}\mathbf{X}(z_0)\mathbf{X}^{-1}(z)$$

$$= \frac{d\mathbf{X}(z)}{dz}\mathbf{X}^{-1}(z) = -j\mathbf{R}\mathbf{X}(z)\mathbf{X}^{-1}(z)$$

$$= -j\mathbf{R}(z) \tag{72}$$

Hence $-j\mathbf{R}(z)$ has been recovered.

It is possible to set up a differential and integral calculus based on these operations. This was done by Volterra in the study of linear differential equations with analytic coefficients.

Exercises

1. Use the Peano expansion to obtain the matricant of a uniform transmission line, with

$$\mathbf{S} = \begin{pmatrix} 0 & -j\beta Z \\ -j\beta/Z & 0 \end{pmatrix}$$

where β and Z are constants.

2. Use the Peano expansion to obtain the matricant with

$$\mathbf{S} = \begin{pmatrix} a & 1 \\ 0 & a \end{pmatrix}$$

3. A system described by

$$\frac{d\mathbf{X}}{dz} = \frac{1}{z - \alpha}\mathbf{S}\mathbf{X}$$

where $\mathbf{S}$ is a constant matrix and α is a constant, possibly complex, is called a *Cauchy* system. Use the substitution

$$w = \ln(z - \alpha)$$

to obtain an explicit expression for the matricant of a Cauchy system.

4. Prove the following formula for the multiplicative integral:

(a) $\displaystyle \int_{z_0}^{\widehat{z_2}} (\mathbf{I} + \mathbf{S}\, dz) = \int_{z_1}^{\widehat{z_2}} (\mathbf{I} + \mathbf{S}\, dz) \int_{z_0}^{\widehat{z_1}} (\mathbf{I} + \mathbf{S}\, dz)$

(b) $\displaystyle \int_{0}^{\widehat{z}} (\mathbf{I} + \mathbf{S}\, dz) = \left[\int_{0}^{\widehat{z_0}} (\mathbf{I} + \mathbf{S}\, dz) \right]^{-1}$

(c) $\displaystyle \int_{z_0}^{\widehat{z_1}} (\mathbf{I} + \mathbf{CSC}^{-1}\, dz) = \mathbf{C} \left[\int_{z_0}^{\widehat{z_1}} (\mathbf{I} + \mathbf{S}\, dz) \right] \mathbf{C}^{-1}$

where $\mathbf{C}$ is a constant matrix.

(d) $\displaystyle \int_{z_0}^{\widehat{z}} \{\mathbf{I} + (\mathbf{S} + D_z\mathbf{X})\, dz\} = \mathbf{X}(z) \left[\int_{z_0}^{\widehat{z}} \{\mathbf{I} + \mathbf{X}^{-1}\mathbf{SX}\, dz\} \right] \mathbf{X}^{-1}(z_0)$

5. Prove the following formulas for the multiplicative derivative:

(a) $D_z(\mathbf{XY}) = D_z(\mathbf{X}) + \mathbf{X} D_z(\mathbf{Y}) \mathbf{X}^{-1}$

(b) $D_z(\mathbf{XC}) = D_z\mathbf{X}$,   where $\mathbf{C}$ is a constant matrix.

(c) $D_z(\mathbf{CX}) = \mathbf{C} D_z(\mathbf{X}) \mathbf{C}^{-1}$, $\mathbf{C}$ a constant matrix.

(d) $D_z(\mathbf{X}^\dagger) = \mathbf{X}^\dagger (D_z\mathbf{X})^\dagger \mathbf{X}^{\dagger-1}$

(e) $D_z(\mathbf{X}^{-1}) = -\mathbf{X}^{-1}(D_z\mathbf{X})\mathbf{X}$

(f) $D_z(\mathbf{X}^{\dagger-1}) = -(D_z\mathbf{X})^\dagger$

6. Find the Peano expansion of $\mathbf{N}(z)$ if

$$\frac{d\mathbf{N}}{dz} = -\mathbf{NS}, \qquad \mathbf{N}(0) = \mathbf{I}$$

What is the relation of $\mathbf{N}$ to the matricant $\mathbf{M}(z, 0)$ of a system whose system operator is $\mathbf{S}$?

7. Show that the solution of

$$\frac{d\mathbf{X}}{dz} = \mathbf{AX} + \mathbf{XB}, \qquad \mathbf{X}(0) = \mathbf{X}_0$$

is given by

$$\mathbf{X} = \mathbf{UX}_0\mathbf{V}$$

where

$$\frac{d\mathbf{U}}{dz} = \mathbf{AU}, \qquad \mathbf{U}(0) = \mathbf{I}$$

$$\frac{d\mathbf{V}}{dz} = \mathbf{VB}, \qquad \mathbf{V}(0) = \mathbf{I}$$

Observe that this is true even if $\mathbf{A}$ and $\mathbf{B}$ are not constant.

CHAPTER VIII

Decomposition Theorems and the Jordan Canonical Form

This chapter will be devoted to picking up some of the loose ends that we have blithely allowed to persist so far. In particular, we shall prove that any matrix has a Jordan canonical form and that this form is unique. This is not to say that the basis that puts a given matrix into the Jordan canonical form is unique, but only that whatever basis is chosen, it puts the given matrix into the same form within a permutation of the Jordan blocks.

To accomplish this, we will develop some of the theory of the invariant cyclic subspaces of a given matrix. We will show that these subspaces permit the complete *decomposition* of the whole space. (The term *decomposition* is being used technically here and will be defined shortly.) It is through this decomposition that the Jordan canonical form is reached, and the use of generalized eigenvectors justified.

For the application of matrix algebra to practical problems of physics or engineering, the analysis that we will give in this chapter may not be necessary. However, the principle of determining the structure of an operator through study of its invariant subspaces is a very powerful one. It is an important tool for the study of the behavior of an operator or of classes of operators.

1. DECOMPOSITION

We start by defining the concept of decomposing a space with respect to a given matrix operator.

Definition. *A linear vector space S is said to be **decomposed** into two linear vector spaces S_1 and S_2 if* (a) *any vector in either S_1 or S_2 is also in S,* (b) *there exists no vector in S except the null vector that is, simultaneously, a member of both S_1 and S_2, and* (c) *any vector in S can be expressed as the sum of a vector in S_1 and a vector in S_2. The spaces S_1 and S_2 are said to be a **decomposition** of S. We also say that S is the **direct sum** of S_1 and S_2, and symbolize this relation by*

$$S = S_1 \oplus S_2 \tag{1}$$

193

We can describe this by saying that (a) requires that S_1 and S_2 be subspaces of S, (b) that they are disjoint, and (c) that together they span S. We can clearly extend the concept of decomposition to more than a pair of spaces. We say that S is decomposed into S_1, S_2, ..., S_k if (a) these spaces are all subspaces of S, (b) they are disjoint, and (c) they span S.

If S is decomposed into S_1 and S_2, then the resolution of a vector $\mathbf{x}$ in S into $\mathbf{x}_1 + \mathbf{x}_2$, where $\mathbf{x}_1$ is in S_1 and $\mathbf{x}_2$ in S_2 is unique. For suppose we could find another resolution:

$$\mathbf{x} = \mathbf{x}_1' + \mathbf{x}_2', \qquad \mathbf{x}_1' \in S_1, \quad \mathbf{x}_2' \in S_2 \qquad (2)^1$$

Then subtracting,

$$0 = (\mathbf{x}_1 - \mathbf{x}_1') + (\mathbf{x}_2 - \mathbf{x}_2') \qquad (3)$$

or

$$(\mathbf{x}_1 - \mathbf{x}_1') = -(\mathbf{x}_2' - \mathbf{x}_2) \qquad (4)$$

But $(\mathbf{x}_1 - \mathbf{x}_1') \in S_1$ and $(\mathbf{x}_2' - \mathbf{x}_2) \in S_2$. Therefore the disjointness of S_1 and S_2 is violated unless $(\mathbf{x}_1 - \mathbf{x}_1')$ and $(\mathbf{x}_2' - \mathbf{x}_2)$ are null.

The converse is also true. For suppose S_1 and S_2 were not disjoint but contained $\mathbf{u}$ in common. Then, if

$$\mathbf{x} = \mathbf{x}_1 + \mathbf{x}_2 \qquad (5)$$

it would be also true that

$$\mathbf{x} = \mathbf{x}_1' + \mathbf{x}_2' \qquad (6)$$

where

$$\mathbf{x}_1' = \mathbf{x}_1 + \mathbf{u} \qquad \in S_1$$
$$\mathbf{x}_2' = \mathbf{x}_2 - \mathbf{u} \qquad \in S_2 \qquad (7)$$

and the decomposition of $\mathbf{x}$ would not be unique.

Hence we can replace disjointness by the requirement that any vector $\mathbf{x}$ can be represented *uniquely* as

$$\mathbf{x} = \mathbf{x}_1 + \mathbf{x}_2, \qquad \mathbf{x}_1 \in S_1, \quad \mathbf{x}_2 \in S_2 \qquad (8)$$

We now make the following definition:

---

[1] The symbol $\in$ means "is a member of."

Definition. *We say that the operator* **A** **decomposes** *the space* S *into* S_1 *and* S_2 *if* S_1 *and* S_2 *are a decomposition of* S, *and if they are both invariant for* **A**.

The significance of decomposition is that it implies that there is a basis in terms of which **A** is quasidiagonal. For consider any basis $\mathbf{x}_1, ..., \mathbf{x}_n$ such that $\mathbf{x}_1, ..., \mathbf{x}_k$ spans S_1 and $\mathbf{x}_{k+1}, ..., \mathbf{x}_n$ spans S_2. Then, on this basis, **A** evidently has the form

$$\mathbf{A} = \begin{pmatrix} \mathbf{A}_1 & 0 \\ 0 & \mathbf{A}_2 \end{pmatrix} \tag{9}$$

where $\mathbf{A}_1$ is $k \times k$ and $\mathbf{A}_2$ is $(n - k \times (n - k)$. Any vector in S_1 is represented as a column vector all of whose nonzero terms are among the first k coefficients. Since S_1 is invariant, **A** operating on such a vector must leave it in S_1—i.e., must yield a vector such that all components from the $(k + 1)$ on must be zero. Hence the submatrix in the lower left corner must be null. Similarly, by considering an arbitrary vector in S_2, we see that the upper right submatrix must be null.

There is another process that is also important, although we shall not use it here. It is, however, easily confused with decomposition. This is the process of reduction.

The matrix **A** is said to *reduce* the space S to the subspace S_1 if S_1 is an invariant subspace for **A**.

The missing part, which distinguishes reduction from decomposition, is that we have not asserted that there exists any S_2 such that $S = S_1 \oplus S_2$ and such that S_2 is invariant.

If, now, **A** reduces S, we can choose a basis for $S_1 : \mathbf{x}_1, ..., \mathbf{x}_k$, and augment it to a basis for S by adding on sufficient linearly independent vectors $\mathbf{x}_{k+1}, ..., \mathbf{x}_n$. Then it is easy to see that on this basis, **A** must have the form

$$\mathbf{A} = \begin{pmatrix} \mathbf{A}_1 & \mathbf{B} \\ 0 & \mathbf{A}_2 \end{pmatrix} \tag{10}$$

where $\mathbf{A}_1$ is $k \times k$ and $\mathbf{A}_2$ $(n - k) \times (n - k)$ and **B** an appropriately dimensioned rectangular matrix.

This is not an important concept for the analysis of a single matrix. Indeed, we can show that it is always possible put any matrix in upper triangular form, thus exhibiting a whole succession of reduction processes.

It does become a vitally important process in such matters as the study of matrix groups (or groups represented as matrices) or of the algebras defined over various classes of matrices. It is then very far from inconsequential to ask if the entire set of matrices being studied is reducible—i.e., whether there exists a basis in terms of which *all* members of the set take the form of Eq. (10).

We mention this here only to emphasize the warning the decomposability and reducibility are quite different properties and must be sharply distinguished. Our primary concern here is with decomposition.

2. DECOMPOSITION INTO EIGENSUBSPACES

We now wish to study how a given matrix may decompose the space on which it operates. We have already observed that a decomposition implies the possible choice of a basis in terms of which the matrix takes the quasidiagonal form of Eq. (9). Thus this seems a step in the right direction for obtaining a canonical form.

Our purpose now, is to relate the decomposition of S by $\mathbf{A}$ to the minimum polynomial of $\mathbf{A}$. We have defined the minimum polynomial over the whole space. It is reasonable to extend this to a subspace:

Definition. *A polynomial $p(x)$ is said to* **annihilate** *a subspace S_1 for $\mathbf{A}$ if, for any vector $\mathbf{x}$ in S_1, $p(\mathbf{A})\mathbf{x} = \mathbf{0}$. The polynomial of lowest degree that annihilates S_1 is called the* **minimum polynomial of $\mathbf{A}$ over S_1.**

We shall now prove the following:

Theorem 1. *If $\mathbf{A}$ has the minimum polynomial $\varphi(\lambda)$ which is factorable into coprime polynomials $\psi_1(\lambda)$, $\psi_2(\lambda)$,*

$$\varphi(\lambda) = \psi_1(\lambda)\psi_2(\lambda) \tag{11}$$

then $\mathbf{A}$ decomposes the whole space S into S_1 and S_2 :

$$S = S_1 \oplus S_2 \tag{12}$$

such that S_1 has the minimum polynomial $\psi_1(\lambda)$ and S_2 , $\psi_2(\lambda)$.

Since ψ_1 and ψ_2 are coprime, there must exist polynomials $\kappa_1(\lambda)$ and $\kappa_2(\lambda)$ such that

$$\kappa_1(\lambda)\psi_1(\lambda) + \kappa_2(\lambda)\psi_2(\lambda) = 1$$

Then, replacing λ by $\mathbf{A}$:

$$\kappa_1(\mathbf{A})\psi_1(\mathbf{A}) + \kappa_2(\mathbf{A})\psi_2(\mathbf{A}) = \mathbf{I} \tag{13}$$

Let $\mathbf{x}$ be arbitrary vector in S and apply Eq. (13) to it:

$$\psi_1(\mathbf{A})\kappa_1(\mathbf{A})\mathbf{x} + \psi_2(\mathbf{A})\kappa_2(\mathbf{A})\mathbf{x} = \mathbf{x} \tag{14}$$

We can then let

$$\mathbf{x}_1 = \psi_2(\mathbf{A})\kappa_2(\mathbf{A})\mathbf{x}$$
$$\mathbf{x}_2 = \psi_1(\mathbf{A})\kappa_1(\mathbf{A})\mathbf{x} \tag{15}$$

and any vector $\mathbf{x}$ is thus expressible as

$$\mathbf{x} = \mathbf{x}_1 + \mathbf{x}_2 \tag{16}$$

We define the set S_1 as the set of all $\mathbf{x}_1$ as $\mathbf{x}$ takes all values in S. Likewise S_2 is the set of all $\mathbf{x}_2$. We need to show, first, that this is a decomposition.

We observe, first, that

$$\psi_1(\mathbf{A})\mathbf{x}_1 = \psi_1(\mathbf{A})\psi_2(\mathbf{A})\kappa_2(\mathbf{A})\mathbf{x} = \varphi(\mathbf{A})\kappa_2(\mathbf{A})\mathbf{x} = 0 \tag{17}$$

$$\psi_2(\mathbf{A})\mathbf{x}_2 = \psi_2(\mathbf{A})\psi_1(\mathbf{A})\kappa_1(\mathbf{A})\mathbf{x} = \varphi(\mathbf{A})\kappa_1(\mathbf{A})\mathbf{x} = 0 \tag{18}$$

so that $\psi_1(\mathbf{A})$ annihilates S_1 and $\psi_2(\mathbf{A})$ annihilates S_2.

Further, suppose there existed a vector $\mathbf{x}_0$ common to both S_1 and S_2. Then we would have

$$\psi_1(\mathbf{A})\mathbf{x}_0 = \psi_2(\mathbf{A})\mathbf{x}_0 = 0 \tag{19}$$

Using $\mathbf{x}_0$ for $\mathbf{x}$ in Eq. (14), and recalling that polynomials of $\mathbf{A}$ commute,

$$\mathbf{x}_0 = \kappa_1(\mathbf{A})\psi_1(\mathbf{A})\mathbf{x}_0 + \kappa_2(\mathbf{A})\psi_2(\mathbf{A})\mathbf{x}_0 = 0 \tag{20}$$

The only common $\mathbf{x}_0$ is the null vector and S_1 and S_2 are disjoint. Taken with Eq. (16), this shows that the separation into S_1 and S_2 is a decomposition. We still need to show that it is a decomposition by $\mathbf{A}$. We need to show, specifically, that S_1 and S_2 are invariant for $\mathbf{A}$.

To show that S_1 is invariant for $\mathbf{A}$, we observe that since $\psi_2(\mathbf{A})$ and $\kappa_2(\mathbf{A})$ are polynomials in $\mathbf{A}$, they commute with $\mathbf{A}$. Hence,

$$\mathbf{A}\mathbf{x}_1 = \mathbf{A}\psi_2(\mathbf{A})\kappa_2(\mathbf{A})\mathbf{x}$$
$$= \psi_2(\mathbf{A})\kappa_2(\mathbf{A})(\mathbf{A}\mathbf{x}) \tag{21}$$

Hence $\mathbf{A}\mathbf{x}_1$ is expressible in the form of Eq. (15), and so is in S_1. Similarly, $\mathbf{A}\mathbf{x}_2$ is in S_2.

Hence, Eq. (15) is a decomposition of the whole space by $\mathbf{A}$. It is, furthermore, a decomposition into subspaces for which ψ_1 and ψ_2 are annihilating polynomials by Eqs. (17) and (18).

There remains to show that ψ_1 and ψ_2 are, in fact, minimum polynomials for S_1 and S_2. Suppose that there existed a polynomial $\theta_1(\lambda)$ of lower degree than $\psi_1(\lambda)$ which annihilates S_1:

$$\theta_1(\mathbf{A})\mathbf{x}_1 = 0 \tag{22}$$

Then, for any vector $\mathbf{x}$,

$$\mathbf{x} = \mathbf{x}_1 + \mathbf{x}_2 \tag{23}$$

we would have

$$\theta_1(\mathbf{A})\mathbf{x} = \theta_1(\mathbf{A})\mathbf{x}_2 \qquad (24)$$

which must be in S_2 since $\mathbf{x}_2$ is in S_2 and $\theta_1(\mathbf{A})$ is a polynomial in $\mathbf{A}$, and S_2 is invariant with respect to $\mathbf{A}$. Hence we have

$$\psi_2(\mathbf{A})\theta_1(\mathbf{A})\mathbf{x} = 0, \qquad \text{all} \quad \mathbf{x} \in S \qquad (25)$$

so that there would exist a polynomial of degree less than that of $\varphi(\lambda)$ that annihilates any vector in S. Hence $\varphi(\lambda)$ would not be the minimum polynomial of S, contrary to assumption.

Hence $\psi_1(\lambda)$ must be the minimum polynomial of S_1. In similar fashion $\psi_2(\lambda)$ is the minimum polynomial of S_2.

This completes the proof of all parts of the theorem.

From this we immediately have the following:

Corollary 1. *If the minimum polynomial $\varphi(\lambda)$ of $\mathbf{A}$ is factorable into a set of coprime polynomials*

$$\varphi(\lambda) = \psi_1(\lambda)\psi_2(\lambda) \cdots \psi_k(\lambda) \qquad (26)$$

then S is decomposable into invariant subspaces

$$S = S_1 \oplus S_2 \oplus \cdots \oplus S_k \qquad (27)$$

such that $\psi_i(\lambda)$ is the minimum polynomial of S_i.

We now need the following theorem:

Theorem 2. *Given a subspace S_i, which may be the whole space, that is invariant with respect to $\mathbf{A}$, and which has the minimum polynomial $\varphi_i(\lambda)$, there exists in S_i a vector whose minimum polynomial is $\varphi_i(\lambda)$.* [*The* **minimum polynomial** *$\varphi(\lambda)$ of a vector $\mathbf{x}$ with respect to $\mathbf{A}$ is the polynomial of lowest degree such that $\varphi(\mathbf{A})\mathbf{x} = 0$.*]

First we note that the theorem is true if the minimum polynomial of S_i is a power of an irreducible polynomial[1]

$$\varphi_i(\lambda) = \{\theta_i(\lambda)\}^{k_i} \qquad (28)$$

---

[1] An *irreducible polynomial* in a field F is a polynomial with coefficients in F that is not factorable into polynomials of lower degree with coefficients in F. If F is an algebraically complete field—cf. page 71—then the irreducible polynomials are of the form $(\lambda - \lambda_i)$. This is true, for example, in the field of complex numbers that generally concerns us here. Since most of the results of this chapter do not depend on the particular field, however, we shall, for the sake of generality, use the term *irreducible polynomial* instead of $(\lambda - \lambda_i)$.

For S_i is a subspace. Hence we can choose a basis $\mathbf{x}_1$, $\mathbf{x}_2$, ..., $\mathbf{x}_k$ and represent any vector $\mathbf{y}$ in S_i as

$$\mathbf{y} = \sum a_i \mathbf{x}_i \tag{29}$$

Then each of the basis vectors must be annihilated by some power of $\theta_i(\lambda)$. The minimum polynomial will be the lowest common multiple of the minimum polynomials of the basis vectors. Hence there must be at least one basis vector that is annihilated by $\varphi_i(\lambda)$ but by no lower power of $\theta_i(\lambda)$. We can therefore find a vector satisfying the theorem for this type of minimum polynomial simply by taking any set of linearly independent vectors that span the subspace, and testing them one at a time. We know that at least one must have the requisite power of $\theta_i(\lambda)$ as its minimum polynomial.

We consider, now, the following lemma:

Lemma. *If the minimum polynomials of two vectors* $\mathbf{x}_1$ *and* $\mathbf{x}_2$ *are the coprime polynomials* $\psi_1(\lambda)$, $\psi_2(\lambda)$, *then the minimum polynomial of* $\mathbf{x} = \mathbf{x}_1 + \mathbf{x}_2$ *is* $\psi_1(\lambda)\psi_2(\lambda)$.

In the first place, $\mathbf{x}$ is annihilated by $(\psi_1\psi_2)$ since polynomials of $\mathbf{A}$ commute:

$$\psi_1(\mathbf{A})\psi_2(\mathbf{A})\mathbf{x} = \psi_2(\mathbf{A})\psi_1(\mathbf{A})\mathbf{x}_1 + \psi_1(\mathbf{A})\psi_2(\mathbf{A})\mathbf{x}_2$$
$$= 0 \tag{30}$$

Now consider any polynomial $\kappa(\lambda)$ that annihilates $\mathbf{x}$:

$$\kappa(\mathbf{A})\mathbf{x} = \kappa(\mathbf{A})\mathbf{x}_1 + \kappa(\mathbf{A})\mathbf{x}_2 = 0 \tag{31}$$

Premultiplying by $\psi_2(\mathbf{A})$ and noting that $\psi_2(\mathbf{A})$ and $\kappa(\mathbf{A})$ commute, being polynomials of $\mathbf{A}$, we see that

$$\psi_2(\mathbf{A})\kappa(\mathbf{A})\mathbf{x}_1 + \kappa(\mathbf{A})\psi_2(\mathbf{A})\mathbf{x}_2 = 0 \tag{32}$$

or

$$\psi_2(\mathbf{A})\kappa(\mathbf{A})\mathbf{x}_1 = 0 \tag{33}$$

and $\psi_2(\mathbf{A})\kappa(\mathbf{A})$ is an annihilating polynomial for $\mathbf{x}_1$. Therefore it contains $\psi_1(\mathbf{A})$ as a factor. However, ψ_1 and ψ_2 are coprime. Hence $\kappa(\lambda)$ must contain $\psi_1(\lambda)$.

In similar fashion $\kappa(\lambda)$ must contain $\psi_2(\lambda)$. Hence every annihilating polynomial for $\mathbf{x}$ must contain the factor $(\psi_1\psi_2)$. Hence $\psi_1\psi_2$ is the minimum polynomial for $\mathbf{x}$, and the lemma is proven.

To prove the theorem, we need simply consider the decomposition of the whole space into coprime invariant subspaces whose minimum polynomials are powers of irreducible polynomials. We have already shown that there must be, in S_i, a vector $\mathbf{x}_i$ whose minimum polynomial is the minimum polynomial of the subspace. Hence the sum of these vectors is a vector whose minimum polynomial is the entire minimum polynomial of the operator.

This gives us a preliminary decomposition of the whole space. Theorem 1 shows that we can decompose the whole space into subspaces according to the irreducible polynomial factors of the minimum polynomial. In an algebraic field, this is a decomposition into subspaces, each of which corresponds to a distinct eigenvalue—sometimes called the *eigensubspaces*. Thus we have achieved a quasi diagonalization according to the eigensubspaces.

Theorem 2 establishes the connection between the minimum polynomial of a space or subspace and a vector in that space or subspace. We shall use this connection, after some further elaboration of it, as the first step in the generation of a basis.

We must now divert, briefly, into consideration of the relation of congruence, vector classes, and factor spaces. We do this as a preliminary to the further decomposition of a space.

3. CONGRUENCE AND FACTOR SPACE

Definition. *Two vectors* $\mathbf{x}$ *and* $\mathbf{y}$ *are said to be congruent modulo* S, *where* S *is a subspace, if their difference is a vector in* S. *We write*

$$\mathbf{x} \equiv \mathbf{y} \bmod S \tag{34}$$

The definition then says that if this is so,

$$\mathbf{x} = \mathbf{y} + \mathbf{z} \tag{35}$$

where $\mathbf{z}$ is some vector in S.

We define the following:

Definition. *Given a vector* $\mathbf{x}_0$ *and a subspace* S, *we call the* **totality** *of vectors* $\mathbf{x}$ *such that*

$$\mathbf{x} \equiv \mathbf{x}_0 \bmod S \tag{36}$$

a **class** *or, where we want to be unambiguous, a* **class modulo** S.

We will denote a class as $\hat{\mathbf{x}}$. The symbol under the caret is then just a typical member of the class and the whole symbol indicates the totality of vectors forming the class.

Multiplication times a scalar carries over directly into the classes. If

$$\mathbf{x} \equiv \mathbf{x}_0 \bmod S \tag{37}$$

or

$$\mathbf{x} = \mathbf{x}_0 + \mathbf{z}, \qquad \mathbf{z} \in S \tag{38}$$

then we see that

$$\alpha\mathbf{x} = \alpha\mathbf{x}_0 + \alpha\mathbf{z} = \alpha\mathbf{x}_0 + \mathbf{z}', \qquad \mathbf{z}' \in S \tag{39}$$

and

$$\alpha\mathbf{x} \equiv \alpha\mathbf{x}_0 \bmod S \tag{40}$$

or

$$(\alpha\mathbf{x})^\wedge = \alpha\hat{\mathbf{x}} \tag{41}$$

where by $(\ )^\wedge$ we mean the class of which the vector in the parentheses is a typical member.

Also, the addition of vectors carries over. If we have

$$\mathbf{x} \equiv \mathbf{x}_0 \bmod S, \qquad \mathbf{y} \equiv \mathbf{y}_0 \bmod S \tag{42}$$

or

$$\mathbf{x} = \mathbf{x}_0 + \mathbf{u}, \qquad \mathbf{y} = \mathbf{y}_0 + \mathbf{v}, \qquad \mathbf{u}, \mathbf{v} \in S \tag{43}$$

then

$$\mathbf{x} + \mathbf{y} = (\mathbf{x}_0 + \mathbf{y}_0) + (\mathbf{u} + \mathbf{v}) \tag{44}$$

But $(\mathbf{u} + \mathbf{v})$ is in S since S is a subspace. Hence

$$\mathbf{x} + \mathbf{y} \equiv (\mathbf{x}_0 + \mathbf{y}_0) \bmod S \tag{45}$$

or

$$(\mathbf{x} + \mathbf{y})^\wedge = \hat{\mathbf{x}} + \hat{\mathbf{y}} \tag{46}$$

Further, it is easy to see that these operations have all the properties—associative, distributivity, etc.—that they had in regard to the original vectors.

Hence the totality of all classes modulo S is itself a vector space!

Definition. *The totality of all classes modulo S_0 is called a* **factor space** *of the whole space. If the whole space is S, we sometimes designate the factor space as (S/S_0) or call it the* **factor space modulo** S_0 *(sometimes called the* **quotient space**.*)*

If the whole space is of dimension n, and S_0 is of dimension k, then the dimensionality of the factor space is $n - k$. For suppose we have a basis for S_0 in S, $\mathbf{x}_1$, $\mathbf{x}_2$, ..., $\mathbf{x}_k$. We extend this by the addition of the $(n - k)$ vectors $\mathbf{x}_{k+1}$, ..., $\mathbf{x}_n$ to provide a basis for the whole space. Then, evidently, $\hat{\mathbf{x}}_{k+1}$, ..., $\hat{\mathbf{x}}_n$ provide a basis for the factor space, modulo S_0.

We are interested in matrices for which S_0 is an invariant subspace. Then, if $\mathbf{z} \in S_0$, so is $\mathbf{Az}$. Hence, if we consider

$$\mathbf{x} \equiv \mathbf{x}_0 \bmod S_0 \tag{47}$$

or

$$\mathbf{x} = \mathbf{x}_0 + \mathbf{z}, \qquad \mathbf{z} \in S_0 \tag{48}$$

then

$$\mathbf{Ax} = \mathbf{Ax}_0 + \mathbf{Az} = \mathbf{Ax}_0 + \mathbf{z}' \tag{'49}$$

and $\mathbf{z}'$ is in S_0 so that

$$\mathbf{Ax} \equiv \mathbf{Ax}_0 \bmod S_0 \tag{50}$$

Hence we can write, formally,

$$\mathbf{A}\hat{\mathbf{x}} = (\mathbf{Ax})^\hat{} \tag{51}$$

That is, the operation of $\mathbf{A}$ on the entire class is the class whose representative member can be taken as the result of applying $\mathbf{A}$ to any representative member of the original class.

It would be better, perhaps, to write the left side as $\hat{\mathbf{A}}\hat{\mathbf{x}}$ to indicate that here the operator is conceptually different from the operator that operates on $\mathbf{x}$. This is not customarily done, however. We will follow normal usage, therefore, and use the same symbol for both meanings. We emphasize, however, that just as $\hat{\mathbf{x}}$ is not a vector, but a class of vectors, so $\mathbf{A}$, when applied to $\hat{\mathbf{x}}$, is no longer properly a matrix. It is simply a linear operator whose domain is the factor space.

We observe that the concepts of the addition and multiplication of two such operators is still valid, providing S_0 is invariant to both. We can properly form polynomials of $\mathbf{A}$, even in the factor space, and, in particular, we can study the minimum polynomial $\psi'(\lambda)$ for the factor space—i.e., the polynomial of lowest degree such that

$$\psi'(\mathbf{A})\hat{\mathbf{x}} = 0 \tag{52}$$

for all $\hat{\mathbf{x}}$, or

$$\psi'(\mathbf{A})\mathbf{x} \equiv 0 \bmod S_0 \tag{53}$$

for all $\mathbf{x}$. We note that $\psi'(\lambda)$ may not be—and generally will not be—indentical with the minimum polynomial of $\mathbf{A}$. The requirement is simply that $\psi'(\mathbf{A})$ transform $\mathbf{x}$ into a vector in S_0 and not that it annihilate it. Since, however, $\psi(\lambda)$ is certainly an annihilating polynomial, mod S_0, since it completely annihilates all $\mathbf{x}$, it follows that $\psi'(\lambda)$, the minimum polynomial modulo S_0, must be a factor of $\psi(\lambda)$.

4. CYCLIC SUBSPACES

We are now almost ready to return to our principal theme—the ultimate decomposition of S by $\mathbf{A}$. Before we do this, however, we need the concept of a cyclic subspace since the ultimate decomposition will be into such subspaces.

Consider a matrix $\mathbf{A}$. Let us take any vector $\mathbf{x}$ and form the subspace S_1 spanned by

$$\mathbf{x}, \quad \mathbf{A}\mathbf{x}, \quad \mathbf{A}^2\mathbf{x}, ..., \mathbf{A}^{p-1}\mathbf{x}, ... \tag{54}$$

Evidently we must eventually reach a point at which we cease to form a vector that is linearly independent of the preceding ones. For the space as a whole is finitely dimensioned so that we must exhaust the possibilities eventually. If $\mathbf{A}^p\mathbf{x}$ is linearly dependent on the preceding ones, so that

$$\mathbf{A}^p\mathbf{x} = -a_p\mathbf{x} - a_{p-1}\mathbf{A}\mathbf{x} - \cdots - a_1\mathbf{A}^{p-1}\mathbf{x} \tag{55}$$

then

$$\begin{aligned}
\mathbf{A}^{p+1}\mathbf{x} &= -a_p\mathbf{A}\mathbf{x} - a_{p-1}\mathbf{A}^2\mathbf{x} - \cdots - a_1\mathbf{A}^p\mathbf{x} \\
&= -a_p\mathbf{A}\mathbf{x} - a_{p-1}\mathbf{A}^2\mathbf{x} - \cdots - a_2\mathbf{A}^{p-1}\mathbf{x} \\
&\quad -a_1(-a_p\mathbf{x} - a_{p-1}\mathbf{A}\mathbf{x} - \cdots - a_1\mathbf{A}^{p-1}\mathbf{x})
\end{aligned} \tag{56}$$

so that all succeeding powers of $\mathbf{A}$ times $\mathbf{x}$ are linearly dependent on $\mathbf{x}, ..., \mathbf{A}^{p-1}\mathbf{x}$.

We define S_1 as the linear envelope of the set $\mathbf{x}, \mathbf{A}\mathbf{x}, \cdots, \mathbf{A}^{p-1}\mathbf{x}$. That is, it is the subspace of all possible linear combinations of these vectors. We call S_1 the *cyclic subspace generated by* $\mathbf{x}$. We considered such subspaces briefly in Chapter IV, Section 6.

Suppose, now, the cyclic subspace S_1 is generated by a vector $\mathbf{x}$, whose minimum polynomial is $\psi(\lambda)$ of degree p. Then the set $\mathbf{x}, \mathbf{A}\mathbf{x}, \cdots, \mathbf{A}^{p-1}\mathbf{x}$ are linearly independent. Otherwise, there would exist a polynomial of degree less than p that would annihilate $\mathbf{x}$, contrary to the assumption that ψ was the minimum polynomial of $\mathbf{x}$. Hence the set $\mathbf{x}, \mathbf{A}\mathbf{x}, \cdots, \mathbf{A}^{p-1}\mathbf{x}$ is a basis for S_1.

Since any vector in S_1 can be expressed as a linear combination of the basis elements, it follows that we can express any $\mathbf{y}$ in S_1 as

$$\mathbf{y} = X(\mathbf{A})\mathbf{x} \tag{57}$$

where $X(\lambda)$ is a polynomial of degree not greater than $(p-1)$, and $\mathbf{x}$ is the generating vector.

It is also evident' that $\psi(\lambda)$ is the minimum polynomial, not only of the generating vector $\mathbf{x}$, but of the whole cyclic subspace generated by $\mathbf{x}$.

Thus the principle properties of the a cyclic subspace are obtained from the properties of the vector generating it.

5. DECOMPOSITION INTO CYCLIC SUBSPACES

We will now prove the following:

Theorem 3. *The whole space can be decomposed into cyclic subspaces with progressively simpler minimum polynomials.*

Let the minimum polynomial of $\mathbf{A}$ be $\psi_1(\lambda)$. We have already shown that there must exist at least one vector, say $\mathbf{x}_1$, whose minimum polynomial is the minimum polynomial of $\mathbf{A}$, $\psi_1(\lambda)$:

$$\psi_1(\mathbf{A})\mathbf{x}_1 = \mathbf{0} \tag{58}$$

Then the space

$$S_1: \quad \mathbf{x}_1, \quad \mathbf{A}\mathbf{x}_1, \quad \mathbf{A}^2\mathbf{x}_1, ..., \mathbf{A}^{p-1}\mathbf{x}_1 \tag{59}$$

is the p-dimensional cyclic subspace generated by $\mathbf{x}_1$, where p is the degree of $\psi_1(\lambda)$.

If $p = n$, where n is the dimensionality of $\mathbf{A}$, then the theorem is proven since the whole space is cyclic.

Suppose p is less than n. Then we must find a suitable vector with which to generate a second cyclic subspace. To do this, we consider the factor space modulo S_1, S/S_1. This is a space of dimensionality $n - p$. It has a minimum polynomial $\psi_2(\lambda)$ that must be a divisor of $\psi_1(\lambda)$. Then, for any vector $\mathbf{u}$ in S,

$$\psi_2(\mathbf{A})\mathbf{u} \equiv \mathbf{0} \bmod S_1 \tag{60}$$

Also, since ψ_2 is a divisor of ψ_1, there must exist a nonnull polynomial such that

$$\psi_1(\lambda) = \psi_2(\lambda)\kappa(\lambda) \tag{61}$$

By Theorem 2, applied to the factor space, there must be a class $\hat{\mathbf{u}}$ for which $\psi_2(\mathbf{A})$ is the minimum polynomial. Let $\mathbf{u}$ be any representative of this class, so that Eq. (60) applies, and such that there exists no polynomial of lower degree which annihilates $\mathbf{u}$ mod S_1.

If now $\psi_2(\mathbf{A})\mathbf{u} = \mathbf{0}$, then $\mathbf{u}$ is the vector we are seeking, as we shall see later. For the sake of generality, assume that $\psi_2(\mathbf{A})\mathbf{u} \neq \mathbf{0}$, but equals, instead, a vector in S_1. We will now show that we can subtract from $\mathbf{u}$ a vector in S_1, and have left a vector for which ψ_2 is the absolute minimum polynomial.

We have seen in Eq. (57), that any vector in S_1 can be expressed as a polynomial in $\mathbf{A}$ times $\mathbf{x}_1$, the generator of S_1. Since $\psi_2(\mathbf{A})\mathbf{u}$ is such a vector, we can find a polynomial P such that

$$\psi_2(\mathbf{A})\mathbf{u} = P(\mathbf{A})\mathbf{x}_1 \tag{62}$$

Multiplying Eq. (62) by $\kappa(\mathbf{A})$, as defined by Eq. (61), we see that

$$\kappa(\mathbf{A})P(\mathbf{A})\mathbf{x}_1 = \kappa(\mathbf{A})\psi_2(\mathbf{A})\mathbf{u} = \psi_1(\mathbf{A})\mathbf{u} = \mathbf{0} \tag{63}$$

since $\psi_1(\lambda)$ is the minimum polynomial of the whole space. The vector $\mathbf{x}_1$ was chosen as a vector whose minimum polynomial is ψ_1. Hence κP must be divisible by ψ_1, so that there must exist a polynomial Q such that

$$\kappa(\mathbf{A})P(\mathbf{A}) = \psi_1(\mathbf{A})Q(\mathbf{A})$$
$$= \kappa(\mathbf{A})\psi_2(\mathbf{A})Q(\mathbf{A}) \tag{64}$$

where we have substituted for ψ_1 from Eq. (61). Hence we have

$$P = \psi_2 Q \tag{65}$$

If we substitute this back into Eq. (62), we obtain

$$\psi_2(\mathbf{A})\{\mathbf{u} - Q(\mathbf{A})\mathbf{x}_1\} = \mathbf{0} \tag{66}$$

Now $Q(\mathbf{A})\mathbf{x}_1$ is a vector in S_1 and $\mathbf{u}$ is not. Hence, if we set

$$\mathbf{x}_2 = \mathbf{u} - Q(\mathbf{A})\mathbf{x}_1 \tag{67}$$

then $\mathbf{x}_2$ is not the null vector. It is, instead, a vector that is annihilated by ψ_2, according to Eq. (66).

We now need to show that $\mathbf{x}_2$ is not only annihilated by ψ_2, but that ψ_2 is its minimum polynomial. Let its minimum polynomial be φ_2. Then, since ψ_2 is an annihilating polynomial for $\mathbf{x}_2$, it must be divisible by φ_2. On the other hand, we have

$$\mathbf{x}_2 \equiv \mathbf{u} \bmod S_1$$

and $\mathbf{u}$ was chosen so that its minimum polynomial, mod S_1, was ψ_2. This must then be true of $\mathbf{x}_2$. But the minimum polynomial mod S_1 must divide into the absolute minimum polynomial, or ψ_2 into φ_2. Since φ_2 is both a divisor of and divisible by ψ_2, the two polynomials must be the same within a scalar factor. Hence ψ_2 is the minimum polynomial of $\mathbf{x}_2$.

Consider the cyclic subspace S_2 generated by $\mathbf{x}_2$:

$$S_2: \quad \mathbf{x}_2, \quad \mathbf{Ax}_2, \quad \mathbf{A}^2\mathbf{x}_2, ..., \mathbf{A}^{q-1}\mathbf{x}_2 \tag{65}$$

where q is the degree of ψ_1.

We know that these vectors are linearly independent. We need to show that they are linearly independent of the vectors in S_1. Suppose they were not. Then there would exist scalars, $c_0, ..., c_{q-1}$ such that

$$\begin{aligned}
c_0\mathbf{x}_2 + c_1\mathbf{Ax}_2 &+ \cdots + c_{q-1}\mathbf{A}^{q-1}\mathbf{x}_2 \\
&= (c_0\mathbf{I} + c_1\mathbf{A} + \cdots + c_{q-1}\mathbf{A}^{q-1})\mathbf{x}_2 \\
&= U(\mathbf{A})\mathbf{x}_2 \equiv 0 \bmod S_1
\end{aligned} \tag{69}$$

where $U(\mathbf{A})$ is a polynomial of degree not greater than $q - 1$. However, ψ_2 is the minimum polynomial, mod S_1, of $\mathbf{x}_2$, and is of degree q. Hence no such set of scalars can exist, and S_1 and S_2 must be linearly independent.

If $p + q = n$, then S_1 and S_2 together span the whole space, and we have obtained a decomposition into cyclic subspaces.

If $p + q < n$, we consider the factor space of $S_1 \oplus S_2$ and repeat the process. We must eventually exhaust the dimensionality of the whole space.

We have, finally, the theorem which we can now state more completely as:

Theorem 3'.   *Given a matrix* $\mathbf{A}$ *the whole space* S *can be decomposed into cyclic subspaces* $S_1, S_2, ..., S_m$ *with minimum polynomials* $\psi_1(\lambda), \psi_2(\lambda), ..., \psi_m(\lambda)$, *where* $\psi_1(\lambda)$ *is the minimum polynomial of* $\mathbf{A}$, *and* $\psi_i(\lambda)$ *is a divisor of* $\psi_{i-1}(\lambda)$.

From this several corollaries follow:

Corollary 1.   *S is cyclic (with respect to* $\mathbf{A}$*) if and only if the degree of the minimum polynomial of* $\mathbf{A}$ *is the same as the dimension of* S.

The sufficiency of the condition follows immediately since S_1 exhausts the space immediately if $\psi_1(\lambda)$ is of degree n. Conversely, if S is cyclic, then there exists an **x** such that S_1 exhausts the space. But the minimum polynomial of **x** must then be of degree n. Since the minimum polynomial of **A** cannot be greater than n, it must then equal n.

Corollary 2. *A cyclic space can be decomposed only into subspaces that are cyclic and whose minimum polynomials are coprime.*

Let S be the whole space being considered. Let it be of dimensionality n with minimum polynomial $\psi(\lambda)$ which is of degree m. Since S is cyclic, then by Corollary 1,

$$m = n \tag{70}$$

Let S be decomposed into S_1 and S_2 :

$$S = S_1 \oplus S_2 \tag{71}$$

where S_1 and S_2 are of dimension n_1 and n_2 , with minimum polynomials $\psi_1(\lambda)$ and $\psi_2(\lambda)$, of degree m_1 and m_2 , respectively. Then we have generally that

$$m_1 \leqslant n_1$$
$$m_2 \leqslant n_2 \tag{72}$$

where the equality applies only if S_1 and S_2 are cyclic. Adding these inequalities, we obtain

$$(m_1 + m_2) \leqslant (n_1 + n_2) = n \tag{73}$$

However, $\psi(\lambda)$ is the least common multiple of ψ_1 and ψ_2 , so that

$$m \leqslant m_1 + m_2 \tag{74}$$

where the equality applies only if ψ_1 and ψ_2 are coprime. Putting Eqs. (70), (73) and (74) together, we find

$$m \leqslant (m_1 + m_2) \leqslant (n_1 + n_2) = n \tag{75}$$

But $m = n$. Hence equality must hold throughout. We must therefore have

$$m_1 = n_1 \tag{76}$$

$$m_2 = n_2 \tag{77}$$

$$m = m_1 + m_2 \tag{78}$$

and the corollary is proven.

Corollary 3. *S is indecomposable with respect to* **A** *if it is cyclic and its minimum polynomial is a power of an irreducible polynomial.*

The converse also follows:

Corollary 4. *If S is indecomposable with respect to* **A**, *then it is cyclic and its minimum polynomial is a power of an irreducible polynomial.*

This follows directly. If it were not cyclic, then the proof of Theorem 3 shows how to decompose it, contrary to assumption. Further, if it were cyclic but its minimum polynomial were the product of powers of distinct irreducible polynomials, then Theorem 1 shows how to decompose it.

We therefore arrive at the following theorem which, in effect, summarizes these conclusions:

Theorem 4. *The whole space S can always be decomposed into subspaces* S_1 , S_2 , ..., S_k *which are cyclic invariant subspaces with respect to* **A**, *each subspace having a minimum polynomial which is a power of an irreducible polynomial. No further decomposition is possible.*

(We are not asserting that a decomposition is always possible. If S is indecomposable, then, by Corollary 3 it already fulfills the rest of the theorem.)

To summarize, then, we have found it possible to decompose S into invariant subspaces with respect to **A** in various ways. We could now go back and use these various decompositions to develop corresponding canonical forms for **A**. This is, in fact, done in the general theory of matrix algebra. We are, however, primarily interested in the Jordan canonical form which evolves from the final decomposition, and it is highly significant that we discovered that no further decomposition is possible. It means that nothing simpler than the Jordan canonical form is possible.

6. THE JORDAN CANONICAL FORM

We have so far left the field unrestricted. Let us now specify that it is algebraically complete—i.e., contains all the roots of all algebraic equations with coefficients in the field. The field of complex numbers is such a field, but the field of real numbers is not.

Then the irreducible polynomials are all of the form $(\lambda - \lambda_i)$.

Theorem 4 states that, with respect to **A**, the entire space S can be decomposed into cyclic invariant subspaces each of which has a minimum polynomial of the form $(\lambda - \lambda_i)^{k_i}$. Symbolically we have

$$S = S_1 \oplus S_2 \oplus \cdots S_m$$
$$\mathbf{A}\mathbf{x} \in S_i \quad \text{if} \quad \mathbf{x} \in S_i \tag{79}$$
$$(\mathbf{A} - \lambda_i \mathbf{I})^{k_i}\mathbf{x}_i = 0 \quad \text{if} \quad \mathbf{x}_i \in S_i$$

Further, for each S_i we have a generator $\mathbf{x}_i$ such that S_i is spanned by

$$S_i: \quad (\mathbf{x}_i, \mathbf{A}\mathbf{x}_i, ..., \mathbf{A}^{k-1}\mathbf{x}_i) \tag{80}$$

Consider the vectors

$$\mathbf{u}_1 = (\mathbf{A} - \lambda_1 \mathbf{I})^{k_1-1}\mathbf{x}_1$$
$$\mathbf{u}_2 = (\mathbf{A} - \lambda_1 \mathbf{I})^{k_1-2}\mathbf{x}_1$$
$$\cdots$$
$$\mathbf{u}_{k_1} = \mathbf{x}_1$$
$$\mathbf{u}_{k_1+1} = (\mathbf{A} - \lambda_2 \mathbf{I})^{k_2-1}\mathbf{x}_2 \tag{81}$$
$$\text{etc.}$$

Evidently $\mathbf{u}_1, ..., \mathbf{u}_{k_1}$ are linearly independent and span S_1. Likewise, $\mathbf{u}_{k_1+1}, ..., \mathbf{u}_{k_1+k_2}$ are linearly independent and span S_2, and so forth. Also,

$$(\mathbf{A} - \lambda_1 \mathbf{I})\mathbf{u}_1 = \psi_1(\mathbf{A})\mathbf{x}_1 = 0$$
$$(\mathbf{A} - \lambda_1 \mathbf{I})\mathbf{u}_2 = (\mathbf{A} - \lambda_1 \mathbf{I})^{k_1-1}\mathbf{x}_1 = \mathbf{u}_1 \tag{82}$$
$$\text{etc.}$$

so that these vectors are chains of generalized eigenvectors.

Suppose we take $\mathbf{u}_1, \mathbf{u}_2, ..., \mathbf{u}_n$ as the basis for the whole space. That is, we express an arbitrary vector $\mathbf{w}$ in terms of them according to the column matrix convention:

$$\mathbf{w} = \begin{pmatrix} w_1 \\ w_2 \\ \vdots \end{pmatrix} = w_1 \mathbf{u}_1 + w_2 \mathbf{u}_2 + \cdots \tag{83}$$

Then we find that

$$\mathbf{A}\mathbf{w} = w_1 \mathbf{A}\mathbf{u}_1 + w_2 \mathbf{A}\mathbf{u}_2 + \cdots$$
$$= w_1(\lambda_1 \mathbf{u}_1) + w_2(\lambda_1 \mathbf{u}_2 + \mathbf{u}_1) + \cdots$$
$$= (\lambda_1 w_1 + w_2)\mathbf{u}_1 + (\lambda_1 w_2 + w_3)\mathbf{u}_2 + \cdots \tag{84}$$

Evidently, expressed according to this convention, $\mathbf{A}$ must be quasidiagonal. That is, it has the form

$$
\mathbf{A} = \begin{pmatrix} \mathbf{A}_1 & 0 & 0 & \\ 0 & \mathbf{A}_2 & 0 & \\ 0 & 0 & \mathbf{A}_3 & \\ & & & \ddots \end{pmatrix} \tag{85}
$$

where $\mathbf{A}_1$ is $k_1 \times k_1$, $\mathbf{A}_2$ is $k_2 \times k_2$, etc., k_1, k_2, etc., being the dimensions of S_1, S_2, etc. Furthermore, $\mathbf{A}_i$ is the upper Jordan block:

$$
\mathbf{A}_i = \begin{pmatrix} \lambda_i & 1 & 0 & \\ 0 & \lambda_i & 1 & \\ 0 & 0 & \lambda_i & \\ & & & \ddots \end{pmatrix}_{k_i \times k_i} \tag{86}
$$

Thus we obtain the Jordan canonical form.

The statement in Theorem 4 that no further decomposition is possible is the assertion that it is not possible to find a quasi-diagonal form with smaller units on the diagonal. Furthermore, the development of the cyclic invariant subspaces makes it clear that the structure of Eq. (79) is unique in that any other decomposition into indecomposable subspaces must give subspaces of the same dimensionality. They may not, however, be the same subspaces if there is degeneracy involved.

This follows from the fact that we may have various options open to us as to how we choose the generating vectors. Suppose, for example, we have decomposed the whole space into a noncyclic subspace S_1 with minimum polynomial $(\lambda - \lambda_1)^k$, plus other subspaces with coprime polynomials.

We have proven that there is in S_1 at least one vector $\mathbf{x}_1$ whose minimum polynomial is $(\lambda - \lambda_1)^k$. But there may be more than one. If so, then any linear combination of them is also such a vector—i.e., a subspace of the subspace. We can then choose as the generating vector any vector in this subspace of S_1.

Thus there may be a great deal of freedom possible in the decomposition of S. The remarkable result, however, is that no matter what choices are made, the resultant decomposition will be into subspaces involving the same number of dimensions. Hence the Jordan canonical form will be the same within a permutation of the order of the blocks, regardless of the choices made.

One further point should be noted. We choose a generator whose minimum polynomial is the minimum polynomial of the subspace. This vector then becomes the generalized eigenvector of highest rank in the chain. The chain, in other words, is determined by its generalized eigenvector of highest rank, and not, as we might think, by the eigenvector with which it ends. This we pointed out in Chapter III.

7. INVARIANT POLYNOMIALS AND ELEMENTARY DIVISORS

For the sake of completeness, we will include a brief mention of the invariant polynomials and the elementary divisors of a matrix.

We consider a matrix $\mathbf{A}$. Form the characteristic matrix $(\mathbf{A} - \lambda\mathbf{I})$. Form the complete set of k-rowed minors of $(\mathbf{A} - \lambda\mathbf{I})$—i.e., the set of determinants obtained by striking out any $(n - k)$ rows and columns. (We do not confine ourselves here to the principal minors, obtained by striking out the same numbered rows as columns.) This gives us a set of polynomials in λ. Consider, now, the greatest common divisor of this set. We normalize it by specifying that the coefficient of the highest power of λ be unity. Call this greatest common divisor of the k-rowed minors of $(\mathbf{A} - \lambda\mathbf{I})$, $D_k(\lambda)$.

We obtain the set of polynomials

$$D_n(\lambda), \quad D_{n-1}(\lambda), ..., D_1(\lambda), \quad D_0(\lambda) = 1 \tag{87}$$

the last one being defined arbitrarily as 1. The first, $D_n(\lambda)$, is the determinant of $(\mathbf{A} - \lambda\mathbf{I})$.

It is now evident that D_k is always divisible by D_{k-1}. For consider any k-rowed minor. If it be expanded on any row or column, the separate terms of the expansion each includes a $(k - 1)$-rowed minor as a factor. But all of the $(k - 1)$-rowed minors are divisible by D_{k-1} since it is a common divisor. Hence any k-rowed minor is divisible by D_{k-1}. Therefore D_{k-1} is a common divisor of all k-rowed minors, and hence is a factor, at least, in D_k.

If we form the quotients

$$p_1(\lambda) = \frac{D_n(\lambda)}{D_{n-1}(\lambda)}$$

$$p_2(\lambda) = \frac{D_{n-1}(\lambda)}{D_{n-2}(\lambda)} \tag{88}$$

$$...$$

$$p_n(\lambda) = \frac{D_1(\lambda)}{D_0(\lambda)} = D_1(\lambda)$$

the set $\{p_i(\lambda)\}$ are polynomials in λ.

It is these polynomials that are called the *invariant polynomials* of A.

We note that $D_n(\lambda)$ is the characteristic equation of **A**. It is evident that the product

$$\prod_{i=1}^{n} p_i(\lambda) = D_n(\lambda) = \mid \mathbf{A} - \lambda \mathbf{I} \tag{89}$$

is the characteristic equation of **A**. Hence the set $\{p_i(\lambda)\}$ is a factorization of the characteristic equation.

It can be shown that the set $\{p_i(\lambda)\}$ is independent of the basis, and is unchanged by a similarity transformation. It is for this reason that they are called *invariant*.

If we factor each of the polynomials into powers of irreducible polynomials

$$p_i(\lambda) = \{\varphi_1(\lambda)\}^{k_{i_1}} \{\varphi_2(\lambda)\}^{k_{i_2}} \cdots \tag{90}$$

then the set of all nonconstant factors appearing in the set are called the *elementary divisors* of **A**. (More properly, of the characteristic equation of **A**.)

Observe that we may have divisors that are identical if the same form, say $(\lambda - \lambda_i)^k$, occurs in more than one of the $p_i(\lambda)$. The elementary divisors are also independent of the basis chosen. The product of all the elementary divisors is, again, the characteristic equation.

The invariant polynomials and the elementary divisors can, as before, be used to effect the decomposition of the space. In fact, they were used, although without identification. Theorem 3′ for example, can be sharpened to:

Theorem 3″. *If* **A** *is a linear operator on the vector space S, then S can be decomposed*:

$$S = S_1 \oplus S_2 \oplus \cdots S_k \tag{91}$$

where S_i is cyclic invariant subspace with the minimum polynomial $\psi_i(\lambda)$, and where the set $\psi_i(\lambda)$ coincides with the set of invariant polynomials (other than 1) of **A**.

Likewise we can sharpen Theorem 4 to:

Theorem 4′. *If* **A** *is a linear operator on the vector space S, and if S is decomposed in any manner into indecomposable invariant subspaces $\{S_i\}$ with minimum polynomials $\psi_i(\lambda)$, then the set $\{\psi_i(A)\}$ is the set of elementary divisors of* **A**.

We shall not prove these theorems here. They are given here merely to illustrate the sense in which either the invariant polynomials or the elementary divisors describe with precision the structure of any matrix.

The invariant polynomials and the elementary divisors are important when we are considering a field that is not algebraically complete—e.g. the field of real numbers. They are also important when we generalize matrix algebra by permitting the scalars to be in something less than a field, usually a ring. In either case, we may not be able to obtain the Jordan canonical form as a member of the algebra since λ_i may not be in the field or ring. We then need other canonical forms that will perform a similar function. The forms that will do this are based on the decompositions of Theorems 3″ and 4′.

8. CONCLUSIONS

While the analysis of this chapter may not be necessary for the study of specific practical problems, it does involve concepts that penetrate quite deeply into the underlying theory. These concepts are vital if matrix algebra is to be used as more than a "crank turning" way. For it is the way in which a given operator decomposes the whole vector space that is the crucial part of its behavior. It is this aspect that determines its structure and that permits a classification of matrices, and problems, that is the necessary prelude to the analysis of a particular problem involving the matrix.

Exercises

1. If S_1 is the linear envelope, over the field of complex numbers, of col(1, 1, 0, 0) and col(1, 0, 0, −1), and S_2 is defined as follows, in which cases do S_1 and S_2 decompose the whole space?

(a) S_2: col(0, 1, −1, 0) and col(0, 0, 1, 1)
(b) S_2: col(0, 1, −1, 0) and col(0, 0, −1, 1)
(c) S_2: col(0, 1, 0, −1) and col(1, 0, 1, 0)
(d) S_2: col(0, 1, 0, −1) and col(1, 2, 0, 1)

In those cases where S_1 and S_2 do not decompose the whole space, find a vector that is common to both subspaces.

2. Find an example of an $n \times n$ matrix **A** which is cyclic.

3. Let S_1 and S_2 be two subspaces, not necessarily disjoint, both of which are invariant for **A**. Let S_3 be the set of all vectors which are a linear combination of vectors in S_1 and S_2—i.e., S_3 is the linear envelope of S_1 and S_2. Prove the S_3 is a subspace and that it is invariant for **A**.

4. Find the invariant subspaces of

$$\mathbf{A} = \begin{pmatrix} 0 & \frac{1}{2}j & \frac{1}{2} & -1 \\ 0 & \frac{3}{2}j & -\frac{1}{2} & 0 \\ 0 & -\frac{1}{2} & \frac{1}{2}j & 0 \\ 1 & \frac{1}{2} & -\frac{1}{2}j & 0 \end{pmatrix}$$

What is the minimum polynomial of **A** and of each of the invariant subspaces?

5. In euclidean 3-space, define

$$\mathbf{e}_1 = \begin{pmatrix} 1 \\ 0 \\ 0 \end{pmatrix}, \qquad \mathbf{e}_2 = \begin{pmatrix} 0 \\ 1 \\ 0 \end{pmatrix}, \qquad \mathbf{e}_3 = \begin{pmatrix} 0 \\ 0 \\ 1 \end{pmatrix}$$

What is

   (a) $\mathbf{e}_1 \bmod \mathbf{e}_2$
   (b) $\mathbf{e}_1 \bmod(\mathbf{e}_2, \mathbf{e}_3)$
   (c) $\operatorname{col}(1, 0, 1) \bmod \mathbf{e}_2$
   (d) $\operatorname{col}(1, 0, 1) \bmod \mathbf{e}_1$
   (e) $\operatorname{col}(1, 0, 1) \bmod(\mathbf{e}_1, \mathbf{e}_3)$
   (f) $\operatorname{col}(1, 0, 1) \bmod(\mathbf{e}_2, \mathbf{e}_3)$

6. Use Theorem 1 of Chapter III (page 71) and the concept of factor space to prove that every matrix can be put into upper triangular form by a suitable change of basis.

CHAPTER IX

The Improper Inner Product

We will here investigate what happens if we define the inner product as we did in Chapter II, except that we permit the metric $\mathbf{K}$ to be indefinite. This type of relation we call an *improper inner product*.

In Chapter II, Section 5, we considered briefly one case in which an improper metric arises. There we were considering the transmission matrix on an $E - I$ basis of a 2-port passive network. We pointed out that we could constrain the network to be lossless by requiring that the quadratic form

$$s = \tfrac{1}{2}(E^*I + EI^*) \tag{1}$$

be invariant, so that its value at one port must equal its value at the other. This suggested that we take as the metric

$$\mathbf{K} = \frac{1}{2}\begin{pmatrix} 0 & 1 \\ 1 & 0 \end{pmatrix} \tag{2}$$

and require that the transmission matrix of the network be K-unitary for this $\mathbf{K}$. The eigenvalues of this $\mathbf{K}$ may be found to be $\pm \tfrac{1}{2}$, however, so it is not positive definite and the resulting inner product is improper.

While this particular situation is simple enough so that there is little need for such sophistication, we can easily generalize it. We can, for example, consider a $(2n)$-port network in which we describe what is happening at n of the ports in terms of the others. Because of the size of the matrix involved $(2n \times 2n)$, it can become quite difficult to determine directly the implications of assuming losslessness.

Or, consider, again, a 2-port lossless passive network, but one in which the elements may be nonlinear. If we drive it at two or more frequencies, the nonlinearity may generate additional frequencies which are integral linear combinations of the driving frequencies $(m\omega_1 + n\omega_2)$. If the driving signal at one frequency is so strong as to dominate, then the system becomes approximately linear, and may be treated as such.

However, to do so we must take as the signal vector the multidimensional one such as

$$
\mathbf{x} = \begin{pmatrix} \vdots \\ E_{-1} \\ E_0 \\ E_1 \\ \vdots \\ I_{-1} \\ I_0 \\ I_1 \\ \vdots \end{pmatrix}
$$

where E_k and I_k are the complex amplitude of the voltage and current at frequency $(\omega_0 + n\omega_p)$ where ω_p is the frequency of the strong signal, usually called the *pump*. This is, then, infinitely dimensional. Under reasonable assumptions, we can ignore the higher order terms, and so limit the dimensionality. Since the system is nonlinear, its linear approximation will include terms that *couple* various components at different frequencies. Such a network so operated is called a *parametric network* since its operation can be described by a time variation of its parameters at frequency ω_p.

If the network is lossless, it can be shown that any parametric network must obey the "Manley-Rowe relations."[1] In the linearized situation, where the pump signal is strong, this requires that the quadratic form

$$
s = \sum_k \frac{1}{\omega_k} (E_k I_k{}^* + E_k{}^* I_k) \tag{3}
$$

shall be conserved. (It should be noted that some of the ω_k will be negative. It is important that the signs of all ω_k be taken properly.)

We can express this law by defining

$$
\mathbf{K} = \begin{pmatrix} 0 & \mathbf{W} \\ \mathbf{W} & 0 \end{pmatrix} \tag{4}
$$

where

$$
\mathbf{W} = \mathrm{diag} \left(\cdots \frac{1}{\omega_k} \cdots \right) \tag{5}
$$

[1] Cf. J. M. Manley and H. E. Rowe, *Proc. IRE* (*Inst. Radio Engrs.*) **44**, 904 (1956).

Then the conservation law requires that the transmission matrix be K-unitary with this K. However, again, the K so defined is indefinite, and the inner product is improper. Its eigenvalues, in fact, are $\pm 1/\omega_k$.

This situation is the equivalent of the quantum mechanical one in which we know that the total number of quanta must be conserved, even though quanta of different frequencies may be involved.

There are many problems in which we would like to be able to use an improper inner product relation. It is for this reason that we will look into the consequences of such a metric.

1. THE IMPROPER INNER PRODUCT

We define the inner product relation

$$\langle \mathbf{x}, \mathbf{y} \rangle = \mathbf{x}^\dagger \mathbf{K} \mathbf{y} \tag{6}$$

where $\mathbf{K}$ is nonsingular and hermitian, but not necessarily positive definite. The essential properties of the relation are:

(A) $\langle \mathbf{x}, \mathbf{x} \rangle$ is real for all $\mathbf{x}$, but may be zero or negative for some nonnull $\mathbf{x}$.

(B) $\langle \mathbf{x}, \mathbf{y} \rangle = \langle \mathbf{y}, \mathbf{x} \rangle^*$.

(C) $\langle \mathbf{x}, \alpha\mathbf{y} + \beta\mathbf{z} \rangle = \alpha\langle \mathbf{x}, \mathbf{y} \rangle + \beta\langle \mathbf{x}, \mathbf{z} \rangle$

Since $\mathbf{K}$ is hermitian, it is semisimple and its eigenvalues are real. Since it is nonsingular, none of its eigenvalues are zero. Hence, by a suitable change of basis, we can express $\langle \mathbf{x}, \mathbf{x} \rangle$, where $\mathbf{x}$ is arbitrary, as the sum and difference of squares.

Under a change of basis, we know that $\mathbf{K}$ transforms conjunctively. And we have seen that we can choose a basis such that $\mathbf{K}$ becomes a parity matrix—i.e., diagonal with ± 1 everywhere along the main diagonal. If the set $\mathbf{y}_i$ is such a basis, and if an arbitrary vector be expanded on this set

$$\mathbf{y} = \sum a_i \mathbf{y}_i \tag{7}$$

then the conservation law is

$$s = \mathbf{y}^\dagger \mathbf{K} \mathbf{y} = \sum \pm |a_i|^2 \tag{8}$$

where the sign is that of the corresponding term of the parity form of $\mathbf{K}$. Hence the a_i has the effect of an amplitude, and the terms of Eq. (8) may be said to describe the "energy" or "power" on the "waves" $\mathbf{y}_i$. We note, however, that it may not be true energy that is involved here, even if the units are those of energy. In the parametric case, for example, the terms, properly normalized, are the power divided by the frequency of the particular wave involved, or the number of quanta per unit time. Such a term is sometimes called the *reduced energy* or *power*, or the *pseudo-energy* or *power*. In addition, we observe that these terms may be negative. Negative energy may seem strange. However, it simply means that if such a wave is excited, the energy of the system as a whole is decreased. Since the steady state, or *dc* power, flow usually drops out in the course of linearizing the problem, the finding of negative energy or power is really not very mysterious.

One other point about the physical interpretation of a conservation law should be noted. Suppose we consider a lossless passive 2-port linear network. Then the *s* given by Eq. (1) is conserved. If we terminate the network reactively, there can be no net real power flow through either port. Since the *s* of Eq. (1) is precisely the net real power flow through a port, it must be zero. However, this does not mean that we cannot have a voltage and current at a port. Hence we can have a nonnull vector $\mathbf{x}$ such that $\mathbf{x}^\dagger \mathbf{K} \mathbf{x} = 0$, and a $\mathbf{K}$ describing this property cannot be positive definite. Again there is nothing particularly mysterious about it, but is precisely what we would expect from the physical situation we are trying to analyze.

2. FAILURE OF CAUCHY-SCHWARTZ AND TRIANGLE INEQUALITIES

The Cauchy-Schwartz and Triangle inequalities, which are important aspects of spaces with proper inner products, may fail with an improper inner product. We can show this best by example.

Consider

$$\mathbf{K} = \begin{pmatrix} 0 & 1 \\ 1 & 0 \end{pmatrix} \tag{9}$$

and let

$$\mathbf{x} = \begin{pmatrix} 1 \\ 0 \end{pmatrix}, \qquad \mathbf{y} = \begin{pmatrix} 0 \\ 1 \end{pmatrix} \tag{10}$$

We see that

$$\langle \mathbf{x}, \mathbf{x} \rangle = \langle \mathbf{y}, \mathbf{y} \rangle = 0 \tag{11}$$

These are both nonnull vectors of zero "length."

We see, however, that

$$\langle \mathbf{x}, \mathbf{y} \rangle = 1 \tag{12}$$

so that

$$|\langle \mathbf{x}, \mathbf{y} \rangle|^2 \quad \text{is not} \quad \leqslant \langle \mathbf{x}, \mathbf{x} \rangle \langle \mathbf{y}, \mathbf{y} \rangle \tag{13}$$

and the Cauchy-Schwartz inequality fails.

Also, we see that

$$\langle \mathbf{x} + \mathbf{y}, \mathbf{x} + \mathbf{y} \rangle = 2 \tag{14}$$

so that

$$\{\langle \mathbf{x} + \mathbf{y}, \mathbf{x} + \mathbf{y} \rangle\}^{1/2} \text{ is not } \leqslant \langle \mathbf{x}, \mathbf{x} \rangle^{1/2} + \langle \mathbf{y}, \mathbf{y} \rangle^{1/2} \tag{15}$$

and the triangle inequality fails.

Also, the definition of the angle between two vectors given in Eq. (7) or (7′) of Chapter II is inapplicable since the denominator may be zero. Fortunately we do not seem to need such a definition.

What we do need is orthogonality:

Definition. *The vectors* $\mathbf{x}$ *and* $\mathbf{y}$ *are said to be* **orthogonal under the K-inner-product**, *or K-orthogonal, if*

$$\langle \mathbf{x}, \mathbf{y} \rangle = \mathbf{x}^\dagger \mathbf{K} \mathbf{y} = 0 \tag{16}$$

This is precisely the same as with the proper inner product. We must recognize, however, that a vector can now be orthogonal to itself.

It is clear that a space with such an inner product has properties that are strikingly different from those we are used to. Such a space is noneuclidean, and cannot be made euclidean by any change of coordinate axes. We sometimes speak of such spaces as being *hyperbolic*, whereas those with a proper inner product are said to be *elliptic*.

We must be very cautious using intuition based on our geometric experience. Nevertheless, we shall find that the study of such spaces is in fact useful.

3. ORTHOGONAL SETS OF VECTORS

The principal value in considering hyperbolic spaces comes from the possibility of obtaining orthogonal sets of vectors.

We can illustrate this by considering the expansion of an arbitrary vector $\mathbf{y}$ in terms of a complete set $\mathbf{x}_i$:

$$\mathbf{y} = \sum a_i \mathbf{x}_i \tag{17}$$

Equation (17) is a set of n inhomogeneous equations in the unknowns a_i . Since the $\mathbf{x}_i$ are assumed to be linearly independent, we know that we can, in principle, always solve for the a_i .

If, however, the dimensionality of the space is large, it may be entirely impractical to solve Eq. (17), even with a digital computer.

If we have an appropriate set of orthogonality relations among the set $\mathbf{x}_i$, we can use these relations to obtain quite easily the solution of Eq. (17).

Suppose we have an inner product relation such that

$$\langle \mathbf{x}_{\sim j} , \mathbf{x}_i \rangle = \alpha_i \delta_{ij} \tag{18}$$

where δ_{ij} is the Kronecker delta and α_j is a nonzero known scalar quantity. We shall defer for the moment detailed discussion of the meaning of the index $\sim j$, except to say that it is a relabeling of the indices, and consider the relation purely formally.

Now if we form the inner product of each $\mathbf{x}_{\sim j}$ in turn with Eq. (17), we get

$$\langle \mathbf{x}_{\sim j} , \mathbf{y} \rangle = \sum a_i \langle \mathbf{x}_{\sim j} , \mathbf{x}_i \rangle = a_j \alpha_j \tag{19}$$

Hence

$$a_j = \langle \mathbf{x}_{\sim j} , \mathbf{y} \rangle / \alpha_j \tag{20}$$

The coefficients of the expansion have been determined explicitly and simply. This is a thoroughly practical technique for finding the expansion of $\mathbf{y}$ in terms of the set $\mathbf{x}_i$, providing we know of a suitable inner product relation.

This illustrates the practical importance of being able to obtain orthogonality. In many problems of great practical importance, we can set up such relations through a physically meaningful inner product which is improper.

4. PAIRWISE ORTHOGONALITY

Let us now consider more carefully the implications of an inner product relation of the form of Eq. (1) where $\mathbf{K}$ may not be positive definite but is restricted only to being nonsingular and hermitian. In particular, we need to justify, and explain, the use of Eq. (18).

We have seen that a vector can be orthogonal to itself. We may have $\langle \mathbf{x}_i , \mathbf{x}_i \rangle = \mathbf{x}_i^{\dagger} \mathbf{K} \mathbf{x}_i = 0$. However, $\mathbf{K}$ is nonsingular so $\mathbf{K} \mathbf{x}_i$ is not the null vector. If the set $\mathbf{x}_i$ is complete, there must be at least one member of it, say $\mathbf{x}_j$, such that

$$\langle \mathbf{x}_j , \mathbf{x}_i \rangle = \mathbf{x}_j^{\dagger} \mathbf{K} \mathbf{x}_i \neq 0 \tag{21}$$

There may be more than one, but there must be at least one for each $\mathbf{x}_i$.

Suppose that for each $\mathbf{x}_i$ there is only one value of the index j such that $\langle \mathbf{x}_j , \mathbf{x}_i \rangle$ does not vanish. We will indicate this value of j as $(\sim i)$, which we may read as "conjugate i." We will also write $i \sim j$, which may be read as "i is conjugate to j."

If i is conjugate to j, then j is conjugate to i. For if Eq. (21) holds, then by property (B) (page 217), $\langle \mathbf{x}_i, \mathbf{x}_j \rangle \neq 0$. Hence the relation $i \sim j$ is a reciprocal one.

We make the following definition:

Definition.   *The complete set of vectors* $\mathbf{u}_i$ *is* **pairwise K-orthogonal**, *if to each value of the index i there corresponds a unique value $(\sim i)$ such that*

$$\langle \mathbf{u}_{\sim j}, \mathbf{u}_i \rangle = \mathbf{u}_{\sim j}^\dagger \mathbf{K} \mathbf{u}_i = \alpha_j \delta_{ij} \tag{22}$$

where the α_j *are nonzero, possibly complex, numbers.*

There is, obviously, nothing that forbids us to have $(\sim i)$ the same as i. What we have done is to admit the possibility that they may be different.

We also note the possibility of the α's being complex, even though $\mathbf{K}$ is hermitian. This is perhaps astonishing since the α's play a role analogous to the square of the length of the vector in unitary space. The hermitian property of $\mathbf{K}$ does, however, mean that $\alpha_{\sim i}$ is the complex conjugate of α_i since

$$\alpha_{\sim i} = \langle \mathbf{x}_i, \mathbf{x}_{\sim i} \rangle = \langle \mathbf{x}_{\sim i}, \mathbf{x}_i \rangle^* = \alpha_i^* \tag{23}$$

Hence, if $i \sim i$, α_i must be real. Complex α can occur only when $i \sim j \neq i$.

Since the α's play the role of a magnitude squared, we can consider the normalization of the set of vectors. Let us define

$$\mathbf{y}_i = \mathbf{x}_i / \langle \mathbf{x}_{\sim i}, \mathbf{x}_i \rangle^{1/2} = \mathbf{x}_i / \alpha_i^{1/2}$$

where the square root is taken with positive real part.

Then

$$\langle \mathbf{y}_j, \mathbf{y}_i \rangle = \mathbf{y}_j^\dagger \mathbf{K} \mathbf{y}_i = \frac{\mathbf{x}_j^\dagger \mathbf{K} \mathbf{x}_i}{(\alpha_j^*)^{1/2}(\alpha_i)^{1/2}}$$

$$= 0 \qquad \text{if } j \text{ not } \sim i$$

$$= \alpha_i / (\lvert \alpha_i \rvert^2)^{1/2} \qquad \text{if } j \sim i \tag{24}$$

If $j \neq i$, $j \sim i$, the normalization factors can be so chosen that $\langle \mathbf{y}_j, \mathbf{y}_i \rangle = 1$. However, if $i \sim i$, then α_i is real. If α_i is negative, then $(\lvert \alpha_i \rvert^2)^{1/2}$ is positive and equal to $-\alpha_i$, so that $\langle \mathbf{y}_j, \mathbf{y}_i \rangle = -1$. Hence the most we can do is to normalize the set $\mathbf{y}_i$ so that

$$\langle \mathbf{y}_{\sim i}, \mathbf{y}_j \rangle = \mathbf{y}_{\sim i}^\dagger \mathbf{K} \mathbf{y}_j = \sigma_i \delta_{ij} \tag{25}$$

where $\sigma_i = \sigma_{\sim i} = \pm 1$.

We shall speak of the set y_i as *maximally normalized*, meaning that the vectors have been normalized to the greatest extent possible under the given inner product.

To illustrate these relations, take K as in Eq. (9). Consider first the two vectors

$$\mathbf{x}_1 = \begin{pmatrix} 1 \\ 1 \end{pmatrix}, \qquad \mathbf{x}_2 = \begin{pmatrix} 1 \\ -1 \end{pmatrix}$$

The inner products are

$$\mathbf{x}_1{}^\dagger \mathbf{K} \mathbf{x}_1 = 2$$
$$\mathbf{x}_2{}^\dagger \mathbf{K} \mathbf{x}_2 = -2$$
$$\mathbf{x}_1{}^\dagger \mathbf{K} \mathbf{x}_2 = \mathbf{x}_2{}^\dagger \mathbf{K} \mathbf{x}_1 = 0$$

The latter relation indicates the orthogonality of the pair, with $1 \sim 1$, $2 \sim 2$. We call such vectors *self-conjugate*.

Normalizing the pair, we obtain

$$\mathbf{y}_1 = \frac{1}{\sqrt{2}} \begin{pmatrix} 1 \\ 1 \end{pmatrix}, \qquad \mathbf{y}_2 = \frac{1}{\sqrt{2}} \begin{pmatrix} 1 \\ -1 \end{pmatrix}$$

and

$$\mathbf{y}_1{}^\dagger \mathbf{K} \mathbf{y}_1 = \sigma_1 = 1$$
$$\mathbf{y}_2{}^\dagger \mathbf{K} \mathbf{y}_2 = \sigma_2 = -1$$
$$\mathbf{y}_1{}^\dagger \mathbf{K} \mathbf{y}_2 = \mathbf{y}_2{}^\dagger \mathbf{K} \mathbf{y}_1 = 0$$

We cannot choose α_2 in any way to change the sign of σ_2.

Consider, on the other hand, the two vectors

$$\mathbf{x}_1 = \begin{pmatrix} 1 \\ j \end{pmatrix}, \qquad \mathbf{x}_2 = \begin{pmatrix} 1 \\ -j \end{pmatrix}$$

Then

$$\mathbf{x}_1{}^\dagger \mathbf{K} \mathbf{x}_1 = \mathbf{x}_2{}^\dagger \mathbf{K} \mathbf{x}_2 = 0$$
$$\mathbf{x}_1{}^\dagger \mathbf{K} \mathbf{x}_2 = -2j = \alpha_2{}^2$$
$$\mathbf{x}_2{}^\dagger \mathbf{K} \mathbf{x}_1 = 2j = \alpha_1{}^2$$

so that the pair is again orthogonal, but now with $1 \sim 2$. We call such a pair of vectors *cross-conjugate*.

Then we can set

$$\mathbf{y}_1 = \frac{1}{2} \begin{pmatrix} 1-j \\ 1+j \end{pmatrix}, \qquad \mathbf{y}_2 = \frac{1}{2} \begin{pmatrix} 1+j \\ 1-j \end{pmatrix}$$

and

$$\mathbf{y}_1{}^\dagger \mathbf{K} \mathbf{y}_1 = \mathbf{y}_2{}^\dagger \mathbf{K} \mathbf{y}_2 = 0$$
$$\mathbf{y}_1{}^\dagger \mathbf{K} \mathbf{y}_2 = \mathbf{y}_2{}^\dagger \mathbf{K} \mathbf{y}_1 = \sigma_1 = \sigma_2 = 1$$

We can also multiply a self-conjugate vector by an arbitrary phase term, $\exp j\varphi_i$, φ_i real, without changing its relations. Likewise, we can multiply one member of a cross-conjugate pair by $\exp(\gamma_i + j\varphi_i)$ if we multiply the other by $\exp(-\gamma_i + j\varphi_i)$. Such factors do not affect Eq. (25), and can be used to simplify the vectors. For example, in place of $\mathbf{y_1}$ and $\mathbf{y_2}$ in the last example we can obtain

$$\mathbf{u_1} = \frac{1}{\sqrt{2}} \begin{pmatrix} j \\ 1 \end{pmatrix}, \qquad \mathbf{u_2} = \frac{1}{\sqrt{2}} \begin{pmatrix} 1 \\ j \end{pmatrix}$$

and find

$$\mathbf{u_1}^\dagger \mathbf{K} \mathbf{u_1} = \mathbf{u_2}^\dagger \mathbf{K} \mathbf{u_2} = 0$$

$$\mathbf{u_1}^\dagger \mathbf{K} \mathbf{u_2} = \mathbf{u_2}^\dagger \mathbf{K} \mathbf{u_1} = 1$$

These examples illustrate that both self-and cross-conjugate vectors are indeed possible and demonstrate the normalization procedure.

5. ADJOINT OPERATOR

We have not, so far, said anything about the origin of such sets of vectors. It is reasonable, however, to expect that they will usually arise as the eigenvectors, or generalized eigenvectors, of matrices. Just as we classified matrices according to their relation to their adjoint, so do we want to do the same thing here.

Definition. *The matrix $\mathbf{A}^{\#}$ is the K-adjoint of $\mathbf{A}$ if, for all $\mathbf{x}$ and $\mathbf{y}$ in the space*

$$\langle \mathbf{x}, \mathbf{A}\mathbf{y} \rangle = \langle \mathbf{A}^{\#}\mathbf{x}, \mathbf{y} \rangle \tag{26}$$

Expanding Eq. (26), we get

$$\mathbf{x}^\dagger \mathbf{K} \mathbf{A} \mathbf{y} = (\mathbf{A}^{\#}\mathbf{x})^\dagger \mathbf{K} \mathbf{y} = \mathbf{x}^\dagger \mathbf{A}^{\#\dagger} \mathbf{K} \mathbf{y}$$

Since this must hold for all $\mathbf{x}$ and $\mathbf{y}$, we must have

$$\mathbf{K}\mathbf{A} = \mathbf{A}^{\#\dagger}\mathbf{K}$$

or

$$\mathbf{A}^{\#} = \mathbf{K}^{-1}\mathbf{A}^\dagger\mathbf{K} \tag{27}$$

Hence the adjoint always exists, since $\mathbf{K}$ is nonsingular, and is unique for a given $\mathbf{K}$.

We define:

Definition. *A matrix* **A** *is* K-**normal** *if it commutes with its* K-*adjoint*

$$\mathbf{A}\mathbf{A}^{\#} = \mathbf{A}^{\#}\mathbf{A}$$
$$\mathbf{A}\mathbf{K}^{-1}\mathbf{A}^{\dagger}\mathbf{K} = \mathbf{K}^{-1}\mathbf{A}^{\dagger}\mathbf{K}\mathbf{A}$$

(28)

Definition. *A matrix is* K-**hermitian** *if it equals its* K-*adjoint*:

$$\mathbf{A} = \mathbf{A}^{\#} = \mathbf{K}^{-1}\mathbf{A}^{\dagger}\mathbf{K}$$
$$\mathbf{K}\mathbf{A} = \mathbf{A}^{\dagger}\mathbf{K}$$

(29)

and is K-**skew-hermitian** *if it is the negative of its* K-*adjoint*:

$$\mathbf{A} = -\mathbf{A}^{\#} = -\mathbf{K}^{-1}\mathbf{A}^{\dagger}\mathbf{K}$$
$$\mathbf{K}\mathbf{A} = -\mathbf{A}^{\dagger}\mathbf{K}$$

(30)

Definition. *A matrix is* K-**unitary** *if it is the reciprocal of its* K-*adjoint*:

$$\mathbf{A}^{\#}\mathbf{A} = \mathbf{K}^{-1}\mathbf{A}^{\dagger}\mathbf{K}\mathbf{A} = \mathbf{I}$$
$$\mathbf{A}^{\dagger}\mathbf{K}\mathbf{A} = \mathbf{K}$$

(31)

These definitions are formally identical with the corresponding definitions for a proper inner product.

With a proper inner product, the corresponding types of matrices have three properties of importance—semisimplicity, orthogonality of the eigenvectors if degeneracies are properly resolved, and the nature of the eigenvalues.

With an improper inner product, we lose semisimplicity, but retain the other properties with some modification.

The loss of semisimplicity is best shown by example. Consider

$$\mathbf{A} = \begin{pmatrix} \lambda & 1 \\ 0 & \lambda \end{pmatrix}$$

so that **A** is a Jordan block and therefore not semisimple. If λ is real, **A** is K-hermitian with

$$\mathbf{K} = \begin{pmatrix} 0 & b \\ b & a \end{pmatrix}$$

where a is any real number and b any nonzero real number. It is K-unitary if $|\lambda|^2 = 1$ and

$$\mathbf{K} = \begin{pmatrix} 0 & ja\lambda^* \\ -ja\lambda & b \end{pmatrix}$$

where a and b are any real numbers.

This shows that the fact that $\mathbf{A}$ is K-normal, K-hermitian, or K-unitary does not permit us to conclude that $\mathbf{A}$ is semisimple. If semisimplicity is important to us, it must be determined by other means.

6. ORTHOGONALITY AND NORMALITY

By analogy to the case of a proper inner product, we would expect that the eigenvectors of a K-normal—and hence of a K-hermitian or K-unitary—matrix $\mathbf{A}$ to be K-orthogonal by pairs. The situation is complicated by the possibility that $\mathbf{A}$ may not be semisimple, and by the possible variations of the conjugacy relations.

We shall not investigate the most general situation but will consider only the case where the eigenvalues are discrete. We have the following:

Theorem 1. *If* $\mathbf{A}$ *is K-normal and semisimple with discrete eigenvalues, then its eigenvectors are K-orthogonal by pairs.*

For if

$$\mathbf{A}\mathbf{x}_i = \lambda_i \mathbf{x}_i$$

then

$$\mathbf{A}^{\#}\mathbf{A}\mathbf{x}_i = \mathbf{A}\mathbf{A}^{\#}\mathbf{x}_i = \lambda_i \mathbf{A}^{\#}\mathbf{x}_i$$

Hence $\mathbf{A}^{\#}\mathbf{x}_i$ is also an eigenvector of $\mathbf{A}$ with eigenvalue λ_i and so must be proportional to $\mathbf{x}_i$, which is therefore an eigenvector of $\mathbf{A}^{\#}$:

$$\mathbf{A}^{\#}\mathbf{x}_i = \mu_i \mathbf{x}_i$$

Then, if $\mathbf{x}_j$ is any other eigenvector,

$$\langle \mathbf{x}_j , \mathbf{A}\mathbf{x}_i \rangle = \langle \mathbf{A}^{\#}\mathbf{x}_j , \mathbf{x}_i \rangle = \lambda_i \langle \mathbf{x}_j , \mathbf{x}_i \rangle = \mu_j{}^* \langle \mathbf{x}_j , \mathbf{x}_i \rangle$$

or

$$(\lambda_i - \mu_j{}^*) \langle \mathbf{x}_j , \mathbf{x}_i \rangle = 0 \tag{32}$$

We now consider what happens to Eq. (32) for a given value of j as i takes all values. Since the λ_i are discrete, there can be only one value of i for which $(\lambda_i - \mu_j{}^*) = 0$. For all other i, we must have $\langle \mathbf{x}_j , \mathbf{x}_i \rangle = 0$. We cannot have $\langle \mathbf{x}_j , \mathbf{x}_i \rangle = 0$ for all i, however, since the set of $\mathbf{x}_i$ are complete, and the inner product is nonsingular. There must be one value of i for which $\langle \mathbf{x}_j , \mathbf{x}_i \rangle \neq 0$, and there can be only one. We call this value of the index $\sim j$.

Hence the eigenvectors of $\mathbf{A}$ are simultaneously eigenvectors of $\mathbf{A}^{\#}$, and the whole set is orthogonal by pairs. The eigenvalues of $\mathbf{A}^{\#}$ are related to those of $\mathbf{A}$ by

$$\mu_{\sim i} = \lambda_i^* \tag{33}$$

The converse theorem is also true:

Theorem 2. *If $\mathbf{A}$ is semisimple, and if it has a complete set of eigenvectors that are K-orthogonal, then $\mathbf{A}$ is K-normal.*

Let $\mathbf{x}_i$ be a complete set of eigenvectors of $\mathbf{A}$. They are, by assumption, K-orthogonal by pairs, which implies that the conjugacy relations are known, so that we understand what we mean by $\sim i$.

Consider the set of vectors

$$\mathbf{y}_i = \mathbf{A}^{\#}\mathbf{x}_i - \lambda_{\sim i}^* \mathbf{x}_i \tag{34}$$

We wish to show that the set $\mathbf{y}_i$ are null vectors.

We form the inner products of a given $\mathbf{y}_i$ with each of the eigenvectors, labeled according to $\sim j$, and use the definition of adjointness to write

$$\langle \mathbf{x}_{\sim j}, \mathbf{y}_i \rangle = \langle \mathbf{A}\mathbf{x}_{\sim j}, \mathbf{x}_i \rangle - \lambda_{\sim i}^* \langle \mathbf{x}_{\sim j}, \mathbf{x}_i \rangle$$

$$= (\lambda_{\sim j}^* - \lambda_{\sim i}^*)\langle \mathbf{x}_{\sim j}, \mathbf{x}_i \rangle$$

This vanishes identically, because of $(\lambda_{\sim j}^* - \lambda_{\sim i}^*)$ if $i = j$, and because of $\langle \mathbf{x}_{\sim j}, \mathbf{x}_i \rangle$ if $i \neq j$. Hence the inner product of $\mathbf{y}_i$ with each of the complete set $\mathbf{x}_i$ vanishes, so that $\mathbf{y}_i$ must be the null vector, and every $\mathbf{x}_i$ an eigenvector of $\mathbf{A}^{\#}$:

$$\mathbf{A}^{\#}\mathbf{x}_i = \lambda_{\sim i}^* \mathbf{x}_i$$

With this result, we can immediately verify that $\mathbf{A}$ commutes with $\mathbf{A}^{\#}$, since

$$\mathbf{A}\mathbf{A}^{\#}\mathbf{x}_i = \lambda_{\sim i}^* \mathbf{A}\mathbf{x}_i = \lambda_i \lambda_{\sim i}^* \mathbf{x}_i$$

$$\mathbf{A}^{\#}\mathbf{A}\mathbf{x}_i = \lambda_i \mathbf{A}^{\#} x_i = \lambda_i \lambda_{\sim i}^* \mathbf{x}_i$$

Since these equations are equal for a complete set of vectors, the operators must be equal, and

$$\mathbf{A}\mathbf{A}^{\#} = \mathbf{A}^{\#}\mathbf{A} \tag{35}$$

so that $\mathbf{A}$ is K-normal.

Theorem 2 does not depend on the discreteness of the eigenvalues. The proof is the same even if $\mathbf{A}$ is degenerate, so long as we have managed to find a complete set of K-orthogonal eigenvectors.

If **A** is degenerate but still semisimple, Theorem 1 requires that we resolve the degeneracy properly. We can infer the possibility of doing this by arguing that any degenerate matrix can be regarded as the limit of a sequence of nondegenerate ones as a perturbation parameter approaches zero. This, however, is not a proof unless or until we show that we can in fact obtain such a sequence that does not upset the K-normality. We suggest this line of thought, therefore, more as a plausibility argument than anything else. We will simply assert the truth of the theorem even in the degenerate case, and say that the degeneracy can always be resolved to give us K-orthogonal eigenvectors. The method of doing this is by a suitable adaptation of the Gram-Schmidt process.

If **A** is not semisimple, then there are additional complications. The principal factor involved is that, in $\mathbf{A}^\#$, the direction of progress along a chain is reversed. Hence, if **A** has a chain of length m, the generalized eigenvector of rank k is always conjugated with a generalized eigenvector of rank $(m - k)$ of a chain of length m. This may be another generalized eigenvector of the same chain, or in another chain of the same length. In addition, we have the possibility of degeneracy between chains and, of course, the degeneracy within the chains. Thus there is a great deal of variety possible. It appears, however, that the following is always true:

Theorem 3. *If* **A** *is K-normal, then its eigenvectors and generalized eigenvectors can be chosen so that they are pairwise K-orthogonal.*

The generalization of Theorem 2 to the nonsemisimple case, on the other hand, involves additional difficulty. It is not enough just that the eigenvectors and generalized eigenvectors be K-orthogonal to assure K-normality. In addition, the conjugacy relations must be appropriate to the structure of the matrix.

7. *K*-HERMITIAN MATRICES

Of greater interest to us is the behavior of K-hermitian and K-unitary matrices. We shall therefore consider here, in some additional detail, the K-hermitian class, and in the next section the K-unitary class.

We ask two questions. If **A** is K-hermitian, what constraints does this imply on the eigenvalues? Is this constraint sufficient to imply that **A** is K-hermitian for some **K**? If so, and we shall see that it is so, then we will be able to test to see when we should seek such a **K**.

In answer to the first question, we will prove the following:

Theorem 4. *The eigenvalues of a K-hermitian matrix, where* **K** *may be indefinite, are either real or else occur in complex conjugate pairs. If the* *matrix is not semisimple, the conjugacy relations must relate vectors in a chain or in chains of the same length in the opposite sequence of rank.*

Suppose the set $\mathbf{x}_i$ are the eigenvectors and generalized eigenvectors of $\mathbf{A}$, chosen to be pairwise K-orthogonal. We can describe this situation by setting

$$\mathbf{A}\mathbf{x}_i = \lambda_i \mathbf{x}_i + \epsilon_i \mathbf{x}_{i-1} \tag{36}$$

where ϵ_i is 0 or 1 depending on whether the rank of $\mathbf{x}_i$ is one or greater. From the self-adjointness of $\mathbf{A}$, we have:

$$\langle \mathbf{x}_j , \mathbf{A}\mathbf{x}_i \rangle = \langle \mathbf{A}\mathbf{x}_j , \mathbf{x}_i \rangle$$

or

$$\lambda_i \langle \mathbf{x}_j , \mathbf{x}_i \rangle + \epsilon_i \langle \mathbf{x}_j , \mathbf{x}_{i-1} \rangle = \lambda_j{}^* \langle \mathbf{x}_j , \mathbf{x}_i \rangle + \epsilon_j \langle \mathbf{x}_{j-1} , \mathbf{x}_i \rangle \tag{37}$$

If we let j be $\sim i$, then only the first terms on each side of Eq. (37) remain, and we see that

$$\lambda_i = \lambda^*_{\sim i} \tag{38}$$

If $\mathbf{x}_i$ is self-conjugate—i.e., $i \sim i$—then λ_i must be real. Otherwise, we only know that if there exists a vector in the set with λ_i, there must also occur one with $\lambda_i{}^*$ which is conjugate with it.

If we set $j = \sim(i-1)$, we are left, in Eq. (37), with

$$\epsilon_i \langle \mathbf{x}_{\sim(i-1)} , \mathbf{x}_{i-1} \rangle = \epsilon_{\sim(i-1)} \langle \mathbf{x}_{\sim(i-1)-1} , \mathbf{x}_i \rangle$$

If $\epsilon_i = 1$, so that $\mathbf{x}_i$ is a generalized eigenvector of rank >1, then the left side does not vanish, so the right side cannot either. Therefore we must have

$$\sim(i-1) - 1 = \sim i$$
$$\epsilon_{\sim(i-1)} = \epsilon_{(\sim i+1)} = 1 \tag{39}$$

The ranking of a chain according to $\sim i$ is in the opposite direction from that according to i.

We have found, in Eq. (38), the necessary constraint on the eigenvalues, and, in Eq. (39), a constraint on the conjugacy relations among the chains of generalized eigenvectors.

In answer to our second question, we can now prove the following:

Theorem 5. *If the eigenvalues of $\mathbf{A}$ are either real or else occur in conjugate pairs such that chains of the same length are associated with each of the complex conjugate pairs of eigenvalues, then there exists a $\mathbf{K}$ for which $\mathbf{A}$ is K-hermitian.*

We shall prove this by showing how the Jordan canonical form can, in principle, be used to determine a **K**. This will not only prove the theorem, but may help to illustrate the significance of the property of being *K*-hermitian.

We note, first, that the property of being *K*-hermitian is invariant under a change of basis. If

$$KA = A^\dagger K \tag{40}$$

and we change the basis by **S**, letting

$$A' = S^{-1}AS$$
$$K' = S^\dagger KS = K'^\dagger \tag{41}$$

as we found in Chapter V, then

$$K'A' = (S^\dagger KS)(S^{-1}AS) = S^\dagger KAS = S^\dagger A^\dagger KS$$
$$= (S^\dagger A^\dagger S^{\dagger-1})(S^\dagger KS) = A'^\dagger K' \tag{42}$$

Hence **A**' is *K*'-hermitian.

Suppose we have chosen a basis such that **A** is in Jordan canonical form:

$$A = \text{quasidiag}(J_{m_1}(\lambda_1), J_{m_2}(\lambda_2), ...) \tag{43}$$

Then

$$A^\dagger = \text{quasidiag}(J_{m_1}^T(\lambda_1^*), J_{m_2}^T(\lambda_2^*), ...) \tag{44}$$

where $J_{m_i}^T(\lambda_i^*)$ is the $m_i \times m_i$ lower Jordan block with λ_i^*:

$$J_{m_i}^T(\lambda_i^*) = \begin{pmatrix} \lambda_i^* & 0 & 0 & \cdots \\ 1 & \lambda_i^* & 0 \\ 0 & 1 & \lambda_i^* \\ \cdots \end{pmatrix} \tag{45}$$

Suppose, first, that all the eigenvalues are real. Then we wish to obtain an **S** that will transform Eq. (44) into the Jordan canonical form. We can do this with a quasidiagonal form with the same size blocks as Eq. (44):

$$K = \text{quasidiag}(K_{m_1}, K_{m_2}, ...) \tag{46}$$

if the individual blocks will transform $J_{m_i}^T$ into the upper Jordan block. A K_{m_i} that will do this is the $m_i \times m_i$ matrix

$$K_{m_i} = \begin{pmatrix} \cdots & 0 & 0 & 1 \\ \cdots & 0 & 1 & 0 \\ \cdots & 1 & 0 & 0 \\ \cdots \end{pmatrix} \tag{47}$$

We note that the $\mathbf{K}$ so defined is nonsingular and hermitian, and therefore we have found, in Eqs. (46) and (47), a suitable $\mathbf{K}$ such that an $\mathbf{A}$ of the form of Eq. (43) is K-hermitian.

We may note that the $\mathbf{K}_{m_i}$ given by Eq. (47) is positive definite only if $m_i = 1$ so that it reduces to the scalar unity. Hence the $\mathbf{K}$ of Eq. (46) is positive definite if, but only if, $\mathbf{A}$ is semisimple.

Suppose, now, that λ_1, for example, is complex. Then there must exist in Eq. (43) another block with the same dimensionality as $\mathbf{J}_{m_1}(\lambda_1)$, but with $\lambda_1{}^*$. Suppose, to be specific, that this block is $\mathbf{J}_{m_2}(\lambda_2)$, so that $m_2 = m_1 = m$ and $\lambda_2 = \lambda_1{}^*$. Then we set

$$\mathbf{K} = \begin{pmatrix} 0 & \mathbf{K}_{m_1} & \cdots \\ \mathbf{K}_{m_1} & 0 & \cdots \\ \cdots & & \end{pmatrix} \tag{48}$$

where $\mathbf{K}_{m_1}$ is again given by Eq. (47). This is a suitable $\mathbf{K}$, which is also nonsingular and hermitian.

Under the given conditions on the eigenvalues, we have found it possible to obtain a $\mathbf{K}$ such that $\mathbf{A}$ is K-hermitian. The specific development was for $\mathbf{A}$ in Jordan canonical form. For the more general case, we can transform this $\mathbf{K}$ back through the change of basis of Eq. (41) and obtain a $\mathbf{K}$ that is suitable for the operator expressed on any basis. Thus the theorem is proven.

The $\mathbf{K}$ so found is not unique. What we have done is to show that one exists, and so verified that the conditions on the eigenvalues given in Theorem 5 are sufficient to assure that $\mathbf{A}$ is K-hermitian for some nonsingular hermitian $\mathbf{K}$.

8. K-UNITARY MATRICES

We shall now prove the analogous theorem to Theorem 4, which is:

Theorem 6. *The eigenvalues of a K-unitary matrix are either of unit magnitude or else occur in pairs such that one is the complex conjugate of the reciprocal of the other*:

$$\lambda_i \lambda_{-i}^* = 1 \tag{49}$$

If the matrix is not semisimple, the conjugacy relations relate vectors in a chain, or in chains of the same length, in opposite sequence of rank.

This can be proven by similar methods to those used on Theorem 4. The comparable theorem to Theorem 5 is the following:

Theorem 7.   *If the eigenvalues of a matrix* **A** *are either of unit magnitude or else occur in pairs satisfying* Eq. (49) *and such that chains of the same length can be conjugated, then there exists a* **K** *such that* **A** *is K-unitary.*

We shall sketch out the proof using the Jordan canonical form as in the proof of Theorem 5. However, we shall not be able to find quite such a simple form as Eqs. (46) and (47).

We observe first that the property of being K-unitary is invariant under a change of basis. If

$$\mathbf{A^\dagger K A = K} \tag{50}$$

and we change the basis according to Eq. (41), then

$$\mathbf{A'^\dagger K' A'} = \mathbf{(S^\dagger A^\dagger S^{\dagger-1})(S^\dagger K S)(S^{-1} A S)}$$
$$= \mathbf{S^\dagger A^\dagger K A S = S^\dagger K S = K'}$$

so that $\mathbf{A'}$ is K'-unitary.

Hence we need only consider an **A** in Jordan canonical form, Eq. (43) We observe that Eq. (50) can be written

$$\mathbf{A = K^{-1} A^{\dagger-1} K} \tag{51}$$

This is valid since, under the conditions stated, none of the eigenvalues of **A** vanish, and it is therefore nonsingular. We are seeking a similarity transformation that will carry $\mathbf{A^{\dagger-1}}$ into **A**.

We can verify that

$$
\mathbf{J}_m^{\dagger-1}(\lambda) =
\begin{pmatrix}
\mu & 0 & 0 & 0 & \cdots \\
-\mu^2 & \mu & 0 & 0 & \cdots \\
\mu^3 & -\mu^2 & \mu & 0 & \cdots \\
-\mu^4 & \mu^3 & -\mu^2 & \mu & \cdots \\
\cdots & & & &
\end{pmatrix}
\tag{52}
$$

where

$$\mu = 1/\lambda^*$$

If λ_i is of unit magnitude, then the corresponding $\mu_i = \lambda_i$. If it is not, then the conditions require that there be another eigenvalue $\lambda_{\sim i}$ that has the same size Jordan block, such that $\lambda_{\sim i} = \mu_i$.

The first thing we need to do is to adjust the order of the blocks in $\mathbf{A}^{-1}$. This we can do with a similarity transformation using the appropriate permutation matrix.

We are left with transforming the matrix of Eq. (52) into $\mathbf{J}_m(\mu)$. This we can do by the methods of Chapter V, after obtaining the chains of Eq. (52). If we write $\mathbf{x}_i$ for the generalized eigenvector of rank i in this chain, we can set

$$\mathbf{x}_m = \begin{pmatrix} 1 \\ 0 \\ 0 \\ \vdots \\ \vdots \end{pmatrix}$$

and

$$(\mathbf{J}_m^{\dagger-1}(\lambda) - \mu\mathbf{I})\mathbf{x}_i = \mathbf{x}_{i-1}$$

so that we obtain a chain of generalized eigenvectors of $\mathbf{J}_m^{\dagger-1}(\lambda)$.

If we set

$$\mathbf{K} = (\mathbf{x}_1 , \mathbf{x}_2 , ..., \mathbf{x}_m) \tag{53}$$

we have a matrix that will transform $\mathbf{J}_m^{\dagger-1}(\lambda)$ into $\mathbf{J}_m(\mu)$.

The $\mathbf{K}$ obtained in this process will not, in general, be hermitian. However, it will be nonsingular and will satisfy Eq. (50).

We can now obtain a hermitian $\mathbf{K}$ from this. For, taking the hermitian conjugate of Eq. (50), we obtain

$$\mathbf{A}^\dagger\mathbf{K}^\dagger\mathbf{A} = \mathbf{K}^\dagger$$

so that, if $\mathbf{K}$ satisfies Eq. (49), so does $\mathbf{K}^\dagger$. We can now form

$$\mathbf{K}_\alpha = e^{j\alpha}\mathbf{K} + e^{-j\alpha}\mathbf{K}^\dagger$$

This is hermitian for any real α. The $\mathbf{K}$ that we found is nonsingular. Let its eigenvalues be η_i, none of which vanish. The eigenvalues of $\mathbf{K}_\alpha$ are, then, $(e^{j\alpha}\eta_i + e^{-j\alpha}\eta_i^*)$. We can always choose α so that none of these values vanish. We have a $\mathbf{K}$ which is hermitian and nonsingular.

The $\mathbf{K}$ so developed is not unique. What is important here is the demonstration that the condition on the eigenvalues is sufficient to assure the existence of a $\mathbf{K}$ for which the matrix is K-unitary.

9. ORTHOGONALIZATION OF A SET OF VECTORS

We shall now consider the problem of the choice of metric in a somewhat broader context. We shall show that it is always possible to choose a $\mathbf{K}$ such that any complete set of vectors are K-orthogonal and maximally normalized with any desired conjugacy and parity.

Suppose $\mathbf{x}_i$ are a complete set of vectors. We have seen (Chapter III, Section 15) that it is always possible to find a reciprocal set $\mathbf{w}_i$ such that

$$\mathbf{w}_i^\dagger\mathbf{x}_j = \delta_{ij} \tag{54}$$

Suppose we desire to obtain a particular relabeling of the indices and a particular sequence of parity terms. That is, we wish to obtain a **K** such that

$$\mathbf{x}^{\dagger}_{\sim i}\mathbf{K}\mathbf{x}_j = \sigma_i\delta_{ij} \tag{55}$$

This will be true providing

$$\mathbf{x}^{\dagger}_{\sim i}\mathbf{K} = \sigma_i\mathbf{w}_i^{\dagger}$$

or

$$\mathbf{K}\mathbf{x}_{\sim i} = \sigma_i\mathbf{w}_i \tag{56}$$

Since this is a mapping of the whole space onto itself, it is soluble. We can write the solution as the product of two matrices:

$$\mathbf{K} = (\sigma_1\mathbf{w}_1\,,\,\sigma_2\mathbf{w}_2\,,\,...)\begin{pmatrix}\mathbf{w}^{\dagger}_{\sim 1}\\ \mathbf{w}^{\dagger}_{\sim 2}\\ \vdots \\ \vdots \end{pmatrix} \tag{57}$$

where $\mathbf{w}_{\sim i}$ is the reciprocal vector to $\mathbf{x}_{\sim i}$. The second factor is the matrix whose kth row is $\mathbf{w}^{\dagger}_{\sim k}$. Its product times $\mathbf{x}_{\sim i}$ gives a vector whose only nonzero term is a one in the kth position. This vector then picks out the kth column of the first factor, which is the vector $\sigma_k\mathbf{w}_k$, as desired.

From this we can infer, although we have not proven it, that any matrix is K-normal to some **K**.

We saw in Chapter III, Section 17, that the vectors that are reciprocal to a chain of generalized eigenvectors of a matrix **A** are a chain of generalized eigenvectors of $\mathbf{A}^{\dagger}$, but in the reverse order of rank. It is this reversal of the sequence of rank that is the source of the reversal of the sequence in the conjugacy relations.

10. RANGE OF **K**

We have indicated that the **K**'s we have developed are not unique. This is indicated by the following:

Theorem 8. *If* **A** *is K-normal, K-hermitian, or K-unitary, and* **S** *is any nonsingular matrix which commutes with* **A**, *then* **A** *is also K'-normal, K'-hermitian, or K'-unitary, respectively, with*

$$\mathbf{K}' = \mathbf{K}\mathbf{S} \tag{58}$$

providing **S** *is such that* **K**' *is hermitian.*

From the nonsingularity of $\mathbf{S}$, if $\mathbf{S}$ commutes with $\mathbf{A}$, so does $\mathbf{S}^{-1}$:

$$\mathbf{S}^{-1}\mathbf{A} = \mathbf{A}\mathbf{S}^{-1}$$

If $\mathbf{A}$ is K-normal, so that

$$\mathbf{A}\mathbf{K}^{-1}\mathbf{A}^{\dagger}\mathbf{K} = \mathbf{K}^{-1}\mathbf{A}^{\dagger}\mathbf{K}\mathbf{A}$$

then

$$\begin{aligned}
\mathbf{A}(\mathbf{KS})^{-1}\mathbf{A}^{\dagger}(\mathbf{KS}) &= \mathbf{A}\mathbf{S}^{-1}\mathbf{K}^{-1}\mathbf{A}^{\dagger}\mathbf{KS} \\
&= \mathbf{S}^{-1}(\mathbf{A}\mathbf{K}^{-1}\mathbf{A}^{\dagger}\mathbf{K})\mathbf{S} \\
&= \mathbf{S}^{-1}(\mathbf{K}^{-1}\mathbf{A}^{\dagger}\mathbf{KA})\mathbf{S} \\
&= (\mathbf{KS})^{-1}\mathbf{A}^{\dagger}(\mathbf{KS})\mathbf{A}
\end{aligned}$$

so that $\mathbf{A}$ is K'-normal.

If $\mathbf{A}$ is K-hermitian so that

$$\mathbf{KA} = \mathbf{A}^{\dagger}\mathbf{K}$$

then

$$(\mathbf{KS})\mathbf{A} = \mathbf{KAS} = \mathbf{A}^{\dagger}(\mathbf{KS})$$

and $\mathbf{A}$ is K'-hermitian.

If $\mathbf{A}$ is K-unitary, so that

$$\mathbf{A}^{\dagger}\mathbf{KA} = \mathbf{K}$$

then

$$\mathbf{A}^{\dagger}\mathbf{KSA} = (\mathbf{A}^{\dagger}\mathbf{KA})\mathbf{S} = \mathbf{KS}$$

and $\mathbf{A}$ is K'-unitary.

In particular, if $\mathbf{K}$ is appropriate to $\mathbf{A}$, so is $\mathbf{K}f(\mathbf{A})$, if it is hermitian, where $f(\mathbf{A})$ is any admissable function of $\mathbf{A}$ that does not generate a singular matrix,—i.e., $f(x)$ is nonzero anywheres on the spectrum of $\mathbf{A}$.

There is a wide choice of possible $\mathbf{K}$. Usually the desire is to find a $\mathbf{K}$, if possible, for which $\mathbf{A}$ has the desired properties, and which does not depend on some of the particular parameters of $\mathbf{A}$.

What is happening here is that a particular matrix $\mathbf{A}$ is being defined as within the intersection of classes associated with the various possible $\mathbf{K}$'s. For example, the class of lossless 2-port networks on an $E - I$ basis can be defined as the systems whose transmission matrix is K-unitary with

$$\mathbf{K}_1 = \begin{pmatrix} 0 & 1 \\ 1 & 0 \end{pmatrix} \tag{59}$$

so the conserved quantity is

$$s_1 = EI^* + E^*I = \frac{1}{2Z}\{|E + ZI|^2 - |E - ZI|^2\} \tag{60}$$

The latter way of writing it is as the difference of the powers flowing in the forward and backward waves, where the waves are defined with reference to an impedance Z.

Another class may be defined as those systems whose transmission matrix is K-unitary with

$$\mathbf{K}_2 = \begin{pmatrix} 1/Z & 0 \\ 0 & Z \end{pmatrix} = \frac{1}{\beta} \mathbf{K}_1 \begin{pmatrix} 0 & \beta Z \\ \beta/Z & 0 \end{pmatrix} \tag{61}$$

This class conserves

$$s_2 = \frac{1}{2Z} \{ | E + ZI |^2 + | E - ZI |^2 \} \tag{62}$$

or the sum, instead of the difference, of the powers in the two waves.

The class of lossless transmission lines with characteristic impedance Z is the intersection of these two classes. The $\mathbf{K}$ of Eq. (59) is, however, generally the more useful of the conservation laws since it is independent of Z, which we normally regard as a parameter of the system.

11. DETERMINATION OF A METRIC

We have given methods that, in principle, allow us to determine a possible $\mathbf{K}$ from the matrix involved. It must be admitted, however, that these are not very practical methods. They depend on putting the matrix into Jordan canonical form. If this has been done, we have the eigenvectors and eigenvalues of the system, and for many problems this is enough to permit an immediate solution. The purpose of these derivations, therefore, has been as a method of analyzing the significance of the $\mathbf{K}$ metric, and to obtain the necessary and sufficient conditions for its existence.

A more practical method of calculation, if $\mathbf{A}$ is to be K-hermitian, is to observe that Eq. (29) requires that if $\mathbf{K}$ is hermitian, so is $(\mathbf{KA})$. This gives us, probably, the most convenient way of obtaining $\mathbf{K}$ if the dimensionality of $\mathbf{A}$ is not too large. We simply write down the general hermitian $\mathbf{K}$ of the required dimensionality, and determine the constraints that will make $(\mathbf{KA})$ hermitian.

If, however, $\mathbf{A}$ is of reasonably large dimensionality, even the work of doing this can be quite formidable.

Fortunately, the physics of the problem often tells us what is being conserved. Or at least it tells us what sort of thing is conserved. We may know that the system conserves energy, or real power, or some reduced power. We can then write down the appropriate conservation law, and immediately obtain the metric. Or, if it is time-varying but lossless, then we know that the Manley-Rowe relations are satisfied and we can again write down a **K** such as that of Eq. (4).

In other problems, we may know conservation laws that apply to various parts of the system. If we are studying the interaction of an electron beam with a lossless distributed circuit (for example, in a traveling wave tube), we know that the circuit, taken by itself, conserves power. Hence we have a metric $\mathbf{K_1}$ that applies to it when uncoupled from the beam. We may also know an appropriate conservation law and hence a metric $\mathbf{K_2}$ for the beam taken by itself. (For the so-called space charge waves, it is "Chu's kinetic power law.") We can then look to see if we can combine these two metrics in the form

$$\mathbf{K} = \begin{pmatrix} \mathbf{K_1} & 0 \\ 0 & a\mathbf{K_2} \end{pmatrix}$$

where a is a real constant, and so obtain a metric for the whole system. We do not know *a priori* that such a **K** exists, but it is simple to try it out and, if it works, to solve for a.

The physics of the problem very often either tells us the metric directly or else suggests its form sufficiently well to make it practical to find it.

Another situation of interest is when we can use the choice of one or more metrics to specify the problem. For example, we might wish to study "ideal" uniformly distributed lossless parametric networks, where by ideal we mean those in which there is no coupling between the forward and backward waves, defined appropriately. Since it is lossless, the Manley-Rowe condition applies and we have the metric of Eq. (4). This conservation law, however, can be expressed similarly to Eq. (60) as the sum of the reduced powers in the forward waves, minus the sum in the backward waves. But if there is to be no coupling between the two sets of waves, the reduced power in each set must be separately conserved. Hence we can also write a conservation law that is the sum of these powers (to make it nonsingular) analogously to Eq. (62). Hence the conditions can be expressed by specifying the simultaneous existence of two metrics, analogous to Eqs. (59) and (61).

Finally, we shall see in the succeeding chapters that the determination of a metric provides us with a powerful tool for the calculation and manipulation of matrices—for example, in the calculation of the functions of a matrix. We are, in fact, able to obtain some important results if we merely know that a metric exists. We shall see this, for example, in Chapter XIV.

Exercises

1. Prove that **A** is K-hermitian if both **K** and **(KA)** are hermitian.

2. Consider the matrix

$$\mathbf{A} = \begin{pmatrix} 0 & \frac{1}{2} & -\frac{1}{2}j & 1 \\ \frac{1}{2} & 0 & 1 & \frac{1}{2}j \\ -\frac{1}{2}j & -1 & 0 & \frac{1}{2} \\ -1 & \frac{1}{2}i & \frac{1}{2} & 0 \end{pmatrix}$$

Verify that **A** is K-hermitian for

$$\mathbf{K} = \begin{pmatrix} 0 & 0 & 0 & 1 \\ 0 & 0 & 1 & 0 \\ 0 & 1 & 0 & 0 \\ 1 & 0 & 0 & 0 \end{pmatrix}$$

Find the eigenvectors and generalized eigenvectors of **A**. Show that they are K-orthogonal and find the conjugacy relations between them. (The eigenvalues of **A** are ± 1, each with multiplicity 2.)

3. Find a metric for which

$$\begin{aligned} \mathbf{x}_1 &= \mathrm{col}(1, 0, j, 0) \\ \mathbf{x}_2 &= \mathrm{col}(1, 0, -j, 0) \\ \mathbf{x}_3 &= \mathrm{col}(0, 1, 0, j) \\ \mathbf{x}_4 &= \mathrm{col}(0, 1, 0, -j) \end{aligned}$$

are K-orthogonal with

   (a) $1 \sim 1$, $2 \sim 2$, $3 \sim 3$, $4 \sim 4$,   and $\sigma_1 = \sigma_2 = \sigma_3 = \sigma_4 = 1$

   (b) $1 \sim 1$, $2 \sim 2$, $3 \sim 3$, $4 \sim 4$,   and $\sigma_1 = \sigma_2 = +1, \sigma_3 = \sigma_4 = -1$

   (c) $1 \sim 2$, $3 \sim 4$

   (d) $1 \sim 4$, $2 \sim 3$

In each case, maximally normalize the set.

4. Using the metric

$$\mathbf{K} = \begin{pmatrix} 0 & 0 & 0 & 1 \\ 0 & 0 & 1 & 0 \\ 0 & 1 & 0 & 0 \\ 1 & 0 & 0 & 0 \end{pmatrix}$$

find the K-orthogonal complements of

    (a) $\mathrm{col}(1, 0, j, 0)$ and $\mathrm{col}(0, 1, 0, j)$

    (b) $\mathrm{col}(1, -1, 0, -j)$ and $\mathrm{col}(1, 0, -j, j)$

    (c) $\mathrm{col}(1, -j, -1, j)$ and $\mathrm{col}(1, j, 1, j)$

    (d) $\mathrm{col}(1, 1, j, -j)$ and $\mathrm{col}(j, 1, 1, j)$

5. If we relax the requirement that **K** be hermitian, observe that the K-hermitian and K-skew-hermitian parts of **K** are each metrics of the system. What does this mean with regard to the conservation law from which **K** may have been derived?

Show that any metric that can be partitioned into

$$\mathbf{K} = \begin{pmatrix} 0 & \mathbf{P} \\ \mathbf{P} & 0 \end{pmatrix}$$

where **P** is square, hermitian, and nonsingular, has signature 0. Find the eigenvalues and eigenvectors of **K** in terms of those of **P**.

(Note the occurrence of this form in Eqs. (2) and (4). It appears to be generally true that metrics that express important physical conservation laws have this property, indicating the occurrence of pairs of modes with opposite parity. Whether this is coincidence, or the expression of some deeper physical truth, we do not know.)

6. Prove Theorem 6.

CHAPTER X

The Dyad Expansion and Its Application

We are ready to consider a technique which is often of great convenience in the solution of various problems. We shall show its application to two types of problems. The first type is the solution of a vector or matrix differential equation with constant coefficient matrices. The second is the determination to the first order of the effect of a perturbation.

These are problems that can, in principle, be solved in many ways. In practice, however, they can become very difficult if the problem has more than a very limited dimensionality, or has many degrees of freedom. The methods that we shall discuss here are not always applicable, but are very useful when they are applicable.

Before considering the problems themselves, we must first discuss what is meant by a *dyad* formed as the *outer product* of two vectors. We will therefore open with a general discussion in which we will briefly explore some of the important properties that are involved.

1. THE OUTER PRODUCT OF TWO VECTORS

What is sometimes called the *outer product* of two vectors $\mathbf{x}$ and $\mathbf{y}$ is the form $\mathbf{x}\mathbf{y}^\dagger$. This is not a scalar, like the inner product $\mathbf{x}^\dagger\mathbf{y}$. It a matrix, but a rather special sort of a matrix.

The vectors $\mathbf{x}$ and $\mathbf{y}$ are $n \times 1$ matrices. The form $\mathbf{x}^\dagger\mathbf{y}$, the inner product, is the product of a $1 \times n$ matrix times an $n \times 1$. It is, therefore, a 1×1 matrix, or a scalar. The outer product $\mathbf{x}\mathbf{y}^\dagger$, on the other hand, is an $n \times 1$ matrix times a $1 \times n$ one. It is therefore $n \times n$. By the usual rules of matrix multiplication, it is the matrix whose kth column is the vector $\mathbf{x}$ times the complex conjugate of the kth component of $\mathbf{y}$. Alternatively, it is the matrix whose jth row is the row vector $\mathbf{y}^\dagger$ times the jth component of $\mathbf{x}$.

Since each column (row) is a scalar times each other column (row), the determinant of the matrix is zero. Further, all minors of rank greater than unity are zero. Hence the rank of $\mathbf{x}\mathbf{y}^\dagger$ is one, assuming neither $\mathbf{x}$ nor $\mathbf{y}$ is the null vector.

Consider the effect of the form $\mathbf{xy}^\dagger$ on a vector $\mathbf{u}$. We can write the product

$$(\mathbf{xy}^\dagger)\mathbf{u} = (\mathbf{y}^\dagger\mathbf{u})\mathbf{x} \tag{1}$$

The latter form arises since $\mathbf{y}^\dagger\mathbf{u}$ is a scalar, being the inner product of $\mathbf{y}$ and $\mathbf{u}$, and therefore commutes with $\mathbf{x}$.

If $\mathbf{x}$ and $\mathbf{y}$ are unit vectors (i.e., of unit length under the unitary inner product relation), the product $(\mathbf{xy}^\dagger)\mathbf{u}$ takes the projection of $\mathbf{u}$ on $\mathbf{y}$ times $\mathbf{y}$, and determines a vector in the $\mathbf{x}$ direction of this length.

If $\mathbf{x}$ and $\mathbf{y}$ are not orthogonal (under the unitary inner product relation), then $\mathbf{xy}^\dagger$ has only a single eigenvector with nonzero eigenvalue. For, if we require that $\mathbf{u}$ and λ be such that

$$(\mathbf{xy}^\dagger)\mathbf{u} = \lambda\mathbf{u} \tag{2}$$

then, from Eq. (1), $\mathbf{u}$ must be proportional to $\mathbf{x}$, and λ must equal $(\mathbf{y}^\dagger\mathbf{x})$.

The $(n-1)$ subspace of vectors orthogonal to $\mathbf{y}$ are a subspace of eigenvectors with zero eigenvalues.

If, now, $\mathbf{x}$ and $\mathbf{y}$ are orthogonal, then $\mathbf{x}$ also is an eigenvector with zero eigenvalue. In this case, however, $\mathbf{y}$ is a generalized eigenvector of the chain lead by the zero-eigenvalued eigenvector $(\mathbf{y}^\dagger\mathbf{y})\mathbf{x}$. We have, in this case, an $(n-2)$ subspace of eigenvectors with zero eigenvalue plus a chain of length two, also with zero eigenvalue.

We call the specialized matrices formed as the outer product of two vectors *dyads*. They are very useful in certain types of problems. Before discussing these applications, however, we shall generalize the concept to the K-metric.

2. K-DYADS

We shall consider the case where we have a complete set of vectors $\mathbf{u}_i$ which are pairwise K-orthogonal and maximally normalized. That is,

$$\begin{aligned}\mathbf{u}_i^\dagger\mathbf{K}\mathbf{u}_j &= 0 \qquad \text{if } j \text{ not} \sim i \\ &= \sigma_i = \sigma_j \qquad \text{if } j \sim i\end{aligned} \tag{3}$$

where

$$\sigma_i = \pm 1$$

That is, to each vector $\mathbf{u}_i$ there corresponds only a single value of j, designated as $\sim i$, such that the inner product $\mathbf{u}_i^\dagger\mathbf{K}\mathbf{u}_j$ does not vanish.

These vectors will very often be the eigenvectors of a matrix appearing in the problem. The metric $\mathbf{K}$ then arises as a metric in terms of which the matrix is K-hermitian, K-unitary, or, at least, K-normal. For the moment, however, let us simply consider the set of vectors and $\mathbf{K}$, as given.

We define the normalized K-dyads $\mathbf{E}_{ij}$ as

$$\mathbf{E}_{ij} = \sigma_i \mathbf{u}_i \mathbf{u}_{\sim j}^{\dagger} \mathbf{K} \tag{4}$$

The inclusion of σ_i in the definition is a convenience only. The indexing of the second term as $\sim j$ instead of j is also a matter of convenience leading to some formal simplification. The inclusion of the factor $\mathbf{K}$ is more fundamental in that it induces orthogonality relations analogous to those of the vectors, Eq. (3). Specifically, we have

$$\mathbf{E}_{ij}\mathbf{E}_{st} = \sigma_i \mathbf{u}_i \mathbf{u}_{\sim j}^{\dagger} \mathbf{K} \sigma_s \mathbf{u}_s \mathbf{u}_{\sim t} \mathbf{K} \tag{5}$$

$$= \sigma_i \sigma_s (\mathbf{u}_{\sim j}^{\dagger} \mathbf{K} \mathbf{u}_s) \mathbf{u}_i \mathbf{u}_{\sim t}^{\dagger} \mathbf{K}$$

where we have isolated the scalar factor. Then, from Eq. (3),

$$\mathbf{E}_{ij}\mathbf{E}_{st} = 0 \quad \text{if} \quad s \neq j$$

$$= \mathbf{E}_{it} \quad \text{if} \quad s = j \tag{6}$$

Equation (6) can be considered as an orthogonality relation between the normalized dyads.

We may also observe that Eq. (6) states that the set of dyads, plus the null matrix, have the group property. They are not a group, however, since the set does not include a unit element.[1] It is possible to combine them in appropriate ways to form elements that do constite a group, but this is another matter.

3. IDEMPOTENCY AND NILPOTENCY

The dyads of Eq. (4) have an important property whose significance we shall see later. Consider, first, $\mathbf{E}_{ii}$. We see that

$$\mathbf{E}_{ii}^2 = (\sigma_i \mathbf{u}_i \mathbf{u}_{\sim i}^{\dagger} \mathbf{K})(\sigma_i \mathbf{u}_i \mathbf{u}_{\sim i}^{\dagger} \mathbf{K}) \tag{7}$$

$$= \sigma_i \mathbf{u}_i \mathbf{u}_{\sim i}^{\dagger} \mathbf{K} = \mathbf{E}_{ii}$$

By induction, any power of $\mathbf{E}_{ii}$ is the same as $\mathbf{E}_{ii}$.

We describe this property by saying that $\mathbf{E}_{ii}$ is *idempotent*, meaning that is has some of the properties of the identity.

---

[1] A set of elements that have the group property but do not form a group are said to form a *semigroup*.

On the other hand, if $i \neq j$, then

$$\mathbf{E}_{ij}\mathbf{E}_{ij} = (\sigma_i\mathbf{u}_i\mathbf{u}^\dagger_{\sim j}K)(\sigma_i\mathbf{u}_i\mathbf{u}^\dagger_{\sim j}\mathbf{K}) = 0 \tag{8}$$

so that the square and higher powers vanish. We say that a matrix with this property is *nilpotent*, meaning that it has some of the properties of the null matrix. (The term nilpotent is sometimes used for a matrix such that some power, not necessarily the square, vanishes.)

As an illustration of the importance of these properties, consider a function with the power series expansion:

$$f(x) = a_0 + a_1x + \cdots = \sum_{n=0}^{\infty} a_n x^n \tag{9}$$

Then

$$f(k\mathbf{E}_{ii}) = a_0\mathbf{I} + \sum_{n=1}^{\infty} k^n\mathbf{E}_{ii}^n = a_0\mathbf{I} + \{f(k) - a_0\}\mathbf{E}_{ii} \tag{10}$$

and, if $i \neq j$,

$$f(k\mathbf{E}_{ij}) = a_0\mathbf{I} + a_1\mathbf{E}_{ij} \tag{11}$$

In particular, we see that

$$e^{-jk\mathbf{E}_{ii}z} = \mathbf{I} + (e^{-jkz} - 1)\mathbf{E}_{ii} \tag{12}$$

and

$$e^{-jk\mathbf{E}_{ij}z} = \mathbf{I} - jk\mathbf{E}_{ij}z, \qquad i \neq j \tag{13}$$

Thus the development of a function of a dyad is particularly easy. This is a direct consequence of their idempotency or nilpotency.

4. EXPANSION OF AN ARBITRARY MATRIX

Since the set $\mathbf{u}_i$ was assumed complete, it is evident that the set $\mathbf{E}_{ij}$ is complete and can therefore be used as the basis for the algebra of $n \times n$ matrices.

An arbitrary matrix $\mathbf{A}$ can be expanded in terms of these dyads:

$$\mathbf{A} = \sum_{ij} a_{ij}\mathbf{E}_{ij} = \sum_{ij} a_{ij}\sigma_i\mathbf{u}_i\mathbf{u}^\dagger_{\sim j}\mathbf{K} \tag{14}$$

We can determine the coefficients directly by premultiplying Eq. (14) by $\mathbf{u}^\dagger_{\sim m}\mathbf{K}$ and post-multiplying it by $\mathbf{u}_n$. We see then that the terms on the right vanish unless $i = m$ and $j = n$, when we have

$$a_{mn} = \sigma_n\mathbf{u}^\dagger_{\sim m}\mathbf{KAu}_n \tag{15}$$

If the vectors are the eigenvectors and generalized eigenvectors of $\mathbf{A}$, this expansion becomes particularly simple. In fact, the matrix of coefficients (a_{ij}) is closely related to the Jordan canonical form. For, suppose $\mathbf{u}_n$ is an eigenvector of $\mathbf{A}$ with eigenvalue λ_r ; then, from Eq. (8),

$$
\begin{aligned}
a_{mn} = \sigma_n \mathbf{u}^\dagger_{\sim m} \mathbf{K} \lambda_n \mathbf{u}_n &= 0 \quad \text{if} \quad m \neq n \\
&= \lambda_n \quad \text{if} \quad m = n
\end{aligned}
\tag{16}
$$

Hence the matrix (a_{mn}) is diagonal in the eigenvalues if $\mathbf{A}$ is semisimple, and

$$
\mathbf{A} = \sum_i \lambda_i \mathbf{E}_{ii}
\tag{17}
$$

On the other hand, suppose $\mathbf{u}_n$ is a generalized eigenvector with eigenvalue λ, and $\mathbf{u}_{n-1}$ is the generalized eigenvector of next lower rank in the chain. That is, suppose

$$
\mathbf{A}\mathbf{u}_n = \lambda \mathbf{u}_n + \mathbf{u}_{n-1}
$$

Then, from Eq. (15),

$$
\begin{aligned}
a_{mn} = \sigma_n \mathbf{u}^\dagger_{\sim m} \mathbf{K}(\lambda \mathbf{u}_n + \mathbf{u}_{n-1}) & \\
&= \lambda \quad \text{if} \quad n = m \\
&= \sigma_n \sigma_{n-1} \quad \text{if} \quad m = n - 1 \\
&= 0 \quad \text{otherwise}
\end{aligned}
\tag{18}
$$

The matrix (a_{mn}), therefore, is still quasidiagonal. The block associated with the given chain has λ on the main diagonal, $\sigma_n \sigma_{n-1} \, (= \pm 1)$ on the next superdiagonal, and zeros elsewhere.

We may note that the identity goes into the identity; that is,

$$
\mathbf{I} = \sum_i \mathbf{E}_{ii}
\tag{19}
$$

so that the corresponding matrix of coefficients is the identity.

It is evident that the transformation to the dyad basis is an isomorphism. We can confirm this by considering

$$
\mathbf{AB} = \left(\sum_{ij} a_{ij} \mathbf{E}_{ij} \right) \left(\sum_{kh} b_{kh} \mathbf{E}_{kh} \right)
$$

The product $\mathbf{E}_{ij}\mathbf{E}_{kh}$ vanishes unless $k = j$ when it equals $\mathbf{E}_{ih}$. Hence we have

$$
\mathbf{AB} = \sum_{ih} \left(\sum_j a_{ij} b_{jh} \right) \mathbf{E}_{ih}
\tag{20}
$$

Hence the product $\mathbf{AB}$ transformed into the product of the matrices of the coefficients, confirming the isomorphism.

5. FUNCTIONS OF A MATRIX

If the set $\mathbf{u}_i$ are eigenvectors of the K-normal matrix $\mathbf{A}$, then we can obtain simple expressions for a function of $\mathbf{A}$, $f(\mathbf{A})$, where $f(x)$ is an admissable function.

This follows directly from the isomorphism. However, it can also be shown easily in the case when $\mathbf{A}$ is semisimple so that Eq. (17) holds. Then we see that

$$\mathbf{A}^2 = \sum_{ij} \lambda_i \lambda_j \mathbf{E}_{ii} \mathbf{E}_{jj} = \sum_i \lambda_i^2 \mathbf{E}_{ii} \tag{21}$$

and, by induction,

$$\mathbf{A}^n = \sum_i \lambda_i^n \mathbf{E}_{ii} \tag{22}$$

If $f(x)$ can be expressed as a power series whose radius of convergence includes all the eigenvalues of $\mathbf{A}$, then it is evident that

$$f(\mathbf{A}) = \sum_i f(\lambda_i) \mathbf{E}_{ii} \tag{23}$$

The dependence on the radius of convergence of the power series can be removed by analytic continuation. It is only necessary that $f(x)$ be analytic in a simply connected region that includes all the eigenvalues of $\mathbf{A}$.

6. EXAMPLE

As a quite simple example of this kind of calculation, let us consider again the transmission line, on an $E - I$ basis, for which

$$\mathbf{R} = \begin{pmatrix} 0 & \beta Z \\ \beta/Z & 0 \end{pmatrix}$$

with β and Z constant. A metric for which this $\mathbf{R}$ is K-hermitian is

$$\mathbf{K} = \begin{pmatrix} 0 & 1 \\ 1 & 0 \end{pmatrix}$$

The maximally normalized eigenvectors, with their eigenvalues, are

$$\mathbf{u}_1 = \frac{1}{\sqrt{2Z}} \begin{pmatrix} Z \\ 1 \end{pmatrix}_\beta, \qquad \mathbf{u}_2 = \frac{1}{\sqrt{2Z}} \begin{pmatrix} -Z \\ 1 \end{pmatrix}_{-\beta}$$

The conjugacy and orthogonality relations are

$$\mathbf{u_1}^\dagger \mathbf{K} \mathbf{u_1} = 1$$

$$\mathbf{u_2}^\dagger \mathbf{K} \mathbf{u_2} = -1$$

$$\mathbf{u_1}^\dagger \mathbf{K} \mathbf{u_2} = \mathbf{u_2}^\dagger \mathbf{K} \mathbf{u_1} = 0$$

The matricant solution is

$$\mathbf{M} = e^{-j\mathbf{R}z} = e^{-j\beta z}\mathbf{u_1}\mathbf{u_1}^\dagger \mathbf{K} - e^{+j\beta z}\mathbf{u_2}\mathbf{u_2}^\dagger \mathbf{K}$$

$$= \tfrac{1}{2}e^{-j\beta z}\begin{pmatrix} 1 & Z \\ 1/Z & 1 \end{pmatrix} - \tfrac{1}{2}e^{j\beta z}\begin{pmatrix} -1 & Z \\ 1/Z & -1 \end{pmatrix}$$

$$= \begin{pmatrix} \cos \beta z & -jZ \sin \beta z \\ -(j/Z) \sin \beta z & \cos \beta z \end{pmatrix}$$

as we have found before.

This case is too simple to require this technique. However, in problems of larger dimensionality, the methods used here can be of great advantage.

7. DIFFERENTIAL EQUATIONS WITH CONSTANT COEFFICIENTS

We shall now consider the differential equation

$$\frac{d\mathbf{x}(z)}{dz} = -j\mathbf{R}\mathbf{x}(z), \qquad \mathbf{x}(0) = \mathbf{x_0} \tag{24}$$

where $\mathbf{R}$ is a square matrix.

Consider the dyads constructed from the maximally normalized eigenvectors and generalized eigenvectors $\mathbf{u}_i$ of $\mathbf{R}$:

$$\mathbf{R} = \sum r_{ij}\mathbf{E}_{ij} \tag{25}$$

where (r_{ij}) is the modified Jordan canonical form developed in the previous section.

Since the vectors $\mathbf{u}_i$ are a complete set, $\mathbf{x}(z)$ can be expanded on them as a basis:

$$\mathbf{x}(z) = \sum \alpha_i(z)\mathbf{u}_i \tag{26}$$

The set $\mathbf{u}_i$ may be taken as constant since $\mathbf{R}$ is assumed constant.

Hence, substituting in Eq. (24), we find

$$\sum_i \frac{d\alpha_i}{dz}\mathbf{u}_i = -j\sum_{ijk} r_{ij}\mathbf{E}_{ij}\alpha_k\mathbf{u}_k$$

$$= -j\sum r_{ij}\alpha_k\sigma_i\mathbf{u}_i\mathbf{u}^\dagger_{-j}\mathbf{K}\mathbf{u}_k$$

$$= -j\sum r_{ij}\alpha_j\sigma_i\sigma_j\mathbf{u}_i \tag{27}$$

Since the $\mathbf{u}_i$ are linearly independent, the coefficient of $\mathbf{u}_k$ in Eq. (27) must vanish for all k:

$$\frac{d\alpha_k}{dz} = -j\sum_i \sigma_k\sigma_i r_{ki}\alpha_i$$

If $\mathbf{R}$ is semisimple, then r_{ij} is diag$(\lambda_1, \lambda_2, ...)$ and

$$\frac{d\alpha_k}{dz} = -j\lambda_k\alpha_k \tag{28}$$

or

$$\alpha_k = e^{-j\lambda_k z}\alpha_k(0) \tag{29}$$

If the boundary condition is applied at $z = 0$ and is equal to $\mathbf{x}_0$, then, from Eq. (26),

$$\mathbf{x}_0 = \sum \alpha_i(0)\mathbf{u}_i \tag{30}$$

Premultiplying by $\sigma_j\mathbf{u}^\dagger_{-j}\mathbf{K}$, we find that

$$\alpha_j(0) = \sigma_j\mathbf{u}^\dagger_{-j}\mathbf{K}\mathbf{x}_0 \tag{31}$$

Hence if $\mathbf{R}$ is semisimple, the complete solution is

$$\mathbf{x}(z) = \sum_i e^{-j\lambda_i z}\sigma_i\mathbf{u}^\dagger_{-i}\mathbf{K}\mathbf{x}_0\mathbf{u}_i$$

$$= \sum_i e^{-j\lambda_i z}(\sigma_i\mathbf{u}_i\mathbf{u}^\dagger_{-i}\mathbf{K})\mathbf{x}_0 \tag{32}$$

since $\alpha_i(0)$ commutes with $\mathbf{u}_i$, or

$$\mathbf{x}(z) = \sum_i e^{-j\lambda_i z}\mathbf{E}_{ii}\mathbf{x}_0 \tag{33}$$

We therefore obtain the exponential dependence involving the eigenvalues without pulling any assumptions out of the air. The expansion in terms of the dyads constructed from the eigenvectors of the system matrix automatically separates the various behaviors, and, for each, sets up an equation of the form of Eq. (28), whose solution is known to be the exponential function.

It will be observed, also, that the solution found here must be the same as that found before, so that

$$e^{-j\mathbf{R}z} = \sum_i e^{-j\lambda_i z} \mathbf{E}_{ii} \tag{34}$$

If, on the other hand, $\mathbf{R}$ is not semisimple, then the problem gets a little more complicated, but not unduly so. Equation (27) still holds, but the r_{ij} now take the values given in Eq. (18). Thus there is set up a chain of differential equations, corresponding to the chain of generalized eigenvectors. The solution then is developed in terms of functions of the form $\varphi_i \exp(-j\lambda_i z)$ where φ_i is a polynomial in z of degree $m - i$, if m is the length of the chain and i the rank of the generalized eigenvector. The problem of fitting such polynomials to the boundary conditions is messy but straightforward.

8. PERTURBATION THEORY, NONDEGENERATE CASE

As a second example of the use of the dyad expansion, we shall consider a perturbed system. We shall restrict ourselves to first order perturbation theory although the method could be extended easily to higher orders.

Suppose we have a system described by Eq. (24) with

$$\mathbf{R} = \mathbf{R}_0 + \epsilon\mathbf{R}_1 \tag{35}$$

Where ϵ is the *perturbation parameter*. Suppose also that we know the solutions for $\mathbf{R}_0$ and want to know the effect of the perturbation for small ϵ.

For example, we might be considering an electron beam coupled to a circuit. If we know, in detail, the solutions to the circuit and the beam, each acting by itself, we can ask what happens as we introduce coupling between them. To do this, we set up a vector of which the first k components are the circuit variables and the rest are the beam variables. Then $\mathbf{R}_0$ is quasi diagonal, the first block being the system matrix of the circuit and the second of the beam. $\mathbf{R}_0$ then describes the system with the circuit and beam totally decoupled.

If $\epsilon\mathbf{R}_1$ describes the effect of coupling the beam to the circuit, our first question concerns the effect of this coupling for small values of ϵ. Does it, for example, cause amplification? If so, which waves are affected?

To treat this problem, we use the eigenvectors $\mathbf{u}_i$ of the unperturbed system. We will here restrict ourselves to the case where $\mathbf{R}_0$ is semisimple so that the set $\mathbf{u}_i$ is complete.

We will consider, first, the completely asynchronous case. We assume that the corresponding eigenvalues λ_i are all distinct.

We determine, by whatever means are available, an appropriate metric for the system—i.e., a $\mathbf{K}$ such that $\mathbf{R}_0$ is K-normal. In actual practice, it is usually possible to find a $\mathbf{K}$ such that $\mathbf{R}$ is K-hermitian for all ϵ with $\mathbf{K}$ independent of ϵ. If, for example, the system is lossless regardless of the coupling, then there is an appropriate power law that is independent of the coupling. However, the only requirement we need is that we know a $\mathbf{K}$ such that $\mathbf{R}_0$ is K-normal.

We will assume that the $\mathbf{u}_i$ are pairwise K-orthogonal and maximally normalized, according to Eq. (3). Then

$$\mathbf{R}_0 = \sum \lambda_i \mathbf{E}_{ii} = \sum \lambda_i \sigma_i \mathbf{u}_i \mathbf{u}_{\sim i}^\dagger \mathbf{K} \tag{36}$$

where the λ_i are all distinct.

The matrix $\mathbf{R}_1$ can also be expanded in terms of these dyads, as in Eqs. (14) and (15), so that

$$\mathbf{R}_1 = \sum_{ij} \sigma_j (\mathbf{u}_{\sim i}^\dagger \mathbf{K} \mathbf{R}_1 \mathbf{u}_j) \mathbf{E}_{ij} \tag{37}$$

We want to know the first order effect on the pth eigenvector and eigenvalue. That is, we want to know $\mathbf{u}_p{}'$ and $\lambda_p{}'$ such that

$$\mathbf{R}\mathbf{u}_p{}' = \lambda_p{}'\mathbf{u}_p{}' \tag{38}$$

where

$$\mathbf{u}_p{}' = \mathbf{u}_p + \epsilon \mathbf{v}_p \tag{39}$$

$$\lambda_p{}' = \lambda_p + \epsilon \mu_p \tag{40}$$

and we seek to determine $\mathbf{v}_p$ and μ_p.

Since the set $\mathbf{u}_i$ is complete, we can expand $\mathbf{v}_p$:

$$\mathbf{v}_p = \sum a_{pi} \mathbf{u}_i \tag{41}$$

If we substitute Eqs. (39) and (40) into Eq. (38), the eigenvector equation for $\mathbf{R}$, we find that the terms independent of ϵ give the eigenvector relation for $\mathbf{R}_0$. Those in the first order in ϵ give

$$\mathbf{R}_1 \mathbf{u}_p + \mathbf{R}_0 \mathbf{v}_p = \mu_p \mathbf{u}_p + \lambda_p \mathbf{v}_p \tag{42}$$

We substitute from Eqs. (36), and (37) for $\mathbf{R}_0$ and $\mathbf{R}_1$, and Eq. (41) for $\mathbf{v}_p$ recognizing that

$$\mathbf{E}_{ij}\mathbf{u}_k = \sigma_i\mathbf{u}_i\mathbf{u}_{\sim j}^\dagger\mathbf{K}\mathbf{u}_k$$

$$= \mathbf{0} \quad \text{if} \quad k \neq j \tag{43}$$

$$= \sigma_i\sigma_j\mathbf{u}_i \quad \text{if} \quad k = j$$

and find

$$\sum_i \sigma_i(\mathbf{u}_{\sim i}^\dagger\mathbf{K}\mathbf{R}_1\mathbf{u}_p)\mathbf{u}_i + \sum_i \lambda_i a_{pi}\mathbf{u}_i = \mu_p\mathbf{u}_p + \sum_i \lambda_p a_{pi}\mathbf{u}_i \tag{44}$$

Since the $\mathbf{u}_i$ are linearly independent, the coefficients of each vector in Eq. (44) must separately vanish. We see that

$$\sigma_i(\mathbf{u}_{\sim i}^\dagger\mathbf{K}\mathbf{R}_1\mathbf{u}_p) + \lambda_i a_{pi} = \mu_p\delta_{pi} + \lambda_p a_{pi} \tag{45}$$

If, now, we choose $i = p$, the second and fourth terms cancel and

$$\mu_p = \sigma_i\mathbf{u}_{\sim i}^\dagger\mathbf{K}\mathbf{R}_1\mathbf{u}_p \tag{46}$$

so that we have determined the first order perturbation of the eigenvalue. If $i \neq p$, the third term of Eq. (45) drops out and we can solve for

$$a_{pi} = \sigma_i\mathbf{u}_{\sim i}^\dagger\mathbf{K}\mathbf{R}_1\mathbf{u}_p/(\lambda_p - \lambda_i) \tag{47}$$

If we put this back into Eq. (39) we see that we have determined $\mathbf{v}_p$, except for a_{pp} , the first order perturbation of the eigenvector.

The coefficient a_{pp} is indeterminate. This is to be expected, however. This terms perturbs the magnitude of $\mathbf{u}_p$ without changing its direction. Since we can change the length of a vector without disturbing the fact of its being an eigenvector of $\mathbf{R}_0$, we would not expect this coefficient to be determined. It may be noted that the magnitude of the vector after the first order perturbation will determine the magnitude of the nonparallel components of the second order perturbation. Hence the choice of a_{pp} will affect the second order terms, but may be chosen arbitrarily as far as the first order terms are concerned. We therefore choose it either to be zero or to preserve the normalization of the vector, as convenient.

We have determined the first order perturbation of the eigenvectors and eigenvalues that results from perturbing the system matrix. It is the dyad expansion that permits us to break up the effect of the perturbing matrix into parts which have a simple effect. The ability to make this expansion in a convenient manner is, in turn, dependent on the K-orthogonality of the eigenvectors of the unperturbed matrix.

9. DEGENERATE CASE

If the eigenvalues are not all distinct, the procedure we have just been through requires some modification. This is indicated by the fact that Eq. (47) contains the denominator $(\lambda_p - \lambda_i)$ and hence will lead to dividing by zero.

This is a very important situation since it is the case where synchronism occurs—which is, often, the most interesting situation.

We shall not try to develop the theory in complete generality since this leads to great complexity of symbology tending to confuse the basic technique.

We shall suppose, instead, that $\mathbf{u}_1$ and $\mathbf{u}_2$ are degenerate for $\mathbf{R}_0$, both having the eigenvalue λ:

$$\mathbf{R}_0 \mathbf{u}_1 = \lambda \mathbf{u}_1$$

$$\mathbf{R}_0 \mathbf{u}_2 = \lambda \mathbf{u}_2$$

(48)

and assume there are no other eigenvectors of $\mathbf{R}_0$ with this eigenvalue. We shall consider the first order perturbation of these eigenvectors and of λ.

We may note that degeneracy among eigenvectors with eigenvalues different from λ does not interfere. We therefore do not restrict ourselves otherwise.

As before, we restrict ourselves to $\mathbf{R}_0$ semisimple, and assume a $\mathbf{K}$ such that $\mathbf{u}_i$ is pairwise K-orthogonal and maximally normalized.

The difficulty arises because the perturbed eigenvectors are not normally degenerate. In fact, the interesting situations are precisely those in which the degeneracy is split. If two waves that propagate synchronously are coupled so that the resultant eigenvectors have different eigenvalues, the separation *may* occur along the imaginary axis. If the original eigenvalue was purely real, so that the original waves propagated with phase shift only, coupling may split the degeneracy so as to give the eigenvalues imaginary components. One wave is now amplified, while the other decays. Thus amplification (or, what is the same thing in a different context, instability) can be a direct result of the splitting of a degeneracy.

Now, in the uncoupled case, any linear combination of $\mathbf{u}_1$ and $\mathbf{u}_2$ is an eigenvector of $\mathbf{R}_0$. But this is not true in the coupled case when the degeneracy is split. If we consider the perturbed eigenvectors as functions of ϵ, we see that they approach specific vectors as ϵ decreases to zero. These vectors are in the subspace spanned by $\mathbf{u}_1$ and $\mathbf{u}_2$ but will not be identical with $\mathbf{u}_1$ and $\mathbf{u}_2$ unless we have been extraordinarily lucky in their choice.

We must find the proper eigenvectors of $\mathbf{R}_0$. We let

$$\mathbf{w} = \mathbf{u}_1 + \alpha\mathbf{u}_2 \tag{49}$$

and require that α be such that we can express the perturbed eigenvector $\mathbf{w}'$ as

$$\mathbf{w}' = \mathbf{w} + \epsilon\mathbf{v} \tag{50}$$

We can expect, in this case, to find two possible values of α, α_1 and α_2 , leading to two unperturbed vectors, $\mathbf{w}_1$ and $\mathbf{w}_2$, which are perturbed to $\mathbf{w}_1'$ and $\mathbf{w}_2'$ through the perturbation vectors $\mathbf{v}_1$ and $\mathbf{v}_2$.

As before, we substitute Eqs. (35), (40), (49), and (50) in the eigenvector equation:

$$(\mathbf{R}_0 + \epsilon\mathbf{R}_1)(\mathbf{u}_1 + \alpha\mathbf{u}_2 + \epsilon\mathbf{v}) = (\lambda + \epsilon\mu)(\mathbf{u}_1 + \alpha\mathbf{u}_2 + \epsilon\mathbf{v}) \tag{51}$$

Again, the terms that are independent of ϵ express the fact that $\mathbf{w}$ is an eigenvector of $\mathbf{R}_0$ with eigenvalue λ. The first order terms give

$$\mathbf{R}_1(\mathbf{u}_1 + \alpha\mathbf{u}_2) + \mathbf{R}_0\mathbf{v} = \lambda\mathbf{v} + \mu(\mathbf{u}_1 + \alpha\mathbf{u}_2) \tag{52}$$

We substitute Eqs. (36), (37), and (41) in Eq. (52) and use the orthogonality relations:

$$\sum_i \sigma_i(\mathbf{u}_{-i}^{\mathsf{t}}\mathbf{KR}_1\mathbf{u}_1)\mathbf{u}_i + \alpha \sum_i \sigma_i(\mathbf{u}_{-i}^{\mathsf{t}}\mathbf{KR}_1\mathbf{u}_2)\mathbf{u}_i + \sum_i a_i\lambda_i\mathbf{u}$$

$$= \lambda \sum_i a_i\mathbf{u}_i + \mu(\mathbf{u}_1 + \alpha\mathbf{u}_2) \tag{53}$$

Pulling out the coefficients of $\mathbf{u}_1$ and $\mathbf{u}_2$, we obtain

$$\sigma_1\mathbf{u}_{-1}^{\mathsf{t}}\mathbf{KR}_1\mathbf{u}_1 + \alpha\sigma_1\mathbf{u}_{-1}^{\mathsf{t}}\mathbf{KR}_1\mathbf{u}_2 = \mu \tag{54}$$

$$\sigma_2\mathbf{u}_{-2}^{\mathsf{t}}\mathbf{KR}_1\mathbf{u}_1 + \alpha\sigma_2\mathbf{u}_{-2}^{\mathsf{t}}\mathbf{KR}_1\mathbf{u}_2 = \alpha\mu \tag{55}$$

We can now solve Eq. (54), for example, for α and substitute in Eq. (55). We obtain a quadratic in μ. The two roots of this equation give the two eigenvalues to the first order of the perturbed system. If there is only a single root, then the perturbation has not split the degeneracy.

Substitutions of these values of μ in either Eq. (54) or (55) give the appropriate value of α. (One must note the possibility that one of the appropriate $\mathbf{w}$'s is, in fact, $\mathbf{u}_2$. In this case, the appropriate α is ∞. This, however, will show up earlier in the analysis if specific values of the terms $\mathbf{u}^{\dagger}_{\sim i}\mathbf{KR}_1\mathbf{u}_j$ are used.)

Finally, the appropriate coefficients of the $\mathbf{v}$ vectors, and hence of the perturbed eigenvectors, can be calculated as before. Again, there is an indeterminancy in that the conditions do not determine a perturbation of, say, $\mathbf{w}_1$ in direction of $\mathbf{w}_1$.

Perhaps the most significant question is the conditions under which the perturbation introduces an imaginary component to a real λ. If $\mathbf{R}$ is a system matrix appropriate to Eq. (24), this will cause one of the perturbed eigenvectors to grow—i.e., amplify—and the other to decay.

If we eliminate α from Eqs. (52) and (53), the discriminant of the resultant quadratic in μ is

$$B^2 - 4AC = \{\sigma_1\mathbf{u}^{\dagger}_{\sim 1}\mathbf{KR}_1\mathbf{u}_1 - \sigma_2\mathbf{u}^{\dagger}_{\sim 2}\mathbf{KR}_1\mathbf{u}_2\}^2$$

$$+ 4\sigma_1\sigma_2(\mathbf{u}^{\dagger}_{\sim 1}\mathbf{KR}_1\mathbf{u}_2)(\mathbf{u}^{\dagger}_{\sim 2}\mathbf{KR}_1\mathbf{u}_1) \qquad (56)$$

If $\mathbf{R}$ is K-hermitian for all ϵ, Eq. (56) is necessarily real. If it is greater than zero, then μ_1 and μ_2 are both real and the coupling does not cause amplification of these modes—at least to the first order. If it is negative, then μ_1 and μ_2 are complex, and λ_1 and λ_2 contain imaginary parts. Then $\mathbf{u}_1'$ amplifies and $\mathbf{u}_2'$ decays.

The first factor on the right of Eq. (56) is necessarily nonnegative. In the second term, the factors in parentheses are complex conjugates of each other if $\mathbf{R}_1$, as well as $\mathbf{R}_0$, is K-hermitian. Hence their product is nonnegative. Therefore, the only way we can make the discriminant negative is by having σ_1 and σ_2 be of opposite sign. This is not a sufficient condition, since the first factor may dominate, but it is a necessary condition. In coupled mode terminology, amplification can be obtained by pairwise coupling only if the modes so coupled have opposite parity. (We have here proved this only on a perturbation basis. It can also be proven generally, even for strong coupling.)

Again we should note the importance of the orthogonality relations obtained by the choice of $\mathbf{K}$ as metric, in making tractible a problem that otherwise would be soluble in principle, but expremely tedious if not quite impractical.

10. APPROXIMATE MATRICANT

The technique we have developed provides a way to obtain an approximation to the matricant of a uniform system that may be very useful.

Suppose we have a system whose matrix $\mathbf{R}$ is large with many nonzero terms. Even though it is always possible, in principle, to obtain the exact matricant solution to this system, it may be quite impractical to do so. We may have much too much difficulty in obtaining its eigenvectors and eigenvalues to hope to apply Eq. (34), or to solve it exactly by any other means.

It may happen, however, that we can split $\mathbf{R}$ up into $\mathbf{R}_0 + \epsilon\mathbf{R}_1$, where $\mathbf{R}_0$ is a matrix whose eigenvectors can be obtained with relative ease, and where both $\mathbf{R}_0$ and $\mathbf{R}$ are K-hermitian for a known $\mathbf{K}$. We can then consider that $\mathbf{R}$ is obtained by perturbing $\mathbf{R}_0$ with $\mathbf{R}_1$, providing the constant ϵ is reasonably small. If now we find the perturbed eigenvectors and eigenvalues to some appropriate order in ϵ, we can use these in Eq. (34) and obtain an approximate solution to the problem.

Properly done, this method yields an approximation whose percentage error may remain small even for large z, even under conditions where the methods of Chapter VII are valid only for small z.

Suppose, for example, that some of the eigenvalues of $\mathbf{R}$ are complex. The corresponding terms in Eq. (34) then contain exponential growth or decay factors. The approximation considered in Chapter VII consisting of the first k terms of the Peano expansion approximates this dependence as a polynomial in z of order $(k-1)$ (since $\mathbf{R}$ is here assumed constant.) It cannot be valid, therefore, for any z greater than that for which such a polynomial in z is a suitable approximation to the exponential functions involved.

On the other hand, we can often choose $\mathbf{R}_0$ to be a matrix which has only real eigenvalues, and which therefore includes only phase effects. The first order perturbation of $\mathbf{R}_0$ by $\mathbf{R}_1$ may, however, include the major part of the imaginary component of the eigenvalues of $\mathbf{R}$. The corresponding terms in the resulting Eq. (34) will then include the major growth or decay factors. Hence the resulting approximation may be valid even to large z.

We can, as usual, check the validity of this approximation by computing the next order perturbation and assuring ourselves that it is negligible.

This method of approximation does give the correct functional dependence of the matricant on z, with the residual error being in the constants of the dependence. It is, therefore, an approximation technique that is often very useful, and that may give a very good approximation.

11. CONCLUSION

The dyad expansion of a matrix is a technique that is often of great value in the analysis of a system. We have illustrated its use in two areas. We have discussed the solution of the general system equation, Eq. (24), with constant coefficients—i.e., a uniform system, and we have discussed the first order perturbation problem. In both cases, the dyad expansion has allowed us to make effective use of the orthogonality relations introduced by the metric **K**. Other applications could be cited also.

It must be admitted that this technique requires knowledge of the eigenvectors involved. In the first example this knowledge need only be approximate. The result will be no better than the approximation, but neither will it be worse.

In the perturbation problem, it is necessary to have the eigenvectors of the unperturbed problem exactly. The first order perturbation is the solution that is correct within any desired error for sufficiently small ϵ. But if the eigenvectors of $\mathbf{R}_0$ are only approximate, then we can pick ϵ small enough so that the error in the eigenvectors is greater than the first order perturbation itself. Hence it is necessary that we start with an exact solution of the unperturbed problem. (However, if only approximate eigenvectors of $\mathbf{R}_0$ are known, it may be legitimate to construct a new $\mathbf{R}_0$ of which they are the exact eigenvectors, and perturb this system.)

Both applications do depend on knowing the eigenvectors and eigenvalues and a **K** that orthogonalizes them. If it is not feasible to obtain them, then other methods must be sought.

In practical terms this is not a method of completely general applicability. When it is applicable, however, it is a method of great convenience.

Exercises

1. Using

$$\mathbf{K} = \begin{pmatrix} 0 & 0 & 0 & 1 \\ 0 & 0 & 1 & 0 \\ 0 & 1 & 0 & 0 \\ 1 & 0 & 0 & 0 \end{pmatrix}$$

and the vectors

$$\mathbf{x}_1 = \mathrm{col}(1, 0, j, 0), \qquad \mathbf{x}_3 = \mathrm{col}(0, 1, 0, j)$$

$$\mathbf{x}_2 = \mathrm{col}(1, 0, -j, 0) \qquad \mathbf{x}_4 = \mathrm{col}(0, 1, 0, -j)$$

construct

(a) a matrix for which $\mathbf{x}_1$, $\mathbf{x}_2$, $\mathbf{x}_3$, and $\mathbf{x}_4$ are eigenvectors with eigenvalues $1, -1, j, -j$, in that order,

(b)   a matrix such that

$$\mathbf{Ax_1} = j\mathbf{x_1}, \qquad \mathbf{Ax_3} = -j\mathbf{x_3}$$
$$\mathbf{Ax_2} = j\mathbf{x_2} + \mathbf{x_1}, \qquad \mathbf{Ax_4} = -j\mathbf{x_4} + \mathbf{x_3}$$

(c)   a matrix such that

$$\mathbf{Ax_1} = j\mathbf{x_1}, \qquad \mathbf{Ax_3} = -j\mathbf{x_3} + \mathbf{x_4}$$
$$\mathbf{Ax_2} = j\mathbf{x_2} + \mathbf{x_1}, \qquad \mathbf{Ax_4} = -j\mathbf{x_4}$$

(d)   a matrix such that

$$\mathbf{Ax_1} = j\mathbf{x_1}, \qquad \mathbf{Ax_3} = j\mathbf{x_3} + \mathbf{x_2}$$
$$\mathbf{Ax_2} = j\mathbf{x_2} + \mathbf{x_1}, \qquad \mathbf{Ax_4} = -j\mathbf{x_4}$$

2.   Let

$$\mathbf{R_0} = \begin{pmatrix} 0 & 1 & 0 & 0 \\ 1 & 0 & 0 & 0 \\ 0 & 0 & a & b \\ 0 & 0 & -1 & 0 \end{pmatrix}, \qquad \mathbf{R_1} = \begin{pmatrix} 0 & 0 & 0 & 0 \\ 0 & 0 & 0 & 1 \\ 1 & 0 & 0 & 0 \\ 0 & 0 & 0 & 0 \end{pmatrix}$$

where a and b are real constants.
If

$$\mathbf{R} = \mathbf{R_0} + \epsilon\mathbf{R_1}$$

where ϵ is small and real, show that $\mathbf{R}$ is K-hermitian, independently of ϵ, for

$$\mathbf{K} = \begin{pmatrix} 0 & 1 & 0 & 0 \\ 1 & 0 & 0 & 0 \\ 0 & 0 & 0 & 1 \\ 0 & 0 & 1 & a \end{pmatrix}$$

Find the eigenvalues and eigenvectors of $\mathbf{R}$ to the first order in ϵ as perturbations of the eigenvalues and eigenvectors of $\mathbf{R_0}$ for the following cases:

(a) $a = 5, \quad b = 6$

(b) $a = 3, \quad b = 2$

(c) $a = \frac{3}{2}, \quad b = \frac{1}{2}$

Note the different parity conditions on the synchronous modes in (b) and (c).

(This is a simplified version of the system matrix that describes the coupling of transverse waves in an electron beam by interaction with a slow-wave circuit. See, for example, M. Pease, *J. Appl. Phys.* **31** 2028–2036 (1960).)

3. Show that any $n \times n$ matrix can be expressed as the sum of not more than n dyads.

(*Comment*: The expansion in terms of the set $\mathbf{E}_{ij}$ involves possibly n^2 dyads.)

(*Caution*: We have not specified semisimplicity.)

4. In Exercise 3, Chapter VII, we considered the Cauchy system, given by

$$\frac{d\mathbf{X}}{dz} = \frac{1}{z - \alpha} \mathbf{SX}, \qquad \mathbf{X}(0) = \mathbf{I}$$

where $\mathbf{S}$ is a constant matrix and α is a possibly complex constant. Assuming $\mathbf{S}$ is semisimple and K-normal, solve this system using the dyad expansion.

5. Suppose K is a proper metric and $\mathbf{E}$ is a dyad that we can write as $\mathbf{uv^\dagger K}$. The equation

$$\mathbf{Ex} = \mathbf{y}$$

has a solution for $\mathbf{x}$ in terms of $\mathbf{y}$ if and only if $\mathbf{y}$ is proportional to $\mathbf{u}$. Show that if this is so, a solution is given by

$$\mathbf{x} = \alpha \mathbf{v}/(\mathbf{v^\dagger K v})$$

where α is a scalar. What is the value of α?

6. We can define an inner product of two dyads by

$$\langle \mathbf{uv^\dagger}, \mathbf{xy^\dagger} \rangle = \langle \mathbf{v}, \mathbf{x} \rangle \langle \mathbf{y}, \mathbf{u} \rangle$$

corresponding to the double contraction of tensor theory. Show that if the vectorial inner product is proper, the dyad inner product satisfies the postulates for a proper inner product in a space of real vectors (Chapter II, Section 4, (A'), (B'), (C'), and (D').)

7. Suppose K is a proper metric and $\mathbf{A}$ is an operator that can be expressed as the sum of a dyad and the identity

$$\mathbf{A} = \mathbf{I} + \mathbf{uv^\dagger K}$$

Under what conditions does the equation

$$\mathbf{Ax} = \mathbf{y}$$

have a solution? If it does, what is the solution?

(*Hint*: If we write the equation to be solved in explicit form, we obtain

$$\mathbf{x} + \mathbf{u}\mathbf{v}^{\dagger}\mathbf{K}\mathbf{x} = \mathbf{y}$$

Premultiplying by $\mathbf{v}^{\dagger}\mathbf{K}$, we can solve for $(\mathbf{v}^{\dagger}\mathbf{K}\mathbf{x})$. This permits us to solve directly for $\mathbf{x}$.)

Outline how this process can be generalized to an operator that is the identity plus k dyads.

8.   Let $\mathbf{E}_{ij}$ be a complete set of dyads for the metric $\mathbf{K}$, formed from a complete set of K-orthogonal maximally normalized vectors according to Eq. (4). If we expand a matrix $\mathbf{A}$ on this set

$$\mathbf{A} = \sum a_{ij}\mathbf{E}_{ij}$$

what conditions on the coefficients a_{ij} are necessary and sufficient to make $\mathbf{A}$ (a) K-hermitian, (b) K-unitary?

CHAPTER XI

Projectors

We shall, in this chapter, develop the theory of a class of operators that we shall call *projectors*. These are, in effect, generalizations of a subclass of the dyads that we considered in the previous chapter. They are also generalizations of the idea of expressing a vector in 3-space in terms of its projections on a set of coordinate axes. The generalization that is involved is, first, that instead of axes, we can use subspaces of any dimension. (A vector in euclidean 3-space can be expressed, for example, in terms of its projection on the xy plane and its z component.) In addition, we are able to do this without any implication of the orthogonality of the axes—i.e., without reference to any inner product.

Aside from the elegance of such an operation, it is also useful in certain problems because the use of projectors may avoid the explicit calculation of the eigenvectors. If, in particular, the system matrix is semisimple, we find that we can develop what we shall call the projectors on its eigenspaces from the minimum polynomial alone—i.e., by knowledge of the eigenvalues only. In some situations, such as high dimensionality, this can give a marked improvement in the computational efficiency.

It is with this purpose in mind that we shall develop the theory of projectors in rather abstract terms. We shall base them on the fundamental operation of decomposing the space. The more usual procedure is to define them as *idempotent* operators (i.e., an operator $\mathbf{P}$ such that $\mathbf{P}^2 = \mathbf{P}$). The latter, however, appears arbitrary unless it be justified in terms of the behavior of the eigenvectors of a given operator. The approach used here seems the more fundamental and general. Later in this chapter we shall see that they have some very useful properties, and we will show their application to certain types of problems.

1. DEFINITION OF A PROJECTOR

As a preliminary to the general definition of a projector, we remind the reader of the definition of the decomposition of a space S into subspaces S_1 and S_2. We say that S is *decomposed* into S_1 and S_2 if any vector $\mathbf{x}$ in S_1 can be written uniquely as $\mathbf{x}_1 + \mathbf{x}_2$, where $\mathbf{x}_1$ is in

S_1 and $\mathbf{x}_2$ in S_2. In place of the requirement of uniqueness, we can assert that there is no vector that is common to S_1 and S_2—i.e., that S_1 and S_2 are *disjoint*.

If S is decomposed into S_1 and S_2, we say that S is the *direct sum* of S_1 and S_2, symbolized

$$S = S_1 \oplus S_2 \tag{1}$$

Definition. *Given a decomposition of S into S_1 and S_2 so that*

$$\mathbf{x} = \mathbf{x}_1 + \mathbf{x}_2, \qquad \mathbf{x}_1 \in S_1, \quad \mathbf{x}_2 \in S_2 \tag{2}$$

for any $\mathbf{x} \in S$, the operator $\mathbf{P}$ that carries $\mathbf{x}$ into $\mathbf{x}_1$ is called the **projector on S_1 along S_2**.

It should be noted that the projector $\mathbf{P}$ depends both on S_1 and on S_2. For example, Fig. 1 shows a vector $\mathbf{u}$ in 2-dimensional euclidean space.

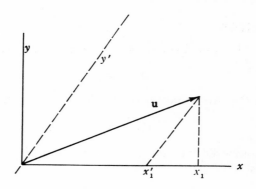

FIG. 1.   The projection of u on x along y and y'.

Its projection on S_1, the subspace of the x axis, clearly depends on whether the other axis S_2 is the y or y' axis.

Theorem 1.   *A projector is a linear homogeneous operator.*

This is evident since, if

$$\mathbf{x} = \mathbf{x}_1 + \mathbf{x}_2, \qquad \mathbf{x}_1 \in S_1, \quad \mathbf{x}_2 \in S_2$$
$$\mathbf{Px} = \mathbf{x}_1$$

then

$$\mathbf{P}(\alpha\mathbf{x}) = \alpha\mathbf{x}_1$$

where α is any scalar in F.

Also, if

$$\mathbf{y} = \mathbf{y}_1 + \mathbf{y}_2 , \qquad \mathbf{y}_1 \in S_1 , \quad \mathbf{y}_2 \in S_2$$

then

$$\mathbf{x} + \mathbf{y} = (\mathbf{x}_1 + \mathbf{y}_1) + (\mathbf{x}_2 + \mathbf{y}_2)$$

so that

$$\mathbf{P}(\mathbf{x} + \mathbf{y}) = \mathbf{x}_1 + \mathbf{y}_1 = \mathbf{Px} + \mathbf{Py}$$

Finally, if $\mathbf{x}$ is the null vector, $\mathbf{Px} = 0$. Hence, $\mathbf{P}$ is a linear homogeneous operator. As an example, the matrix

$$\mathbf{P} = \begin{pmatrix} \mathbf{I} & \mathbf{0} \\ \mathbf{0} & \mathbf{0} \end{pmatrix}$$

where $\mathbf{I}$ is $k \times k$, is a projector on the subspace of vectors, all of whose components beyond the kth are zero, along the space of vectors whose first k components are zero.

2. IDEMPOTENCY

Theorem 2. *A linear operator* $\mathbf{P}$ *is a projector if and only if it is idempotent—i.e.,*

$$\mathbf{P}^2 = \mathbf{P}$$

For suppose $\mathbf{P}$ is the projector on S_1 along S_2. Let $\mathbf{x}$ be any vector. Then

$$\mathbf{Px} = \mathbf{x}_1$$

But if $\mathbf{x}_1$ is decomposed into components in S_1 and S_2, we get $(\mathbf{x}_1 + \mathbf{0})$. Hence, we must have

$$\mathbf{P}^2\mathbf{x} = \mathbf{Px}_1 = \mathbf{x}_1 = \mathbf{Px}$$

for all $\mathbf{x}$ in S. Hence

$$\mathbf{P}^2 = \mathbf{P}$$

and $\mathbf{P}$ is idempotent.

Conversely, suppose $\mathbf{P}$ is idempotent. Let S_1 be the set of all vectors $\mathbf{x}_1$ such that

$$\mathbf{Px}_1 = \mathbf{x}_1 \tag{3}$$

and S_2 be the set of all vectors $\mathbf{x}_2$ such that

$$\mathbf{Px}_2 = 0 \tag{4}$$

Both S_1 and S_2 are evidently subspaces. We need to prove that, together, they are a decomposition of the whole space.

Suppose, first, that there were a vector **u** that was common to S_1 and S_2. Then, since it is in S_1,

$$\mathbf{Pu} = \mathbf{u}$$

But since it is also in S_2,

$$\mathbf{Pu} = \mathbf{0}$$

Hence, **u** is the null vector, and S_1 and S_2 are disjoint.

Consider an arbitrary **x**. Then we can write

$$\mathbf{x} = \mathbf{Px} + (\mathbf{I} - \mathbf{P})\mathbf{x}$$

If we write

$$\mathbf{x}_1 = \mathbf{Px}, \qquad \mathbf{x}_2 = (\mathbf{I} - \mathbf{P})\mathbf{x}$$

Then $\mathbf{x}_1$ is certainly in S_1 since

$$\mathbf{Px}_1 = \mathbf{P}^2\mathbf{x} = \mathbf{Px} = \mathbf{x}_1$$

Also, we see that $\mathbf{x}_2$ is in S_2 since

$$\mathbf{Px}_2 = (\mathbf{P} - \mathbf{P}^2)\mathbf{x} = \mathbf{Px} - \mathbf{Px} = \mathbf{0}$$

Hence, we have shown how any vector can be written as

$$\mathbf{x} = \mathbf{x}_1 + \mathbf{x}_2, \qquad \mathbf{x}_1 \in S_1, \quad \mathbf{x}_2 \in S_2$$

and S is decomposed into S_1 and S_2.

From this we immediately obtain the following:

Corollary 1. *If* **P** *is the projector on* S_1 *along* S_2, *where* $S = S_1 \oplus S_2$, *then* **P** *is semisimple with only the eigenvalues 1 and 0, and* S_1 *is spanned by the eigenvectors with unit eigenvalue,* S_2 *by the eigenvectors with zero eigenvalue.*

This follows immediately from Eqs. (3) and (4) which determine S_1 and S_2.

We have also the following:

Corollary 2. *If* **P** *is the projector on* S_1 *along* S_2, *then* $(\mathbf{I} - \mathbf{P})$ *is the projector on* S_2 *along* S_1.

3. COMBINATIONS OF PROJECTORS

In the theorems that follow, we will use a little different symbology. We will let $\mathbf{P}_1$ be the projector on R_1 (for range) along N_1 (for null space), and $\mathbf{P}_2$ on R_2 along N_2.

Theorem 3. $(\mathbf{P}_1 + \mathbf{P}_2)$ *is a projector if and only if*

$$\mathbf{P}_1\mathbf{P}_2 = \mathbf{P}_2\mathbf{P}_1 = 0$$

If so, then it is the projector on $R_1 \oplus R_2$ *along* $N_1 \cap N_2$.

(The symbol $N_1 \cap N_2$ means the *intersection of* N_1 *and* N_2—i.e., the subspace of vectors that are simultaneously in N_1 and N_2.)

If $\mathbf{P}_1 + \mathbf{P}_2$ is a projector, then we require that

$$(\mathbf{P}_1 + \mathbf{P}_2)^2 = \mathbf{P}_1{}^2 + \mathbf{P}_1\mathbf{P}_2 + \mathbf{P}_2\mathbf{P}_1 + \mathbf{P}_2{}^2 = \mathbf{P}_1 + \mathbf{P}_2 \qquad (5)$$

Since $\mathbf{P}_1$ and $\mathbf{P}_2$ are projectors, this requires that

$$\mathbf{P}_1\mathbf{P}_2 + \mathbf{P}_2\mathbf{P}_1 = 0 \qquad (6)$$

Premultiplying by $\mathbf{P}_1$, we find that

$$\mathbf{P}_1\mathbf{P}_2 + \mathbf{P}_1\mathbf{P}_2\mathbf{P}_1 = 0$$

and post-multiplying by $\mathbf{P}_1$

$$\mathbf{P}_1\mathbf{P}_2\mathbf{P}_1 + \mathbf{P}_2\mathbf{P}_1 = 0$$

Subtracting these two equations, we see that $\mathbf{P}_1$ and $\mathbf{P}_2$ commute:

$$\mathbf{P}_1\mathbf{P}_2 - \mathbf{P}_2\mathbf{P}_1 = 0$$

Combining this with Eq. (6), we find

$$\mathbf{P}_1\mathbf{P}_2 = \mathbf{P}_2\mathbf{P}_1 = 0 \qquad (7)$$

Therefore, if $(\mathbf{P}_1 + \mathbf{P}_2)$ is a projector, then Eq. (7) is true.

Conversely, if Eq. (7) is true, then Eq. (6) is also true, so that, as in Eq. (5),

$$(\mathbf{P}_1 + \mathbf{P}_2)^2 = \mathbf{P}_1 + \mathbf{P}_2$$

and $(\mathbf{P}_1 + \mathbf{P}_2)$ is a projector.

The first part of the theorem is proven. We must now determine what are the spaces involved.

If $\mathbf{P} = \mathbf{P}_1 + \mathbf{P}_2$ is a projector, consider a $\mathbf{z}$ that is separately decomposed by $\mathbf{P}_1$ and $\mathbf{P}_2$ according to

$$\begin{aligned}
\mathbf{z} &= \mathbf{x}_1 + \mathbf{y}_1, & \mathbf{x}_1 \in R_1, & \quad \mathbf{y}_1 \in N_1 \\
&= \mathbf{x}_2 + \mathbf{y}_2, & \mathbf{x}_2 \in R_2, & \quad \mathbf{y}_2 \in N_2
\end{aligned}$$

If $\mathbf{z}$ is in R, the range of $\mathbf{P}$, or the set of vectors such that $\mathbf{Pz} = \mathbf{z}$, then

$$\begin{aligned}
\mathbf{z} = \mathbf{Pz} &= (\mathbf{P}_1 + \mathbf{P}_2)\mathbf{z} = \mathbf{P}_1\mathbf{z} + \mathbf{P}_2\mathbf{z} \\
&= \mathbf{P}_1(\mathbf{x}_1 + \mathbf{y}_1) + \mathbf{P}_2(\mathbf{x}_2 + \mathbf{y}_2) \\
&= \mathbf{x}_1 + \mathbf{x}_2
\end{aligned}$$

Hence $\mathbf{z}$ is written as the sum of a vector in R_1 and a vector in R_2, and R is included in the sum of R_1 and R_2.

Conversely, if $\mathbf{z} = \mathbf{x}_1 + \mathbf{x}_2$, then

$$\begin{aligned}
\mathbf{Pz} &= \mathbf{P}_1\mathbf{z} + \mathbf{P}_2\mathbf{z} \\
&= \mathbf{P}_1(\mathbf{x}_1 + \mathbf{y}_1) + \mathbf{P}_2(\mathbf{x}_2 + \mathbf{y}_2) \\
&= \mathbf{P}_1\mathbf{x}_1 + \mathbf{P}_2\mathbf{x}_2 \\
&= \mathbf{x}_1 + \mathbf{x}_2 = \mathbf{z}
\end{aligned}$$

so that, if $\mathbf{z}$ is the sum of any vector in R_1 and any vector in R_2, it is in R. Hence the sum of R_1 and R_2 includes R. With the previous result, R must equal $R_1 + R_2$.

Finally, if $\mathbf{z}$ is in both R_1 and R_2, so that

$$\mathbf{P}_1\mathbf{z} = \mathbf{P}_2\mathbf{z} = \mathbf{z}$$

then

$$\mathbf{z} = \mathbf{P}_1\mathbf{z} = \mathbf{P}_1\mathbf{P}_2\mathbf{z} = \mathbf{0}$$

since $\mathbf{P}_1\mathbf{P}_2 = \mathbf{0}$ by the first part of the theorem. Therefore, R_1 and R_2 are disjoint, and

$$R = R_1 \oplus R_2$$

It remains to show that N, the set of all vectors such that $\mathbf{Pz} = \mathbf{0}$, is $N_1 \cap N_2$. If $\mathbf{z}$ is in $N_1 \cap N_2$, then $\mathbf{Pz} = (\mathbf{P}_1 + \mathbf{P}_2)\mathbf{z} = 0$. Let $\mathbf{z}$ be such that

$$\mathbf{Pz} = \mathbf{P}_1\mathbf{z} + \mathbf{P}_2\mathbf{z} = 0$$

Premultiplying by $\mathbf{P}_1$ and $\mathbf{P}_2$, we obtain

$$\mathbf{P}_1^{\,2}\mathbf{z} + \mathbf{P}_1\mathbf{P}_2\mathbf{z} = \mathbf{P}_1\mathbf{z} = 0$$

and

$$\mathbf{P}_2\mathbf{P}_1\mathbf{z} + \mathbf{P}_2^2\mathbf{z} = \mathbf{P}_2\mathbf{z} = 0$$

since $\mathbf{P}_1\mathbf{P}_2 = \mathbf{P}_2\mathbf{P}_1 = 0$. Hence $\mathbf{z}$ is in both N_1 and N_2, i.e., in $N_1 \cap N_2$. The theorem is proven.

Theorem 4. $(\mathbf{P}_1 - \mathbf{P}_2)$ *is a projector if and only if*

$$\mathbf{P}_1\mathbf{P}_2 = \mathbf{P}_2\mathbf{P}_1 = \mathbf{P}_2 \tag{8}$$

If so, then $R = R_1 \cap N_2$ *and* $N = N_1 \oplus R_2$.

$(\mathbf{P}_1 - \mathbf{P}_2)$ is a projector if and only if

$$\mathbf{I} - (\mathbf{P}_1 - \mathbf{P}_2) = (\mathbf{I} - \mathbf{P}_1) + \mathbf{P}_2$$

is a projector. By Theorem 3, this is so if and only if

$$\mathbf{P}_2(\mathbf{I} - \mathbf{P}_1) = (\mathbf{I} - \mathbf{P}_1)\mathbf{P}_2 = 0$$

which requires that Eq. (8) be true.

The space R, which is the range of $\mathbf{P}$, is then the null space of $\mathbf{I} - \mathbf{P} = \mathbf{I} - (\mathbf{P}_1 - \mathbf{P}_2) = (\mathbf{I} - \mathbf{P}_1) + \mathbf{P}_2$. Hence, by Theorem 3, R is the intersection of N_2 and the null space of $(\mathbf{I} - \mathbf{P}_1)$, which is R_1:

$$R = R_1 \cap N_2$$

Likewise N, the null space of $\mathbf{P}$, is the range of $(\mathbf{I} - \mathbf{P})$ which, by Theorem 3 is the direct sum of R_2 and the range of $(\mathbf{I} - \mathbf{P}_1)$ which is N_1

$$N = R_2 \oplus N_1$$

Hence the theorem is proven.

Theorem 5. $\mathbf{P} = \mathbf{P}_1\mathbf{P}_2$ *is a projector if*

$$\mathbf{P}_1\mathbf{P}_2 = \mathbf{P}_2\mathbf{P}_1 \tag{9}$$

If so, then $R = R_1 \cap R_2$ *and* $N = N_1 + N_2$.

Note that N here is the simple sum of N_1 and N_2, not the direct sum—i.e., we do not assert disjointness. For example, if we set $\mathbf{P}_1 = \mathbf{P}_2$, then $\mathbf{P} = \mathbf{P}_1^2 = \mathbf{P}_1$ is a projector, but $N_1 = N_2$, the antithesis of disjointness. Also, we do not assert the necessity of Eq. (9).

If Eq. (9) is true, then

$$\mathbf{P}^2 = (\mathbf{P_1P_2})(\mathbf{P_2P_1}) = \mathbf{P_1P_2}^2\mathbf{P_1}$$
$$= (\mathbf{P_1P_2})\mathbf{P_1} = (\mathbf{P_2P_1})\mathbf{P_1} = \mathbf{P_2P_1} = \mathbf{P_1P_2} = \mathbf{P}$$

Therefore $\mathbf{P}$ is a a projector if Eq. (9) is true.

To determine its range, let $\mathbf{z}$ be in R, so that

$$\mathbf{z} = \mathbf{Pz}$$

Then we see that

$$\mathbf{P_1z} = \mathbf{P_1Pz} = \mathbf{P_1}^2\mathbf{P_2z} = \mathbf{P_1P_2z} = \mathbf{z}$$

so that $\mathbf{z}$ is in R_1. Similarly, it is in R_2.

Conversely, if $\mathbf{z}$ is in R_1 and R_2,

$$\mathbf{P_1z} = \mathbf{z} = \mathbf{P_2z}$$
$$\mathbf{z} = \mathbf{P_1z} = \mathbf{P_1P_2z} = \mathbf{Pz}$$

Hence we find that

$$R = R_1 \cap R_2$$

To determine its null space, let $\mathbf{z}$ be in N, so that

$$\mathbf{Pz} = \mathbf{P_1P_2z} = 0$$

Then $\mathbf{P_2z}$ is in N_1. Similarly $\mathbf{P_1z}$ is in N_2.

We can split any vector $\mathbf{z}$ into two parts:

$$\mathbf{z} = \mathbf{P_2z} + (\mathbf{I} - \mathbf{P_2})\mathbf{z}$$

But we have already seen that if $\mathbf{z}$ is in N, then $\mathbf{P_2z}$ is in N_1. Also, $(\mathbf{I} - \mathbf{P_2})\mathbf{z}$ is always in N_2. Hence any $\mathbf{z}$ in N can be split into the sum of a vector in N_1 and one in N_2.

Conversely, if $\mathbf{z}$ can be written as

$$\mathbf{z} = \mathbf{z_1} + \mathbf{z_2}, \qquad \mathbf{z_1} \in N_1, \quad \mathbf{z_2} \in N_2$$

Then

$$\mathbf{Pz} = \mathbf{P_2P_1z_1} + \mathbf{P_1P_2z_2} = 0$$

and $\mathbf{z}$ is in N. Hence,

$$N = N_1 + N_2$$

and the proof is complete.

4. INVARIANT SUBSPACES

There is a direct relation between the invariant subspaces of a matrix **A** and projectors. We have:

Theorem 6. *If S_1 is invariant with respect to* **A**, *then*

$$\mathbf{PAP} = \mathbf{AP} \qquad\qquad (10)$$

for every projector onto S_1.

Suppose S_2 is any subspace such that

$$S = S_1 \oplus S_2$$

and let **P** be the projector onto S_1 along S_2. Let

$$\mathbf{x} = \mathbf{x}_1 + \mathbf{x}_2, \qquad \mathbf{x}_1 \in S_1, \quad \mathbf{x}_2 \in S_2$$

be any vector in S. Then, by the definition of a projector

$$\mathbf{Px} = \mathbf{x}_1$$

and

$$\mathbf{PAPx} = \mathbf{P}(\mathbf{Ax}_1) = \mathbf{Ax}_1$$

since S_1 is invariant for **A**, so that $\mathbf{Ax}_1$ is in S_1. Hence

$$\mathbf{PAPx} = \mathbf{Ax}_1 = \mathbf{APx}$$

for all **x**, so that

$$\mathbf{PAP} = \mathbf{AP}$$

The converse is also true:

Theorem 7. *If, for some projector* **P** *onto a subspace S_1 along S_2,*

$$\mathbf{PAP} = \mathbf{AP}$$

then S_1 is invariant for **A**.

Again, let

$$S = S_1 \oplus S_2$$

where **P** is the projector onto S_1 along S_2.

If **x** is any vector in S_1, so that $\mathbf{x} = \mathbf{Px}$, then

$$\mathbf{PAx} = \mathbf{PAPx} = \mathbf{APx} = \mathbf{Ax}$$

so that **Ax** is in S_1. Hence S_1 is invariant for **A**.

Finally, there is a theorem relating projectors to decompositions:

Theorem 8. *If* $S = S_1 \oplus S_2$, *then* **A** *decomposes the whole space into the invariant subspaces* S_1 *and* S_2 *if and only if*

$$PA = AP$$

where **P** *is the projector onto* S_1 *along* S_2.

We recall the definition of a decomposition by an operator which requires that both S_1 and S_2 be invariant, where $S = S_1 \oplus S_2$.

To prove sufficiency, let x_1 be any vector in S_1. Then

$$Ax_1 = APx_1 = PAx_1$$

so that Ax_1 is in S_1, and S_1 is invariant. If x_2 is any vector in S_2, then

$$PAx_2 = APx_2 = 0$$

so that Ax_2 is in S_2, and S_2 is invariant. Hence **A** is decomposed.

To prove the necessity, assume **A** is decomposed by S_1 and S_2. Since S_1 is invariant, Theorem 6 applies and

$$PAP = AP$$

Since S_2 is also invariant, Theorem 6 applies for $(I - P)$:

$$(I - P)A(I - P) = A(I - P)$$

or

$$A - PA - AP + PAP = A - AP$$

Substituting Eq. (10):

$$PA = AP$$

5. EIGENSUBSPACES

The space $S_A{}^\lambda$ of all vectors **x** such that

$$(A - \lambda I)^k x = 0 \tag{11}$$

for some integer k is called an *eigensubspace of* **A**. It is the subspace spanned by all eigenvectors and chains of generalized eigenvectors with eigenvalue λ. The lowest value of k that can be used to define a given eigenspace is the length of the longest chain with the specified eigenvalue.

An eigenspace of **A** is, evidently, invariant with respect to **A**. That is, if **x** is in $S_A{}^\lambda$, so is (Ax).

The totality of all the eigenspaces of a matrix $\mathbf{A}$ is a decomposition of the whole space. Since the set of all eigenvectors and generalized eigenvectors are complete, an arbitrary vector can be expanded in terms of them. The vectors of the expansion can be grouped according to their eigenvalues. Hence an arbitrary vector can be expressed as the sum of vectors in the eigenspaces. Since there is no vector that is a generalized eigenvector with more than one eigenvalue, the separation is disjoint, and the eigenspaces decompose the whole space.

This leads us to consider the projector on an eigenspace along the direct sum of the other eigenspaces. We define $\mathbf{P}_i$ as the projector on $S_A^{\lambda_i}$ along $\Sigma_{\lambda_j \neq \lambda_i} \oplus S_A^{\lambda_j}$.

The range of $\mathbf{P}_i$ is spanned by the eigenvectors and generalized eigenvectors of $\mathbf{A}$ with eigenvalue λ_i. Its null space is spanned by all other eigenvectors and generalized eigenvectors of $\mathbf{A}$.

Evidently,

$$\mathbf{P}_i \mathbf{P}_j = 0 \quad \text{if} \quad i \neq j \tag{12}$$

From Theorem 3, $(\mathbf{P}_i + \mathbf{P}_j)$ is a projector and its range is the direct sum of S^{λ_i} and S^{λ_j}.

By induction, $\Sigma_i \mathbf{P}_i$ is a projector whose range is the direct sum of all the eigenspaces, which is the whole space. Hence, we see that

$$\sum_i \mathbf{P}_i = \mathbf{I} \tag{13}$$

This gives us a set of projectors that are particularly significant for the analysis of systems involving the system matrix $\mathbf{A}$ (or $\mathbf{R}$ in our usual symbology).

6. SEMISIMPLE MATRICES

If $\mathbf{A}$ is semisimple, we can expand it on the set $\{\mathbf{P}_i\}$ as

$$\mathbf{A} = \sum_i \lambda_i \mathbf{P}_i \tag{14}$$

This is the correct expansion since, if $\mathbf{x}_j$ is an eigenvector with eigenvalue λ_j, we see that

$$\mathbf{A}\mathbf{x}_j = \sum_i \lambda_i \mathbf{P}_i \mathbf{x}_j = \lambda_j \mathbf{x}_j$$

We find also, using Eq. (12),

$$\mathbf{A}^2 = \sum_{ij} \lambda_i \lambda_j \mathbf{P}_i \mathbf{P}_j = \sum_i \lambda_i^2 \mathbf{P}_i$$

or, by induction,

$$\mathbf{A}^n = \sum_i \lambda_i^n \mathbf{P}_i$$

Finally, if $f(x)$ is an admissable function (e.g., if it is analytic in a simply connected region that contains all the eigenvalues of $\mathbf{A}$),

$$f(\mathbf{A}) = \sum_i f(\lambda_i)\mathbf{P}_i \qquad (15)$$

Consider as an example of the use of this expansion the matricant equation

$$\frac{d}{dz}\mathbf{M}(z) = -j\mathbf{R}\mathbf{M}, \qquad \mathbf{M}(0) = \mathbf{I} \qquad (16)$$

Let $\mathbf{R}$ be expanded according to Eq. (14) on the projectors on its eigenspaces. Let us assume that its eigenspaces, and hence the set $\mathbf{P}_i$, are not functions of z. This is somewhat weaker than our usual assumption that $\mathbf{R}$ is constant. Specifically, it permits the eigenvalues to be functions of z.

Let us assume that $\mathbf{M}(z)$ can also be expanded according to Eq. (15):

$$\mathbf{M}(z) = \sum_i m_i(z)\mathbf{P}_i \qquad (17)$$

By Eq. (13) this will satisfy the boundary condition in Eq. (16) if

$$m_i(0) = 1 \qquad \text{for all } i \qquad (18)$$

Substituting Eq. (17) in Eq. (16), since $\mathbf{P}_i$ is constant, we obtain

$$\sum_i \frac{dm_i}{dz}\mathbf{P}_i = -j\sum_{ik}\lambda_i \mathbf{P}_i m_k \mathbf{P}_k$$

$$= -j\sum_i \lambda_i m_i \mathbf{P}_i$$

If we multiply by $\mathbf{P}_k$, we eliminate the summation and find that the solution that satisfies Eq. (18) is

$$m_i = \exp\left\{-j\int_0^z \lambda_i \, dz\right\}$$

and

$$\mathbf{M}(z) = \sum_i \exp\left\{-j\int_0^z \lambda_i \, dz\right\}\mathbf{P}_i \qquad (19)$$

Hence, we have found that the matricant is obtained as an expansion over the projectors.

7. NONSEMISIMPLE MATRICES

If $\mathbf{A}$ is not semisimple we cannot expand $\mathbf{A}$ simply in terms of the projectors on the eigenspaces. We can show, however, that we can make an expansion if we augment the set $\mathbf{P}_i$ by the set $\mathbf{H}_i$ where $\mathbf{H}_i$ is an operator (not a projector) that annihilates a vector in any eigensubspace except that for λ_i, that annihilates any eigenvector with eigenvalue λ_i, and that reduces by one the rank of any generalized eigenvector with eigenvalue λ_i. We find that we can write

$$\mathbf{A} = \sum_i (\lambda_i \mathbf{P}_i + \mathbf{H}_i) \tag{20}$$

The properties of the $\mathbf{H}_i$ and $\mathbf{P}_i$ are as follows:

$$
\begin{aligned}
\mathbf{P}_i{}^2 &= \mathbf{P}_i \\
\mathbf{P}_i \mathbf{P}_j &= 0, && \neq j \\
\mathbf{P}_i \mathbf{H}_j &= \mathbf{H}_j \mathbf{P}_i = 0, && i \neq j \\
\mathbf{P}_i \mathbf{H}_i &= \mathbf{H}_i = \mathbf{H}_i \mathbf{P}_i \\
\mathbf{H}_i{}^k &= 0, && k \geqslant k_i
\end{aligned}
\tag{21}
$$

where k_i is the length of the longest chain with eigenvalue λ_i.

Then we see that

$$
\begin{aligned}
\mathbf{A}^2 &= \sum_{ij} (\lambda_i \mathbf{P}_i + \mathbf{H}_i)(\lambda_j \mathbf{P}_j + \mathbf{H}_j) \\
&= \sum_i (\lambda_i{}^2 \mathbf{P}_i + 2\lambda_i \mathbf{H}_i + \mathbf{H}_i{}^2)
\end{aligned}
$$

and, by induction,

$$\mathbf{A}^n = \sum_i \left\{ (\lambda_i{}^n)\mathbf{P}_i + \sum_{j=1}^{k_i-1} \binom{n}{j} \lambda_i{}^{n-j} \mathbf{H}_i{}^j \right\} \tag{22}$$

the expression terminating because $\mathbf{H}_i^{k_i} = 0$.

Consequently, if $f(x)$ is an admissible function, then

$$f(\mathbf{A}) = \sum_i \left\{ f(\lambda_i)\mathbf{P}_i + \sum_{j=1}^{k_i-1} \frac{f^{(j)}(\lambda_i)}{j!} \mathbf{H}_i{}^j \right\} \tag{23}$$

where $f^{(j)}(\lambda_i)$ is the jth derivative of $f(x)$, evaluated at λ_i. This follows from the Taylor expansion of $f(x)$, using, if necessary, analytic continuation.

8. DETERMINATION OF P_i, A SEMISIMPLE

If **A** is semisimple, the set of projectors on the eigensubspaces $\mathbf{P}_i$ can be determined directly from the minimum polynomial $\varphi(\lambda)$ of **A**. The minimum polynomial $\varphi(\lambda)$ of **A** has the form

$$\varphi(\lambda) = \prod_i (\lambda - \lambda_i) \tag{24}$$

where the product is taken over all *discrete* λ_i. This can be written

$$\varphi(\lambda) = a_n(\lambda - \lambda_n)\theta_n(\lambda)$$

where $\theta_n(\lambda)$ is a polynomial that does not contain λ_n as a root. We can normalize $\theta_n(\lambda)$ to

$$\theta_n(\lambda) = \prod_{i \neq n} \frac{(\lambda - \lambda_i)}{(\lambda_n - \lambda_i)} \tag{25}$$

by letting

$$a_n = \prod_{i \neq n} (\lambda_n - \lambda_i)$$

and observing that a_n is necessarily nonzero.

We claim that $\theta_n(\mathbf{A})$ is $\mathbf{P}_n$:

$$\theta_n(\mathbf{A}) = \prod_{i \neq n} \frac{(\mathbf{A} - \lambda_i\mathbf{I})}{(\lambda_n - \lambda_i)} = \mathbf{P}_n \tag{26}$$

We observe, first, that if $\mathbf{x}_m$ is an eigenvector of **A** with eigenvalue $\lambda_m \neq \lambda_i$, there is a factor in $\mathbf{P}_n$ that causes $\mathbf{P}_n\mathbf{x}_m$ to vanish. If, on the other hand, we consider an eigenvector $\mathbf{x}_n$ with eigenvalue λ_n, we find that $\mathbf{P}_n\mathbf{x}_n = \mathbf{x}_n$. Since **A** is assumed semisimple, these are the only cases to be considered.

Hence the projectors on the eigenspaces of a semisimple matrix can be obtained by a suitable factorization and renormalization of the minimum polynomial.

This can be of considerable significance. If the system matrix is constant, there are many ways of solving Eq. (16). Most of these require specific knowledge of the eigenvectors, however. The use of Eq. (26) with Eq. (19) depends only on knowledge of the eigenvalues and the minimum polynomial.

9. A NOT SEMISIMPLE

If $\mathbf{A}$ is not semisimple, the determination of the $\mathbf{P}_i$, other than by direct computation with the eigenvectors and generalized eigenvectors, is more involved, but still possible in principle.

We shall not attempt a general solution but will discuss a simple case to demonstrate the technique that can be used.

Suppose the minimum polynomial of $\mathbf{A}$ is

$$\varphi(\lambda) = (\lambda - \lambda_1)^2 (\lambda - \lambda_2)^2$$

Then

$$\mathbf{A} = \lambda_1 \mathbf{P}_1 + \lambda_2 \mathbf{P}_2 + \mathbf{H}_1 + \mathbf{H}_2$$

as in Eq. (20). From Eq. (13)

$$\begin{aligned}
\mathbf{A} - \lambda_1 \mathbf{I} &= (\lambda_2 - \lambda_1)\mathbf{P}_2 + \mathbf{H}_1 + \mathbf{H}_2 \\
\mathbf{A} - \lambda_2 \mathbf{I} &= (\lambda_1 - \lambda_2)\mathbf{P}_1 + \mathbf{H}_1 + \mathbf{H}_2
\end{aligned} \tag{27}$$

so that, multiplying, respectively, by $\mathbf{P}_1$ and $\mathbf{P}_2$,

$$\begin{aligned}
\mathbf{H}_1 &= (\mathbf{A} - \lambda_1 \mathbf{I})\mathbf{P}_1 \\
\mathbf{H}_2 &= (\mathbf{A} - \lambda_2 \mathbf{I})\mathbf{P}_2
\end{aligned} \tag{28}$$

Squaring Eqs. (27) and recognizing that in this case $\mathbf{H}_1{}^2 = \mathbf{H}_2{}^2 = \mathbf{0}$, we find

$$\begin{aligned}
(\mathbf{A} - \lambda_1 \mathbf{I})^2 &= (\lambda_2 - \lambda_1)^2 \mathbf{P}_2 + 2(\lambda_2 - \lambda_1)\mathbf{H}_2 \\
(\mathbf{A} - \lambda_2 \mathbf{I})^2 &= (\lambda_1 - \lambda_2)^2 \mathbf{P}_1 + 2(\lambda_1 - \lambda_2)\mathbf{H}_1
\end{aligned}$$

If we substitute for $\mathbf{H}_1$ and $\mathbf{H}_2$ from Eq. (28), we obtain

$$\begin{aligned}
(\mathbf{A} - \lambda_1 \mathbf{I})^2 &= 2(\lambda_2 - \lambda_1)\{\mathbf{A} - \tfrac{1}{2}(\lambda_1 + \lambda_2)\mathbf{I}\}\mathbf{P}_2 \\
(\mathbf{A} - \lambda_2 \mathbf{I})^2 &= 2(\lambda_1 - \lambda_2)\{\mathbf{A} - \tfrac{1}{2}(\lambda_1 + \lambda_2)\mathbf{I}\}\mathbf{P}_1
\end{aligned} \tag{29}$$

Since $\tfrac{1}{2}(\lambda_1 + \lambda_2)$ is not an eigenvalue of $\mathbf{A}$, the matrix $\{\mathbf{A} - \tfrac{1}{2}(\lambda_1 + \lambda_2)\mathbf{I}\}$ is nonsingular and so has an inverse. Hence we can solve Eqs. (29) for $\mathbf{P}_1$ and $\mathbf{P}_2$ and, with Eqs. (28), for $\mathbf{H}_1$ and $\mathbf{H}_2$.

More complicated systems can be solved by similar means. Whether this is a practical method or not depends on the particular situation. It is at least possible in principle to determine the $\mathbf{P}_i$ and $\mathbf{H}_i$ by direct calculation from knowledge of the eigenvalues and the lengths of the longest chains associated with each eigenvalue.

10. THE RESOLVANT

We will mention another method of obtaining the projectors of an operator $\mathbf{A}$ which may, in some cases, be convenient although it is more commonly used for operators in an infinitely dimensioned Hilbert space.
We consider the matrix valued function of λ:

$$\mathbf{F}(\lambda) = (\lambda\mathbf{I} - \mathbf{A})^{-1} \qquad (30)$$

This function is called the *resolvant*. We consider it as a function of the complex variable λ. It is not difficult to see that the components of $\mathbf{F}(\lambda)$ are functions that are analytic except at the eigenvalues of $\mathbf{A}$.
Consider the contour integral

$$\frac{1}{2\pi j} \oint \mathbf{F}(\lambda)\, d\lambda$$

By this we mean the matrix whose coefficients are $(1/2\pi j)$ times the contour integrals of the coefficients of $\mathbf{F}(\lambda)$, each integral being taken over the same contour. The coefficients will be the residues of those simple poles of the coefficients of $\mathbf{F}(\lambda)$ that lie within the contour.
We can now use Eq. (15) to expand $\mathbf{F}(\lambda)$, if $\mathbf{A}$ is semisimple:

$$\mathbf{F}(\lambda) = \sum_i (\lambda - \lambda_i)^{-1}\mathbf{P}_i$$

or, if $\mathbf{A}$ is not semisimple, we can use Eq. (23):

$$\mathbf{F}(\lambda) = \sum_i \left\{ (\lambda - \lambda_i)^{-1}\mathbf{P}_i + (\lambda - \lambda_i)^{-2}\mathbf{H}_i + (\lambda - \lambda_i)^{-3}\mathbf{H}_i^2 + \cdots \right\}$$

In either case, the residue of the pole at $\lambda = \lambda_i$ is simply $\mathbf{P}_i$. Hence

$$\mathbf{P}_i = \frac{1}{2\pi j} \oint_i \mathbf{F}(\lambda)\, d\lambda \qquad (31)$$

where the contour encloses only the single root λ_i.
If the contour encloses more than one root, say λ_1 and λ_2, the integral gives $(\mathbf{P}_1 + \mathbf{P}_2)$.
We can then obtain $\mathbf{H}_i$ as in Eq. (28) as

$$\mathbf{H}_i = (\mathbf{A} - \lambda_i\mathbf{I})\mathbf{P}_i \qquad (32)$$

or as the contour integral

$$\mathbf{H}_i = \frac{1}{2\pi j} \oint_i (\lambda - \lambda_i)(\lambda\mathbf{I} - \mathbf{A})^{-1}\, d\lambda \qquad (33)$$

Whether or not these formulas provide a convenient method of calculating the $\mathbf{P}_i$ depends on the ability to calculate $\mathbf{F}(\lambda)$. It is, however, a method of general validity that, again, obtains the projectors without explicit determination of the eigenvectors.

11. ORTHOGONALITY

One reason for using the given definition of a projector is that it frees the development from dependence any concept of orthogonality.

An alternative definition that is more closely connected to the elementary concepts of geometry would involve projecting a vector onto an axis, plane, hyperplane, etc. This was, in fact, done in the discussion of Fig. 1. This viewpoint, however, almost presupposes that we are dealing with a set of cartesian coordinates, or with coordinates that can be taken as cartesian with proper choice of a metric.

In Fig. 1, for example, x_1 is the projection of $\mathbf{u}$ on x in the (x, y) coordinate system, which is cartesian. In the case of the skewed axes (x, y'), x_1' is the projection on x. We have shown previously that skewed axes can be studied conveniently by proper choice of a metric $\mathbf{K}$ that is positive definite. The projection is then defined as x_1' such that the vector $(u - x_1')$ is orthogonal to any x.

This definition is satisfactory as long as the metric is proper, and can easily be extended to the projection on any subspace.

If the metric that we wish to use is improper, we may be in serious trouble. Consider, for example, the two-dimensional space with the metric diag$(1, -1)$ so that if the vector is col(x, t), its length l, squared, is

$$l^2 = x^2 - t^2$$

This is the case, for example, in the two-dimensional Minkowski space of relativity.

The vectors

$$\mathbf{u}_1 = \begin{pmatrix} 1 \\ 1 \end{pmatrix}, \qquad \mathbf{u}_2 = \begin{pmatrix} 1 \\ -1 \end{pmatrix}$$

are both of zero length, if we ignore the concept of conjugacy that we developed in Chapter IX:

$$\langle \mathbf{u}_1 \mathbf{u}_1 \rangle = \mathbf{u}_1{}^\dagger \begin{pmatrix} 1 & 0 \\ 0 & -1 \end{pmatrix} \mathbf{u}_1 = 0$$

$$\langle \mathbf{u}_2 \mathbf{u}_2 \rangle = 0$$

If, now, we wish to project an arbitrary vector $\begin{pmatrix} x \\ t \end{pmatrix}$ onto S_1 along S_2, where S_1 is the subspace spanned by $\mathbf{u}_1$, and S_2 by $\mathbf{u}_2$, we must be careful. We cannot define the projection as that vector in S_1 such that the other component is orthogonal to all vectors is S_1. The only vectors that are orthogonal to a vector in S_1 are vectors in S_1.

Basing the definition on a decomposition of the space, however, avoids all difficulty. We can decompose the vector into a vector in S_1 and a vector in S_2:

$$\begin{pmatrix} x \\ t \end{pmatrix} = \tfrac{1}{2}(x + t)\begin{pmatrix} 1 \\ 1 \end{pmatrix} + \tfrac{1}{2}(x - t)\begin{pmatrix} 1 \\ -1 \end{pmatrix}$$

Hence we find immediately and trivially that

$$\mathbf{P}_1 = \frac{1}{2}\begin{pmatrix} 1 & 1 \\ 1 & 1 \end{pmatrix}, \qquad \mathbf{P}_2 = \frac{1}{2}\begin{pmatrix} 1 & -1 \\ -1 & 1 \end{pmatrix} = \mathbf{I} - \mathbf{P}_1$$

That these operators are idempotent is obvious. Further, we see that $\mathbf{P}_1\mathbf{P}_2 = \mathbf{0}$.

This method of defining the projectors thus avoids all questions of the orthogonality of vectors. The concept of the metric does not enter at all.

It is possible, now, to reintroduce the metric by considering the K-*adjoint projectors*, $\mathbf{P}_i^\#$, defined by

$$\mathbf{P}_i^\# = \mathbf{K}^{-1}\mathbf{P}_i^\dagger\mathbf{K} \tag{34}$$

and studying the possible relation between the sets $\mathbf{P}_i^\#$ and $\mathbf{P}_i$.

If $\mathbf{A}$ is not semisimple, we must also consider the K-adjoint set of $\mathbf{H}_i$:

$$\mathbf{H}_i^\# = \mathbf{K}^{-1}\mathbf{H}_i^\dagger\mathbf{K} \tag{35}$$

Suppose $\mathbf{K}$ has been chosen so that it is possible to relabel the index from i to $(\sim i)$ so that

$$\mathbf{P}_i^\# = \mathbf{P}_{\sim i}$$
$$\mathbf{H}_i^\# = \mathbf{H}_{\sim i} \tag{36}$$
$$\lambda_i^* = \lambda_{\sim i}$$

Then $\mathbf{A}$ is K-hermitian, for

$$\mathbf{A}^\# = \sum(\lambda_i\mathbf{P}_i + \mathbf{H}_i)^\# = \sum(\lambda_i^*\mathbf{P}_i^\# + \mathbf{H}_i^\#)$$

$$= \sum(\lambda_{\sim i}\mathbf{P}_{\sim i} + \mathbf{H}_{\sim i}) = \mathbf{A}$$

More generally, the transformation of Eq. (34) preserves the property of being a projector since $\mathbf{P}_i^{\#2} = \mathbf{P}_i^\#$. Also, it preserves the disjointness of the projectors since

$$\mathbf{P}_i^\#\mathbf{P}_j^\# = \mathbf{K}^{-1}(\mathbf{P}_j\mathbf{P}_i)^\dagger\mathbf{K} = \mathbf{0} \qquad \text{if} \quad i \neq j$$

and Eqs. (34) and (35) preserve the relations of Eq. (21).

Conversely, if **A** is K-hermitian, then, if it is expressed in the form of Eq. (20), there must be a relabeling of the index such that Eq. (36) applies.

Thus the properties of K-hermitian matrices flow from the behavior of the projectors under the transformations of Eqs. (34) and (35).

12. CONCLUSIONS

The projectors have properties that, in a sense, are analogous to those of the eigenvectors. More precisely, they are generalizations of the dyads formed as in Chapter X from the eigenvectors. Their advantage is that they include in their structure any degeneracy that may be present, and so avoid the complications that degeneracy otherwise introduces into subsequent operations.

The practical advantage that develops is due to the possibility of obtaining the projectors on the eigenspaces as polynomials of the matrix involved, the appropriate polynomial being obtained as a factor of the minimum polynomial (if the matrix is semisimple). Thus we avoid the necessity of obtaining an explicit evaluation of the eigenvectors. In some cases this can lead to a considerable simplification of the necessary calculation.

Exercises

1. Find the projector onto the space M along the space N, where:

    (a) M is the linear envelope of col(1, 1, 0); col(1, −1, 1); and N is the linear envelope of col(1, 0, 1).
    (b) M is the linear envelope of col(1, 1, 0); col(1, −1, 1); and N is the linear envelope of col(0, 1, 1).
    (c) M is the linear envelope of col(1, 0, 1); and N is the linear envelope of col(2, 0, 1); col(0, 2, −1).
    (d) M is the linear envelope of col(1, 1, j, 0); col(0, 1, j, j); and N is the linear envelope of col(0, 1, j, 0); col(1, 0, j, −j).

    In each case, check the idemotency of your results.

2. Suppose

$$\mathbf{A} = \mathbf{I} + \mathbf{u}\mathbf{v}^\dagger\mathbf{K}$$

where **u** and **v** are vectors such that

$$\mathbf{v}^\dagger\mathbf{K}\mathbf{u} = -1$$

Show that $\mathbf{A}$ is a projector. Generalize this result to an operator $\mathbf{A}$ that is $\mathbf{I}$ plus the sum of k dyads:

$$\mathbf{A} = \mathbf{I} + \mathbf{u_1v_1}^\dagger\mathbf{K} + \cdots + \mathbf{u}_k\mathbf{v}_k^\dagger\mathbf{K}$$

where

$$\mathbf{v}_i^\dagger\mathbf{Ku}_j = 0$$

if $i \neq j$.

(Cf. Chapter X, Exercise 7.)

3. If $\mathbf{P}$ is a projector, and $\mathbf{Q} = \mathbf{I} - \mathbf{P}$, prove the identity:

$$\mathbf{A} = \mathbf{PAP} + \mathbf{PAQ} + \mathbf{QAP} + \mathbf{QAQ}$$

Use this identity to prove the formula for the product of two partitioned matrices:

$$\begin{pmatrix} \mathbf{A} & \mathbf{B} \\ \mathbf{C} & \mathbf{D} \end{pmatrix}\begin{pmatrix} \mathbf{A'} & \mathbf{B'} \\ \mathbf{C'} & \mathbf{D'} \end{pmatrix} = \begin{pmatrix} \mathbf{AA'} + \mathbf{BC'} & \mathbf{AB'} + \mathbf{BD'} \\ \mathbf{CA'} + \mathbf{DC'} & \mathbf{CB'} + \mathbf{DD'} \end{pmatrix}$$

4. If $\mathbf{P}_1$ and $\mathbf{P}_2$ are projectors that commute, prove that $(\mathbf{P}_1 + \mathbf{P}_2 - \mathbf{P}_1\mathbf{P}_2)$ is a projector.

5. The matrix $\mathbf{U}$ is called an *involution* if $\mathbf{U}^2 = \mathbf{I}$. Show that the relation

$$\mathbf{U} = 2\mathbf{P} - \mathbf{I}$$

is a one-to-one correspondance between the set of all $n \times n$ involutions and the set of all $n \times n$ projectors.

6. Prove that if $\mathbf{P}$ is a projector, there is a basis in terms of which $\mathbf{P}$ takes the form

$$\mathbf{P} = \begin{pmatrix} \mathbf{I} & 0 \\ 0 & 0 \end{pmatrix}$$

On this basis, what is the form of the involution obtained from $\mathbf{P}$ as $(2\mathbf{P} - \mathbf{I})$? (Cf. Exercise 5)

7. What is the minimum polynomial of a projector? Of an involution? (Cf. Exercise 5.)

8. If $\mathbf{P}$ is a projector, show that the inverse of $(\mathbf{I} + \alpha\mathbf{P})$ is given by

$$(\mathbf{I} + \mathbf{P})^{-1} = \mathbf{I} - \frac{\alpha}{1 + \alpha}\mathbf{P}$$

What happens if $\alpha = -1$?

9.   Let $\mathbf{P}_1$, $\mathbf{P}_2$, $\mathbf{P}_3$ be three projectors such that

$$\mathbf{P}_1 + \mathbf{P}_2 + \mathbf{P}_3 = \mathbf{I}$$

Show that

$$\mathbf{P}_1\mathbf{P}_2 = \mathbf{P}_2\mathbf{P}_1 = \mathbf{P}_1\mathbf{P}_3 = \mathbf{P}_3\mathbf{P}_1 = \mathbf{P}_2\mathbf{P}_3 = \mathbf{P}_3\mathbf{P}_2 = 0$$

CHAPTER XII

Singular and Rectangular Operators

In this chapter we shall be concerned with the solution for **v**, given **u**, of the equation

$$\mathbf{u} = \mathbf{T}\mathbf{v} \tag{1}$$

where **T** is a linear homogeneous operator.

If **T** is a nonsingular square matrix, then Eq. (1) is solved by obtaining $\mathbf{T}^{-1}$. However, the problem as stated may still be meaningful when **T** has no inverse, either because it is singular or because it is rectangular. In these cases, it is necessary to restrict the vector **u** to a subspace. Also, the solution obtained for a given **u** may not be unique. The general solution for a particular **u** may be an entire subspace. Our purpose is to understand these possible complications, and to discover how to handle them.

Such problems arise in a number of different contexts. In vector analysis we may wish to find $\vec{v}$, given $\vec{u}$, for a fixed vector $\vec{a}$, when

$$\vec{u} = \vec{a} \times \vec{v} \tag{2}$$

The operator $(\vec{a} \times)$ is easily seen to be a linear operator. It is a singular one since the cross product vanishes if $\vec{v}$ is a scalar times $\vec{a}$. Yet it is possible to solve Eq. (2) providing $\vec{u}$ is suitable—i.e., perpendicular to $\vec{a}$. The solution, however, is not unique. We can add to a given $\vec{v}$ any vector parallel to $\vec{a}$ without affecting $\vec{u}$.

Another problem that is of considerable interest is to find the matrix **V**, given **U**, when

$$\mathbf{V} = j[\mathbf{RU}] = j(\mathbf{RU} - \mathbf{UR}) \tag{3}$$

i.e., when **V** is j times the commutator of **R** and **U**.[1] The space of $n \times n$ matrices can be considered a linear vector space. The operator

$$\mathbf{T} = j[\mathbf{R},] \tag{4}$$

---

[1] We shall use square brackets, [,], to denote the commutator
$$[\mathbf{A}, \mathbf{B}] = \mathbf{AB} - \mathbf{BA} \tag{6}$$

is a linear operator. It is, however, singular since **V** vanishes for any **U** that commutes with **R**, such as **R** itself.

This form arises in various quantum mechanical problems. It also occurs in coupled mode theory since the class of systems with system matrix **R**, such that a matrix **A** exists such that

$$\frac{d\mathbf{R}}{dz} = j[\mathbf{R}, \mathbf{A}] \tag{5}$$

is a class of nonuniform systems which are considerably simpler than the general nonuniform system. The class of systems whose system matrix obeys Eq. (5) with a constant **A** includes most of the solved nonuniform systems, such as the exponentially tapered transmission line and the distributed parametric amplifier. This a class of systems that justifies intensive study.

It can be shown that the necessary and sufficient condition that a given $\mathbf{R}(z)$ can be expressed as the solution of an equation of the form of Eq. (5) is that its eigenvalues and their structures shall be independent of z. (We shall have more to say about this in Chapter XIII.) This, however, does not immediately tell us what the matrix **A** may be. To find **A** we must solve Eq. (5), given $d\mathbf{R}/dz$ and the singular operator [**R**,].

Many other examples illustrating the importance of this type of problem could be given. These will illustrate the scope of its application.

The problem of solving Eq. (1) when **T** is a rectangular matrix is essentially the same. If **T** is $n \times m$, with n the number of rows and m the number of columns, and $n < m$, then we can add to the bottom of **T** enough rows of zeros to make it square, and to the bottom of **u** enough zeros to make it the same dimension as **v**. The augmented **T** so generated is automatically singular with rank not greater than m, and with the augmented **u** automatically confined to a subspace of the whole m-dimensional space.

If, on the other hand, $n > m$, then we can add columns of zeros on the right of **T**, and zeros to the bottom of **v**, and so, again, reduce the problem to the question of solving Eq. (1) with singular square **T**.

Therefore, we shall confine our explicit discussion to the case of **T** square but singular and simply acknowledge that this case subsumes under it the case of a rectangular **T**.

1. ABSTRACT FORMULATION

We will start by defining certain important concepts:

Definition. *The* **domain** S_D *of an operator* **T** *is the subspace of vectors such that the operation of* **T** *is defined.*

Normally, we consider the domain of a matrix operator to be the whole space. We do this because there is really no reason to do otherwise. In the present situation, however, we are seeking an operator whose operand is known to be confined to a given subspace. This operator will have significant meaning only for the domain that is spanned by the possible vectors $\mathbf{u}$.

Definition. *The* **range** S_R *of an operator* $\mathbf{T}$ *is the subspace spanned by the vectors obtained by* $\mathbf{T}$ *operating on any vector in its domain. We can express this formally by writing*

$$S_R = \mathbf{T}S_D$$

or by saying that the range of $\mathbf{T}$ *is* $\mathbf{T}$ *operating on its domain.*

The singularity of $\mathbf{T}$ is expressed by saying that its range is a proper subspace—i.e., is not the whole space.

Definition. *The* **null space** S_N *of an operator* $\mathbf{T}$ *is the subspace of its domain such that* $\mathbf{T}$ *operating on any vector in* S_N *vanishes*:

$$\mathbf{Tx} = 0 \qquad \text{if } \mathbf{x} \text{ is in } S_N$$

The singularity of $\mathbf{T}$ can also be expressed by stating that the null space of $\mathbf{T}$ is a proper subspace—i.e., not the space containing only the null vector.

Definition. *A set of linearly independent vectors* $\mathbf{x}_1, ..., \mathbf{x}_k$ *are called* progenitors *of the range of* $\mathbf{T}$ *if the set* $\mathbf{Tx}_1, \mathbf{Tx}_2, ..., \mathbf{Tx}_k$ *form a basis for the range of* $\mathbf{T}$.

Note that the specification that $\mathbf{Tx}_1, ..., \mathbf{Tx}_k$ form a basis implies that (a) they are linearly independent, and (b) none is the null vector. Hence a set of progenitors must contain exactly k vectors, if k is the dimensionality of the range.

Further, the vectors $\mathbf{x}_1, ..., \mathbf{x}_k$ must be linearly independent. For, if there existed a nontrivial set of scalars c_i such that

$$\sum c_i \mathbf{x}_i = 0 \tag{7}$$

then, since $\mathbf{T}$ is linear, we would have

$$\mathbf{T} \sum c_i \mathbf{x}_i = \sum c_i(\mathbf{Tx}_i) = 0 \tag{8}$$

and the set $\mathbf{Tx}_i$ would not be linearly independent.

Hence, any set of progenitors spans a subspace which we will call a progenitor space. This space is not uniquely defined if $\mathbf{T}$ is singular. We can add to any progenitor a vector in the null space of $\mathbf{T}$ without changing its mapping into the range of $\mathbf{T}$. It has, however, the virtue that the operation of $\mathbf{T}$ on any progenitor space is nonsingular. That is, to every vector in any given progenitor space there corresponds one and only one vector in the range of $\mathbf{T}$, and vice versa.

In solving Eq. (1), we know that $\mathbf{u}$ is in the range of $\mathbf{T}$. For a particular solution to Eq. (1) we need to specify, for each $\mathbf{u}$, a unique $\mathbf{v}$. That is, we wish to specify a particular progenitor space. The mapping of the progenitor space onto the range is one-to-one, and we can seek an operator that, taking as its domain the range of $\mathbf{T}$, exhibits the inverse mapping.

The general solution is then obtained by adding to the particular solution an arbitrary vector in the null space of $\mathbf{T}$. Alternatively, given a particular solution $\mathbf{v}$, we can say that the general solution is the class $\hat{\mathbf{v}}$, modulo S_N.

2. SEMISIMPLE T

We will consider first the case when $\mathbf{T}$ is semisimple. We observe that we can take as a progenitor space the range of $\mathbf{T}$. We can take as a basis for the whole space S a complete set $\mathbf{x}_i$ of eigenvectors of $\mathbf{T}$. Then the space S_1 that is the linear envelope of those members of the set $\mathbf{x}_i$ that have nonzero eigenvalues is the range of $\mathbf{T}$ and is also a progenitor space.

Thus $\mathbf{T}$ maps S_1 onto itself. The operation is, in this domain, non-singular, so that the singularity of $\mathbf{T}$ now enters in the fact that S_1 is not the whole space. If we can find an operator that maps S_1 onto itself in the reverse way, then we will be able to solve Eq. (1).

We can do this quite easily with the projectors $\mathbf{P}_i$ on the eigenspaces of $\mathbf{T}$ that we developed in the previous chapter. We discovered there that, since $\mathbf{T}$ is semisimple, it can written as

$$\mathbf{T} = \sum_{i=1}^{m} \lambda_i \mathbf{P}_i \tag{9}$$

the summation being over all discrete nonzero values of λ_i. There will be, in addition, a projector onto the eigenspace with zero eigenvalue that does not appear in Eq. (9).

We then have

$$\mathbf{u} = \mathbf{T}\mathbf{v} = \sum_{i=1}^{m} \lambda_i \mathbf{P}_i \mathbf{v}$$

If we premultiply this by any $\mathbf{P}_k$ of the set, we get

$$\mathbf{P}_k\mathbf{v} = \frac{1}{\lambda_k}\mathbf{P}_k\mathbf{u} \tag{10}$$

Suppose we sum Eq. (10) over all k associated with nonzero eigenvalues. The sum of the projectors is also a projector. It is the projector onto the range of $\mathbf{T}$ along the null space of $\mathbf{T}$. If we specify that $\mathbf{v}$ shall be in the range of $\mathbf{T}$, then we see that

$$\sum_{k=1}^{m}\mathbf{P}_k\mathbf{v} = \mathbf{v} = \sum_{k=1}^{m}\frac{1}{\lambda_k}\mathbf{P}_k\mathbf{u}$$

and we have a particular solution of Eq. (1). The general solution is

$$\mathbf{v} = \sum_{i=1}^{m}\frac{1}{\lambda_i}\mathbf{P}_i\mathbf{u} + \mathbf{v}_0 \tag{11}$$

where the summation is over the nonzero discrete eigenvalues, and $\mathbf{v}_0$ is an arbitrary vector in the null space of $\mathbf{T}$.

Alternatively, we can write the general solution as

$$\hat{\mathbf{v}} \equiv \sum_{i=1}^{m}(1/\lambda_i)\mathbf{P}_i\mathbf{u}, \qquad \mathrm{mod}\ S_N \tag{11'}$$

We may note that the product of $\mathbf{T}$ with the operator of Eq. (11) is not the identity, but is, instead, $(\mathbf{I} - \mathbf{P}_0)$ where $\mathbf{P}_0$ is the projector onto the null space of $\mathbf{T}$. The operator gives the desired mapping of S_1 onto itself, and annihilates the same space as does $\mathbf{T}$.

We discovered, in Chapter XI, Section 8, that the projectors on the eigenspaces of $\mathbf{T}$ can be developed from the minimum polynomial of $\mathbf{T}$. We can use this fact to put Eq. (11) into convenient form.

Since $\mathbf{T}$ is singular and semisimple, its minimum polynomial is

$$\varphi(\lambda) = \lambda\prod{}'(\lambda - \lambda_i) \tag{12}$$

where the product is over all nonzero discrete values of λ_i. It is convenient to renormalize this and to write it as

$$\varphi(\lambda) = \lambda\{1 - \lambda\theta(\lambda)\} \tag{13}$$

where $\theta(\lambda)$ is a polynomial of degree two less than that of $\varphi(\lambda)$.

This says that

$$\varphi(\mathbf{T}) = 0 = \mathbf{T}\{\mathbf{I} - \mathbf{T}\theta(\mathbf{T})\}$$

or

$$\mathbf{T} = \theta(\mathbf{T})\mathbf{T}^2 \tag{14}$$

since $\mathbf{T}$ commutes with the polynomial $\theta(\mathbf{T})$.

We may note that the polynomial $\theta(\mathbf{T})\mathbf{T}$ is a projector since

$$\{\theta(\mathbf{T})\mathbf{T}\}^2 = \theta(\mathbf{T})\{\theta(\mathbf{T})\mathbf{T}^2\} = \theta(\mathbf{T})\mathbf{T} \tag{15}$$

Evidently it is the projector on the range of $\mathbf{T}$, and so gives us $\sum_i^m \mathbf{P}_i$. Also $\{\mathbf{I} - \theta(\mathbf{T})\mathbf{T}\}$ is the projector on the null space of $\mathbf{T}$.

Now we have seen that we can specify the progenitor space of a semi-simple operator to be its range. Hence, in Eq. (1), we can specify that $\mathbf{v}$ be expressible as $\mathbf{T}$ operating on some vector, $\mathbf{x}$:

$$\mathbf{u} = \mathbf{T}\mathbf{v} = \mathbf{T}^2\mathbf{x} \tag{16}$$

Multiplying Eq. (16) by $\theta(\mathbf{T})$ and using Eq. (14), we find that

$$\theta(\mathbf{T})\mathbf{u} = \theta(\mathbf{T})\mathbf{T}^2\mathbf{x} = \mathbf{T}\mathbf{x} = \mathbf{v} \tag{17}$$

so that we have a particular solution of Eq. (1). For the general solution we add to this an arbitrary vector in the null space of $\mathbf{T}$, which we can obtain from an arbitrary vector in the whole space by the projector on the null space:

$$\mathbf{v} = \theta(\mathbf{T})\mathbf{u} + \{\mathbf{I} - \theta(\mathbf{T})\mathbf{T}\}\mathbf{y} \tag{18}$$

where $\mathbf{y}$ is any vector.

Providing $\mathbf{T}$ is semisimple, we are able to obtain an operator that will solve Eq. (1) for $\mathbf{v}$ given any $\mathbf{u}$ that is a possible vector in Eq. (1).

3. EXAMPLE

Before proceeding to the more general case where $\mathbf{T}$ may not be semi-simple, let us consider as an example Eq. (2). This will not only provide an illustration of this technique, but will illustrate the development of vector algebra in matrix form, which is an interesting process in itself.

In vector terms, we can solve Eq. (2) by forming the cross product of $\vec{a}$ with Eq. (2):

$$\vec{a} \times \vec{u} = \vec{a} \times (\vec{a} \times \vec{v}) = \vec{a}(\vec{a} \cdot \vec{v}) - \vec{v}(\vec{a} \cdot \vec{a})$$

If now, $\vec{v}$ is specified to be perpendicular to $\vec{a}$, then

$$v = -\vec{a} \times \vec{u}/(\vec{a} \cdot \vec{a}) = -\vec{a} \times \vec{u}/a^2$$

or, for the general solution,

$$\vec{v} = -\vec{a} \times \vec{u}/a^2 + k\vec{a}$$

where k is any constant.

To put this problem in the context of matrix algebra, we consider cartesian coordinates and establish the vectors

$$\mathbf{u} = \begin{pmatrix} u_x \\ u_y \\ u_z \end{pmatrix}, \qquad \mathbf{v} = \begin{pmatrix} v_x \\ v_y \\ v_z \end{pmatrix}, \qquad \mathbf{a} = \begin{pmatrix} a_x \\ a_y \\ a_z \end{pmatrix}$$

Equation (2) becomes

$$\mathbf{u} = \begin{pmatrix} a_y v_z - a_z v_y \\ a_z v_x - a_x v_z \\ a_x v_y - a_y v_x \end{pmatrix} = \begin{pmatrix} 0 & -a_z & a_y \\ a_z & 0 & -a_x \\ -a_y & a_x & 0 \end{pmatrix} \times \begin{pmatrix} v_x \\ v_y \\ v_z \end{pmatrix}$$

so that $\mathbf{T}$, on this basis, represents $(\vec{a} \times \ )$ as

$$\mathbf{T} = \begin{pmatrix} 0 & -a_z & a_y \\ a_z & 0 & -a_x \\ -a_y & a_x & 0 \end{pmatrix}$$

This is a singular operator since $\mathbf{Ta} = \mathbf{0}$. Its minimum polynomial is

$$\lambda^3 + a^2\lambda = 0$$

$$a^2 = a_x{}^2 + a_y{}^2 + a_z{}^2$$

so that

$$-\frac{1}{a^2}\,\mathbf{T}^3 = \mathbf{T}$$

We find that the θ of Eq. (13) is

$$\theta(\mathbf{T}) = -\frac{1}{a^2}\,\mathbf{T}$$

The particular solution is then

$$\mathbf{v} = -\frac{1}{a^2}\,\mathbf{Tu}$$

which is the same as we found before, since $\mathbf{T}$ is a representation of $(\vec{a} \times \ )$.

We shall defer until Chapter XIII detailed consideration of the other example cited in Eq. (3) or (15) involving the commutator.

4. NOT SEMISIMPLE

If $\mathbf{T}$ is not semisimple, the procedure given so far *may* not work. It will work if the failure of semisimplicity does not involve the zero eigenvalue. The question is not the semisimplicity of the operator as a whole, but whether or not the eigensubspace with eigenvalue zero, S_T^0, has a complete set of eigenvectors. If it does, we can still write the minimum polynomial in the form of Eq. (13), and so develop the solution given in Eq. (18). If, however, there is a chain associated with the zero eigenvalue, the minimum polynomial will contain as a factor λ to the power of the length of the longest such chain, and the expression of φ as Eq. (13) will not be valid.

More fundamentally, if there is a chain of length greater than one with eigenvalue zero, then the eigenvector that heads this chain is in both the null space and the range of $\mathbf{T}$. It is annihilated by $\mathbf{T}$, and so is in the null space. It is generated by $\mathbf{T}$ operating on the generalized eigenvector of rank two, and so is in the range. Hence the operator we seek is required to map, not S_1 onto itself, but S_1 onto another subspace S_2 of the same dimensionality.

We shall show that, given a *proper* inner product, the range of $\mathbf{T}$ is in the orthogonal complement of the null space of $\mathbf{T}^{\#}$, the adjoint $\mathbf{T}$. Hence we can premultiply Eq. (1) by $\mathbf{T}^{\#}$:

$$\mathbf{T}^{\#}\mathbf{u} = \mathbf{T}^{\#}\mathbf{Tv} \tag{19}$$

and be assured that $(\mathbf{T}^{\#}\mathbf{u})$ is nonnull if $\mathbf{u}$ is.

The operator $(\mathbf{T}^{\#}\mathbf{T})$ is semisimple since the inner product is assumed proper and the operator is self-adjoint:

$$(\mathbf{T}^{\#}\mathbf{T})^{\#} = \mathbf{T}^{\#}\mathbf{T} \tag{20}$$

Hence the problem has been reduced to the semisimple case.

If $\mathbf{S} = \mathbf{T}^{\#}\mathbf{T}$, we know that its minimum polynomial can be written as

$$\mathbf{S} = \mathbf{S}^2\theta(\mathbf{S}) \tag{21}$$

where θ is a polynomial. We also know $\mathbf{v}$ can now be written as $\mathbf{Sx}$, where $\mathbf{x}$ is some vector. Then premultiplying Eq. (19) by $\mathbf{S}$, we find that

$$\theta(\mathbf{S})\mathbf{T}^{\#}\mathbf{u} = \theta(\mathbf{S})\mathbf{Sv} = \theta(\mathbf{S})\mathbf{S}^2\mathbf{x} = \mathbf{Sx} = \mathbf{v}$$

so that

$$\mathbf{v} \equiv \theta(\mathbf{T}^{\#}\mathbf{T})\mathbf{T}^{\#}\mathbf{u}, \qquad \text{mod } S_N \qquad (22)$$

where S_N is the null space of $\mathbf{T}$.

This depends on the statement that if $\mathbf{u}$ is a nonnull vector in the range of $\mathbf{T}$, then $\mathbf{T}^{\#}\mathbf{u}$ is nonnull. The proof of this is somewhat devious.

We remind the reader of the definition of the orthogonal complement of a subspace:

Definition. *Given an inner product relation and a subspace S_1, then S_2 is the* **orthogonal complement** *of S_1 if, for any $\mathbf{x}$ in S_1, and any $\mathbf{y}$ in S_2*

$$\langle \mathbf{x}, \mathbf{y} \rangle = 0$$

It is evident that S_2 is a subspace. We now prove the following:

Theorem. (the "projection theorem"). *If the given inner product relation is a proper one, then a subspace S_1 and its orthogonal complement S_2 is a decomposition of the whole space.*

We are saying, in other words, that if the inner product is proper, then orthogonality is a useable tool for constructing projectors. That the inner product relation must be proper is reasonable when we consider that, under an improper relation, a vector can be orthogonal to itself, and so in both S_1 and S_2.

To prove the theorem, we note first that S_1 and S_2 are necessarily disjoint since no nonnull vector can be orthogonal to itself. We therefore need only to show that any vector can be resolved into components in S_1 and S_2.

Now evidently any vector $\mathbf{u}$ can be expressed as the sum of a vector in S_1, $\mathbf{u}_1$, and some other vector, $\mathbf{v}$:

$$\mathbf{u} = \mathbf{u}_1 + \mathbf{v}$$

Then, since the relation is proper

$$\langle \mathbf{v}, \mathbf{v} \rangle = \langle \mathbf{u} - \mathbf{u}_1, \mathbf{u} - \mathbf{u}_1 \rangle > 0 \qquad (23)$$

There must be at least one vector $\mathbf{u}_1$ in S_1, say $\mathbf{u}_0$, for which $\langle \mathbf{v}, \mathbf{v} \rangle$ takes its minimum value. We shall show that this $\mathbf{u}_0$ is the projection of $\mathbf{u}$ on S_1, by showing that $(\mathbf{u} - \mathbf{u}_0)$ is in S_2.

Consider any other $\mathbf{u}_1$. We can express this as

$$\mathbf{u}_1 = \mathbf{u}_0 + \alpha\mathbf{w}$$

where $\mathbf{w}$ is in S_1 and α a scalar. Conversely, for any nonnull $\mathbf{w}$ in S_1, this gives us a $\mathbf{u}_1$ such that the length, squared, of $(\mathbf{u} - \mathbf{u}_1)$ must be not less than the minimum value:

$$\langle \mathbf{u} - \mathbf{u}_0 - \alpha\mathbf{w}, \mathbf{u} - \mathbf{u}_0 - \alpha\mathbf{w} \rangle = \langle \mathbf{u} - \mathbf{u}_0, \mathbf{u} - \mathbf{u}_0 \rangle - \alpha^*\langle \mathbf{w}, \mathbf{u} - \mathbf{u}_0 \rangle$$
$$-\alpha\langle \mathbf{u} - \mathbf{u}_0, \mathbf{w} \rangle + |\alpha|^2\langle \mathbf{w}, \mathbf{w} \rangle$$
$$\geqslant \langle \mathbf{u} - \mathbf{u}_0, \mathbf{u} - \mathbf{u}_0 \rangle$$

Since this must be true for any α, it is true, in particular, for

$$\alpha = \frac{\langle \mathbf{w}, \mathbf{u} - \mathbf{u}_0 \rangle}{\langle \mathbf{w}, \mathbf{w} \rangle} \tag{24}$$

since $\langle \mathbf{w}, \mathbf{w} \rangle \neq 0$. Substituting this value, we find

$$\frac{-|\langle \mathbf{w}, \mathbf{u} - \mathbf{u}_0 \rangle|^2}{\langle \mathbf{w}, \mathbf{w} \rangle} \geqslant 0 \tag{25}$$

and we must have

$$\langle \mathbf{w}, \mathbf{u} - \mathbf{u}_0 \rangle = 0 \tag{26}$$

Hence $\mathbf{u} - \mathbf{u}_0$ is orthogonal to any $\mathbf{w}$ in S_1. Therefore $\mathbf{u} - \mathbf{u}_0$ is in S_2. We can therefore express any $\mathbf{u}$ as

$$\mathbf{u} = \mathbf{u}_0 + (\mathbf{u} - \mathbf{u}_0) \tag{27}$$

where $\mathbf{u}_0 \in S_1$ and $(\mathbf{u} - \mathbf{u}_0) \in S_2$.

The theorem is thus proven.

The application of this theorem is in the following:

Theorem. *If $\mathbf{u}$ is in the range of $\mathbf{T}$, and $\mathbf{K}$ is a proper metric, then $\mathbf{u}$ is K-orthogonal to all $\mathbf{w}$ that are solutions of $\mathbf{T}^{\#}\mathbf{w} = 0$, where $\mathbf{T}^{\#}$ is the K-adjoint operator. Conversely, if $\mathbf{u}$ is K-orthogonal to all such $\mathbf{w}$, then $\mathbf{u}$ is in the range of $\mathbf{T}$.*

It should be carefully noted that the theorem is restricted to proper inner products.

Proving the direct theorem first, consider a $\mathbf{u}$ which is in the range of $\mathbf{T}$ and so can be written as $\mathbf{Tv}$, for some $\mathbf{v}$. Then

$$\langle \mathbf{u}, \mathbf{w} \rangle = \langle \mathbf{Tv}, \mathbf{w} \rangle = \langle \mathbf{v}, \mathbf{T}^{\#}\mathbf{w} \rangle \tag{28}$$

However, by assumption, $\mathbf{w}$ is such that $\mathbf{T}^{\#}\mathbf{w}$ vanishes. Hence $\langle \mathbf{v}, \mathbf{T}^{\#}\mathbf{w} \rangle = 0$, and $\mathbf{u}$ is K-orthogonal to $\mathbf{w}$.

For the converse part of the theorem, suppose

$$\langle \mathbf{u}, \mathbf{w} \rangle = 0$$

for all $\mathbf{w}$ such that $\mathbf{T}^{\#}\mathbf{w} = \mathbf{0}$. Let S_1 be the range of $\mathbf{T}$ and S_2 its orthogonal complement. By Theorem 1 this is a decomposition and we can write

$$\mathbf{u} = \mathbf{u}_1 + \mathbf{u}_2, \qquad \mathbf{u}_1 \in S_1, \quad \mathbf{u}_2 \in S_2$$

Then $\mathbf{u} - \mathbf{u}_1 = \mathbf{u}_2$ is orthogonal to any $\mathbf{x}$ in the range of $\mathbf{T}$, or to $\mathbf{Ty}$, where $\mathbf{y}$ is any vector

$$\langle \mathbf{u} - \mathbf{u}_1, \mathbf{Ty} \rangle = \langle \mathbf{T}^{\#}(\mathbf{u} - \mathbf{u}_1), \mathbf{y} \rangle = 0$$

Since $\mathbf{y}$ is any vector, this requires that

$$\mathbf{T}^{\#}(\mathbf{u} - \mathbf{u}_1) = \mathbf{0} \tag{29}$$

so that $\mathbf{u} - \mathbf{u}_1$ is a solution of the homogeneous adjoint equation—i.e., is a $\mathbf{w}$. Hence $\mathbf{u} - \mathbf{u}_1$ is orthogonal to $\mathbf{u}$ and we can write

$$\langle \mathbf{u}, \mathbf{u} - \mathbf{u}_1 \rangle = \langle \mathbf{u} - \mathbf{u}_1, \mathbf{u} - \mathbf{u}_1 \rangle + \langle \mathbf{u}_1, \mathbf{u} - \mathbf{u}_1 \rangle = 0$$

Now $\mathbf{u}_1$ is in S_1 and $\mathbf{u} - \mathbf{u}_1 = \mathbf{u}_2$ is in S_2. Hence the second term in the above vanishes, and we are left with

$$\langle \mathbf{u} - \mathbf{u}_1, \mathbf{u} - \mathbf{u}_1 \rangle = 0 \tag{30}$$

Therefore $\mathbf{u} - \mathbf{u}_1$ must be the null vector, and $\mathbf{u}$ must equal $\mathbf{u}_1$. Hence $\mathbf{u}$ is in the range of $\mathbf{T}$ and the theorem is proven.

This gives us the result we need. It states that, if $\mathbf{u}$ is in the range of $\mathbf{T}$, it is orthogonal to all vectors that are annihilated by $\mathbf{T}^{\#}$. We can, therefore, operate on $\mathbf{u}$ with $\mathbf{T}^{\#}$ without risk of annihilating $\mathbf{u}$. Hence Eq. (19) is justified. From this the solution to Eq. (1) given in Eq. (22) is obtained.

Whether, or under what conditions, these results can be generalized to include an improper inner product is not known.

5. EXAMPLE

As a simple example of the process, consider the case when $\mathbf{T}$ is an $n \times n$ Jordan block:

$$\mathbf{T} = \begin{pmatrix} 0 & 1 & 0 & \cdots \\ 0 & 0 & 1 & \cdots \\ \vdots & & & \\ 0 & 0 & 0 & \cdots & 1 \\ 0 & 0 & 0 & \cdots & 0 \end{pmatrix}$$

The range is the subspace whose nth component is zero:

$$\mathbf{u} = \begin{pmatrix} a \\ b \\ \vdots \\ m \\ 0 \end{pmatrix}$$

If we use the unitary inner product, then

$$\mathbf{T}^{\#} = \mathbf{T}^{\dagger} = \begin{pmatrix} 0 & 0 & 0 & & 0 & 0 \\ 1 & 0 & 0 & & & \\ 0 & 1 & 0 & & 0 & 0 \\ & \vdots & & & & \\ 0 & 0 & 0 & \cdots & 1 & 0 \end{pmatrix}$$

and

$$\mathbf{T}^{\dagger}\mathbf{u} = \begin{pmatrix} 0 \\ a \\ b \\ \vdots \\ m \end{pmatrix}$$

Also,

$$\mathbf{T}^{\dagger}\mathbf{T} = \mathrm{diag}(0, 1, 1, ..., 1) = \begin{pmatrix} 0 & 0 \\ 0 & \mathbf{I} \end{pmatrix}$$

Hence $\mathbf{v}$ is the same as $\mathbf{T}^{\dagger}\mathbf{u}$, mod S_N:

$$\mathbf{v} = \begin{pmatrix} 0 \\ a \\ b \\ \vdots \\ m \end{pmatrix}, \qquad \mathrm{mod} \begin{pmatrix} 1 \\ 0 \\ 0 \\ \vdots \end{pmatrix}$$

as was evident by inspection.

With more involved operators, or ones expressed on a less convenient basis, the answer may be far from obvious, but the procedure will give the correct answer.

6. CONCLUSIONS

We have found methods for the solution of $\mathbf{u} = \mathbf{T}\mathbf{v}$ that are applicable even when $\mathbf{T}$ is singular or rectangular, providing $\mathbf{u}$ is a vector which is in the range of **T**. If **T** is singular, the solution is not unique but is any vector in a subspace formed by adding to any particular solution any vector in the null space of **T**—i.e., is the class, modulo the null space of **T**.

Exercises

1. Find the range and null space of

$$A = \begin{pmatrix} 1 & 0 & -j & 0 \\ 1 & -j & j & 1 \\ -j & 0 & -1 & 0 \\ j & -1 & -1 & -j \end{pmatrix}$$

Find the intersection of the range and null space. Solve

$$Ax = \begin{pmatrix} 1 \\ -j \\ -j \\ 2j-1 \end{pmatrix}$$

2. What are the range and null space of

$$A = \begin{pmatrix} 0 & j & 0 & 1 \\ 1 & 0 & -j & 0 \\ 0 & 1 & 0 & -j \\ j & 0 & 1 & 0 \end{pmatrix}?$$

For which of the following vectors, **a**, does the equation

$$Ax = u$$

have a solution? For those cases, find the general solution.

(a) $a = \text{col}(1, -1, -j, j)$

(b) $a = \text{col}(1, 1, -j, j)$

(c) $a = \text{col}(1 + j, 1 - j, 1 - j, -1 - j)$

(d) $a = \text{col}(1, 1 - j, -j, 1 - j)$

3. If **E** is a dyad, expressible as $uv^\dagger$, what are its range and null space? (*Caution*: There are two distinct cases to be considered.)

4. In Exercise 5, Chapter X, we asserted that, if $\mathbf{E} = \mathbf{u}\mathbf{v}^\dagger\mathbf{K}$, where $\mathbf{K}$ is a proper metric, then the equation

$$\mathbf{E}\mathbf{x} = \mathbf{y}$$

has a solution for $\mathbf{x}$ in terms of $\mathbf{y}$ if and only if $\mathbf{y}$ is proportional to $\mathbf{u}$. We proved there a particular solution of the equation.

Prove that this condition is necessary and sufficient. Find the general solution.

5. If $\mathbf{P}$ is a projector, under what conditions does

$$\mathbf{P}\mathbf{x} = \mathbf{a}$$

have a solution? What is its general solution?

CHAPTER XIII

The Commutator Operator

We shall, in this chapter, consider the equation

$$\frac{d\mathbf{W}}{dz} = [\mathbf{S}, \mathbf{W}] = \mathbf{SW} - \mathbf{WS} \tag{1}$$

where the square brackets indicate the commutator and $\mathbf{S}$ may be either constant or a prescribed function of z.

This type of equation occurs in some important applications, such as in quantum mechanics where the time derivative of the *density matrix* is equal to $(1/i\hbar)$ times the commutator of the Hamiltonian with the density matrix.

It is also important as a way of suppressing undesired aspects of the problem. We may, for example, wish to study the propagation of noise through a distributed system described by the usual system equation

$$\frac{d\mathbf{x}}{dz} = \mathbf{Sx} \tag{2}$$

If the components of $\mathbf{x}$ are noise, they will be "pathological" functions of frequency. In particular, it is the phase part that is pathological. While there are ways of handling such functions—by Lebesque integration and the like—it is often more convenient, and quite satisfactory, simply to suppress the phase information.

If $\mathbf{S}$ is K-skew-hermitian for a known $\mathbf{K}$, one can do this quite easily. We consider the dyad

$$\mathbf{W} = \mathbf{xy}^\dagger\mathbf{K} \tag{3}$$

where $\mathbf{x}$ and $\mathbf{y}$ are solutions of Eq. (2), possibly the same. We find that

$$\frac{d\mathbf{W}}{dz} = \frac{d\mathbf{x}}{dz}\mathbf{y}^\dagger\mathbf{K} + \mathbf{x}\left(\frac{d\mathbf{y}}{dz}\right)^\dagger\mathbf{K} = \mathbf{Sxy}^\dagger\mathbf{K} + \mathbf{xy}^\dagger\mathbf{S}^\dagger\mathbf{K}$$

$$= \mathbf{Sxy}^\dagger\mathbf{K} - \mathbf{xy}^\dagger\mathbf{KS} = [\mathbf{S}, \mathbf{W}] \tag{4}$$

We can form the appropriate average over the ensemble of $\mathbf{W}$'s, and find that this average obeys Eq. (1). Since the components of $\mathbf{W}$ are now power spectrum densities, the phase information has been suppressed, and the **W** for a noise signal will be a well-behaved function of frequency.

As another source of Eq. (1), consider the matricant equation

$$\frac{d\mathbf{M}}{dz} = \mathbf{SM}, \qquad \mathbf{M}(0) = \mathbf{I} \tag{5}$$

where **S** may be a function of z, so that the system is nonuniform. If we form the matrix

$$\mathbf{W} = \mathbf{MW_0M}^{-1} \tag{6}$$

where $\mathbf{W_0}$ is the boundary condition, we find that **W** obeys Eq. (1).

Again information has been suppressed. We can, in Eq. (6), post-multiply **M** by any nonsingular z-dependent matrix that everywhere commutes with $\mathbf{W_0}$ without affecting **W**. However, we are left with some of the information contained in $\mathbf{M}(z)$. If we can handle Eq. (1) more easily or effectively then Eq. (5), we shall have found some of the properties of the system being studied. If these are the properties that are important to us, we will be very much ahead of the game.

As a final example, we shall discover that Eq. (5) itself, or Eq. (2), becomes tractible even if **S** is a function of z—the nonuniform case—if **S** is governed by the equation

$$\frac{d\mathbf{S}}{dz} = [\mathbf{A}, \mathbf{S}] \tag{7}$$

providing **A** can be taken as sufficiently simple. Indeed, most of the solved nonuniform systems are of this type with **A** constant. This is true, for example, in the exponentially tapered transmission line.

Thus Eq. (1) is a type of equation that has considerable importance. Also, its study will provide us with a useful exercise to broaden understanding of the analytic methods we have developed.

Properly speaking, the investigation of Eq. (1) will carry us into the subject of *Lie algebras*, which may be roughly defined as the kind of algebra that develops when we use the operation of commutation in place of matrix multiplication. This subject, in its full generality, goes well beyond the scope of this book. However, it will be helpful to discuss some of the underlying concepts and properties. We shall start with a very sketchy account of the nature and significance of Lie groups and algebras.

1. LIE GROUPS

We have previously (Chapter IV, Section 3) defined a group G as a collection of elements $(\mathbf{A}, \mathbf{B}, ...)$ for which a product relation has been defined and which has the following three properties:

1. The product of any two elements of the group is an element in the group (the group property).
2. There exists a unique element $\mathbf{I}$ such that its product with any element of the group is the element.
3. With every element $\mathbf{X}$ of the group there is associated a unique element of the group, $\mathbf{X}^{-1}$, whose product with the given element is the identity.

Groups may be either finite or infinite. We are here concerned only with infinite groups—i.e., groups that contain an infinite number of distinct elements. Note that we are *not* saying that there is an infinite number of linearly independent elements, but, instead, *distinct* elements. We are limiting ourselves to groups with a finite number of linearly independent elements. We are concerned with groups of *finite dimensionality*.

We suppose that it is possible to parametrize the elements of a group G at least locally. That is, we suppose that it is possible to write an arbitrary element $\mathbf{X}$ in at least a part of G as

$$\mathbf{X} = \mathbf{X}(\alpha_1, \alpha_2, ..., \alpha_k) \tag{8}$$

where $\alpha_1, ..., \alpha_k$ are numbers within designated ranges of a field, so that for any such set of $\alpha_1, ..., \alpha_k$, the resulting $\mathbf{X}$ is a member of the group. Further, we suppose that, within some range, the parametrization is singlevalued, so that a given element $\mathbf{X}$ is designated by a unique set of parameters. We suppose further that it is possible to do this in a set of regions (open sets) that completely cover the group. In the different regions, different parametrizations may be required, but, where regions overlap, it is possible to transform smoothly from one parametrization to the other.

We also assume that the parametrization can be taken to be differentiable. A full discussion of the abstract meaning of this assumption would take us too far afield. However, we shall not in general be discussing abstract groups, but their realizations as sets of matrices. The assumption then requires that every component of each member of the group shall be a differentiable function of the parameter.

The question of whether, or when, it is possible to obtain a parametrization that is *global*—i.e., which covers the whole of G—will not concern us here. It is a question of vital importance for group theory but leads into subtleties that would carry us rather far afield. We shall only assume that there is at least a *local* parametrization that is valid in some region that includes the identity.

Such a group is called a *Lie* or *continuous* group. Put abstractly, a Lie group is a topological group which is everywhere differentiably parametrizable, at least locally.

As an example, consider the set of all $n \times n$ matrices with nonzero determinant, with the matrix product relation. The matrix product of two such matrices is a member of the set since it is also $n \times n$ and its determinant is the product of the determinants of the matrices being multiplied and so is nonzero. Hence the set has the group property. The $n \times n$ **I** is a member of the set. Since the determinant of any element **X** is nonzero, **X**$^{-1}$ exists and is a member of the set. Hence the set is a group. It is designated as $GL(n)$ (for *general linear group* in n-dimensional space).

The set of $n \times n$ matrices with determinant equal to one is another group designated as $SL(n)$ (for *special linear group*), and also known as the *unimodular group*.

The set of all $n \times n$ unitary matrices is a group, the group $U(n)$, or *unitary group*. It is the group of $n \times n$ matrices whose determinant has absolute magnitude one.

The set of all $n \times n$ orthogonal matrices—i.e., matrices, whose components are real numbers and whose determinant is ± 1—is a group, $O(n)$. The group $O(3)$ is the *reflection-rotation* group. We should note that this group consists of two distinct parts, the operations of rotations alone, and those of rotation with reflection. These two parts are realized by the subgroup of matrices with determinant $+1$, and the set (not a subgroup) with determinant -1. Evidently, we cannot set up a continuous parametrization over any region that includes some of both parts. Hence the topology is split into two disjoint parts. Nevertheless, the whole group is still a Lie group.

There are other important groups as well, but this is enough to illustrate the concept.

A set of matrices that combine under matrix multiplication in the same way as do the abstract elements is called a *representation* of the abstract group. There are always many different ways in which a given abstract group can be represented. We can use matrices of various sizes, with elements from different fields. We can even have representations involving other kinds of operators than matrices, e.g., differential or integral operators. It is one of the principal concerns of group theory to determine and classify the various types of representations that are possible. However, it will be enough for our purposes here simply to observe that we can have representations of the same group which bear little superficial resemblance to each other.

A representation is *faithful* if to each distinct element of the abstract group there corresponds a distinct element of the representation, so that the correspondence is an isomorphism. As an extreme example of an unfaithful representation, we can represent every element of any group G by 1. The relation in G that $AB = C$ then is imaged by the relation that $1^2 = 1$, which is trivial but true. This is a valid representation, although an unfaithful one, of every group.

It can be proven that every Lie group (in fact, every group of finite dimensionality) can be faithfully represented as a subgroup of $GL(n)$ for some suitably large n. Thus every Lie group can be represented by matrices with the matrix product.

We shall also mention at this point the broader concept of a *realization* of an abstract group. In the discussion given of representations, we have included the requirement that the rule of combination shall be matrix multiplication. (More broadly, so as to include differential and integral operators, we require that the product of two operators shall be given by the successive application of the operators separately.) We can also consider sets of matrices which behave like a given abstract group under some other rule of combination, such as the star product discussed in Chapter I, Section 14. We speak of such a set as being a *realization* of the abstract group. The distinction will become particularly significant when we come to Lie algebras.

2. INFINITESIMAL TRANSFORMATIONS OF A LIE GROUP

Every Lie group is at least locally parametrizable in a region that includes the identity. Furthermore, the parametrization is differentiable, and hence expandable in a multivariable Taylor's series.

If we choose the parametrization of Eq. (1), as we obviously can, so that

$$\mathbf{X}(0, 0, ..., 0) = \mathbf{I} \tag{9}$$

then, for an $\mathbf{X}$ sufficiently close to $\mathbf{I}$—i.e., for small enough $\alpha_1, ..., \alpha_k$, we can approximate

$$\mathbf{X}(\alpha_1, ..., \alpha_k) = \mathbf{I} + \sum \alpha_i \frac{\partial \mathbf{X}}{\partial \alpha_i}\bigg|_{\alpha_1 = \alpha_2 = \cdots = \alpha_k = 0} \tag{10}$$

We can then describe any $\mathbf{X}$ sufficiently close to the identity as a linear combination of the elements $\partial \mathbf{X}/\partial \alpha_i$, evaluated at $\alpha_1 = \cdots = \alpha_k = 0$.

These elements, which we will designate as $\mathbf{X}_i$, are the *infinitesimal transformations* of G. Suppose that we have a system described by the equation

$$\frac{d}{dz}\mathbf{M}(z, z_0) = \mathbf{SM}(z, z_0), \qquad \mathbf{M}(z_0, z_0) = \mathbf{I} \tag{11}$$

so that $\mathbf{M}(z, z_0)$ is the matricant. $\mathbf{S}$ may, in this case, be a function of z but not of z_0.

Suppose we know that $\mathbf{M}(z, z_0)$ is within some Lie group G. For a fixed z_0, it is a *curve* in G. The question we wish to consider is what we can say about $\mathbf{S}$.

For z sufficiently close to z_0, the expansion of Eq. (10) is valid, and we can write

$$\mathbf{M}(z, z_0) = \mathbf{I} + \sum \alpha_i \mathbf{X}_i + \cdots \tag{12}$$

where α_i is a function of $(z - z_0)$.

Then we can write Eq. (11) as

$$\sum \frac{\partial \alpha_i}{dz}\mathbf{X}_i = \mathbf{S} + \sum \alpha_i \mathbf{SX}_i + \cdots \tag{13}$$

Evaluating this at $z = z_0$, where α_i becomes zero, we find that

$$\mathbf{S} = \sum \mathbf{X}_i \frac{\partial \alpha_i}{\partial z}\bigg|_{z=z_0} \tag{14}$$

$\mathbf{S}$ is then expandable also in terms of $\mathbf{X}_i$. This does not mean that $\mathbf{S}$ is in G, however. At least some of the terms

$$\gamma_i(z) = \frac{\partial \alpha_i}{\partial z}\bigg|_{z=z_0} \tag{15}$$

are not zero, if $\mathbf{S}(z)$ is to be nontrivial, and the expression of Eq. (10) was assumed valid only for infinitesmal α_i.

Instead, we can only say that $\mathbf{S}(z)$ is in the subspace spanned by $\mathbf{X}_i$—i.e., is a linear combination of the $\mathbf{X}_i$.

In geometric terms, the matricant is a *curve* in an appropriately dimensioned *surface* in some space, and $\mathbf{S}$ is a *curve* to the appropriately dimensioned *plane* that is tangent to the surface at $\alpha_1 = \alpha_2 = \cdots = \alpha_k = 0$.

The space spanned by the $\mathbf{X}_i$—the space in which $\mathbf{S}(z)$ is a curve— is the *Lie algebra associated with the group* G.

We need to determine more specifically the nature of this restriction on $\mathbf{S}(z)$.

3. ROLE OF THE COMMUTATOR

We shall now show that the infinitesmal transformations of a Lie group have the very important property that their commutator is also an infinitesimal transformation.

Suppose that $\mathbf{M}$ and $\mathbf{N}$ are two elements of G lying close to $\mathbf{I}$—close being interpreted by some proper measure on the parameters. Then, to the second order in the parameters, we can write

$$\mathbf{M} = \mathbf{I} + \sum_i \alpha_i \mathbf{X}_i + \sum \alpha_{ij} \mathbf{P}_{ij} + \cdots$$

$$\mathbf{N} = \mathbf{I} + \sum \beta_i \mathbf{X}_i + \sum \beta_{ij} \mathbf{Q}_{ij} + \cdots$$

where α_{ij} and β_{ij} are some scalars that are second order in the parameters, and $\mathbf{P}_{ij}$ and $\mathbf{Q}_{ij}$ some operators or matrices whose nature does not concern us here, except to note that these sums are the total of the second order terms in the Taylor expansion of $\mathbf{M}$ and $\mathbf{N}$ as functions of their parameters.

The inverses of $\mathbf{M}$ and $\mathbf{N}$ must be in the group. We can write them as

$$\mathbf{M}^{-1} = \mathbf{I} - \sum_i \alpha_i \mathbf{X}_i + \sum \mu_{ij} \mathbf{U}_{ij}$$

$$\mathbf{N}^{-1} = \mathbf{I} - \sum \beta_i \mathbf{X}_i + \sum \eta_{ij} \mathbf{V}_{ij}$$

For these to be inverses, we find that we must have

$$\sum_{ij} \{\alpha_{ij} \mathbf{P}_{ij} - \alpha_i \alpha_j \mathbf{X}_i \mathbf{X}_j + \mu_{ij} \mathbf{U}_{ij}\} = 0 \tag{16}$$

$$\sum_{ij} \{\beta_{ij} \mathbf{Q}_{ij} - \beta_i \beta_j \mathbf{X}_i \mathbf{X}_j + \eta_{ij} \mathbf{V}_{ij}\} = 0 \tag{17}$$

Consider, now $\mathbf{M}^{-1}\mathbf{N}^{-1}\mathbf{M}\mathbf{N}$. This again must be a member of the group. Using these equations, we find that, to the second order in the parameters,

$$\mathbf{M}^{-1}\mathbf{N}^{-1}\mathbf{M}\mathbf{N} = \mathbf{I} + \sum_{ij} (\alpha_{ij} \mathbf{P}_{ij} - \alpha_i \alpha_j \mathbf{X}_i \mathbf{X}_j + \mu_{ij} \mathbf{U}_{ij})$$

$$+ \sum_{ij} (\beta_{ij} \mathbf{Q}_{ij} - \beta_i \beta_j \mathbf{X}_i \mathbf{X}_j + \eta_{ij} \mathbf{V}_{ij})$$

$$+ \sum_{ij} (\alpha_i \beta_j - \beta_i \alpha_j) \mathbf{X}_i \mathbf{X}_j$$

$$+ \cdots$$

By Eqs. (16) and (17), the first two sums vanish. The final sum can be simplified by relabeling the indices in the second part to interchange i and j. We find, if we do this, that

$$\mathbf{M^{-1}N^{-1}MN} = \mathbf{I} + \sum_{ij} \alpha_i \beta_j (\mathbf{X}_i \mathbf{X}_j - \mathbf{X}_j \mathbf{X}_i) + \cdots$$

$$= \mathbf{I} + \sum_{ij} \alpha_i \beta_j [\mathbf{X}_i, \mathbf{X}_j] + \cdots. \tag{18}$$

Since $\mathbf{M^{-1}N^{-1}MN}$ is an element of the group, this must be of the form of Eq. (12):

$$\mathbf{M^{-1}N^{-1}MN} = \mathbf{I} + \sum \gamma_i \mathbf{X}_i + \cdots \tag{19}$$

Further, this must be true for any α_i and β_j that are in the appropriate field and range. Therefore it follows that each term of the sum—i.e., the commutator of any pair of the infinitesimal transformations of G—must be a linear combination of the set of infinitesimal transformations:

$$[\mathbf{X}_i, \mathbf{X}_j] = \sum_k c_{ij}^k \mathbf{X}_k \tag{20}$$

where c_{ij}^k are constants in the appropriate field.

It is this property, discovered by Lie, that provides the means for characterizing a Lie algebra.

The constants c_{ij}^k in Eq. (20) are called the *structure constants* of the algebra.

4. LIE ALGEBRAS

An *algebra* in general is a linear vector space that is also a ring with respect to some defined multiplicative process.[1] If the multiplication process is associative—that is, if

$$\mathbf{A(BC)} = \mathbf{(AB)C}$$

then it is an *associative algebra*.

---

[1] It will be recalled that a *linear vector space* is a set of elements that is closed under linear combination over a field, F. That is, if A and B are any elements of the linear vector space, and if a and b any members of the field, then $(aA + bB)$ is a member of the set. A *ring* is a set that is closed under a defined product relation. If A and B are any members of the set, and (A, B) is a product relation, then (A, B) is in the set.

However, the multiplicative process need not be associative. (At least it need not be if we relax the definition of a ring to eliminate the postulate that it is.)

We define the *Lie product* of **A** and **B**, which we will symbolize as [**A, B**], by the postulates:

(A) $$[a\mathbf{A} + b\mathbf{B}, \mathbf{C}] = a[\mathbf{A}, \mathbf{C}] + b[\mathbf{B}, \mathbf{C}] \qquad (21)$$

a and b being scalars in the appropriate field.

(B) $$[\mathbf{A}, \mathbf{B}] = -[\mathbf{B}, \mathbf{A}] \qquad (22)$$

(C) $$[\mathbf{A}, [\mathbf{B}, \mathbf{C}]] + [\mathbf{B}, [\mathbf{C}, \mathbf{A}]] + [\mathbf{C}, [\mathbf{A}, \mathbf{B}]] = 0 \qquad (23)$$

Postulate (A) is the postulate of linearity, while (B) is that of skew-symmetry. Together, they imply bilinearity, i.e., that the Lie product is linear in the second term also.

It is a consequence of these two postulates also that, for any **A**,

$$[\mathbf{A}, \mathbf{A}] = 0 \qquad (24)$$

Postulate (C) is the *Jacobi Identity*. It, in effect, specifies the manner in which associativity fails. In fact, using (B), we can write (C) as

$$[\mathbf{A}, [\mathbf{B}, \mathbf{C}]] - [[\mathbf{A}, \mathbf{B}], \mathbf{C}] = [[\mathbf{C}, \mathbf{A}], \mathbf{B}] \qquad (25)$$

If the product were associative, the right-hand side would be zero. The Jacobi identity specifies the exact nature of the departure from associativity.

A *Lie algebra*, then, is a linear vector space over a given field that is also a ring under a Lie product.

5. THE PRODUCT RELATION

The Lie product has been defined abstractly above. Postulates (A), (B), and (C) are sufficient for this purpose when taken with the postulates defining a field, a linear vector space, and a ring. We are not interested, however, in quite such complete abstraction.

We might observe, first, that there is an example of a Lie product—and a Lie algebra—that the student has been familiar with for some time, although not under that name. This is the cross product of two vectors. Postulates (A) and (B) are obvious, and the Jacobi identity can be readily verified:

$$\vec{u} \times (\vec{v} \times \vec{w}) + \vec{v} \times (\vec{w} \times \vec{u}) + \vec{w} \times (\vec{u} \times \vec{v})$$

$$= \vec{v}(\vec{u} \cdot \vec{w}) - \vec{w}(\vec{u} \cdot \vec{v}) + \vec{w}(\vec{v} \cdot \vec{u}) - \vec{u}(\vec{v} \cdot \vec{w}) + \vec{u}(\vec{w} \cdot \vec{v}) - \vec{v}(\vec{w} \cdot \vec{u}) = 0$$

Hence this is a Lie product and vector algebra in real euclidean 3-space is a Lie algebra. We may observe that it is this fact that makes the cross product a useful relation in vector algebra. The purposes for which we require the cross product involve the properties that are implied by saying that vector algebra is a Lie algebra.

Of more concern to us here is the fact that, in matrix algebra, the commutator is a Lie product, as we have anticipated by using the symbol [**A, B**] for the general Lie product. If we define

$$[\mathbf{A}, \mathbf{B}] = \mathbf{AB} - \mathbf{BA}$$

where **AB** means matrix multiplication, the postulates (A) and (B) are obvious. The Jacobi identity also follows immediately:

$$[\mathbf{A}, [\mathbf{B}, \mathbf{C}]] + [\mathbf{B}, [\mathbf{C}, \mathbf{A}]] + [\mathbf{C}, [\mathbf{A}, \mathbf{B}]]$$

$$= \mathbf{A}(\mathbf{BC} - \mathbf{CB}) - (\mathbf{BC} - \mathbf{CB})\mathbf{A}$$

$$+ \mathbf{B}(\mathbf{CA} - \mathbf{AC}) - (\mathbf{CA} - \mathbf{AC})\mathbf{B}$$

$$+ \mathbf{C}(\mathbf{AB} - \mathbf{BA}) - (\mathbf{AB} - \mathbf{BA})\mathbf{C} = \mathbf{0} \qquad (26)$$

Hence we can define the Lie product of two matrices as the commutator. Any set of matrices which is closed under linear combination over some field and is also closed under commutation is a Lie algebra.

We must be careful here of the distinction between a representation and a realization. One Lie algebra, for example, is the set of all $n \times n$ matrices with complex coefficients. It is designated as $L^{(n)}$ and called the *full linear algebra of order n*. However, the set of all $n \times n$ matrices is *not* a representation of this algebra, but a realization since the product relation is the commutator, not the matrix product.

As an example, consider $L^{(2)}$. We have that

$$\left[\begin{pmatrix} a & b \\ c & d \end{pmatrix}, \begin{pmatrix} e & f \\ g & h \end{pmatrix}\right] = \begin{pmatrix} bg - cf & (a-d)f - b(e-h) \\ c(e-h) - (a-d)g & cf - bg \end{pmatrix}$$

The operand can be written as the column vector

$$\mathbf{x} = \begin{pmatrix} e \\ f \\ g \\ h \end{pmatrix}$$

We can now write the Lie product as

$$\mathbf{y} = \mathbf{Ax}$$

where

$$\mathbf{A} = \begin{pmatrix} 0 & -c & b & 0 \\ -b & a-d & 0 & b \\ c & 0 & -a+d & -c \\ 0 & c & -b & 0 \end{pmatrix}$$

so that

$$\mathbf{y} = \begin{pmatrix} bg - cf \\ (a-d)f - b(e-h) \\ c(e-h) - (a-d)g \\ cf - bg \end{pmatrix}$$

The 4×4 matrix $\mathbf{A}$, is a representation of $L^{(2)}$.

We should note that there is no requirement that all elements of an algebra be expressible as the commutator of two elements of it, only that the commutator of any two elements be an element. The $n \times n$ identity is an element of $L^{(n)}$, for example, but cannot be expressed as a commutator.

Another example of a Lie algebra is the set of all $n \times n$ real matrices over the field of real numbers.

A third example is any set of commuting matrices, such as the set of $n \times n$ diagonal matrices.

A less trivial example is the set of all $n \times n$ matrices whose trace is zero. Since it can be easily shown that the trace of any commutator is zero, this set is closed under commutation. (This algebra is normally designated as A_{n-1}, for reasons that we will not go into here.)

Finally, we may note that Eq. (26) depends only on $\mathbf{AB}$ being an associative product relation. We have based our discussion on the process of matrix multiplication, but this is not necessary. If we take any associative product—e.g., the star product (cf. page 28)—we can form a Lie product by making a commutator out of it.

In fact, we can go further. It has been proven by Ado that any Lie algebra, defined in accordance with the postulates, can be *embedded* in some appropriate associative algebra, whether or not the Lie product has been obtained explicitly from an associative product relation.

6. *K*-SKEW-HERMITIAN ALGEBRA

We have previously observed that if the system described by Eq. (2) has a conservation law of the form

$$s = \mathbf{x}^\dagger \mathbf{K} \mathbf{x} \tag{27}$$

where **K** is constant, hermitian, and nonsingular, then the matricant is
K-unitary and **S** is K-skew-hermitian (or $\mathbf{R} = j\mathbf{S}$ is K-hermitian).
The converse is also true.

The proper statement of this fact is that Eq. (27) defines a group,
that the matricant is a curve in this group, and that the system operator
S is a point or curve in the corresponding Lie algebra.

The proof of all statements except the last has been given before and
will not be repeated here. We do need to show, however, that the set of
all K-skew-hermitian matrices do form a Lie algebra over the field of
real numbers.

The field must be the real numbers for the set to be closed under
linear combination—i.e., to be a linear vector space.

Suppose **A** and **B** are K-skew-hermitian, so that

$$\mathbf{KA} + \mathbf{A}^\dagger \mathbf{K} = 0, \qquad \mathbf{KB} + \mathbf{B}^\dagger \mathbf{K} = 0 \tag{28}$$

Then we see that

$$\mathbf{K}[\mathbf{A}, \mathbf{B}] + [\mathbf{A}, \mathbf{B}]^\dagger \mathbf{K}$$
$$= \mathbf{K}(\mathbf{AB} - \mathbf{BA}) + (\mathbf{AB} - \mathbf{BA})^\dagger \mathbf{K}$$
$$= \mathbf{KAB} - \mathbf{KBA} + \mathbf{B}^\dagger \mathbf{A}^\dagger \mathbf{K} - \mathbf{A}^\dagger \mathbf{B}^\dagger \mathbf{K}$$
$$= -\mathbf{A}^\dagger \mathbf{KB} + \mathbf{B}^\dagger \mathbf{KA} - \mathbf{B}^\dagger \mathbf{KA} + \mathbf{A}^\dagger \mathbf{KB} = 0 \tag{29}$$

Hence $[\mathbf{A}, \mathbf{B}]$ is K-skew-hermitian, and the set is ring under the Lie
product that is the commutator.

Hence the set is a Lie algebra.

It may be noted that the set of K-hermitian matrices is not a Lie
algebra. It is for this reason that we have switched to $\mathbf{S} = -j\mathbf{R}$ for the
system operator.

The results here are quite independent of uniformity. We have not
assumed that **S** is independent of z, only that **K** is.

The role of a conservation law of the type of Eq. (27) can then be
described as determining the group in which the matricant is embedded,
and the Lie algebra in which the system operator is embedded.

7. THE Ad OPERATOR

Suppose we have a Lie algebra L of which **A**, **B**, etc., are elements.
We note that these elements are used in two ways. They are elements
of the linear vector space, and so are the things manipulated. They are
also the things that are multiplied times the elements by the Lie product,
and so are the operators.

To distinguish these roles, we define the operator Ad_A , corresponding to the element **A**, by the relation

$$\text{Ad}_A \mathbf{X} = [\mathbf{A}, \mathbf{X}] \tag{30}$$

where **X** is any element of the algebra. This is normally called the *adjoint operator*. This use of the word *adjoint*, however, should not be confused with its use in connection with the inner product of Chapter II.

The adjoint operator has some interesting properties. First, it is a *derivation*. An operator D is a derivation for some product relation $\{\mathbf{A}, \mathbf{B}\}$ if

$$D\{\mathbf{A}, \mathbf{B}\} = \{D\mathbf{A}, \mathbf{B}\} + \{\mathbf{A}, D\mathbf{B}\} \tag{31}$$

The name comes from analogy to the derivative relation

$$\frac{d}{dz}(fg) = \frac{df}{dz}g + f\frac{dg}{dz}$$

The adjoint operator is a derivation not only for the Lie product, but also for the associative product:

$$\text{Ad}_A(\mathbf{BC}) = [\mathbf{A}, \mathbf{BC}] = \mathbf{ABC} - \mathbf{BCA}$$

$$= \mathbf{ABC} - \mathbf{BAC} + \mathbf{BAC} - \mathbf{BCA}$$

$$= [\mathbf{A}, \mathbf{B}]\mathbf{C} + \mathbf{B}[\mathbf{A}, \mathbf{C}]$$

$$= (\text{Ad}_A\mathbf{B})\mathbf{C} + \mathbf{B}(\text{Ad}_A\mathbf{C}) \tag{32}$$

Further, it is an *inner derivation*, since it is a derivation obtained from an element that is also a part of the set.

It can be shown that all inner derivations of a Lie algebra can be expressed in this manner—i.e., as the adjoint operator obtained from some element of the set. That is to say, any derivation that is obtained by some combination of operations with members of algebra L can be expressed as Ad_X where **X** is some member of the algebra L.

Another important formula for the manipulation of these operators is

$$\text{Ad}_{\text{Ad}_A B} = [\text{Ad}_A , \text{Ad}_B] = \text{Ad}_A \text{Ad}_B - \text{Ad}_B \text{Ad}_A \tag{33}$$

This is actually an expression of the Jacobi identity, Eq. (19) or (21), although it is hardly recognizable as such. However, we see that

$$\text{Ad}_{\text{Ad}_A B}\mathbf{X} = [\text{Ad}_A\mathbf{B}, \mathbf{X}] = [[\mathbf{A}, \mathbf{B}], \mathbf{X}]$$

$$= -[\mathbf{X}, [\mathbf{A}, \mathbf{B}]] = [\mathbf{A}, [\mathbf{B}, \mathbf{X}]] + [\mathbf{B}, [\mathbf{X}, \mathbf{A}]]$$

from the Jacobi identity,

$$= [\mathbf{A}, [\mathbf{B}, \mathbf{X}]] - [\mathbf{B}, [\mathbf{A}, \mathbf{X}]]$$

$$= (\mathrm{Ad}_A \, \mathrm{Ad}_B - \mathrm{Ad}_B \, \mathrm{Ad}_A)\mathbf{X}$$

8. LINEARITY

We have, from the definition, that an algebra is a linear vector space and a ring. Also, we see that Ad_A is a linear homogenous operator—i.e.,

$$\mathrm{Ad}_A(a\mathbf{X}) = a \, \mathrm{Ad}_A\mathbf{X} \qquad (34)$$

for any a in the field.

Hence Ad_A is a linear homogenous operator whose domain is a linear vector space. Therefore *all* of the results of the preceding chapters that flow from this property of the operator, rather than the form of a particular representation, apply directly. For example, we know immediately that we can choose a basis for the space. In fact, any complete set of dyads is such a basis.

Also, we know that we can apply Theorem 1 of Chapter III. This theorem stated that if the field is algebraically complete, any linear operator that maps a given space onto or into itself has at least one eigenvector in that space. This means, here, that there must be at least one scalar λ_i and one matrix $\mathbf{X}_i$ such that

$$\mathrm{Ad}_A\mathbf{X}_i = [\mathbf{A}, \mathbf{X}_i] = \lambda_i\mathbf{X}_i \qquad (35)$$

This is the eigenvector equation for the commutator operator.

The general results of Chapter VIII must also apply. In particular, a given Ad_A must decompose the whole space of $n \times n$ matrices into cyclic invariant subspaces, each of which has as its minimum polynomial some power of an irreducible polynomial (Theorem 4, Chapter VIII). This theorem led, in Chapter VIII, to the Jordan canonical form. However, this form was a consequence of the particular representation of the operator as a matrix, and so is inapplicable. The basis that accomplished the reduction to canonical form may still be a useful one, however, providing the field involved is algebraically complete.

What is a polynomial of Ad_A may be puzzling, at first glance. We recall, however, that the power of an operator is obtained as that operator that has the effect of an n-fold application of the given operator. It follows that

$$(\mathrm{Ad}_A)^2\mathbf{X} = \mathrm{Ad}_A(\mathrm{Ad}_A\mathbf{X}) = [\mathbf{A}, [\mathbf{A}, \mathbf{X}]]$$

$$(\mathrm{Ad}_A)^3\mathbf{X} = \mathrm{Ad}_A(\mathrm{Ad}_A{}^2\mathbf{X}) = [\mathbf{A}, [\mathbf{A}, [\mathbf{A}, \mathbf{X}]]] \qquad (36)$$

$$(\mathrm{Ad}_A)^n\mathbf{X} = \mathrm{Ad}_A(\mathrm{Ad}_A^{n-1}\mathbf{X})$$

Further, to be consistent, we must define

$$(\mathrm{Ad}_A)^0 \mathbf{X} = \mathbf{X}$$

$\mathrm{Ad}_A{}^n \mathbf{X}$ is sometimes called the n-commutator of $\mathbf{A}$ with $\mathbf{X}$. We therefore can define a polynomial of Ad_A :

$$p(\mathrm{Ad}_A)\mathbf{X} = (a_0 \mathbf{I} + a_1 \,\mathrm{Ad}_A + a_2 \,\mathrm{Ad}_A{}^2 + \cdots)\mathbf{X}$$

$$= a_0 \mathbf{X} + a_1 [\mathbf{A}, \mathbf{X}] + a_2 [\mathbf{A}, [\mathbf{A}, \mathbf{X}]] + \cdots$$

Therefore a minimum polynomial of Ad_A exists, and its roots are the eigenvalues of Ad_A. As before, if the minimum polynomial has only simple roots, then Ad_A is *semisimple* and the linearly independent set of $\mathbf{X}_i$ that solve Eq. (35) form a complete set that spans the whole space of $n \times n$ matrices.

On the other hand, it is quite possible that Ad_A is not semisimple. In fact, we shall see that it is not if $\mathbf{A}$ is not. In this case, Ad_A has one or more chains of generalized eigenvectors, $\mathbf{X}_i$, $\mathbf{X}_{i1}$, $\mathbf{X}_{i2}$, ... such that

$$\mathrm{Ad}_A \mathbf{X}_i = \lambda_i \mathbf{X}_i$$

$$\mathrm{Ad}_A \mathbf{X}_{i1} = \lambda_i \mathbf{X}_{i1} + \mathbf{X}_i \tag{37}$$

$$\mathrm{Ad}_A \mathbf{X}_{i2} = \lambda_i \mathbf{X}_{i2} + \mathbf{X}_{i1}$$

$$\text{etc.}$$

Again, if the length of the longest chain with eigenvalue λ_i is m_i, then λ_i is the root of the minimum polynomial of Ad_A with multiplicity m_i.

In other words, the entire body of theory that we have developed from the abstract concept of linear operators carries over quite directly. The parts that do not carry over are those that depend on the particular form of the operator. Thus we find that we can define the trace of Ad_A as the sum of the eigenvalues, multiplicities included, and know that it is the negative of the coefficient of λ^{n-1} in the characteristic equation. It is, however, meaningless to attempt to interpret the trace as the "sum of the coefficients on the main diagonal."

9. EIGENVALUES AND EIGENVECTORS

The first question that arises is: What is the relation between the eigenvalues and eigenvectors of Ad_A and those of $\mathbf{A}$?

Suppose, first, that $\mathbf{A}$ is semisimple and K-hermitian. Then we can choose a complete set of eigenvectors of $\mathbf{A}$, $\mathbf{u}_i$ that are K-orthogonal and maximally normalized:

$$\mathbf{Au}_i = \lambda_i \mathbf{u}_i$$

$$\mathbf{u}_i{}^\dagger \mathbf{Ku}_j = \delta_{ij}\sigma_i$$

We assert that the dyad

$$\mathbf{W}_{ij} = \sigma_i \mathbf{u}_i \mathbf{u}_{\sim j}^\dagger \mathbf{K} \tag{38}$$

is an eigenvector of Ad_A . We can easily see that this is so:

$$
\begin{aligned}
\mathrm{Ad}_A \mathbf{W}_{ij} &= \sigma_i \mathbf{Au}_i \mathbf{u}_{\sim j}^\dagger \mathbf{K} - \sigma_i \mathbf{u}_i \mathbf{u}_{\sim j}^\dagger \mathbf{KA} \\
&= \sigma_i \mathbf{Au}_i \mathbf{u}_{\sim j}^\dagger \mathbf{K} - \sigma_i \mathbf{u}_i \mathbf{u}_{\sim j}^\dagger \mathbf{A}^\dagger \mathbf{K} \\
&= \sigma_i \lambda_i \mathbf{u}_i \mathbf{u}_{\sim j}^\dagger \mathbf{K} - \sigma_i \lambda_{\sim j}^* \mathbf{u}_i \mathbf{u}_{\sim j}^\dagger \mathbf{K} \\
&= (\lambda_i - \lambda_j)\mathbf{W}_{ij} \tag{39}
\end{aligned}
$$

Hence $\mathbf{W}_{ij}$ is an eigenvector of Ad_A with eigenvalue $(\lambda_i - \lambda_j)$. We note that $\mathbf{W}_{ii}$ is an eigenvector with zero eigenvalue. Hence Ad_A is a singular operator whose null space is, *at least*, the space spanned by all the $\mathbf{W}_{ii}$.

To be more general, let $\mathbf{A}$ be semisimple with eigenvectors $\mathbf{u}_i$ and eigenvalues λ_i :

$$\mathbf{Au}_i = \lambda_i \mathbf{u}_i$$

Let the reciprocal eigenvectors be $\mathbf{v}_i$ so that, as in Chapter III, Section 16,

$$\mathbf{v}_i{}^\dagger \mathbf{u}_j = \delta_{ij}$$

$$\mathbf{v}_i{}^\dagger \mathbf{A} = \lambda_i \mathbf{v}_i{}^\dagger$$

Then we see that if we let

$$\mathbf{W}_{ij} = \mathbf{u}_i \mathbf{v}_j{}^\dagger$$

we have

$$
\begin{aligned}
\mathrm{Ad}_A \mathbf{W}_{ij} &= \mathbf{Au}_i \mathbf{v}_j{}^\dagger - \mathbf{u}_i \mathbf{v}_j{}^\dagger \mathbf{A} = (\lambda_i - \lambda_j)\mathbf{u}_i \mathbf{v}_j{}^\dagger \\
&= (\lambda_i - \lambda_j)\mathbf{W}_{ij}
\end{aligned}
$$

as before.

If $\mathbf{A}$ is semisimple, the set of $\mathbf{W}_{ij}$ so defined spans the whole space. Hence, if $\mathbf{A}$ is semisimple, so is Ad_A .

Suppose $\mathbf{A}$ is not semisimple. Instead of attempting a general solution, let us look at a specific situation. Suppose $\mathbf{A}$ has a chain of length 2:

$$\mathbf{Au}_1 = \lambda \mathbf{u}_1$$
$$\mathbf{Au}_2 = \lambda \mathbf{u}_2 + \mathbf{u}_1$$

Then, as we found in Chapter III, Section 17, the reciprocal vectors are also a chain of length 2, but in the opposite sequence of rank:

$$\mathbf{v}_1{}^\dagger \mathbf{u}_1 = \mathbf{v}_2{}^\dagger \mathbf{u}_2 = 1$$
$$\mathbf{v}_1{}^\dagger \mathbf{u}_2 = \mathbf{v}_2{}^\dagger \mathbf{u}_1 = 0$$

and

$$\mathbf{v}_1{}^\dagger \mathbf{A} = \lambda \mathbf{v}_1{}^\dagger + \mathbf{v}_2$$
$$\mathbf{v}_2{}^\dagger \mathbf{A} = \lambda \mathbf{v}_2{}^\dagger$$

We consider the dyads:

$$\mathbf{W}_{11} = \mathbf{u}_1 \mathbf{v}_1{}^\dagger, \qquad \mathbf{W}_{12} = \mathbf{u}_1 \mathbf{v}_2{}^\dagger$$
$$\mathbf{W}_{21} = \mathbf{u}_2 \mathbf{v}_1{}^\dagger, \qquad \mathbf{W}_{22} = \mathbf{u}_2 \mathbf{v}_2{}^\dagger$$

We find that

$$\mathrm{Ad}_A \mathbf{W}_{11} = \mathbf{Au}_1 \mathbf{v}_1{}^\dagger - \mathbf{u}_1 \mathbf{v}_1{}^\dagger \mathbf{A} = -\mathbf{u}_1 \mathbf{v}_2{}^\dagger = -\mathbf{W}_{12}$$
$$\mathrm{Ad}_A \mathbf{W}_{12} = \mathbf{Au}_1 \mathbf{v}_2{}^\dagger - \mathbf{u}_1 \mathbf{v}_2{}^\dagger \mathbf{A} = 0$$
$$\mathrm{Ad}_A \mathbf{W}_{21} = \mathbf{Au}_2 \mathbf{v}_1{}^\dagger - \mathbf{u}_2 \mathbf{v}_1{}^\dagger \mathbf{A} = \mathbf{W}_{11} - \mathbf{W}_{22}$$
$$\mathrm{Ad}_A \mathbf{W}_{22} = \mathbf{Au}_2 \mathbf{v}_2{}^\dagger - \mathbf{u}_2 \mathbf{v}_2{}^\dagger \mathbf{A} = \mathbf{W}_{12}$$

The situation here is not immediately apparent. We can find that we can set

$$\mathbf{X}_3 = \mathbf{W}_{21}$$
$$\mathbf{X}_2 = \mathrm{Ad}_A \mathbf{X}_3 = \mathbf{W}_{11} - \mathbf{W}_{22} \qquad (40)$$
$$\mathbf{X}_1 = \mathrm{Ad}_A \mathbf{X}_2 = -2\mathbf{W}_{12}$$

and obtain a chain of length 3 with zero eigenvalue. In addition, $(\mathbf{W}_{11} + \mathbf{W}_{22})$ is an isolated eigenvector with zero eigenvalue.

Similar results are obtained if the chain is longer than two, or if other chains are involved. Hence, if $\mathbf{A}$ is not semisimple, neither is Ad_A. Further, the nonsemisimplicity of Ad_A always involves the eigensubspace with zero eigenvalue.

10. THE EQUATION $U = Ad_AV$

We have, in the preceding section, emphasized the behavior of Ad_A in its eigensubspace of zero eigenvalue so that we might apply the results of Chapter XII to the solution of

$$U = Ad_A V \tag{41}$$

for V, given U. We said, for example, that we shall show that a non-uniform system becomes tractible if S obeys an equation of the form of Eq. (7), providing A is sufficiently simple. This requires that we be able to solve Eq. (7) for A.

The operator Ad_A is always singular, since A necessarily commutes with any admissable function of itself. Hence the solution of Eq. (41) for V, or Eq. (7) for A, necessarily requires the use of the techniques of Chapter XII.

This poses no particular problem if A is semisimple. Then Ad_A is semisimple and we can apply the results of Chapter XII, Section 2. We obtain the minimum polynomial of Ad_A—if in no other way, from its distinct eigenvalues which we know from the eigenvalues of A. We normalize this polynomial so that we can write it as

$$Ad_A\{I - \theta(Ad_A)Ad_A\} = 0 \tag{42}$$

where θ is a polynomial. We also know that we can obtain a particular solution to Eq. (41) which is in the range of Ad_A, so that we can write

$$V = Ad_A X$$

where X is some element in the algebra. Multiplying Eq. (36) by $\theta(Ad_A)$, then, we obtain

$$\theta(Ad_A)U = \theta(Ad_A) Ad_A^2 X$$

$$= Ad_A X = V$$

To this we can add any V in the null space of Ad_A, i.e., which commutes with A, to obtain the general solution.

If A is not semisimple, then the method of Chapter XII, Section 4 involves the adjoint operator under some suitable inner product. The question is, then, what inner product should be used.

An inner product relation is a scalar function of two vectors with the properties listed in Chapter II, Section 3. (It will be recalled that in Chapter XII we required that the inner product be proper.) The vectors in this case are matrices. We have developed various scalar invariants of matrices (Chapter III, Section 12) that might be reasonable candidates. However, the inner product relation must be linear in the second term, and antilinear in the first. It is not unreasonable to consider defining the inner product of $\mathbf{A}$ and $\mathbf{B}$ as

$$\langle \mathbf{A}, \mathbf{B} \rangle = \mathrm{tr}(\mathbf{A}^\dagger \mathbf{B}) \tag{43}$$

We find that

$$\langle \mathbf{A}, \mathbf{A} \rangle = \mathrm{tr}\left(\sum_j A_{ji}^* A_{jk} \right)$$

$$= \sum_{ij} |A_{ji}|^2 \geqslant 0 \tag{44}$$

This is real and nonnegative for all $\mathbf{A}$. It is also positive definite. Further,

$$\langle \mathbf{A}, \mathbf{B} \rangle = \mathrm{tr}\left(\sum_j A_{ji}^* B_{jk} \right)$$

$$= \sum_{ij} (A_{ji}^* B_{ji}) = \langle \mathbf{B}, \mathbf{A} \rangle^* \tag{45}$$

Also, it is evidently linear in the second factor:

$$\langle \mathbf{A}, b\mathbf{B} + c\mathbf{C} \rangle = b\langle \mathbf{A}, \mathbf{B} \rangle + c\langle \mathbf{A}, \mathbf{C} \rangle \tag{46}$$

Therefore this is a suitable proper inner product.

We want to find an operator $\mathrm{Ad}_A{}^\#$ such that for any $\mathbf{X}$ and $\mathbf{Y}$

$$\langle \mathbf{X}, \mathrm{Ad}_A \mathbf{Y} \rangle = \langle \mathrm{Ad}_A{}^\# \mathbf{X}, \mathbf{Y} \rangle \tag{47}$$

Expanding the left side, we get

$$\langle \mathbf{X}, \mathrm{Ad}_A \mathbf{Y} \rangle = \mathrm{tr}\, \mathbf{X}^\dagger (\mathbf{AY} - \mathbf{YA})$$

$$= \mathrm{tr}\, \mathbf{X}^\dagger \mathbf{AY} - \mathrm{tr}\, \mathbf{X}^\dagger \mathbf{YA} \tag{48}$$

Now the trace of the product of two matrices is, in general, independent of their order:

$$\mathrm{tr}\, \mathbf{AB} = \mathrm{tr} \sum_j A_{ij} B_{jk} = \sum_{ij} A_{ij} B_{ji} = \mathrm{tr}\, \mathbf{BA} \tag{49}$$

It therefore follows that the trace of the product of any number of matrices is unchanged by a cyclic permutation of their order (but *not*, in general, for any other permutation). In particular,

$$\text{tr}(\mathbf{ABC}) = \text{tr } \mathbf{A(BC)} = \text{tr}(\mathbf{BC})\mathbf{A} = \text{tr}(\mathbf{BCA}) \tag{50}$$

We can then write Eq. (48) as

$$\begin{aligned}
\langle \mathbf{X}, \text{Ad}_A \mathbf{Y} \rangle &= \text{tr } \mathbf{X}^\dagger \mathbf{AY} - \text{tr } \mathbf{AX}^\dagger \mathbf{Y} \\
&= \text{tr}(\mathbf{X}^\dagger \mathbf{A} - \mathbf{AX}^\dagger)\mathbf{Y} \\
&= \text{tr}(\mathbf{A}^\dagger \mathbf{X} - \mathbf{XA}^\dagger)^\dagger \mathbf{Y} \\
&= \langle \text{Ad}_{A^\dagger} \mathbf{X}, \mathbf{Y} \rangle
\end{aligned} \tag{51}$$

Hence the operator that is adjoint to Ad_A under this inner product is

$$\text{Ad}_A{}^{\#} = \text{Ad}_{A^\dagger} \tag{52}$$

With this definition of the adjoint to Ad_A, we can apply the whole of Chapter XII to the solution of Eq. (41), regardless of whether $\mathbf{A}$ is semisimple or not. Providing $\mathbf{U}$ is, in fact, in the range of Ad_A, we can always solve Eq. (41) for the possible $\mathbf{V}$.

11. THE KILLING FORM

We will interject, here a few brief remarks on the so-called *Killing form* or the *scalar product of Cartan*. We shall not use this form, but it is extremely important in the general theory of Lie algebras and therefore requires mention, if for no other reason than to emphasize its difference from the inner product relation defined in the preceding section.

This form is defined as

$$\langle \mathbf{A}, \mathbf{B} \rangle = \text{tr}(\text{Ad}_A \, \text{Ad}_B) \tag{53}$$

One may wonder what is meant by the trace of an operator of the form $(\text{Ad}_A \, \text{Ad}_B)$. However, this is quite meaningful if we take as the definition of the trace that it is the sum of the eigenvalues. It can also be given meaning in terms of the structure constants defined in terms of Eq. (20), which we shall not go into here.

We will also mention the fact that if the Lie algebra is one of several types, it can be proven that

$$\langle \mathbf{A}, \mathbf{B} \rangle = k \, \text{tr}(\mathbf{AB}) \tag{54}$$

i.e., the Killing form is proportional to the trace of the matrix product, (**AB**). The proportionality constant depends on the particular algebra involved.

The essential distinction between Eqs. (54) and (43) is that in Eq. (43), **A** appears as **A**†. This distinction is very far from trivial. Equation (54) is linear in both terms, whereas Eq. (43) is antilinear in the first term. Hence Eq. (54) is *not* an inner product relation as we have defined the term in Chapter II. It does *not* make a Lie algebra into a Hilbert space.

We shall not go into the implications of this difference, or into why the Killing form is the appropriate type of relation for the general study of Lie algebras. We simply wish to caution the student against confusing it with an inner product relation, and against confusing Eq. (43) with the Killing form.

12. THE EXPONENTIAL OF Ad$_s$

We are now ready to consider in some detail Eq. (1) which we may write as

$$\frac{d\mathbf{W}}{dz} = \mathrm{Ad}_S\mathbf{W} \tag{55}$$

If $\mathbf{S} = \mathbf{S}_0$, a constant, then the solution is

$$\mathbf{W} = \exp(z\,\mathrm{Ad}_{S_0})\mathbf{W}_0 \tag{56}$$

Since $z\,\mathrm{Ad}_S$ is a linear homogeneous operator on a linear vector space, the arguments of Chapter VI apply, so that the exponential function is well defined and Eq. (56) is, in fact, the solution of Eq. (55). It is reasonable to ask, however, if this solution can be related to some appropriate form involving **S**, rather than Ad$_S$.

There is a useful device that enables us to treat such questions very easily. We define the two operators L_S and R_S as, respectively, left and right multiplication by **S**:

$$L_S\mathbf{X} = \mathbf{S}\mathbf{X} \tag{57}$$

$$R_S\mathbf{X} = \mathbf{X}\mathbf{S} \tag{58}$$

These are both linear homogeneous operators that act on the linear vector space of $n \times n$ matrices—i.e., in the associative algebra in which the Lie algebra is embedded. Hence they are operators of the general kind we have been considering. We see that for any admissable function $f(x)$,

$$f(L_S)\mathbf{X} = f(\mathbf{S})\mathbf{X}$$
$$f(R_S)\mathbf{X} = \mathbf{X}f(\mathbf{S}) \tag{59}$$

Furthermore, they are commuting operators regardless of the matrix involved—i.e.,

$$L_A R_B \mathbf{X} = R_B L_A \mathbf{X} = \mathbf{AXB} \tag{60}$$

Hence the theorems in Chapter VI, Section 11, regarding commuting operators apply. In particular, we can factor the exponential. Since

$$\mathrm{Ad}_S = L_S - R_S \tag{61}$$

this means that

$$\exp(z\,\mathrm{Ad}_S) = \{\exp(zL_S)\}\{\exp(-zR_S)\} \tag{62}$$

Hence

$$\exp(z\,\mathrm{Ad}_{S_0})\mathbf{W}_0 = \exp(zL_S)\exp(-zR_S)\mathbf{W}_0 = \exp(z\mathbf{S}_0)\mathbf{W}_0\exp(-z\mathbf{S}_0) \tag{63}$$

This is the solution of Eq. (1) or (55) when $\mathbf{S} = \mathbf{S}_0$, a constant matrix. It may be verified directly.

It may be noted that Eq. (63) implies that any similarity transformation can be expressed as a multiplicative operator of the form $\exp(\mathrm{Ad}_A)$. We should also note that $\exp(\mathrm{Ad}_A)$ is an isomorphism, as is the similarity transformation

$$(e^{\mathrm{Ad}_A}\mathbf{B})(e^{\mathrm{Ad}_A}\mathbf{C}) = (e^{\mathbf{A}}\mathbf{B}e^{-\mathbf{A}})(e^{\mathbf{A}}\mathbf{C}e^{-\mathbf{A}})$$
$$= e^{\mathbf{A}}(\mathbf{BC})e^{-\mathbf{A}} = e^{\mathrm{Ad}_A}(\mathbf{BC}) \tag{64}$$

13. SIMPLE NONUNIFORMITY

We shall say that a system described by Eq. (1), (2), or (5) has *simple nonuniformity* if the system operator $\mathbf{S}$ is not constant, but is describable by Eq. (7) with a constant $\mathbf{A}$. A typical example of such a system is the exponentially tapered transmission line.

We should note that the requirement is that $\mathbf{A}$ *can* be chosen to be constant. Since the solution of Eq. (7) for $\mathbf{A}$ given $\mathbf{S}$ and $d\mathbf{S}/dz$ is determined only within a subspace modulo the null space of Ad_S, there is considerable latitude in the choice of $\mathbf{A}$. The requirement then is that among the possible $\mathbf{A}$, there is at least one that is constant.

If this is so, then by the preceding section

$$\mathbf{S} = e^{z\mathrm{Ad}_A}\mathbf{S}_0 \tag{65}$$

where $\mathbf{S}_0 = \mathbf{S}(0)$, a constant matrix. Then Eq. (1) becomes

$$\frac{d\mathbf{W}}{dz} = (e^{z\mathrm{Ad}_A}\mathbf{S}_0)\mathbf{W} - \mathbf{W}(e^{z\mathrm{Ad}_A}\mathbf{S}_0) \tag{66}$$

If, now, we make the substitution

$$\mathbf{W} = e^{z\,\mathrm{Ad}_A}\mathbf{X} \tag{67}$$

Eq. (66) becomes

$$e^{z\,\mathrm{Ad}_A}\,\mathrm{Ad}_A\mathbf{X} + e^{z\,\mathrm{Ad}_A}\frac{d\mathbf{X}}{dz} = (e^{z\,\mathrm{Ad}_A}\mathbf{S}_0)(e^{z\,\mathrm{Ad}_A}\mathbf{X}) - (e^{z\,\mathrm{Ad}_A}\mathbf{X})(e^{z\,\mathrm{Ad}_A}\mathbf{S}_0)$$
$$= e^{z\,\mathrm{Ad}_A}(\mathrm{Ad}_{S_0}\mathbf{X})$$

by Eq. (64). The transformation of Eq. (67) is to a z-dependent basis such that $\mathbf{S}$ becomes constant. Then we have

$$\frac{d\mathbf{X}}{dz} = (\mathrm{Ad}_{S_0} - \mathrm{Ad}_A)\mathbf{X} = \mathrm{Ad}_{(S_0-A)}\mathbf{X} \tag{68}$$

and since $\mathbf{A}$ is assumed constant,

$$\mathbf{X} = \exp(z\,\mathrm{Ad}_{(S_0-A)})\mathbf{X}_0 \tag{69}$$

or, from Eq. (67),

$$\mathbf{W} = \exp(z\,\mathrm{Ad}_A)\exp(z\,\mathrm{Ad}_{(S_0-A)})\mathbf{X}_0$$
$$= \exp(z\,\mathrm{Ad}_A)\exp(z\,\mathrm{Ad}_{(S_0-A)})\mathbf{W}_0$$
$$= \exp(z\mathbf{A})\exp(z(\mathbf{S}_0-\mathbf{A}))\mathbf{W}_0\exp(-z(\mathbf{S}_0-\mathbf{A}))\exp(-z\mathbf{A}) \tag{70}$$

It is also possible to find that the solution to Eq. (2) is

$$\mathbf{x} = \exp(z\mathbf{A})\exp(z(\mathbf{S}_0-\mathbf{A}))\mathbf{x}(0) \tag{71}$$

and that of Eq. (5) is

$$\mathbf{M}(z) = \exp(z\mathbf{A})\exp(z(\mathbf{S}_0-\mathbf{A})) \tag{72}$$

so that in this case, it is not necessary to go to Eq. (1). The important aspect, however, is Eq. (7) which is of the type being considered.

We can continue the process and consider systems in which $\mathbf{S}$ is a solution of Eq. (7) but such that $\mathbf{A}$ cannot be taken as constant, but can be written as

$$\frac{d\mathbf{A}}{dz} = [\mathbf{A}, \mathbf{B}] \tag{73}$$

where $\mathbf{B}$ can be chosen as constant, and so on. The complexity of the problem increases very rapidly, but the problem, at least in principle, remains soluble, at least in terms of the exponential of an infinite series of matrices.

We can observe that since the exponential of an Ad operator is a similarity transformation, a necessary condition for a system to have simple nonuniformity is that the eigenvalues of $\mathbf{W}$ or $\mathbf{S}$ be constant.

It can be shown without too much difficulty that this is generally true. A necessary and sufficient condition on $\mathbf{W}$ for an $\mathbf{S}$ to exist satisfying Eq. (1) is that the structure and eigenvalues of $\mathbf{W}$ be constant.

The general conditions for simple nonuniformity, or for the development of Eq. (1) into a finite sequence of equations of the form of Eqs. (7) and (73) have not yet been worked out.

14. THE EXPONENTIALLY TAPERED TRANSMISSION LINE

We will conclude by considering when the z-dependent transmission line has simple nonuniformity. For this purpose, we will consider the system matrix

$$\mathbf{S} = \begin{pmatrix} 0 & -j\beta Z \\ -j\beta/Z & 0 \end{pmatrix}$$

as we have before (Chapter VI, Section 1).

The eigenvalues of $\mathbf{S}$ are $\pm\beta$. These must be constant, so that it is necessary that the distributed inductance and capacity vary inversely. We are concerned with Z being a function of z. We have

$$\frac{d\mathbf{S}}{dz} = -j\beta\kappa \begin{pmatrix} 0 & Z \\ -1/Z & 0 \end{pmatrix}$$

where

$$\kappa = Z'/Z$$

We could use the methods of Chapter XII to find $\mathbf{A}$. However, it is easy to proceed directly. If we set

$$\mathbf{A} = \begin{pmatrix} A & B \\ C & D \end{pmatrix}$$

we find that Eq. (7) is satisfied if

$$ZC - (B/Z) = 0$$
$$A - D = \kappa$$

For $\mathbf{A}$ to be constant, we must set $B = C = 0$ and κ must be constant. We can let

$$\mathbf{A} = \tfrac{1}{2}\kappa \begin{pmatrix} 1 & 0 \\ 0 & -1 \end{pmatrix}$$

That κ is constant means that

$$Z = e^{\kappa z} Z_0$$

where Z_0 is the value at $z = 0$. Hence the condition that the nonuniformity be simple implies that the line is exponentially tapered. (If we permit the line to be lossy, then κ can be a complex constant as well.)

To solve the problem we evaluate the exponentials of $z\mathbf{A}$ and $z(\mathbf{S}_0 - \mathbf{A})$ by any of the methods worked out before:

$$e^{z\mathbf{A}} = \begin{pmatrix} e^{\frac{1}{2}\kappa z} & 0 \\ 0 & e^{-\frac{1}{2}\kappa z} \end{pmatrix}$$

$$e^{z(\mathbf{S}_0 - \mathbf{A})} = \begin{pmatrix} \cos \gamma z - \dfrac{1}{2}\dfrac{\kappa}{\gamma} \sin \gamma z & -j\dfrac{\beta}{\gamma} Z_0 \sin \gamma z \\ -\dfrac{j\beta}{\gamma Z_0} \sin \gamma z & \cos \gamma z + \dfrac{1}{2}\dfrac{\kappa}{\gamma} \sin \gamma z \end{pmatrix}$$

where

$$\gamma^2 = \beta^2 - \tfrac{1}{4}\kappa^2$$

The matricant for the exponentially tapered line is, from Eq. (72),

$$\mathbf{M}(z) = \begin{pmatrix} e^{\frac{1}{2}\kappa z}\left(\cos \gamma z - \dfrac{1}{2}\dfrac{\kappa}{\gamma} \sin \gamma z\right) & -j\dfrac{\beta Z_0}{\gamma} e^{\frac{1}{2}\kappa z} \sin \gamma z \\ -\dfrac{j\beta}{\gamma Z_0} e^{-\frac{1}{2}\kappa z} \sin \gamma z & e^{-\frac{1}{2}\kappa z}\left(\cos \gamma z + \dfrac{1}{2}\dfrac{\kappa}{\gamma} \sin \gamma z\right) \end{pmatrix}$$

We note that, if $\kappa = 0$, this reduces to our usual solution for the uniform line.

15. CONCLUSIONS

We have ventured very briefly into the subject of Lie algebras. We have done so for two reasons. Firstly, it gives us an example of the way in which some of the concepts we have developed can be extended. We have discovered that what we have really been talking about was the algebra of linear operators acting on a linear vector space. It does not really matter what is the particular form of the operators, or of the elements of the linear vector space. The situation that we found here lead us to consider as the vectors of the space a set of matrices. The linear operators were the somewhat peculiar looking ones that we have symbolized by Ad_A, R_A, and L_A. Since these are linear operators acting on a linear vector space, the entire results of our previous work can be applied to them as appropriate.

From the more practical and immediate standpoint, we have found it possible to treat certain kinds of nonuniformity by these means. The particular kind that we have solved is what we have called *simple non-uniformity*. This was typified by the exponentially tapered transmission line, but includes many other interesting situations as well. These form a type of nonuniform system for which an exact solution can be obtained.

Exercises

1.   Find the eigenvalues and eigenvectors, μ_i and $\mathbf{X}_i$, of Ad_A i.e., which solve

$$\mathrm{Ad}_A\mathbf{X}_i = \mu_i\mathbf{X}_i$$

where:

(a) $\mathbf{A} = \begin{pmatrix} 0 & 1 \\ 1 & 0 \end{pmatrix}$ (b) $\mathbf{A} = \begin{pmatrix} 0 & 0 & 1 \\ 0 & 1 & 0 \\ 1 & 0 & 0 \end{pmatrix}$ (c) $\mathbf{A} = \begin{pmatrix} 0 & 1 & 0 \\ 0 & 0 & 1 \\ 1 & 0 & 0 \end{pmatrix}$

2.   Find the minimum polynomial, $\varphi(x)$, of Ad_A where

$$\mathbf{A} = \begin{pmatrix} 0 & 1 \\ 1 & 0 \end{pmatrix}$$

Verify your result by showing that

$$(\mathrm{Ad}_A)\mathbf{X} = \mathbf{0}$$

for all $\mathbf{X}$. Use $\varphi(x)$ to solve

$$\mathrm{Ad}_A\mathbf{U} = \begin{pmatrix} 0 & 1 \\ -1 & 0 \end{pmatrix}$$

for $\mathbf{U}$.

3.   Find the eigenvalues and eigenvectors of Ad_A where

$$\mathbf{A} = \begin{pmatrix} 0 & 0 & 1 \\ 0 & 2 & 0 \\ 1 & 0 & 0 \end{pmatrix}$$

Find the minimum polynomial of Ad_A.

4.   The general rotation operator in euclidean 2-space is given by

$$\mathbf{M} = \begin{pmatrix} \cos\theta & \sin\theta \\ -\sin\theta & \cos\theta \end{pmatrix}$$

Obtain the operators that describe the transformations that leave unchanged a regular *n*-gon. Show that these operators form a group.

5. Show that the group property is preserved under a similarity transformation.

6. Suppose D is any derivation. Show that

$$D^n[\mathbf{A}, \mathbf{B}] = \sum_{k=0}^{n} \binom{n}{k}[D^k\mathbf{A}, D^{n-k}\mathbf{B}]$$

From this, show that

$$e^D[\mathbf{A}, \mathbf{B}] = [e^D\mathbf{A}, e^D\mathbf{B}]$$

assuming that the series expression for e^D converges. (It can be shown that it does, in fact, converge for D any linear mapping on a finite-dimensional algebra. The expression found here, of which Eq. (64) is a particular case, is *Leibniz' rule*.)

7. Consider the matrix

$$\mathbf{S} = \begin{pmatrix} 0 & -j\omega & a\cos\theta & jb\cos\theta \\ -j\omega & 0 & -ja\sin\theta & b\sin\theta \\ -a\cos\theta & -ja\sin\theta & 0 & 0 \\ jb\cos\theta & -b\sin\theta & 0 & 0 \end{pmatrix}$$

where a, b, θ, and ω are real constants or functions of z.

Show that we can define $\mathbf{X}_1$, $\mathbf{X}_2$, $\mathbf{X}_3$ so that

$$\mathbf{S} = \mathbf{X}_1 \cos\theta + \mathbf{X}_2 \sin\theta + \omega\mathbf{X}_3$$

and that $\mathbf{X}_1$, $\mathbf{X}_2$, $\mathbf{X}_3$ form a Lie algebra. Show that this algebra can also be realized by

$$\mathbf{X}_1' = \frac{1}{2}c\begin{pmatrix} 0 & 1 \\ -1 & 0 \end{pmatrix}, \qquad \mathbf{X}_2' = \frac{1}{2}c\begin{pmatrix} 0 & j \\ j & 0 \end{pmatrix}, \qquad \mathbf{X}_3' = \frac{1}{2}\begin{pmatrix} j & 0 \\ 0 & -j \end{pmatrix}$$

where c is a suitable constant. Find the $\mathbf{S}'$ that is equivalent to $\mathbf{S}$ on this representation.

Find a $\mathbf{K}'$ for which $\mathbf{X}_1'$, $\mathbf{X}_2'$, $\mathbf{X}_3'$ are K'-skew-hermitian. Find a $\mathbf{K}$ for which $\mathbf{S}$ is K-skew-hermitian.

If

$$\frac{d\mathbf{W}}{dz} = [\mathbf{S}, \mathbf{W}]$$

and if $\mathbf{W}_0$ is in the space spanned by $\mathbf{X}_1$, $\mathbf{X}_2$, $\mathbf{X}_3$, show how the solution can be found from the solution, if available, of

$$\frac{d\mathbf{W}'}{dz} = [\mathbf{S}', \mathbf{W}']$$

8. Solve for the matricant by the methods of this chapter, when

$$\mathbf{S} = \begin{pmatrix} 0 & \gamma e^{-j\beta z} \\ \gamma e^{j\beta z} & 0 \end{pmatrix}$$

β and γ being real constants.

CHAPTER XIV

The Direct Product and Kronecker Sum

We shall here develop the concept of the so-called *direct product* and the *Kronecker sum* of two matrices. These are concepts whose principal applications are in group theory and the theory of Lie algebras, respectively, which are beyond the scope of this book. Nevertheless, the technique, as we shall develop it, certainly does fall within the scope of matrix algebra. It is, furthermore, also of great use in certain types of problems that do arise in matrix algebra.

1. THE DIRECT PRODUCT

Suppose we have two operations on a 2-dimensional vector space, described by the vector equations

$$\mathbf{x} = \begin{pmatrix} x_1 \\ x_2 \end{pmatrix} = \begin{pmatrix} A_1 & B_1 \\ C_1 & C_1 \end{pmatrix} \begin{pmatrix} u_1 \\ u_2 \end{pmatrix} = \mathbf{A_1 u} \tag{1}$$

$$\mathbf{y} = \begin{pmatrix} y_1 \\ y_2 \end{pmatrix} = \begin{pmatrix} A_2 & B_2 \\ C_2 & D_2 \end{pmatrix} \begin{pmatrix} v_1 \\ v_2 \end{pmatrix} = \mathbf{A_2 v} \tag{2}$$

The two matrices involved may be the same or different.

We can now, if we like, seek a way to keep track of what is happening in both vector equations simultaneously. One way is to define the 4-vectors

$$\boldsymbol{\xi} = \begin{pmatrix} x_1 y_1 \\ x_1 y_2 \\ x_2 y_1 \\ x_2 y_2 \end{pmatrix}, \qquad \boldsymbol{\eta} = \begin{pmatrix} u_1 v_1 \\ u_1 v_2 \\ u_2 v_1 \\ u_2 v_2 \end{pmatrix} \tag{3}$$

Then, if we can find how these vectors are related, we will be able to reconstruct the separate vectors $\mathbf{x}$ and $\mathbf{y}$, for any given $\mathbf{u}$ and $\mathbf{y}$, within a scale factor.

It is evident that the transformation of $\boldsymbol{\eta}$ to $\boldsymbol{\xi}$ is a linear homogeneous one. If we multiply $\boldsymbol{\eta}$ by any scalar k, this is equivalent, for instance, to multiplying $\mathbf{u}$ by k and $\mathbf{v}$ by 1, which multiplies $\mathbf{x}$ by k and $\mathbf{y}$ by 1, which means that $\boldsymbol{\xi}$ is multiplied by k.

The transformation, furthermore, is homogeneous. Hence the transformation can be expressed as a 4×4 matrix. The components of this matrix can be computed directly from Eqs. (1) and (2):

$$
\begin{aligned}
x_1 y_1 &= (A_1 u_1 + B_1 u_2)(A_2 v_1 + B_2 v_2) \\
&= A_1 A_2 (u_1 v_1) + A_1 B_2 (u_1 v_2) + B_1 A_2 (u_2 v_1) + B_1 B_2 u_2 v_2
\end{aligned}
\tag{4}
$$

etc.

We find, specifically, that

$$
\boldsymbol{\xi} =
\begin{pmatrix}
A_1 A_2 & A_1 B_2 & B_1 A_2 & B_1 B_2 \\
A_1 C_2 & A_1 D_2 & B_1 C_2 & B_1 D_2 \\
C_1 A_2 & C_1 B_2 & D_1 A_2 & D_1 B_2 \\
C_1 C_2 & C_1 D_2 & D_1 C_2 & D_1 D_2
\end{pmatrix}
\boldsymbol{\eta}
\tag{5}
$$

Symbolically, we can write this as

$$
\boldsymbol{\xi} =
\begin{pmatrix}
A_1 \mathbf{A}_2 & B_1 \mathbf{A}_2 \\
C_1 \mathbf{A}_2 & D_1 \mathbf{A}_2
\end{pmatrix}
\boldsymbol{\eta}
\tag{6}
$$

where each component of $\mathbf{A}_1$ is multiplied by the whole of $\mathbf{A}_2$.

We call the matrix in Eq. (5) or (6) the *direct product* or *Kronecker product* of $\mathbf{A}_1$ and $\mathbf{A}_2$ and write it as

$$
\mathbf{A}_1 \times \mathbf{A}_2
\tag{7}
$$

More generally, let

$$
\mathbf{A} = (a_{ij}), \qquad \mathbf{B} = (b_{ij})
\tag{8}
$$

and

$$
\mathbf{x}_i = \sum_j a_{ij} \mathbf{u}_j, \qquad \mathbf{y}_i = \sum_j b_{ij} \mathbf{v}_j
\tag{9}
$$

Then, if we define $\boldsymbol{\xi}$ and $\boldsymbol{\eta}$ as column vectors whose components are indicated by a two index symbol (ij) ordered in some agreed upon fashion,

$$
\xi_{ij} = x_i y_j, \qquad \eta_{ij} = u_i v_j
\tag{10}
$$

and

$$
\xi_{ij} = (\mathbf{A} \times \mathbf{B}) \eta_{kh}
\tag{11}
$$

we define

$$
(\mathbf{A} \times \mathbf{B})_{ij;kh} = a_{ik} b_{jh}
\tag{12}
$$

the same ordering convention for the 2-index symbols being used throughout.

2. JUSTIFICATION OF "PRODUCT"

By calling the relation of Eq. (12) the direct product, we are implying that the relation has the properties that we expect of a product. This is so, and we can easily verify from Eq. (12) the following:

A. The relation is distributive with respect to addition in either component:

$$(A + B) \times C = A \times C + B \times C \tag{13}$$

$$A \times (B + C) = A \times B + A \times C \tag{14}$$

B. It is also associative:

$$A \times (B \times C) = (A \times B) \times C \tag{15}$$

C. There exists a zero and an identity that can be obtained, although not uniquely, as

$$0 = 0 \times 0$$

$$I = I \times I$$

which have the usual properties of the null and identity operators.

We can also discover that there is a relation between the direct product and the matrix product. Providing the dimensionalities of the matrices involved are such as to give meaning to the various terms, we find that

$$(A \times B)(C \times D) = (AC) \times (BD) \tag{16}$$

This follows since

$$\{(A \times B)(C \times D)\}_{ij,mn} = \sum_{rs} \{A \times B\}_{ij,rs}\{(C \times D)_{rs,mn}\}$$

$$= \sum_{rs} \{A_{ir}B_{js}C_{rm}D_{sn}\}$$

$$= \left\{\sum_{r} A_{ir}C_{rm}\right\}\left\{\sum_{s} B_{js}D_{sn}\right\}$$

$$= \{(AC)_{im}\}\{(BD)_{jn}\}$$

$$= \{(AC) \times (BD)\}_{ij,mn}$$

This relation is quite important. If, for example, we have

$$AB = C, \quad MN = P \tag{17}$$

where **A**, **B**, and **C** are $n \times n$ matrices, and **M**, **N**, and **P** are $m \times m$, then

$$(\mathbf{A} \times \mathbf{M})(\mathbf{B} \times \mathbf{N}) = (\mathbf{AB}) \times (\mathbf{MN}) = \mathbf{C} \times \mathbf{P} \qquad (18)$$

so that the relations are preserved. If, for, example $\mathbf{M} = \mathbf{N} = \mathbf{P} = \mathbf{I}$, then Eq. (18) says that the mapping of **A** into **A** × **I**, **B** into **B** × **I**, etc., is an isomorphism.

More generally, suppose α, β, and γ are abstract elements of a group such that $\alpha\beta = \gamma$ and **A**, **B**, and **C** and **M**, **N**, and **P** are the corresponding elements in any two representations of the group. Then Eq. (18) says that (**A** × **M**), (**B** × **N**), and (**C** × **P**) are also possible representations of these same elements. Thus simple representations of a group can be combined to form more complicated ones.

By induction we can generalize Eq. (18) to any finite number of factors:

$$(\mathbf{A} \times \mathbf{M})(\mathbf{B} \times \mathbf{N})(\mathbf{C} \times \mathbf{P})... = (\mathbf{ABC}...) \times (\mathbf{MNP}...) \qquad (19)$$

assuming that the dimensionalities are compatible—usually that **A**, **B**, **C**, ... are all $n \times n$ matrices, and **M**, **N**, **P**, ... are all $m \times m$.

3. THE PRODUCT OF MATRICANTS AND THE KRONECKER SUM

To lead up to the operation that we will define as the *Kronecker sum*, we will consider the direct product of the matricants of two systems which may be identical or distinct. We will ask if, or when, this product can itself be regarded as the matricant of some system, and, if so, what is its system operator?

Suppose we have the systems described by

$$\frac{d\mathbf{M}}{dz} = -j\mathbf{AM}, \qquad \mathbf{M}(z_1) = \mathbf{I}_m$$

$$\frac{d\mathbf{N}}{dz} = -j\mathbf{BN}, \qquad \mathbf{N}(z_2) = \mathbf{I}_n \qquad (20)$$

where the first is m-dimensional and the second n-dimensional.

We ask if **M** × **N** is a matricant. It is evident that

$$\frac{d}{dz}(\mathbf{M} \times \mathbf{N}) = \left(\frac{d\mathbf{M}}{dz}\right) \times \mathbf{N} + \mathbf{M} \times \left(\frac{d\mathbf{N}}{dz}\right)$$

$$= -j(\mathbf{AM}) \times \mathbf{N} - j\mathbf{M} \times (\mathbf{BN}) \qquad (21)$$

This can be written as

$$\frac{d}{dz}(\mathbf{M} \times \mathbf{N}) = -j(\mathbf{AM}) \times (\mathbf{I}_n\mathbf{N}) - j(\mathbf{I}_m\mathbf{M}) \times (\mathbf{BN})$$

$$= -j(\mathbf{A} \times \mathbf{I}_n)(\mathbf{M} \times \mathbf{N}) - j(\mathbf{I}_m \times \mathbf{B})(\mathbf{M} \times \mathbf{N})$$

$$= -j(\mathbf{A} \times \mathbf{I}_n + \mathbf{I}_m \times \mathbf{B})(\mathbf{M} \times \mathbf{N}) \qquad (22)$$

where we have used Eq. (16).

The direct product $(\mathbf{M} \times \mathbf{N})$ is at least an integral solution of a system whose system operator is $\mathbf{C}$:

$$\mathbf{C} = \mathbf{A} \times \mathbf{I}_n + \mathbf{I}_m \times \mathbf{B} \qquad (23)$$

If $z_1 = z_2$, so that the boundary conditions are applied to both $\mathbf{M}$ and $\mathbf{N}$ at the same value of z, then at this value, $(\mathbf{M} \times \mathbf{N})$ becomes $\mathbf{I}_m \times \mathbf{I}_n = \mathbf{I}_{m+n}$ and the direct product is a matricant.

The particular significance of Eq. (22) lies in the possibility that the system operator of the system we are studying can be written in the form of Eq. (23). If so, we can break the problem into two parts with the smaller system operators $\mathbf{A}$ and $\mathbf{B}$. If we can now solve these parts separately for their matricants $\mathbf{M}$ and $\mathbf{N}$, then the solution to the whole problem will be the direct product of the separate solutions.

The relation indicated in Eq. (23) is called the *Kronecker sum* of $\mathbf{A}$ and $\mathbf{B}$. The name is perhaps unfortunate since the relation does not have the properties that we expect from an additive relation. For example, it is not commutative. Nevertheless, it is an important relation that does play a role that, in many situations, is analogous to a sum.

4. GROUP THEORETIC SIGNIFICANCE

The relationships that we have developed have a very deep significance. The matricant, we have observed, can be regarded as a curve in a group. The system operator is a point or a curve in the corresponding Lie algebra.

What we really want to know is the solution in the abstract group—i.e., the abstract operator that is represented by a particular matricant solution. For it is the abstract operator that is involved with the actual physical situation.

There are many ways of representing a given abstract operator. We have seen some of the possible variations when we studied the effect of the basis. It is only the representation, not the abstract operator, that is affected by a change of basis. But this is not the only kind of variation possible. In addition, we can easily develop representations in terms of matrices of higher dimensionality. We can, for example, simply add rows and columns to the given matricant. If we do this in a way that does not affect the previous solution, we have not changed anything, and the same abstract operator is represented.

A very simple way of doing this is to replace the matricant $\mathbf{M}$ by $\mathbf{M}' = \text{quasidiag}(\mathbf{M}\,\mathbf{I}_n)$ where $\mathbf{I}_n$ is an $n \times n$ identity, n any number. If we replace the system operator $\mathbf{S}$ by $\mathbf{S}' = \text{quasidiag}(\mathbf{S}\,\mathbf{0}_n)$, where $\mathbf{0}_n$ is the $n \times n$ null matrix, we have not basically changed anything.

A more general way of doing this is to replace $\mathbf{M}$ by $(\mathbf{M}' \times \mathbf{M}'')$, where $\mathbf{M}'$ and $\mathbf{M}''$ are any representations of the abstract operator, and replace $\mathbf{S}$ by the Kronecker sum of $\mathbf{S}'$ and $\mathbf{S}''$, the corresponding representations of the abstract system operator. The results of the last section show that this is a valid process.

Hence the direct product gives us a way of combining representations of a group. Then the corresponding way of combining representations of the corresponding Lie algebra is by the Kronecker sum.

To explore this a little further, let $\mathbf{M}$ and $\mathbf{N}$ be matricants of the system or systems described by Eq. (20). Let the boundary conditions in both be applied at z_0, and let us look at their values at z very close to z_0, so that $\mathbf{M}$ and $\mathbf{N}$ are very close to their respective identities:

$$\mathbf{M} = \mathbf{I}_m + \epsilon\mathbf{A}$$
$$\mathbf{N} = \mathbf{I}_n + \epsilon\mathbf{B} \tag{24}$$

where ϵ is a small number. We know that $\mathbf{A}$ and $\mathbf{B}$ are elements in the associated representations of the Lie algebra involved.

Then, from Eq. (14), we find that

$$(\mathbf{M} \times \mathbf{N}) = (\mathbf{I}_m + \epsilon\mathbf{A}) \times (\mathbf{I}_n + \epsilon\mathbf{B})$$
$$= \mathbf{I}_m \times \mathbf{I}_n + \epsilon\{\mathbf{A} \times \mathbf{I}_n + \mathbf{I}_m \times \mathbf{B}\} + \epsilon^2\mathbf{A} \times \mathbf{B}$$
$$= \mathbf{I}_{m+n} + \epsilon\{\mathbf{A} \times \mathbf{I}_n + \mathbf{I}_m \times \mathbf{B}\} \tag{25}$$

to the first order in ϵ. We note the emergence of the Kronecker sum.

Hence the matrix that describes the infinitesimal variation of the matricant $(\mathbf{M} \times \mathbf{N})$ around its value at z_0, which is the identity, is given by the Kronecker sum of the infinitesimal variations of $\mathbf{M}$ and $\mathbf{N}$. Hence the Kronecker sum plays the same role for the Lie algebra that the direct product does for the group.

5. EXPONENTIATION

The fundamental connection between a group and its associated Lie algebra can be described by saying that the group is the result of *exponentiating* the algebra. We shall not explore this statement in depth, but it is worth demonstrating here that the exponential of a Kronecker sum is the direct product of exponentials. Specifically, if we have

$$\mathbf{C} = \mathbf{A} \times \mathbf{I}_n + \mathbf{I}_m \times \mathbf{B} \tag{23}$$

then

$$e^{\mathbf{C}} = e^{\mathbf{A}} \times e^{\mathbf{B}} \tag{26}$$

To show this, we note first that

$$(\mathbf{A} \times \mathbf{I}_m)(\mathbf{I}_n \times \mathbf{B}) = (\mathbf{A}\mathbf{I}_n) \times (\mathbf{I}_m\mathbf{B}) = \mathbf{A} \times \mathbf{B}$$
$$(\mathbf{I}_n \times \mathbf{B})(\mathbf{A} \times \mathbf{I}_m) = (\mathbf{I}_n\mathbf{A}) \times (\mathbf{B}\mathbf{I}_m) = \mathbf{A} \times \mathbf{B} \tag{27}$$

Hence $(\mathbf{A} \times \mathbf{I}_m)$ and $(\mathbf{I}_n \times \mathbf{B})$ commute, and we are therefore justified in using the binomial theorem on powers of their sum.

If we expand exp $\mathbf{C}$ in powers of $\mathbf{C}$, we obtain

$$e^{\mathbf{C}} = \mathbf{I}_{m+n} + \mathbf{C} + \frac{1}{2!}\mathbf{C}^2 + \cdots$$

$$= \sum_{p=0}^{\infty} \frac{1}{p!}\{\mathbf{A} \times \mathbf{I}_n + \mathbf{I}_m \times \mathbf{B}\}^p$$

$$= \sum_{p=0}^{\infty}\sum_{k=0}^{p} \frac{1}{k!(p-k)!}(\mathbf{A} \times \mathbf{I}_n)^k(\mathbf{I}_m \times \mathbf{B})^{p-k}$$

$$= \sum_{p=0}^{\infty}\sum_{k=0}^{p} \frac{1}{k!(p-k)!}\mathbf{A}^k \times \mathbf{B}^{p-k} \tag{28}$$

from Eq. (19). Note that $\mathbf{A}^0 = \mathbf{I}_n$ and $\mathbf{B}^0 = \mathbf{I}_m$. The right-hand side of Eq. (26) expands to give

$$e^{\mathbf{A}} \times e^{\mathbf{B}} = \left\{\mathbf{I}_n + \mathbf{A} + \frac{1}{2!}\mathbf{A}^2 + \cdots\right\} \times \left\{\mathbf{I}_m + \mathbf{B} + \frac{1}{2!}\mathbf{B}^2 + \cdots\right\}$$

$$= \sum_{r=0}^{\infty}\sum_{s=0}^{\infty} \frac{1}{r!s!}\mathbf{A}^r \times \mathbf{B}^s$$

$$= \sum_{p=0}^{\infty}\sum_{k=0}^{p} \frac{1}{k!(p-k)}\mathbf{A}^k \times \mathbf{B}^{p-k} \tag{29}$$

if we rearrange the series to collect terms of the same order in $\mathbf{A}$ and $\mathbf{B}$ combined. (Let $r = k$ and $s = p - k$. Summing first over k for fixed p, we can only sum k to p since s is nonnegative.)

Comparing Eqs. (29) and (28), the equality is proven.

6. EIGENVECTORS AND EIGENVALUES OF THE DIRECT PRODUCT

We shall now consider just what it is we have done by taking the direct product or Kronecker sum of the two matrices.

Suppose first that $\mathbf{A}$ and $\mathbf{B}$ are semisimple matrices of dimensions n and m, respectively. Suppose, further, that

$$
\begin{aligned}
\mathbf{A}\mathbf{x}^{(r)} &= \lambda_r \mathbf{x}^{(r)} \\
\mathbf{B}\mathbf{y}^{(s)} &= \mu_s \mathbf{y}^{(s)}
\end{aligned}
\tag{30}
$$

In detail, this says that

$$
\begin{aligned}
\sum_j A_{ij} x_j^{(r)} &= \lambda_r x_i^{(r)} \\
\sum_k B_{kh} y_h^{(s)} &= \mu_s y_k^{(s)}
\end{aligned}
\tag{31}
$$

Then we see that

$$
\sum_{ih} A_{ij} B_{kh} x_j^{(r)} y_h^{(s)} = \sum_{jh} (\mathbf{A} \times \mathbf{B})_{ik,jh} x_j^{(r)} y_h^{(s)}
$$
$$
= \lambda_r \mu_s x_i^{(r)} y_k^{(s)}
\tag{32}
$$

Define the vector

$$
u_{ij}^{(r,s)} = x_i^{(r)} y_j^{(s)}
\tag{33}
$$

where, as before, (ij) is to be considered as a double index notation of what is "really" a single index.

Then Eq. (32) becomes

$$
(\mathbf{A} \times \mathbf{B})\mathbf{u}^{(r,s)} = (\lambda_r \mu_s)\mathbf{u}^{(r,s)}
\tag{34}
$$

Hence $\mathbf{u}^{(r,s)}$ is an eigenvector of $\mathbf{A} \times \mathbf{B}$ with eigenvalue $\lambda_r \mu_s$.

Since $\mathbf{A}$ and $\mathbf{B}$ are assumed semisimple, there exist n linearly independent $\mathbf{x}^{(r)}$ and m $\mathbf{y}^{(s)}$, and hence (mn) linearly independent eigenvectors $\mathbf{u}^{(r,s)}$ of $\mathbf{A} \times \mathbf{B}$. Hence $\mathbf{A} \times \mathbf{B}$ is semisimple.

Every eigenvalue of $\mathbf{A} \times \mathbf{B}$ is the product of an eigenvalue of $\mathbf{A}$ times an eigenvalue of $\mathbf{B}$, and all possible such combinations occur.

If $\mathbf{A}$ and $\mathbf{B}$ are not semisimple, the problem becomes slightly more complicated. If $\mathbf{A}$ is semisimple and $\mathbf{B}$ not, then each chain of $\mathbf{B}$ is simply imaged into a multiplicity of chains in **A × B**. If neither is semisimple, there are some further complications of detail, though nothing intrinsically new is added. The relation between the eigenvalues of **A** and **B** and **A × B** is, in any case, the same regardless of semisimplicity.

7. EIGENVECTORS AND EIGENVALUES OF THE KRONECKER SUM

The eigenvectors and eigenvalues of the Kronecker sum are found in a similar way. We are considering the matrix of Eq. (23) whose terms, in a double index notation, are

$$C_{ij,kh} = A_{ik}\delta_{jh} + \delta_{ik}B_{jh}$$

where δ_{ij} is the Kronecker delta which equals one if $i = j$, zero, otherwise.

We assume again that **A** and **B** are semisimple.

If Eq. (30) or (31) describes the eigenvectors of **A** and **B**, then

$$\sum_{kh} C_{ij,kh}x_k^{(r)}y_h^{(s)} = \lambda_r x_i^{(r)}y_j^{(s)} + x_i^{(r)}\mu_s y_j^{(s)}$$

$$= (\lambda_r + \mu_s)x_i^{(r)}y_j^{(s)}$$

and, with Eq. (33), we can write

$$\mathbf{C}\mathbf{u}^{(r,s)} = (\mathbf{A} \times \mathbf{I} + \mathbf{I} \times \mathbf{B})\mathbf{u}^{(r,s)} = (\lambda_r + \mu_s)\mathbf{u}^{(r,s)} \tag{35}$$

The double-indexed vectors $\mathbf{u}^{(r,s)}$ are the eigenvectors of the Kronecker sum. Again, there are a sufficient number of them so that if **A** and **B** are semisimple, so is the Kronecker sum.

Every eigenvalue of the Kronecker sum of **A** and **B** is the sum of an eigenvalue of **A** with an eigenvalue of **B**, and all possible combinations exist.

Again, if **A** and **B** are not semisimple, the details of what happens are more complicated, but nothing essentially new is added.

8. NECESSARY CONDITION

We have seen that if we can express the **C** of Eq. (24) as the Kronecker sum of **A** and **B**, the solution of Eq. (24), **P**, can be expressed as the direct product of the solutions of the systems whose system operators are **A** and **B**. We have not provided any test for when this kind of partition of **C** can be effected. The preceding section gives us at least a necessary condition for this to be possible, although not a sufficient one. Suppose the eigenvalues of $\mathbf{C}$, taken with their full multiplicities, are η_i, $i = 1, ..., mn$. Then we require that there exist numbers λ_i, $i = 1, ..., m$, and μ_i, $i = 1, ..., n$, such that every η_i is the sum of some λ_j and some μ_k.

It may be readily seen that this is a singular condition. For example, suppose $\mathbf{C}$ is 4×4 with eigenvalues η_1, η_2, η_3, η_4. We require that we be able to find a λ_1 and λ_2 and μ_1 and μ_2 such that

$$\lambda_1 + \mu_1 = \eta_1$$
$$\lambda_2 + \mu_1 = \eta_2$$
$$\lambda_1 + \mu_2 = \eta_3$$
$$\lambda_2 + \mu_2 = \eta_4$$

These equations can be written as

$$\begin{pmatrix} 1 & 0 & 1 & 0 \\ 0 & 1 & 1 & 0 \\ 1 & 0 & 0 & 1 \\ 0 & 1 & 0 & 1 \end{pmatrix} \begin{pmatrix} \lambda_1 \\ \lambda_2 \\ \mu_1 \\ \mu_2 \end{pmatrix} = \begin{pmatrix} \eta_1 \\ \eta_2 \\ \eta_3 \\ \eta_4 \end{pmatrix}$$

The matrix on the left is singular. The vector on the right must be in the range of the matrix. The range can be easily found to be all vectors of the form

$$\eta = \begin{pmatrix} a + b + c \\ a + c \\ a - c \\ a - b - c \end{pmatrix}$$

from which we can find that we must have

$$\eta_1 - \eta_2 - \eta_3 + \eta_4 = 0$$

If the η_i do not fit this pattern, no such partition of the eigenvalues is possible, and $\mathbf{C}$ cannot be expressed as the Kronecker sum of any $\mathbf{A}$ and $\mathbf{B}$.

If the η_i do fit this pattern, there is still no guarantee that $\mathbf{C}$ can be so interpreted. The eigenvectors of $\mathbf{C}$ may not fit the required pattern. However, it is then worth investigating the possibility.

We should note here that what we have said does not depend on the constancy of $\mathbf{C}$. If the system is nonuniform, so that $\mathbf{C}$ is a function of z, it is still worthwhile to consider if the problem can be split into simpler pieces. The condition that we have developed here as being necessary for this type of splitting must then apply at all z.

There is a great deal more that could be said about this problem. However, such problems are best tackled by the methods of Lie algebras which are beyond the scope of this book.

9. MIXED INVERSES

As an example of the application of these methods to a very different kind of problem, consider the question of solving for $\mathbf{X}$ the equation

$$\mathbf{AX} + \mathbf{XB^\dagger} = \mathbf{C} \tag{36}$$

If we had only one term on the left, this would simply involve finding the inverse of $\mathbf{A}$ or $\mathbf{B^\dagger}$, providing the one present is nonsingular. If it is singular, we can still solve the equation by the methods of Chapter XII, providing the equation has a solution at all—i.e., providing $\mathbf{C}$ is in the range of $\mathbf{A}$, if $\mathbf{B^\dagger} = 0$, or $\mathbf{C^\dagger}$ in the range of $\mathbf{B}$ if $\mathbf{A} = 0$.

The problem of solving Eq. (36) when neither $\mathbf{A}$ nor $\mathbf{B}$ is the null matrix is the problem of finding what we may call the "mixed inverse."

Using subscripts we can write Eq. (36) as

$$\sum_k A_{ik}X_{kj} + \sum_h X_{ih}B_{jh}^* = C_{ij} \tag{37}$$

The indices on $\mathbf{B}$ are reversed since $\mathbf{B}$ appears in Eq. (36) as $\mathbf{B^\dagger}$.

We can isolate the $\mathbf{X}$ terms by writing Eq. (37) as

$$\sum_{kh} (A_{ik}\delta_{jh} + \delta_{ik}B_{jh}^*)X_{kh} = C_{ij} \tag{38}$$

We recognize the left-hand side as the Kronecker sum:

$$\sum_{kh} (\mathbf{A} \times \mathbf{I} + \mathbf{I} \times \mathbf{B}^*)_{ij,kh} X_{kh} = C_{ij}$$

In this equation we now regard X_{kh} and C_{ij} no longer as $n \times n$ square matrices, but as n^2-dimensional vectors with a double index notation.

We then need only to invert the $n^2 \times n^2$ matrix $(\mathbf{A} \times \mathbf{I} + \mathbf{I} \times \mathbf{B}^*)$ if it is nonsingular, or to apply to it the methods of Chapter XII if singular.

The eigenvalues of $(\mathbf{A} \times \mathbf{I} + \mathbf{I} \times \mathbf{B}^*)$ are all combinations of the form $(\lambda_i + \mu_j^*)$ where λ_i are the eigenvalues of $\mathbf{A}$ and μ_i of $\mathbf{B}$. The

Kronecker sum is singular if there exists any combination such that $\lambda_r + \mu_s{}^* = 0$. For Eq. (36) to be soluble for any $\mathbf{C}$, it is necessary and sufficient that no eigenvalue of $\mathbf{B}$ be the negative of the complex conjugate of any eigenvalue of $\mathbf{A}$.

We could, perhaps, have been lead to suspect that the solution of Eq. (36) might involve the Kronecker sum by considering the properties of the form $(\mathbf{AX} + \mathbf{XB}^\dagger)$. If we have

$$\mathbf{Ax} = \lambda\mathbf{x}$$

$$\mathbf{By} = \mu\mathbf{y}$$

we can form the dyad $\mathbf{xy}^\dagger$ and find that it is an "eigendyad" of the mixed operator

$$\mathbf{A}(\mathbf{xy}^\dagger) + (\mathbf{xy}^\dagger)\mathbf{B}^\dagger = (\lambda + \mu^*)\mathbf{xy}^\dagger$$

We find that the eigenvalue of this eigendyad involves the sum of eigenvalues of $\mathbf{A}$ and $\mathbf{B}^\dagger$, which therefore suggests that the Kronecker sum is involved.

10. SUMMARY

We have, in this chapter, developed the concepts of the direct product and the Kronecker sum of two matrices. These concepts are of great importance in group theory and in the theory of Lie algebras. Since both of these topics are beyond the scope of this book, we have only briefly hinted at this application, hoping that we have said enough to permit the student to recognize when he has a problem of this nature.

The process is also important whenever we have a problem that involves constructing a matrix whose eigenvalues are the product or sum of the eigenvalues of two smaller matrices. Unfortunately, it is not always clear when this is the case, unless the problem is posed in precisely those terms. As an example, we have used the Kronecker sum in solving Eq. (36). We did find, in this case, that if we considered the dyads that are preserved—i.e., eigendyads—of $(\mathbf{AX} + \mathbf{XB}^\dagger)$, then the sum of eigenvalues is in fact involved. Hence, a preliminary analysis of the properties of the operator involved could have suggested the use of the Kronecker sum.

Exercises

1. If $\mathbf{A}$ is an $n \times n$ matrix, and $\mathbf{B}$ an $m \times m$ one, show that:

    (a) $(\mathbf{A} \times \mathbf{B})^{-1} = \mathbf{A}^{-1} \times \mathbf{B}^{-1}$
    (b) $\text{tr}(\mathbf{A} \times \mathbf{B}) = (\text{tr } \mathbf{A})(\text{tr } \mathbf{B})$
    (c) $\mathbf{A} \times \mathbf{B} = |\mathbf{A}|^m |\mathbf{B}|^n$

2. Show that the eigenvalues of Ad_A are the same as those of $(\mathbf{A} \times \mathbf{I} - \mathbf{I} \times \mathbf{A})$.

3. If $\mathbf{A}$ and $\mathbf{B}$ are unitary, show that $(\mathbf{A} \times \mathbf{B})$ is also.

4. Let

$$\mathbf{A} = \begin{pmatrix} 1 & 1 \\ 0 & 1 \end{pmatrix}, \qquad \mathbf{B} = \begin{pmatrix} 1 & 0 \\ 2 & 1 \end{pmatrix}$$

$$\mathbf{C} = \begin{pmatrix} 1 & -1 \\ 0 & 1 \end{pmatrix}, \qquad \mathbf{D} = \begin{pmatrix} 1 & 0 \\ -2 & 1 \end{pmatrix}$$

Determine $(\mathbf{A} \times \mathbf{B})$ and $(\mathbf{C} \times \mathbf{D})$. Verify Eq. (16) or (18).

5. Let

$$\mathbf{A} = \begin{pmatrix} 0 & 1 \\ 1 & 0 \end{pmatrix}, \qquad \mathbf{B} = \begin{pmatrix} 0 & ab \\ a/b & 0 \end{pmatrix}$$

Find the eigenvalues and eigenvectors of $\mathbf{A}$ and $\mathbf{B}$. From these, compute the eigenvalues and eigenvectors of $(\mathbf{A} \times \mathbf{B})$. Compute $(\mathbf{A} \times \mathbf{B})$ and verify that these are, in fact, its eigenvalues and eigenvectors.

Compute the Kronecker sum of $\mathbf{A}$ and $\mathbf{B}$. What should its eigenvalues and eigenvectors be? Verify.

6. Consider the matrix

$$\mathbf{A} = \begin{pmatrix} 6 & 4 & 3 & 2 \\ 8 & 2 & 4 & 1 \\ 3 & 2 & 6 & 4 \\ 4 & 1 & 8 & 2 \end{pmatrix}$$

Observe that it is a Kronecker product of two matrices. Find its eigenvalues and eigenvectors. Verify.

7. Consider the matrix

$$\mathbf{A} = \begin{pmatrix} 1 & 0 & 1 & 0 \\ 0 & 0 & 0 & 1 \\ 1 & 0 & 1 & 0 \\ 0 & 1 & 0 & 0 \end{pmatrix}$$

Is it possible for this matrix to be the Kronecker sum of two 2×2 matrices?

8. Solve

$$\mathbf{AX} + \mathbf{XB}^\dagger = \mathbf{C}$$

for $\mathbf{X}$, given

$$\mathbf{A} = \begin{pmatrix} 0 & 1 \\ 1 & 0 \end{pmatrix}, \qquad \mathbf{B} = \begin{pmatrix} 1 & j \\ -j & 0 \end{pmatrix}, \qquad \mathbf{C} = \begin{pmatrix} j & -2j \\ 0 & 2j \end{pmatrix}$$

9. Suppose $\mathbf{u}$ and $\mathbf{v}$ are 2-dimensional vectors related by

$$\mathbf{u} = \mathbf{A}\mathbf{v}$$

How is $\text{col}(u_1{}^2, u_1 u_2, u_2{}^2)$ related to $\text{col}(v_1{}^2, v_1 v_2, v_2{}^2)$? How is the vector $\text{col}(u_1{}^3, u_1{}^2 u_2, u_1 u_2{}^2, u_2{}^3)$ related to the vector $\text{col}(v_1{}^3, v_1{}^2 v_2, v_1 v_2{}^2, v_2{}^3)$?

(*Comment*: The matrices so developed are also known as Kronecker powers. They are often symbolized as $\mathbf{A}_{[2]}$, $\mathbf{A}_{[3]}$, etc., to distinguish them from the more usual Kronecker powers, $\mathbf{A}^{[2]} = \mathbf{A} \times \mathbf{A}$, etc. The process can be generalized to the mth power of an $n \times n$ matrix, although the explicit expression of the result is cumbersome.)

CHAPTER XV

Periodic Systems

In this chapter, we will consider systems whose parameters vary periodically with the independent variable. Such systems have certain simplicities, compared to the case of an unrestricted nonuniformity, that can be used to advantage. In particular, it becomes possible to define what we shall call the "Floquet modes" which are vectors that have some of the properties of the modes of a uniform system. The determination of these vectors is not simple, being dependent on the solution of a generalization of Hill's determinant. However, although their calculation is devious, it can be made in many cases of practical interest. Furthermore, it is an important and useful consequence to know that such vectors exist since some of their general properties demonstrate significant aspects of the behavior of the system.

1. REDUCIBILITY IN THE SENSE OF LYAPUNOV

We consider the vector differential equation

$$\frac{d\mathbf{x}}{dz} = -j\mathbf{R}\mathbf{x} \tag{1}$$

where $\mathbf{R}$ is an $n \times n$ matrix that is a function of z.

From this we can derive the integral matrix equation

$$\frac{d\mathbf{X}}{dz} = -j\mathbf{R}\mathbf{X}, \qquad \det \mathbf{X}(0) \neq 0 \tag{2}$$

where $\mathbf{X}$ is a matrix whose columns are a set of n linearly independent solutions of Eq. (1). (It is sufficient that they be independent at the boundary. Providing $\mathbf{R}(z)$ is reasonably well behaved, specifically providing its coefficients obey the Lipschitz condition, they will remain linearly independent, as discussed in Chapter VII.)

If $\mathbf{X}(0) = \mathbf{I}$, then $\mathbf{X}(z)$ is the matricant of the system, but we need not assume this here.

335

We consider possible z-dependent transformations of the coordinate axes by letting

$$\mathbf{x} = \mathbf{L}(z)\mathbf{y} \tag{3}$$

or

$$\mathbf{X} = \mathbf{L}(z)\mathbf{Y} \tag{4}$$

The $n \times n$ matrix $\mathbf{L}(z)$ is said to be a *Lyapunov* matrix or transformation if, in the range of interest,

(a) $\mathbf{L}(z)$ is continuously differentiable.
(b) Both $\mathbf{L}(z)$ and its derivative are bounded.
(c) The magnitude of the determinant of $\mathbf{L}(z)$ has a lower bound.

We say now that the system of Eq. (1) or (2) is *reducible in the sense of Lyapunov* if there exists a Lyapunov matrix, $\mathbf{L}(z)$, such that

$$\mathbf{L}^{-1}\mathbf{R}\mathbf{L} - j\mathbf{L}^{-1}\frac{d\mathbf{L}}{dz} = \mathbf{A} \tag{5}$$

where $\mathbf{A}$ is a constant matrix.

If such an $\mathbf{L}(z)$ exists and we can find it, we can make the substitution in Eq. (3) or (4) and find that

$$\frac{d\mathbf{Y}}{dz} = -j\mathbf{A}\mathbf{Y} \tag{6}$$

so that

$$\mathbf{Y} = e^{-j\mathbf{A}z} \tag{7}$$

and

$$\mathbf{X} = \mathbf{L}(z)e^{-j\mathbf{A}z} \tag{8}$$

The difficulty, of course, is to find out what is the appropriate Lyapunov transformation, even after we know that it exists. This is a problem that has not been solved in practical terms for the general case. Nevertheless, there is a good deal we can do with the general method of approach.

2. PERIODIC SYSTEMS

We shall show, first, that if $\mathbf{R}(z)$ is continuous and periodic in z with period l, so that

$$\mathbf{R}(z + l) = \mathbf{R}(z) \tag{9}$$

for all z, then the system is reducible. This is, in effect, a generalization of Floquet's theorem for linear differential equations with periodic coefficients.

Consider Eq. (2), replacing z by $(z + l)$:

$$\frac{d\mathbf{X}(z + l)}{dz} = -j\mathbf{R}(z + l)\mathbf{X}(z + l)$$

$$= -j\mathbf{R}(z)\mathbf{X}(z + l) \tag{10}$$

Hence, $\mathbf{X}(z + l)$ is also an integral solution of Eq. (2). By Lemma 1 of Chapter VII it can therefore be expressed as some constant, nonsingular matrix $\mathbf{C}$ times $\mathbf{X}(z)$:

$$\mathbf{X}(z + l) = \mathbf{X}(z)\mathbf{C} \tag{11}$$

Since $\mathbf{C}$ is nonsingular, we can find an $\mathbf{A}$ such that

$$\mathbf{C} = e^{-j\mathbf{A}l} \tag{12}$$

so that

$$\mathbf{C}^{z/l} = e^{-j\mathbf{A}z}$$

Then

$$\mathbf{C}^{(z+l)/l} = e^{-j\mathbf{A}(z+l)} = e^{-j\mathbf{A}z}e^{-j\mathbf{A}l}$$

$$= e^{-j\mathbf{A}z}\mathbf{C} \tag{13}$$

The function $\mathbf{C}^{z/l}$ is multiplied by $\mathbf{C}$ over a period, as is $\mathbf{X}(z)$. We define

$$\mathbf{L}(z) = \mathbf{X}(z)\mathbf{C}^{-z/l} = \mathbf{X}(z)e^{j\mathbf{A}z} \tag{14}$$

Then

$$\mathbf{L}(z + l) = \mathbf{X}(z + l)e^{j\mathbf{A}(z+l)}$$

$$= \mathbf{X}(z)\mathbf{C}\mathbf{C}^{-1}e^{j\mathbf{A}z}$$

$$= \mathbf{L}(z) \tag{15}$$

for all z. Hence $\mathbf{L}(z)$, so defined, is periodic.

Further, $\mathbf{L}(z)$ is nonsingular. It is also differentiable and obeys the other conditions to be a Lyapunov matrix.

Hence the integral matrix can be factored according to

$$\mathbf{X}(z) = \mathbf{L}(z)e^{-j\mathbf{A}z} \tag{16}$$

where $\mathbf{L}(z)$ is periodic, with the same period as $\mathbf{R}(z)$, and $\mathbf{A}$ is constant. Equation (2) then becomes

$$\frac{d\mathbf{X}}{dz} = \frac{d\mathbf{L}}{dz}e^{-j\mathbf{A}z} - j\mathbf{L}\mathbf{A}e^{-j\mathbf{A}z} = -j\mathbf{R}\mathbf{L}e^{-j\mathbf{A}z} \tag{17}$$

so that $\mathbf{L}$ must satisfy

$$\frac{d\mathbf{L}}{dz} = j(\mathbf{L}\mathbf{A} - \mathbf{R}\mathbf{L}) \tag{18}$$

If we solve Eq. (18) for $\mathbf{A}$, we obtain Eq. (5).

We assert that the $\mathbf{L}$ so obtained is a Lyapunov matrix that reduces the system, regardless of the particular integral solution involved. Suppose $\mathbf{U}$ is any other integral solution. Let

$$\mathbf{U} = \mathbf{L}\mathbf{V} \tag{19}$$

where $\mathbf{L}$ is obtained from a particular $\mathbf{X}$ by Eq. (14). If we substitute Eq. (19) in Eq. (2) with $\mathbf{U}$ in place of $\mathbf{X}$, we obtain

$$\begin{aligned} \frac{d\mathbf{V}}{dz} &= -\mathbf{L}^{-1}\frac{d\mathbf{L}}{dz}\mathbf{L}^{-1}\mathbf{U} + \mathbf{L}^{-1}\frac{d\mathbf{U}}{dz} \\ &= \left(-\mathbf{L}^{-1}\frac{d\mathbf{L}}{dz} - j\mathbf{L}^{-1}\mathbf{R}\mathbf{L}\right)\mathbf{V} \\ &= -j\mathbf{A}\mathbf{V} \end{aligned} \tag{20}$$

Hence $\mathbf{L}$, defined with $\mathbf{X}$, is an Lyapunov matrix that reduces the whole system.

We have shown that, if the system operator is continuous and periodic, then the system is reducible in the sense of Lyapunov. Further, the process of reduction yields Floquet's theorem which can be stated as saying that any solution can be expressed as the product of a periodic factor times another factor which can be expressed as $\exp(-j\mathbf{A}z)$ where $\mathbf{A}$ is constant.

3. FORM OF THE FLOQUET FACTORS

We are now interested in knowing what restrictions, other than those already stated, can be placed on the Floquet factors.

Suppose $\mathbf{R}(z)$ is everywhere K-hermitian where, as usual, $\mathbf{K}$ is non-singular, hermitian, and constant.

Then we know that the matricant is K-unitary. (This is not true of an integral matrix of the system unless the boundary condition is K-unitary.)

If $\mathbf{M}(z)$ is the matricant, then $\mathbf{M}(z + l)$ is also. Hence both are K-unitary and from Eq. (11)

$$\mathbf{C} = \mathbf{M}(z)^{-1}\mathbf{M}(z + l) \tag{21}$$

is K-unitary since, for any K-unitary matrices $\mathbf{M}$ and $\mathbf{N}$ we see that

$$(\mathbf{M}^{-1}\mathbf{N})^\dagger \mathbf{K}(\mathbf{M}^{-1}\mathbf{N}) = \mathbf{N}^\dagger \mathbf{M}^{\dagger-1}\mathbf{K}\mathbf{M}^{-1}\mathbf{N}$$
$$= \mathbf{N}^\dagger \mathbf{K}\mathbf{N} = \mathbf{K}$$

Since $\mathbf{C}$ is K-unitary, we can choose $\mathbf{A}$, in Eq. (12), so that it is K-hermitian. If we apply Eq. (16) to the matricant, which we know to be K-unitary, then

$$\mathbf{K} = \mathbf{M}^{\dagger-1}\mathbf{K}\mathbf{M}^{-1} = \mathbf{L}^{\dagger-1}\exp[-j\mathbf{A}^\dagger z]\mathbf{K}\exp[j\mathbf{A}z]\mathbf{L}^{-1}$$
$$= \mathbf{L}^{\dagger-1}\mathbf{K}\mathbf{L}^{-1} \qquad (22)$$

so that $\mathbf{L}^{-1}$, and hence $\mathbf{L}(z)$, must be K-unitary.

Hence the Floquet factorization of the matricant, when $\mathbf{R}$ is K-hermitian, is into two K-unitary factors.

4. DETERMINATION FROM THE MATRICANT

If we had the matricant of the system, then we could immediately obtain the Floquet factorization.

From Eq. (16), setting $z = 0$, we see that

$$\mathbf{L}(0) = \mathbf{I} \qquad (23)$$

From Eqs. (15) and (16),

$$\mathbf{M}(l) = \mathbf{L}(l)e^{-j\mathbf{A}l} = e^{-j\mathbf{A}l} \qquad (24)$$

We can solve this for $\mathbf{A}$, and so find $\exp(-j\mathbf{A}z)$. $\mathbf{L}(z)$ is then obtained from Eq. (14).

This, of course, is not a practical solution, since we have no need of such methods if we have the matricant. However, it provides a demonstration that the factorization is possible and theoretically obtainable.

5. THE FLOQUET MODES

Consider a set of eigenvectors of $\mathbf{A}$, which we shall here assume to be semisimple:

$$\mathbf{A}\mathbf{u}_i = \beta_i \mathbf{u}_i \qquad (25)$$

We can take, in turn, each of these eigenvectors as a boundary condition and obtain a complete set of vector solutions from the matricant of Eq. (16):

$$\mathbf{x}^{(i)}(0) = \mathbf{u}_i$$
$$\mathbf{x}^{(i)}(z) = \mathbf{M}(z)\mathbf{u}_i = \mathbf{L}(z)e^{-j\mathbf{A}z}\mathbf{u}_i$$
$$= e^{-j\beta_i z}\{\mathbf{L}(z)\mathbf{u}_i\} \qquad (26)$$

from Eq. (25).

Such a solution is called a *Floquet mode* of the system.

Since $\mathbf{L}(z)$ is periodic and $\mathbf{u}_i$ constant, the vector part of Eq. (26), $\mathbf{L}\mathbf{u}_i$, is periodic with period l. In particular, we see that

$$\mathbf{x}^{(i)}(nl) = e^{-j\beta_i nl}\mathbf{u}_i \tag{27}$$

While this is not a mode of the system in the usual sense of being an eigenvector of the matricant, it approximates the properties of the eigenvector, and is, in fact, an eigenvector for the matricant of a section that is an integral number of periods long.

6. SPACE HARMONICS

Since $\mathbf{L}(z)$ is periodic in z with period l, we can expand each of its coefficients as a Fourier series, and write the whole as a Fourier series of matrices:

$$\mathbf{L}(z) = \sum \mathbf{L}_n e^{-j2\pi nz/l} \tag{28}$$

where

$$\mathbf{L}_n = \frac{1}{l}\int_0^l \mathbf{L}(z)e^{j2\pi nz/l}\,dz \tag{29}$$

If we substitute Eq. (28) in Eq. (26), we find that

$$\mathbf{x}^{(i)}(z) = e^{-j\beta_i z}\sum_n \mathbf{L}_n e^{-j2\pi nz/l}\mathbf{u}_i$$

$$= \sum_n e^{-j(\beta_i + 2\pi n/l)z}(\mathbf{L}_n\mathbf{u}_i) \tag{30}$$

Letting

$$\beta_i^{(n)} = \beta_i + 2\pi n/l$$

$$\mathbf{u}_i^{(n)} = \mathbf{L}_n\mathbf{u}_i \tag{31}$$

Eq. (30) becomes

$$\mathbf{x}^{(i)}(z) = \sum_n \exp(-j\beta_i^{(n)}z)\mathbf{u}_i^{(n)} \tag{32}$$

This is the resolution of the Floquet mode in terms of its *space harmonics*, which is the set of constant vectors, $\mathbf{u}_i^{(n)}$, each of which has the propagation constant $\beta_i^{(n)}$.

We have found that if the system has a conservation law $\mathbf{K}$, $\mathbf{A}$ is K-hermitian. The set β_i are the eigenvalues of $\mathbf{A}$. Hence the set β_i are constrained by the usual conditions on the eigenvalues of a K-hermitian matrix.

The set $\beta_i^{(n)}$ is then displaced from β_i along the real axis at intervals of $2\pi/l$ according to Eq. (31).

The vectors $\mathbf{u}_i^{(n)}$ are not modes of the system. They do, however, behave like modes in that they propagate through the system without change with the propagation constant $\beta_i^{(n)}$. The difference is that they cannot be independently excited. Instead, we can only excite the Floquet modes, each of which can then be resolved into a fixed set of space harmonics.

7. ORTHOGONALITY RELATIONS

Suppose $\mathbf{R}$, and hence $\mathbf{A}$, is K-hermitian. Then we know that we can choose the set $\mathbf{u}_i$ to be K-orthogonal and maximally normalized so that

$$\mathbf{u}_i^\dagger \mathbf{K} \mathbf{u}_{\sim j} = \sigma_i \delta_{ij}, \qquad \sigma_i = \pm 1 \tag{33}$$

From Eq. (26),

$$
\begin{aligned}
\mathbf{x}^{(i)\dagger} \mathbf{K} \mathbf{x}^{(\sim j)} &= \exp[j\beta_i^* z] \exp[-j\beta_{\sim j} z] \mathbf{u}_i^\dagger \mathbf{L}^\dagger \mathbf{K} \mathbf{L} \mathbf{u}_{\sim j} \\
&= \exp[j(\beta_i^* - \beta_{\sim j}) z] \mathbf{u}_i^\dagger \mathbf{K} \mathbf{u}_{\sim j} \\
&= \exp[j(\beta_{\sim i} - \beta_{\sim j}) z] \sigma_i \delta_{ij} \\
&= \sigma_i \delta_{ij}
\end{aligned}
\tag{34}
$$

since $\mathbf{L}$ is K-unitary, and since, for the eigenvalues of a K-hermitian matrix, $\beta_i^* = \beta_{\sim i}$.

Hence the set $\{\mathbf{x}^{(i)}\}$ is K-orthogonal and maximally normalized for all z.

It also follows that the system can amplify or decay only if $\mathbf{K}$ is indefinite and the Floquet modes involved are of opposite parity.

Substituting Eq. (32) in Eq. (34), we find that

$$\sum_{n,m} \exp[j\beta_i^{*(n)} z] \mathbf{u}_i^{(n)\dagger} \mathbf{K} \exp[-j\beta_{\sim j}^{(m)}] \mathbf{u}_{\sim j}^{(m)} = \sum_{n,m} \exp[j(\beta_{\sim i}^{(n)} - \beta_{\sim j}^{(m)}) z] \mathbf{u}_i^{(n)\dagger} \mathbf{K} \mathbf{u}_{\sim j}^{(m)}$$

$$= \sigma_i \delta_{ij} \tag{35}$$

When $i = j$ this simplifies to

$$\sum_{n,m} e^{j2\pi(n-m)z/l} \mathbf{u}_i^{(n)\dagger} \mathbf{K} \mathbf{u}_i^{(m)} = \sigma_i \tag{36}$$

Since $\mathbf{u}_i^{(n)}$ and σ_i are constant, we see that we must have

$$\sum_n \mathbf{u}_i^{(n)\dagger} \mathbf{K} \mathbf{u}_{\sim i}^{(n)} = \sigma_i \tag{37}$$

and

$$\sum_n \mathbf{u}_i^{(n)\dagger}\mathbf{K}\mathbf{u}_{\sim i}^{(n-k)} = 0$$

$$k \text{ an integer} \neq 0 \tag{38}$$

These are, in effect, orthogonality relations that apply among the space harmonics of a given Floquet mode. Similar relations can be worked out between different Floquet modes, although we must then be careful to include all terms in Eq. (35) that have the same exponential dependence. (The possibility that, at some frequencies, quite different Floquet modes may have space harmonics that have the same dependence in Eq. (35) leads to some interesting effects closely related to the so-called "Woods anomaly" of diffraction gratings.)

In the analysis given so far, we have proven the existence of an appropriate matrix $\mathbf{A}$, and have assumed that we know what it is. Or, we have assumed that we know the solutions to Eq. (1), or the matricant of the system, from which $\mathbf{A}$ can be obtained easily.

In general this is not true, or if it is true, we do not need the detailed analysis we have given, although the resolution of the solution into Floquet modes and their space harmonics may still be useful.

We shall now consider the problem of determining the Floquet modes directly, or their space harmonics.

We have shown the existence of a solution of the form of Eq. (32), where $\beta_i^{(n)}$ is given by Eq. (31) in terms of some set β_i.

Since $\mathbf{R}(z)$ is periodic, we can also make a Fourier expansion of it:

$$\mathbf{R}(z) = \sum_n \mathbf{R}_n e^{-j2\pi nz/l} \tag{39}$$

where

$$\mathbf{R}_n = \frac{1}{l} \int_0^l \mathbf{R}(z) e^{j2\pi nz/l}\, dz$$

and the $\mathbf{R}_n$ are constant matrices.

We substitute Eqs. (32) and (39) in Eq. (1) and find

$$\sum_n (-j)\beta_i^{(n)} \exp[-j\beta_i^{(n)}z]\mathbf{u}_i^{(n)} = -j\sum_{nm} \mathbf{R}_n \exp[-j2\pi nz/l] \exp[-j\beta_i^{(m)}z]\mathbf{u}_i^{(m)}$$

$$= -j\sum_{n,m} \exp[-j\beta_i^{(m+n)}z]\mathbf{R}_n \mathbf{u}_i^{(m)}$$

$$= -j\sum_{n,m} \exp[-j\beta_i^{(n)}z]\mathbf{R}_{n-m}\mathbf{u}_i^{(m)} \tag{40}$$

by a shift in the value of n, and where we have used the fact, evident from Eq. (31), that

$$\beta_i^{(m)} + 2\pi n/l = \beta_i^{(m+n)} \tag{41}$$

Isolating terms with the same exponential factors, we obtain the relations

$$\beta_i^{(n)}\mathbf{u}_i^{(n)} = \sum_m{}' \mathbf{R}_{n-m}\mathbf{u}_i^{(m)}$$

or

$$\sum_m{}' (\mathbf{R}_{n-m} - \beta_i^{(m)}\delta_{nm}\mathbf{I})\mathbf{u}_i^{(m)} = 0 \tag{42}$$

This is, in effect, an eigenvalue equation. For Eq. (42) to have a nontrivial situation, it is necessary that

$$|(\mathbf{R}_{n-m} - \beta_i^{(m)}\delta_{n,m}\mathbf{I})| = 0 \tag{43}$$

We write this as a determinant over the indices n and m which have infinite range. We should note, however, that if $\mathbf{R}(z)$ was an $N \times N$ matrix, each term of Eq. (43) is also an $N \times N$ matrix, and the zero on the right is the $N \times N$ null matrix.

Equation (43) is a generalization of the well-known Hill's determinant.

The solution of Eq. (43) in a given case is usually a formidable task. Further, we have not here investigated its convergence, or whether, or how, it can be made to converge by multiplying Eq. (42) by appropriate factors. However, it does give us a method that is valid in principle, and that may be practical in particular circumstances.

8. EXAMPLE

To illustrate the technique, consider

$$\mathbf{R} = \begin{pmatrix} 0 & \gamma e^{-j\beta z} \\ \gamma e^{j\beta z} & 0 \end{pmatrix} \tag{44}$$

which is K-hermitian for

$$\mathbf{K} = \mathbf{I}$$

e.g., is hermitian. We assume β and γ to be real constants.

This is an example we could solve directly, since it has simple non-uniformity (see Chapter XIII, Section 13, and Exercise 8.) We shall solve it here by the use of the Floquet modes.

The Fourier expansion of $\mathbf{R}$ is over the period $l = 2\pi/\beta$, and has only the two terms

$$\mathbf{R}_1 = \begin{pmatrix} 0 & \gamma \\ 0 & 0 \end{pmatrix}$$

$$\mathbf{R}_{-1} = \begin{pmatrix} 0 & 0 \\ \gamma & 0 \end{pmatrix}$$

$$\mathbf{R}(z) = \mathbf{R}_1 e^{-j\beta z} + \mathbf{R}_{-1} e^{j\beta z}$$

Equation (42) then becomes

$$\mathbf{R}_1 \mathbf{u}_i^{n-1} - \beta_i^n \mathbf{u}_i^n + \mathbf{R}_{-1} \mathbf{u}_i^{n+1} = 0 \tag{45}$$

for any i and all n. We require the set β_i for which this set of recursion formulas shall have a nontrivial solution for the set $\mathbf{u}_i^{(n)}$.

We can simplify this set by multiplying it, in turn, by $\mathbf{R}_1$ and $\mathbf{R}_{-1}$ and solving for

$$\mathbf{R}_1 \mathbf{u}_i^{(n-1)} = \frac{\mathbf{R}_1 \mathbf{R}_{-1} \mathbf{u}_i^{(n)}}{\beta_i^{(n-1)}} \tag{46}$$

$$\mathbf{R}_{-1} \mathbf{u}_i^{(n+1)} = \frac{\mathbf{R}_{-1} \mathbf{R}_1 \mathbf{u}_i^{(n)}}{\beta_i + (n-1)\beta} = \frac{\mathbf{R}_{-1} \mathbf{R}_1 \mathbf{u}_i^{(n)}}{\beta_i^{(n+1)}} \tag{47}$$

Putting these back in Eq. (45), we find that we require that

$$\begin{pmatrix} \beta_i^{(n+1)}(\gamma^2 - \beta_i^{(n)}\beta_i^{(n-1)}) & 0 \\ 0 & \beta_i^{(n-1)}(\gamma^2 - \beta_i^{(n+1)}\beta_i^{(n)}) \end{pmatrix} \mathbf{u}_i^{(n)} = 0 \tag{48}$$

There is freedom in how we choose to index the components. We can therefore require that $\mathbf{u}_i^{(0)} \neq 0$. Then, either

$$\gamma^2 = \beta_i^{(0)}\beta_i^{(-1)} = \beta_i^{(0)}(\beta_i^{(0)} - \beta)$$

or

$$\gamma^2 = \beta_i^{(1)}\beta_i^{(0)} = (\beta_i^{(0)} + \beta)\beta_i^{(0)}$$

Solving these, we find that

$$\beta_i^{(0)} = \tfrac{1}{2}\{\pm\beta \pm \sqrt{\beta^2 + 4\gamma^2}\}$$

Two pairs of these differ by exactly β, and are, therefore, space harmonics. Let us set

$$\beta_+ = \tfrac{1}{2}\{\sqrt{\beta^2 + 4\gamma^2} - \beta\}$$
$$\beta_- = -\beta_+ \tag{49}$$

Normally, one regards as the "fundamental" space harmonic the fastest one—i.e., the one with smallest β. If γ^2 is not less than $3\beta^2/4$, the β_+ and β_- given are not the fundamental space harmonics. However, we shall ignore this possibility. Also we shall not discuss here in detail what happens if $(\beta_+ - \beta_-)$ is itself a multiple of β. This is not a major disaster, however. It simply means that the situation is degenerate. (The resulting behavior is sometimes described as π-mode operation.)

If we consider the β_+ value, then Eq. (48) becomes

$$\begin{pmatrix} \beta_+^{-1}(\gamma^2 - \beta^0\beta^{-1}) & 0 \\ 0 & 0 \end{pmatrix} \mathbf{u}_+^{(0)} = 0$$

so that $\mathbf{u}_+^{(0)}$ can have the form

$$\mathbf{u}_+^{(0)} = k_+ \begin{pmatrix} 0 \\ 1 \end{pmatrix} \tag{50}$$

k_+ being a normalization constant.

From Eq. (46), with $n = 1$, we find that $\mathbf{u}_+^{(1)}$ can have the form

$$\mathbf{u}_+^{(1)} = \frac{k_+}{(\beta_+ + \beta)} \begin{pmatrix} \gamma \\ c_1 \end{pmatrix}$$

where c_1 is arbitrary. We find that this does also fit Eq. (47). Again from Eq. (46), with $n = 2$, we find that

$$\mathbf{u}_+^{(2)} = \frac{k_+ c_1 \gamma}{(\beta_+ + \beta)(\beta_+ + 2\beta)} \begin{pmatrix} 1 \\ 0 \end{pmatrix} + \begin{pmatrix} 0 \\ c_2 \end{pmatrix}$$

However, this does not fit Eq. (47) unless $c_1 = 0$. In similar fashion, we find that $c_2 = 0$. Likewise, we find that all higher space harmonics are identically zero. Also we find that all negative harmonics are identically zero.

By the same kind of reasoning, we can find the space harmonics for the β_- Floquet mode. The nonnull space harmonics are, in summary,

$$\mathbf{u}_+^{(0)} = k_+ \begin{pmatrix} 0 \\ 1 \end{pmatrix}, \qquad \mathbf{u}_+^{(1)} = \frac{k_+ \gamma}{\beta_+ + \beta} \begin{pmatrix} 1 \\ 0 \end{pmatrix}$$

$$\mathbf{u}_-^{(0)} = k_- \begin{pmatrix} 1 \\ 0 \end{pmatrix}, \qquad \mathbf{u}_-^{(-1)} = \frac{k_- \gamma}{(\beta_- - \beta)} \begin{pmatrix} 0 \\ 1 \end{pmatrix}$$

and the unnormalized solutions are, from Eq. (32),

$$\mathbf{x}_+(z) = k_+ \begin{pmatrix} \dfrac{\gamma}{(\beta_+ + \beta)}\, e^{-j(\beta_+ + \beta)z} \\ e^{-j\beta_+ z} \end{pmatrix}$$

$$\mathbf{x}_-(z) = k_- \begin{pmatrix} e^{-j\beta_- z} \\ \dfrac{\gamma}{\beta_- - \beta}\, e^{-j(\beta_- - \beta)z} \end{pmatrix}$$

We can directly verify that these are indeed solutions of Eq. (1) for the **R** of Eq. (44), providing β_+ and β_- are as given in Eq. (49).

9. CONCLUSIONS

The methods discussed here not easy unless the periodic behavior of the system is of a particularly simple type, as with the $\mathbf{R}(z)$ of Eq. (44) in the example. Nevertheless, they do provide a method of analysis that does have general validity, and that very often can be pushed through to a specific answer.

The method is also important as establishing some important properties of a general periodic system. The possibility of the Floquet factorization is itself an important result, as in the finding that if **R** is K-hermitian, $\mathbf{L}(z)$ is K-unitary, and **A** can be made K-hermitian.

The concept of the Floquet modes is also of considerable importance in that it provides a meaningful and useful extension of the concept of modes—which arises in uniform systems—to the case of periodic nonuniformity. Thus we are able to describe the behavior of such systems in a way that relates them to the more familiar uniform systems.

Exercises

1. As a generalization of Section 3, show that if **L** is such that

$$\mathbf{L}^{\dagger}\mathbf{KL} = \mathbf{H}$$

where **H** is hermitian, constant, and nonsingular, and where **R** is K-hermitian, then **A** is H-hermitian.

2. Show that if a matrix **A** is constant and semisimple, and has eigenvalues that are pure imaginary, then $\exp(\mathbf{A}z)$ is a Lyapunov matrix.

3. Under what conditions on the f_i is a matrix of the form

$$\mathbf{R} = \mathrm{diag}(f_1(z), f_2(z), ...)$$

reducible in the sense of Lyapunov?

4. Show that **R**, given by

$$\mathbf{R} = \begin{pmatrix} 0 & \beta Z \\ \beta/Z & 0 \end{pmatrix}$$

is reducible in the sense of Lyapunov if β is constant and $\kappa = (dZ/dz)/Z$ is constant—so that we are here dealing again with the exponentially tapered transmission line. What is a Lyapunov matrix that accomplishes this reduction? Solve for the matricant $\mathbf{M}(z)$, given by

$$\frac{d\mathbf{M}}{dz} = -j\mathbf{R}\mathbf{M}, \qquad \mathbf{M}(0) = \mathbf{I}$$

using this method.

5. Let

$$\mathbf{R} = \begin{pmatrix} 0 & a + 2b \cos \beta z \\ a - 2b \cos \beta z & 0 \end{pmatrix}$$

where a, b, and β are real constants. Set up the recursion formula equivalent to Eq. (47). Solve for $\beta_i^{(0)}$. Solve for the unnormalized vectors.

CHAPTER XVI

Application to Electromagnetic Theory

In this chapter we shall be concerned with the application of matrix techniques to electromagnetic theory. We shall develop a formalism that is adapted to the manipulation of Maxwell's equations, and shall show the derivation of the equations for the various potentials.

We must emphasize that the development of such a formalism adds nothing that is new to the basic theory. It is simply a different way of saying the same things that are more normally expressed in vector algebra. Its virtue is that it systematizes certain procedures—notably that of changing the coordinate system—and that by providing a different viewpoint, it may suggest different ways of attacking a problem.

A second, but perhaps more immediately important, purpose is to provide an example of the application of matrix methods to problems that do not, at first glance, appear algebraic. What we shall develop here is, in fact, an algebra of operators. This approach is foreshadowed in the vector notation that manipulates the operators ∇, $\nabla\times$, and $\nabla\cdot$ as if ∇ were a vector. It is not, of course, and the unrestrained use of the analogy between ∇ and a vector will lead to error. However, properly used, the analogy is a useful one.

1. CARTESIAN SYSTEM

We shall first develop the formalism for a cartesian coordinate system and use it to write Maxwell's equations. Later we shall consider other coordinate systems.

We define the vector $\mathbf{E}$ as

$$\mathbf{E} = \begin{pmatrix} E_x \\ E_y \\ E_z \end{pmatrix} \tag{1}$$

and correspondingly for $\mathbf{H}$, $\mathbf{D}$, $\mathbf{B}$, and $\mathbf{J}$.

We need to be able to take the curl of such a vector. We see that we can do this with an operator, which we shall symbolize as $\varDelta$, which we define as

$$\varDelta = \begin{pmatrix} 0 & -\partial/\partial z & \partial/\partial y \\ \partial/\partial z & 0 & -\partial/\partial x \\ -\partial/\partial y & \partial/\partial x & 0 \end{pmatrix} \tag{2}$$

348

The formal application of this operator to a vector $\mathbf{E}$, $\Delta\mathbf{E}$, by normal matrix multiplication, yields a vector whose components are those that we want in the curl of $\mathbf{E}$.

We are deliberately choosing a symbol, Δ, that suggests the vector symbol ∇, but is not identical with it since we wish to emphasize the difference of form and concept involved.

We also wish to be able to take the divergence of $\mathbf{E}$. For this purpose we need another operator, that we will symbolize as δ', which we define as

$$\delta' = (\partial/\partial x \quad \partial/\partial y \quad \partial/\partial z) \tag{3}$$

The formal application of δ' to a vector $\mathbf{E}$, $\delta'\mathbf{E}$, yields a scalar function that is what we require for div $\mathbf{E}$.

Finally, we wish to be able to take the gradient of a scalar function, φ. For this purpose we define the operator δ as

$$\delta = \begin{pmatrix} \partial/\partial x \\ \partial/\partial y \\ \partial/\partial z \end{pmatrix} \tag{4}$$

and see that $(\delta\varphi)$ is a vector with the proper components.

It is tempting to observe that, formally, δ' is the transpose of δ. It appears also to be the hermitian conjugate of δ. This is deceptive, however. The transpose, or hermitian conjugate of the vector $(\delta\varphi)$, for example, is not the formal transpose or conjugate of δ times φ. The formal application of the rules of transpositions would yield $\varphi\delta^T$ which is not a vector but an operator. In fact, we shall see later that the formal identity of δ' and the transpose of δ is not true in all coordinate systems. Therefore we use a symbol that does not falsely suggest this relationship.

These three operators are not independent. A direct connection can be made through the skew-symmetric unit third order tensor (i.e., ϵ_{ijk}, where $\epsilon_{ijk} = 0$ if any two of the indices are identical, $+1$ if ijk is an even permutation of 123, and -1 if ijk is an odd permutation of 123). This does not seem to serve any immediate purpose here, though, and we shall not elaborate on it.

Instead, we shall simply observe that the matrix products $\Delta\delta$ and $\delta'\Delta$ vanish identically:

$$\Delta\delta \equiv 0 \tag{5}$$

$$\delta'\Delta \equiv 0 \tag{6}$$

These relations state that the curl of a gradient, and the divergence of a curl always vanish.

It is also important to note that we can find by formal multiplication that

$$\Delta^2 = \delta\delta' - \delta'\delta\mathbf{I} \tag{7}$$

which states that $\nabla \times (\nabla \times) = \nabla \nabla \cdot - \nabla^2$. The first term is an operator analogue of a dyad. The second term is a scalar operator times the identity. The lack of symmetry in the second term is disturbing. We shall, in fact, see later that this term should be written a little differently—specifically as $\mathbf{I} \delta' \delta \mathbf{I}$.

Other vector identities can be developed from these relations.

2. MAXWELL'S EQUATIONS

We can, with these operators, write down Maxwell's equations directly. In rationalized MKS units, they are

$$\Delta \mathbf{H} = \mathbf{J} + \frac{\partial}{\partial t} \mathbf{D} \tag{8}$$

$$\Delta \mathbf{E} = - \frac{\partial}{\partial t} \mathbf{B} \tag{9}$$

$$\delta' \mathbf{D} = \rho \tag{10}$$

$$\delta' \mathbf{B} = 0 \tag{11}$$

with the associated equations

$$\mathbf{D} = \epsilon_0 \mathbf{E} + \mathbf{P} = \epsilon \mathbf{E} \tag{12}$$

$$\mathbf{B} = \mu_0 \mathbf{H} + \mathbf{M} = \mu \mathbf{H} \tag{13}$$

If the region under study has no free charge or current, then ρ and $\mathbf{J}$ are everywhere zero. If, in addition, the region is homogeneous and isotropic, then ϵ and μ are scalar constants independent of time and position. (If the medium were anisotropic, we would have to take ϵ and μ as matrices rather than scalars.) Finally, if all quantities vary at frequency ω, then we may take only the part that varies as $\exp(j\omega t)$, and retain only the amplitude part of these terms. We are left with

$$\Delta \mathbf{H} = j\omega\epsilon \mathbf{E} \tag{14}$$

$$\Delta \mathbf{E} = -j\omega\mu \mathbf{H} \tag{15}$$

$$\delta' \mathbf{E} = 0 \tag{16}$$

$$\delta' \mathbf{H} = 0 \tag{17}$$

In Eqs. (8) to (13), the quantities are all physically observable and hence must be real. In Eqs. (14) to (17), however, we have taken only a part of the physically observable fields and have removed a complex time varying phase. In consequence, the fields may now be complex. The physically observable electric field, for example, is the real part of the product of $\mathbf{E}$ and $\exp(j\omega t)$.

Since ϵ and μ are assumed independent of position, we can separate these fields by operating on Eq. (15) with $\varDelta$ and using Eqs. (7) and (14):

$$\varDelta^2\mathbf{E} = (\delta\delta' - \delta'\delta)\mathbf{E}$$
$$= -j\omega\mu_0\varDelta\mathbf{H} = \omega^2\mu_0\epsilon_0\mathbf{E} \tag{18}$$

Using Eq. (16) we find that

$$(\delta'\delta + \omega^2\mu_0\epsilon_0)\mathbf{E} = 0 \tag{19}$$

In similar fashion we find that

$$(\delta'\delta + \omega^2\mu_0\epsilon_0)\mathbf{H} = 0 \tag{20}$$

Equations (19) and (20) are the homogeneous wave equations.

3. MAGNETIC HERTZIAN VECTOR POTENTIAL

We may also analyze the field in terms of the Hertzian vector potentials. For the "magnetic" potential, $\mathbf{\Pi}_h$, we require

$$\mathbf{E} = -j\omega\mu\,\varDelta\mathbf{\Pi}_h \tag{21}$$

so that Eq. (16) is satisfied directly by Eq. (6).

Equation (14) is satisfied with Eq. (21) if we set

$$\mathbf{H} = \omega^2\mu\epsilon\mathbf{\Pi}_h + \delta\psi_h \tag{22}$$

where ψ_h is an appropriate scalar potential.

Equation (15) then becomes, using Eq. (7) and after rearranging,

$$\delta(\delta'\mathbf{\Pi}_h - \psi_h) = (\delta'\delta + \omega^2\mu\epsilon)\mathbf{\Pi}_h$$

If we take as the gauge condition

$$\psi_h = \delta'\mathbf{\Pi}_h \tag{23}$$

then we obtain the wave equation

$$(\delta'\delta + \omega^2\mu\epsilon)\mathbf{\Pi}_h = 0 \tag{24}$$

If we put Eqs. (23) and (24) in Eq. (22), we see that

$$\mathbf{H} = -\delta'\delta\mathbf{\Pi}_h + \delta\delta'\mathbf{\Pi}_h = \varDelta^2\mathbf{\Pi}_h \tag{25}$$

Hence Eq. (17) is satisfied by Eq. (6), thus justifying the choice of gauge in Eq. (23).

The fields are thus determined by Eqs. (21) and (25) in terms of a vector potential, $\mathbf{\Pi}_h$, that is required only to satisfy the vector wave equation (24).

4. ELECTRIC HERTZIAN VECTOR POTENTIAL

We may also seek a solution in terms of the electric Hertzian potential, $\mathbf{\Pi}_e$. We require

$$\mathbf{H} = j\omega\epsilon \, \varDelta\mathbf{\Pi}_e \tag{26}$$

Then Eq. (17) is satisfied directly. From Eq. (15), we set

$$\mathbf{E} = \omega^2\epsilon\mu\mathbf{\Pi}_e + \delta\psi_e \tag{27}$$

From Eq. (14) we have

$$\delta(\delta'\mathbf{\Pi}_e - \psi_e) = (\delta'\delta + \omega^2\epsilon\mu)\mathbf{\Pi}_e \tag{28}$$

from which we are lead to set the gauge condition as

$$\psi_e = \delta'\mathbf{\Pi}_e \tag{29}$$

so that we obtain, again, the wave equation

$$(\delta'\delta + \omega^2\epsilon\mu)\mathbf{\Pi}_e = 0 \tag{30}$$

Using Eqs. (29) and (30), Eq. (27) becomes

$$\mathbf{E} = -\delta'\delta\mathbf{\Pi}_e + \delta\delta \, \mathbf{\Pi}_e = \varDelta^2\mathbf{\Pi}_e \tag{31}$$

so that Eq. (16) is satisfied. The fields are determined in terms of a single vector field $\mathbf{\Pi}_e$ that satisfies the wave equation (30).

We will inject here a cautionary note. We have not proven that all solutions can be expressed in these forms. As a matter of fact, we have not even shown that any solution of these forms exist. We have only shown that if a solution to the vector wave equation exists, then solutions for the fields can be found.

These observations are trivial for the case considered. We can, however, extend this analysis, in whole or in part, to more complex situations such as, for example, certain types of inhomogeneous media. If ϵ or μ is not constant, then one is lead to more complicated gauge conditions and to variations of the wave equation. It is then necessary to consider questions of existence and completeness with some care.

Similar questions arise if the media contains sources—i.e., space charge—or can support currents—i.e., has nonzero conductivity. They become even more complicated if the medium is anistropic in ϵ, μ, or the conductivity σ. In the case of, for example, a medium with anistropic permeability, the scalar μ in Eqs. (8) to (13) is replaced by a matrix, and the analysis must be undertaken with due care of this aspect. Again, one must consider with some care the problems of existence and completeness.

Such problems are beyond the scope of our purpose here, and we shall do no more than to point them out.

5. CHANGE OF BASIS

We are interested particularly in the possible use of other coordinate systems, generally for the purpose of finding solutions appropriate to various boundary conditions. The translation of the equations to another coordinate system can, in general, be described as a change in the basis of the system. Caution is required, however, since the basis may itself be a function of position.

Consider, for example, cylindrical coordinates

$$\theta = \tan^{-1}(y/x)$$
$$r = (x^2 + y^2)^{1/2}$$
$$z = z$$

We can easily find that

$$\hat{\mathbf{E}} = \begin{pmatrix} E_r \\ E_\theta \\ E_z \end{pmatrix} = \begin{pmatrix} \cos\theta & \sin\theta & 0 \\ -\sin\theta & \cos\theta & 0 \\ 0 & 0 & 1 \end{pmatrix} \begin{pmatrix} E_x \\ E_y \\ E_z \end{pmatrix} \tag{32}$$
$$= \mathbf{SE}$$

The transformation matrix $\mathbf{S}$ contains θ explicitly. Hence we must be careful to preserve its order with respect to all differential operators, even the scalar ones.

If we look at Eq. (14) or (15) and set

$$\hat{\mathbf{H}} = \mathbf{SH} \qquad \hat{\mathbf{E}} = \mathbf{SE} \tag{33}$$

then clearly $\varDelta$ must transform to $\hat{\varDelta}$ where

$$\hat{\varDelta} = \mathbf{S}\,\varDelta\mathbf{S}^{-1} \tag{34}$$

to preserve the form.

One may wonder why it is necessary to preserve the form of an equation such as Eq. (14). Proper justification depends on the covariance of physical laws under a change of coordinate system. The derivatives involved here are, strictly speaking, covariant derivatives, and must transform as such.

The transformation of δ' can be obtained from Eq. (16). Again, to preserve the form, we must have

$$\delta' = \delta' \mathbf{S}^{-1} \tag{35}$$

since a scalar density function cannot change. We note that Eq. (6) is preserved by this transformation.

The transformation of δ can be obtained from Eq. (5) as

$$\delta = \mathbf{S}\delta \tag{36}$$

Equation (7) then transforms to

$$\Delta^2 = \delta\delta' - \mathbf{S}\delta' \,\delta\mathbf{S}^{-1} \tag{37}$$

As mentioned before, this rather than Eq. (7) indicates the proper form of this relation. The form of Eq. (7) is valid for $\mathbf{S} = \mathbf{I}$. More generally, since $\delta'\delta$ is a scalar differential operator, it commutes with $\mathbf{S}$ or $\mathbf{S}^{-1}$ if, but only if, $\mathbf{S}$ is independent of position. If $\mathbf{S}$ is constant over space, then the form of Eq. (7) is valid.

Also we may note that, in general, δ' will not even appear to be the transpose of δ.

We may further note that $\mathbf{S}\delta'\delta\mathbf{S}^{-1}$ is diagonal only under rather stringent conditions. This reflects the fact that the vector Laplacian operator is not, in general, the scalar Laplacian applied to the separate components. In a curvilinear coordinate system, the components of a vector are, in general, coupled by the Laplacian operator, and the vector wave equation does not separate.

With these transformations, the expression of the field equations in terms of the vector potentials translate without change of form, except that, where $\delta'\delta$ appears, it becomes $\mathbf{S}\delta'\delta\mathbf{S}^{-1}$. Equation (24), for example, which is the vector wave equation for the magnetic Hertzian vector potential, becomes

$$(\mathbf{S}\delta'\delta\mathbf{S}^{-1} + \omega^2\mu\epsilon)\mathbf{\Pi}_h = 0 \tag{38}$$

and the same for Eq. (30) but with $\mathbf{\Pi}_e$.

6. POLARIZATION COORDINATES

We shall conclude this chapter with a brief tabulation of the properties of what have been called the *polarization* coordinates. This coordinate system has been used in optics and for certain electromagnetic problems such as the cylindrically symmetric dielectric waveguide. It has also been used for certain electrodynamic problems such as a filamentary electron beam in a finite magnetic field in which account must be taken of transverse motion. In this case, the beam modes include the so-called cyclotron and synchronous waves that are conveniently described in polarization coordinates.

The polarization coordinates are defined by z and

$$r_+ = \frac{1}{\sqrt{2}}(x + jy)$$

$$r_- = \frac{1}{\sqrt{2}}(x - jy) \tag{39}$$

The corresponding coefficients of a vector, say **E**, are

$$E_+ = \frac{1}{\sqrt{2}}(E_y + jE_y)$$

$$E_- = \frac{1}{\sqrt{2}}(E_y - jE_y) \tag{40}$$

and E_z. Hence we see that the transformation matrix is

$$\mathbf{S} = \begin{pmatrix} 1/\sqrt{2} & j/\sqrt{2} & 0 \\ 1/\sqrt{2} & -j/\sqrt{2} & 0 \\ 0 & 0 & 1 \end{pmatrix} \tag{41}$$

From Eq. (39), we find

$$\frac{\partial}{\partial r_+} = \frac{\partial x}{\partial r_+}\frac{\partial}{\partial x} + \frac{\partial y}{\partial r_+}\frac{\partial}{\partial y}$$

$$= \frac{1}{\sqrt{2}}\left(\frac{\partial}{\partial x} - j\frac{\partial}{\partial y}\right)$$

$$\frac{\partial}{\partial r_-} = \frac{\partial x}{\partial r_-}\frac{\partial}{\partial x} + \frac{\partial y}{\partial r_-}\frac{\partial}{\partial y}$$

$$= \frac{1}{\sqrt{2}}\left(\frac{\partial}{\partial x} + j\frac{\partial}{\partial y}\right) \tag{42}$$

From Eqs. (34)–(36) then we find that

$$
\hat{\Delta} = \begin{pmatrix} j\,\dfrac{\partial}{\partial z} & 0 & -j\,\dfrac{\partial}{\partial r_-} \\[2mm] 0 & -j\,\dfrac{\partial}{\partial z} & j\,\dfrac{\partial}{\partial r_+} \\[2mm] -j\,\dfrac{\partial}{\partial r_+} & j\,\dfrac{\partial}{\partial r_-} & 0 \end{pmatrix}
\tag{43}
$$

$$
\hat{\delta}' = \left(\dfrac{\partial}{\partial r_+} \quad \dfrac{\partial}{\partial r_-} \quad \dfrac{\partial}{\partial z} \right)
\tag{44}
$$

$$
\hat{\delta} = \begin{pmatrix} \dfrac{\partial}{\partial r_-} \\[2mm] \dfrac{\partial}{\partial r_+} \\[2mm] \dfrac{\partial}{\partial z} \end{pmatrix}
\tag{45}
$$

We can immediately verify Eqs. (5) and (6). Since **S** is independent of the coordinates, the form of Eq. (7) is sufficient, as can be verified. We find that the significant part, the Laplacian, is

$$
\hat{\delta}'\hat{\delta} = 2\,\dfrac{\partial^2}{\partial r_+ \partial r_-} + \dfrac{\partial^2}{\partial z^2}
\tag{46}
$$

It is this form that is to be used in Eq. (19), (20), (24), or (30).

The value of this coordinate system lies in the simplicity of the behavior in it of the cylindrical harmonic functions. We note, from Eq. (39), that

$$
r = \sqrt{x^2 + y^2} = \sqrt{2r_+ r_-}
\tag{47}
$$

and

$$
e^{j\theta} = \cos\theta + j\sin\theta = (x + jy)/r = \sqrt{\dfrac{r_+}{r_-}}
\tag{48}
$$

Hence we can write the cylindrical harmonic function $F_n(r, \theta, z)$ in the form

$$
\begin{aligned}
F_n &= Z_n(\gamma r) e^{j(n\theta - \beta z)} \\
&= Z_n\{\gamma\,\sqrt{2r_+ r_-}\,\} r_+^{n/2} r_-^{-n/2} e^{-j\beta z}
\end{aligned}
\tag{49}
$$

where Z_n is an nth order Bessel function. We find that

$$\frac{\partial F_n}{\partial r_+} = \frac{\gamma}{\sqrt{2}} F_{n-1}$$

$$\frac{\partial F_n}{\partial r_-} = -\frac{\gamma}{\sqrt{2}} F_{n+1}$$

(50)

Hence we find immediately that the Laplacian, Eq. (46), operating on F_n gives

$$\delta'\delta F_n = -(\gamma^2 + \beta^2)F_n$$

(51)

We can use this to obtain solutions to Maxwell's equations.

The development of these formulas illustrates the ease with which we can manipulate through various coordinate systems in the matrix formalism.

7. CONCLUSIONS

We could now proceed to the development of boundary conditions appropriate to metallic walls or to dielectric media. We could also consider the significance of Poynting's vector as a possibly useful metric for the system. These are interesting problems, but they lie more in the field of electromagnetic theory than of matrix algebra. Since our purpose here was to illustrate the means of establishing a matrix formalism for a subject like electromagnetic theory, we have, hopefully, accomplished our purpose. The results have, perhaps, a direct utility in giving a convenient method whereby we can transform coordinate systems with relative ease.

The results also illustrate the possibility of establishing a matrix algebra of operators. In Eq. (2), for example, we have a matrix whose components are the partial differential operators. We were quite cautious here, taking care to justify each step of the way. This is necessary to do. The matrix algebra that we have developed is based on the properties of a field—i.e., a collection of elements among which addition, subtraction, multiplication, and division except by zero are always possible. The partial differential operators do not form a field. Addition is always possible (with reasonable restrictions on the operand) and so is subtraction. Multiplication is possible and is commutative. Division, however, is meaningless, at least in the ordinary sense of the word. Hence we are dealing here with a matrix whose elements are taken from something other than a field (a ring with addition.) We must be cautious lest we inadvertently imply properties that the set does not have.

In this situation, we must not blindly use the results of ordinary matrix algebra. We can, and do, use these results to suggest what may be demonstrable, but we take care to investigate the validity of the results we wish to use for the particular set of elements that we are using.

Exercises

1. Verify Eq. (32).

2. Defining polar coordinates by

$$x = r \sin \theta \cos \varphi$$

$$y = r \sin \theta \sin \varphi$$

$$z = r \cos \theta$$

show that the **S** matrix of Eq. (33) is given by

$$\mathbf{S} = \begin{pmatrix} \sin \theta \cos \varphi & \sin \theta \sin \varphi & \cos \theta \\ \cos \theta \cos \varphi & \cos \theta \sin \varphi & -\sin \theta \\ -\sin \varphi & \cos \varphi & 0 \end{pmatrix}$$

3. Compute Δ, $\hat{\delta}$, and $\hat{\delta}'$ explicitly for cylindrical coordinates.

4. Compute Δ, $\hat{\delta}$, and $\hat{\delta}'$ explicitly for polar coordinates.

5. With the formalism employed here, verify the vector identities:

$$\nabla \cdot (\varphi \vec{u}) = \varphi \nabla \cdot \vec{u} + \vec{u} \cdot (\nabla \varphi)$$

$$\nabla \times (\varphi \vec{u}) = \varphi (\nabla \times \vec{u}) + (\nabla \varphi) \times \vec{u}$$

$$\nabla \cdot (\vec{u} \times \vec{v}) = \vec{v} \cdot (\nabla \times \vec{u}) - \vec{u} \cdot (\nabla \times \vec{v})$$

6. In this formalism, what operators describe the directional derivatives $(\vec{u} \cdot \nabla)$ and $(\vec{u} \nabla \cdot)$? How do they transform under a change of basis? Verify the vector identities:

$$\nabla(\vec{u} \cdot \vec{v}) = \vec{u} \times (\nabla \times \vec{v}) + (\vec{u} \cdot \nabla)\vec{v} + \vec{v} \times (\nabla \times \vec{u}) + (\vec{v} \cdot \nabla)\vec{u}$$

$$\nabla \times (\vec{u} \times \vec{v}) = (\vec{v} \cdot \nabla)\vec{u} - (\vec{u} \cdot \nabla)\vec{v} - \vec{v}(\nabla \cdot \vec{u}) + \vec{u}(\nabla \cdot \vec{v})$$

7. Verify Eqs. (5)–(7) by formal multiplication—i.e., by treating the differential operators as elements in a noncommutative ring.

CHAPTER XVII

Sturm-Liouville Systems

We shall now consider the general Sturm-Liouville equation in one dimension:

$$\frac{d}{dz}\left(p\,\frac{df}{dz}\right) - qf - \lambda rf = 0 \tag{1}$$

where p, q, and r may be functions of z, defined over an interval (a, b), and $f(z)$ is the unknown function to be solved subject to boundary conditions at $z = a$ and $z = b$.

This type of equation appears in many of the most important problems of physics. Schroedinger's equation in one dimension is one of these. The equation for an electromagnetic wave propagating in the z direction through a medium whose properties, dielectric constant, etc., are functions of position with suitable symmetry about the z axis can often be reduced to an equation of this type. The spatial part of an equation of a loaded vibrating string is such an equation where p is the modulus of elasticity, r is the mass per unit length, and $q = 0$.

The application of matrix methods to this equation is very enlightening. Obviously it will not give us a general solution—the problem is much too difficult for that. But it will enable us to obtain some of the important properties of such systems as direct consequences of the basic form, and without undue elaboration of analysis.

As Eq. (1) stands, it is not adapted to an algebra of finite dimensionality. It requires, instead, that we consider a vector space such as the space of all continuous, square-integrable functions. This is a Hilbert space of infinite dimensionality.

It is intuitively evident, however, that we can designate N points in the interval (a, b) and consider only what happens at these points. We can, for example, decide to choose the points at equal intervals and set $z_n = a + nh$ $(n = 0, 1, ..., N)$, where $a = z_0$, $b = z_N$, $h = (b - a)/N$. The behavior of the functions can be approximated by their values at the set z_n, and the system approximated by a system that relates what happens at these points. We would expect this approximation to be valid providing h is sufficiently small. We may describe this approximation as the analysis of the system in an $(N + 1)$-dimensional vector space, with the assumption that this finite-dimensional approximation goes to the continuous case in the limit as $N \to \infty$.

A rigorous justification of this assumption requires a detailed study of the resultant errors and the demonstration that under suitable restrictions on the functions involved, the error goes to zero in the limit. Also, as a method of computation, we would like to have some bound on the error so that we can determine how large N must be to be sure of the desired accuracy.

Both of these questions depend on the behavior in the continuous case, and so are beyond our scope. We shall here be concerned only with the behavior of the approximation. We shall assume that the approximation does converge correctly as $N \to \infty$, and that we have chosen the points z_n so that the resulting accuracy will satisfy our needs.

1. APPROXIMATION IN A FINITELY DIMENSIONED VECTOR SPACE

We are going to consider the values of the functions and of $f(z)$ only on a set of points z_n where $n = 1, 2, ..., N$. (We have omitted $n = 0$ for simplicity.) Clearly, we can define the vector

$$\mathbf{f} = \begin{pmatrix} f_1 \\ f_2 \\ \vdots \\ f_{N-1} \\ f_N \end{pmatrix} \tag{2}$$

which describes the unknown function by its values at the selected values of z.

In Eq. (1), λ is a scalar since it has the same value for all z. The functions p, q, and r depend upon z and multiply term by term the values of $f(z)$. Further, each function affects only the value of $f(z)$ at the given point, independent of its value at neighboring points. Hence, their effect can be described by diagonal matrices:

$$\begin{aligned} \lambda &= \lambda \mathbf{I} \\ \mathbf{P} &= \operatorname{diag}(p_1, p_2, ..., p_N) \\ \mathbf{Q} &= \operatorname{diag}(q_1, q_2, ..., q_n) \\ \mathbf{R} &= \operatorname{diag}(r_1, r_2, ..., r_N) \end{aligned} \tag{3}$$

The question that now remains is how we are to represent the derivative. We can do this in terms of differences. The precise manner of doing it depends on how we select the points z_n. The simplest way is to divide the total range into equal segments. However, let us retain generality, at least for the present, and set

$$z_n = \sum_{1}^{n} d_n \tag{4}$$

so that we have divided the range into segments of size d_n.

Providing all of the d_n are sufficiently small, we can make the Taylor expansions:

$$f(z_{n+1}) = f(z_n + d_{n+1}) = f(z_n) + d_{n+1} f'(z_n) \tag{5}$$

$$f(z_{n-1}) = f(z_n - d_n) = f(z_n) - d_n f'(z_n) \tag{6}$$

where the prime indicates the derivative.

If we set

$$f(z_n) = f_n \tag{7}$$

we see that

$$f'(z_n) = f_n' = \frac{1}{d_{n+1}} (f_{n+1} - f_n) \tag{8}$$

or

$$f'(z_n) = f_n' = \frac{1}{d_n} (f_n - f_{n-1}) \tag{9}$$

We have two possible forms for the derivative of f in terms of its coefficients. Equation (8) becomes ambiguous at $n = N$, since f_{N+1} and d_{n+1} are then involved, and Eq. (9) at $n = 1$ since f_0 and $d_1 = x_1 - x_0$ are involved.

We handle this problem by reference to the boundary conditions. If we have Newmann conditions, specifying that the derivatives at the boundary are zero, we put these values in. If we have Dirichlet conditions, specifying that $f_1 = f_N = 0$, we set $f_1' = f_2/d_2$ and $f_N' = -f_{N-1}/d_N$. Other conditions we handle as seems appropriate.

We have, from Eq. (8),

$$f_1' = \frac{1}{d_2} (f_2 - f_1)$$

$$\vdots \tag{10}$$

$$f_N' = -f_N/d_{N+1}$$

where d_{N+1} is taken as appropriate to the boundary condition. We write

$$
\begin{pmatrix} f_1' \\ f_2' \\ \cdot \\ \cdot \\ \cdot \\ f_{N-1} \\ f_N \end{pmatrix} = \begin{pmatrix} -\dfrac{1}{d_2} & \dfrac{1}{d_2} & 0 & & & \\ 0 & -\dfrac{1}{d_3} & \dfrac{1}{d_3} & & & \\ 0 & 0 & -\dfrac{1}{d_4} & \cdots & & \\ & & & \vdots & & \\ & & & & -\dfrac{1}{d_N} & \dfrac{1}{d_N} \\ & & & & & -\dfrac{1}{d_{N+1}} \end{pmatrix} \begin{pmatrix} f_1 \\ f_2 \\ \cdot \\ \cdot \\ \cdot \\ f_{N-1} \\ f_N \end{pmatrix} \qquad (11)
$$

which can be written as

$$\mathbf{f}_+' = \mathbf{D}_+ \mathbf{f}$$

where

$$(\mathbf{D}_+)_{ij} = \left(\frac{1}{d_{i+1}}\right)(-\delta_{ij} + \delta_{i,j-1}) \qquad (12)$$

Similarly, from Eq. (9), we have

$$f_1' = \frac{1}{d_1} f_1$$

$$f_2' = \frac{1}{d_2}(f_2 - f_1) \qquad (13)$$

$$\vdots$$

$$f_N' = \frac{1}{d_N}(f_N - f_{N-1})$$

which we write as

$$
\begin{pmatrix} f_1' \\ f_2' \\ f_3' \\ \vdots \\ f_N' \end{pmatrix} = \begin{pmatrix} \dfrac{1}{d_1} & 0 & 0 & & \\ -\dfrac{1}{d_2} & \dfrac{1}{d_2} & 0 & & \\ 0 & -\dfrac{1}{d_3} & \dfrac{1}{d_3} & \cdots & \\ & & \vdots & & \\ & & & -\dfrac{1}{d_N} & \dfrac{1}{d_N} \end{pmatrix} \begin{pmatrix} f_1 \\ f_2 \\ f_3 \\ \vdots \\ f_N \end{pmatrix} \qquad (14)
$$

or

$$\mathbf{f\_}' = \mathbf{D\_f}$$

where

$$(\mathbf{D}_-)_{ij} = \frac{1}{d_i}(\delta_{ij} - \delta_{i,j+1}) \tag{15}$$

In writing Eq. (1) in terms of these operators, we use both $\mathbf{D}_+$ and $\mathbf{D}_-$ to minimize the effect of the ambiguities at the boundaries:

$$\mathbf{D_+PD\_f} - \mathbf{Qf} - \lambda\mathbf{Rf} = 0 \tag{16}$$

or

$$\mathbf{D\_PD_+f} - \mathbf{Qf} - \lambda\mathbf{Rf} = 0 \tag{17}$$

If we premultiply these by $\mathbf{R}^{-1}$, then both equations become eigenvalue equations:

$$\mathbf{Hf} = \lambda\mathbf{f} \tag{18}$$

where

$$\mathbf{H} = \mathbf{R}^{-1}(\mathbf{D_+PD_-} - \mathbf{Q}) \tag{19}$$

or

$$\mathbf{H} = \mathbf{R}^{-1}(\mathbf{D\_PD_+} - \mathbf{Q}) \tag{20}$$

We note that although $\mathbf{D}_+$ and $\mathbf{D}_-$ represent differential operators, they are conventional matrices (not formal matrices such as, for example, that used in Chapter XVI for the curl operator). Hence, it is fully meaningful to ask for the eigenvalues and eigenvectors of $\mathbf{H}$.

2. MODIFIED STURM-LIOUVILLE EQUATION

Equation (1) can be simplified by the transformations

$$g = p^{1/4}r^{1/4}f \tag{21}$$

$$w = \int r^{+1/2}p^{-1/2}\,dz = w(z) \tag{22}$$

$$V(w) = -\frac{q}{r} + \frac{3}{16}\left\{\left(\frac{p'}{p}\right)^2 + \left(\frac{r'}{r}\right)^2\right\} - \frac{1}{8}\frac{p'}{p}\frac{r'}{r} - \frac{1}{4}\left(\frac{p''}{p} + \frac{r''}{r}\right) \tag{23}$$

where the prime indicates differentiation with respect to w. We assume that the integral for w converges throughout the range and that w and $V(w)$ are single valued and continuous.

Then Eq. (1) becomes

$$\left\{\frac{d^2}{dw^2} + V(w)\right\}g = \lambda g \tag{24}$$

The operator $\mathbf{D}_2$ for d^2/dw^2 can either be obtained as before as $\mathbf{D}_+\mathbf{D}_-$ or $\mathbf{D}_-\mathbf{D}_+$ or obtained directly from the Taylor expansion. The latter derivation becomes particularly simple if the range of w, (a, b), is divided into equal segments ($w_n = nh$). Then

$$g_{n+1} = g(w_n + h) = g_n + hg_n' + \frac{1}{2!}h^2g_n'' + \cdots$$

$$g_{n-1} = g(w_n - h) = g_n - hg_n' + \frac{1}{2!}h^2g_n'' + \cdots$$

so that

$$g_{n+1} + g_{n-1} = 2g_n + h^2g_n'' + \cdots$$

and, approximately,

$$g_n'' = \frac{1}{h^2}(g_{n+1} - 2g_n + g_{n-1}) \tag{25}$$

We therefore approximate the second derivative by the operator

$$\mathbf{D}_2 = \frac{1}{h^2}\begin{pmatrix} -2 & 1 & 0 & 0 & \\ 1 & -2 & 1 & 0 & \\ 0 & 1 & -2 & 1 & \\ 0 & 0 & 1 & -2 & \\ & & & & \ddots \\ & & & & & -2 \end{pmatrix} \tag{26}$$

Again, we are sliding over detailed consideration of the boundary conditions which should be used to determine the first and last rows and columns of $\mathbf{D}_2$.

Equation (24) becomes

$$\mathbf{H}\mathbf{g} = \lambda\mathbf{g} \tag{27}$$

where

$$\mathbf{H} = \mathbf{D}_2 + \text{diag}(V_1, V_2, \dots)$$

$$= \begin{pmatrix} V_1 - 2 & 1 & 0 & \\ 1 & V_2 - 2 & 1 & \\ 0 & 1 & V_3 - 2 & \\ & & & \ddots \\ & & & & V_n - 2 \end{pmatrix} \tag{28}$$

The formal similarity of Eqs. (27) and (28) to the Schroedinger equation is no accident. The form is appropriate to any Sturm-Liouville system which can be taken into the modified form, Eq. (24).

The important properties of the system are implied in the matrix **H**, given by Eq. (28).

3. THE CHARACTERISTIC EQUATION OF **H**

The characteristic equation of **H** is obtained by evaluating

$$p_n(\lambda) = |\,\mathbf{H} - \lambda \mathbf{I}\,| = \begin{vmatrix} V_1 - 2 - \lambda & 1 & 0 & & \\ 1 & V_2 - 2 - \lambda & 1 & & \\ 0 & 1 & V_3 - 2 - \lambda & & \\ & & & \ddots & \\ & & & & V_n - 2 - \lambda \end{vmatrix}$$

$$(29)$$

where **H** is $n \times n$.

Let $p_k(\lambda)$ be the $k \times k$ determinant obtained from Eq. (29) by removing the last $n - k$ rows and columns. Then, expanding on the last column,

$$p_k(\lambda) = (V_k - 2 - \lambda) \begin{vmatrix} V_1 - 2 - \lambda & 1 & & \\ 1 & V_2 - 2 - \lambda & & \\ & & \ddots & \\ & & & V_{k-1} - 2 - \lambda \end{vmatrix}$$

$$- \begin{vmatrix} V_1 - 2 - \lambda & 1 & & & & \\ 1 & V_2 - 2 - \lambda & & & & \\ & & \ddots & & & \\ & & & V_{k-3} - 2 - \lambda & 1 & 0 \\ & & & 1 & V_{k-2} - 2 - \lambda & 1 \\ & & & 0 & 0 & 1 \end{vmatrix}$$

$$= (V_k - 2 - \lambda) p_{k-1} - p_{k-2} \qquad (30)$$

with the boundary conditions

$$p_1 = V_1 - 2 - \lambda$$
$$p_2 = (V_1 - 2 - \lambda)(V_2 - 2 - \lambda) - 1 \qquad (31)$$

Equation (30) with (31) is a recursion formula determining the characteristic equation of the operator **H**. If all the V_k's were the same, **H** would be what is called a *Jacobi matrix* and we could solve Eq. (30) explicitly and conveniently.

In the general case, where the V_k are different, we cannot obtain a convenient solution. However, the general form of **H** in Eq. (28) and of the recursion relation in Eq. (30) do contain some regularities which can be exploited to prove some of the important general properties of Sturm-Liouville systems.

We can, for example, observe, that the **H** of Eq. (28) is hermitian if the V_i are all real. Hence its eigenvalues are real and its eigenvectors orthogonal under the unitary inner product.

We do not know at this point that it may not have degeneracies, but this we can prove by the theory of Sturm chains.

4. STURM CHAINS

If all of the V_k in the sequence are real, then the sequence of polynomials $p_n(\lambda)$ form what is known as a Sturm chain. In general terms, if we have a sequence $p_n(\lambda)$ of real polynomials, each of which is of degree n, then it is a *Sturm chain* if

(a) For any λ inside the interval $(a < \lambda < b)$ if, for a given k, $p_k(\lambda) = 0$, then $p_{k+1}(\lambda)$ and $p_{k-1}(\lambda)$ are nonvanishing and have opposite signs.

(b) There exists a minimum value of k, say $p_0(\lambda)$, such that $p_0(\lambda)$ has no roots in the interval.

We make a Sturm chain out of the sequence $p_k(\lambda)$ defined by Eq. (30) by defining

$$p_0(\lambda) = 1$$

so that Eq. (30) holds for $k = 2$ as well as all higher k. This satisfies the second condition. To see that the first is satisfied, we observe that if $p_k(\lambda)$ and $p_{k+1}(\lambda)$ are both zero for some λ, then, from Eq. (30), all the p's are zero for that λ. Since $p_0(\lambda)$ is not equal to zero, this cannot happen. We also observe, from Eq. (30), that if $p_{k-1}(\lambda) = 0$ for some λ, then p_k and p_{k-2} must have opposite signs for that λ.

The significance of identifying the sequence as a Sturm chain is that we can apply Sturm's theorem involving the Cauchy indices.

The Cauchy index of a rational function $R(x)$ over a real range (a, b), $I_a^b R(\lambda)$, is the difference of the number of times $R(x)$ jumps from $-\infty$ to $+\infty$, and the number of times it jumps from $+\infty$ to $-\infty$, as the variable λ moves from a to b, extreme values not included.

Let $n(a)$ be the number of times $p_k(a)$ changes sign as k goes from 0 to n.

The Sturm theorem then says that if $p_k(\lambda)$ is a Sturm chain, then

$$I_a^b \left(\frac{p_{n-1}(\lambda)}{p_n(\lambda)} \right) = n(a) - n(b) \tag{32}$$

That is, the Cauchy index of p_{n-1}/p_n over the range (a, b), where the set p_n is a Sturm chain, is equal to the difference of the number of variations of sign along the chain at the two end points.

To see this, let us increase b to b'. If in the process, p_i passes through zero, then, in the neighborhood, p_{i+1} and p_{i-1} have opposite signs. If $i \neq n$, this does not affect $n(b)$, it merely shifts the location of a change of sign along the chain. If $i = n$, we must consider several cases. If $p_{n-1}(b) > 0$, and $p_n(b)$ goes from $+$ to $-$ through 0 as b increases, then $n(b)$ increases by one unit, and the Cauchy index decreases by one unit. Similarly, by considering all other combinations of signs of p_{n-1} and direction of change of p_n, we can verify Eq. (32) for all cases.

If we consider the $p_k(\lambda)$ defined by Eq. (30), we see that as $\lambda \to -\infty$, all of the $p_k(\lambda)$ become positive. Hence, for a sufficiently large negatively, $n(a) = 0$. As $\lambda \to +\infty$, $p_k(\lambda)$ becomes either large positive or negative according to whether k is even or odd. Hence, for b sufficiently positive, $n(b)$ for the chain up to $p_n(\lambda)$ is equal to n. Hence, the Cauchy index of p_{n-1}/p_n for a sufficiently positive is $-n$. By Sturm's theorem, since p_{n-1} is finite in any finite range, p_n must have exactly n distinct roots.

We have already seen that since $\mathbf{H}$ is hermitian it is semisimple with real eigenvalues. We have now shown that it must have n distinct roots, since a root of multiplicity k will contribute only either 0 or -1, depending on whether k is even or odd, to the Cauchy index. Hence $\mathbf{H}$ must be nondegenerate. Since $\mathbf{H}$ is hermitian without degeneracy, its eigenvectors must be orthogonal.

Further, we can see that between every adjacent pair of roots of p_k, there must be a root of p_{k-1}. This follows since p_k must cross zero in opposite directions at neighboring roots. Hence, p_{k-1} must have opposite signs at these two values of λ, or it would sometimes contribute $+1$ and sometimes -1 to the Cauchy index.

It is sometimes possible to deduce $n(a)$ or $n(b)$ at some λ other than large negative or positive. If so, then we can use this fact to limit the possible locations of the roots.

We find that for a Sturm-Liouville system, with $V(z)$ real, the operator $\mathbf{H}$ is always semisimple and nondegenerate with real eigenvalues and orthogonal eigenvectors. If we consider n as a variable, the eigenvalues for $(n - 1)$ interleave those of n. These results are entirely independent of the potential function $V(z)$ providing it is real and reasonably well behaved.

5. RECURSION FORMULA

The detailed solution of a problem such as those we are considering depends on the solution of the recursion formula, Eq. (30), for the characteristic equation. This, therefore, seems like a good time at which to consider the general problem of recursion formulas.

Suppose we have a second order recursion formula

$$x_n = a_n x_{n-1} + b_n x_{n-2} \tag{33}$$

where the a_n and b_n are known functions of n.

Being a second order difference equation, Eq. (33) is analogous to a second order differential equation. We have seen (Chapter VI, Section 2) that we can always reduce a second order differential equation to a first order one at the expense of dimensionality. It is reasonable to do the same here.

The easiest way to do this here is to define

$$y_n = x_{n-1} \tag{34}$$

Then Eq. (33) can be written

$$x_n = a_n x_{n-1} + b_n y_{n-1} \tag{35}$$

and Eqs. (34) and (35) together become

$$\mathbf{u}_n = \begin{pmatrix} x_n \\ y_n \end{pmatrix} = \begin{pmatrix} a_n & b_n \\ 1 & 0 \end{pmatrix} \begin{pmatrix} x_{n-1} \\ y_{n-1} \end{pmatrix} = \mathbf{P}_n \mathbf{u}_{n-1} \tag{36}$$

where $\mathbf{P}_n$ is the matrix of coefficients.

If $\mathbf{P}_n = \mathbf{P}$, constant, so that the coefficients of the original equation were constant, then the solution evidently is

$$\mathbf{u}_n = \mathbf{P}^{n-1}\mathbf{u}_1 = \mathbf{P}^{n-1} \begin{pmatrix} x_1 \\ x_0 \end{pmatrix} \tag{37}$$

and it is simply a question of evaluating the $(n-1)$ power of $\mathbf{P}$ by the methods already developed.

We could also solve Eq. (36) if the eigenvectors of $\mathbf{P}_n$ were independent of n. This is not helpful, however, since a little study will show that this is possible only if a_n and b_n are independent of n.

We may note that Eq. (36) is redundant. The sequence of y_n contains the same information as the sequence of x_n. We can avoid this by letting n take only odd values, so that

$$\mathbf{u}_n = \mathbf{P}_n \mathbf{P}_{n-1} \mathbf{u}_{n-2} \tag{38}$$

Then

$$\mathbf{P}_n\mathbf{P}_{n-1} = \begin{pmatrix} a_n a_{n-1} + b_n & a_n b_{n-1} \\ a_{n-1} & b_{n-1} \end{pmatrix} \tag{39}$$

This is sometimes useful for computational purposes. It is of little theoretic value since the conditions that the eigenvectors of $\mathbf{P}_n\mathbf{P}_{n-1}$ be constant are the same as that $\mathbf{P}_n$ be constant—i.e., that a_n and b_n be constant.

We can sometimes solve Eq. (36), or put it into soluble form, by finding an n-dependent change of basis that will lead to a matrix with constant eigenvectors. This is equivalent to replacing x_n and y_n by two linear forms on x_n and x_{n-1} with coefficients that depend on n. It is analogous to finding a Lyapunov transformation of a differential equation (cf. Chapter XV, Section 1).

As an example, let us set, instead of Eq. (34),

$$y_n = k_n x_{n-1} \tag{40}$$

where the k_n are to be determined. Equation (36) then becomes

$$\begin{pmatrix} x_n \\ y_n \end{pmatrix} = \begin{pmatrix} a_n & b_n/k_{n-1} \\ k_n & 0 \end{pmatrix}\begin{pmatrix} x_{n-1} \\ y_{n-1} \end{pmatrix} \tag{41}$$

If it happens that

$$b_n = k a_n a_{n-1} \tag{42}$$

where k is some constant, then we can set $k_n = a_n$ and find that

$$\mathbf{P}_n = a_n \begin{pmatrix} 1 & k \\ 1 & 0 \end{pmatrix} \tag{43}$$

With this b_n, the original equation, Eq. (33), was

$$x_n = a_n x_{n-1} + k a_n a_{n-1} x_{n-2} \tag{44}$$

The scalar factor a_n in $\mathbf{P}_n$ indicates the presence in x_n of the factor $\prod^n a_n$. If we set

$$x_n = w_n \prod^n a_n \tag{45}$$

then Eq. (44) reduces to

$$w_n = w_{n-1} + k w_{n-2} \tag{46}$$

which has constant coefficients generating the matrix part of $\mathbf{P}_n$ in Eq. (43). This can now be solved directly.

While such techniques do permit us to solve certain problems, the solution of the general recursion problem is at least as difficult, and perhaps more so, than the analogous differential problem, which is that of the general nonuniform system. The difficulty, it should be observed, is essentially the same type—that if the eigenvectors cannot be taken as constant, then adjacent pieces of the problem do not "match." The difficulty is the precise evaluation and accounting of the cummulative effects of this mismatch.

Exercises

1.   The general Jacobi matrix of order n is the $n \times n$ matrix of the form

$$\mathbf{J}_n = \begin{pmatrix} a & b & 0 & 0 \\ c & a & b & 0 \\ 0 & c & a & b \\ 0 & 0 & c & a \\ & & & & \ddots \end{pmatrix}$$

where a, b, and c are possibly complex constants. Find the eigenvalues of $\mathbf{J}_n$.

(*Hint*: Use the method of Section 3 to develop the recursion formula.)
Find the eigenvectors of $\mathbf{J}_n$.

(*Hint*: Develop a recursion formula for the kth coefficient of the eigenvector with the mth eigenvalue.)

2.   If all the d_i of Eq. (11) are equal to d, what are the eigenvalues and structure of $\mathbf{D}_+$?

3.   Suppose the minimum polynomial of a matrix, $\mathbf{R}$, is

$$\mathbf{R}^4 + a\mathbf{R}^3 + b\mathbf{R}^2 + c\mathbf{R} + d\mathbf{I} = 0$$

Obtain the set of first order recursion formulas that will determine $\mathbf{R}^n$. Write these analogously to Eq. (36).

(*Hint*: Let

$$\mathbf{R}^n = f_n\mathbf{R}^3 + g_n\mathbf{R}^2 + h_n\mathbf{R} + k_n\mathbf{I}$$

where f_n, g_n, h_n, k_n are functions of n to be determined.)
Solve this system explicitly for $a = b = c = 0$, $d = -1$.

CHAPTER XVIII

Markoff Matrices and Probability Theory

In this chapter we wish to call attention to a rather remarkable class of matrices which provide a tool for the study of certain types of probabilistic problems. A considerable body of theory has been developed concerning these matrices. We shall not attempt even to survey this knowledge, since to do so would require much more space than appears justified here. Instead, our intent is to provide the means for recognizing a problem for which this approach is appropriate, to state briefly how such a problem is set up, and to show some of the properties of its solution.

We consider random or *stochastic* processes of a restricted type known as Markoff processes or chains. A *Markoff process* is one in which the future is determined only by the present. We do not need to know anything about the past history to compute the statistics of its future.

This may appear a rather drastic restriction. However, there are a great many problems which concern processes that are at least approximately Markoff. Others may be put in this category by properly defining the present state. That is, the description and categorization of the state at time t may be made to include not only the observable situation at time t, but the manner in which it was reached.

The general class of Markoff processes include those with a continuum of possible states, and with continuous transition from one state to another. Brownian motion, in which the motion of a set of masses— ideally point masses—are determined by a set of unpredictable, and hence random, factors acting discretely but at random intervals, is an example.

We shall not here concern ourselves with such a broad class of processes. Instead, we shall be concerned with processes in which transitions occur at fixed intervals of time—or of whatever is the independent variable. We shall assume, furthermore, that these transitions are among a finite set of possible states. At least we shall assume that the physical problem can be so approximated.

As is so often the case in probability problems, we can best illustrate this by a problem of gambling. Let the state of a gambler's pocketbook at time t be $N(t)$. That is, he has \$N. Once a minute he makes a bet. On each bet, there is a known probability that he will win \$K, where K is one of some set of integers. If K is negative, then this is a probability of loss. Hence, if he has $\$N(t)$ at time t, we know the probability that he will have $\$(N + K)$ at time $(t + 1)$.

We can then ask various questions. If, for example, he starts with $\$N_0$ at $t = 0$, and vows to quit when he has $\$M$, we can ask: What is the probability that he will go broke before reaching his goal? (We cannot, however, ask the probability that he will keep his vow if he is lucky!) This is the so-called *Problem of the Gambler's Ruin*.

There are many areas where similar problems arise that are of greater cultural significance. For example, consider an atomic pile. A neutron is generated at some point inside it. This neutron, after being moderated to thermal energy, bounces around in a random fashion. It collides with various types of nuclei. At each collision, it may simply bounce, or it may be absorbed without further effect, or it may be absorbed with subsequent fission and the release of new neutrons. Furthermore, if it bounces long enough, it may irreversibly escape from the boundary. We may say that the neutron has "won" if it induces a new fission, "lost" if it is captured without fission or escapes, and remains in a neutral state if it simply bounces. We are vitally interested in the probability that a neutron generated at a random point in the pile will win. If the probability of winning is high enough, taking into account the average number of neutrons generated in a fission, then the pile will run away. If it is too small, then the pile will be quenched. It is obviously of great interest to know just where is the balance point.

Again, for example, consider a length of transmission line terminated in a known impedance. There are joints in it every so often. Each joint contributes some degree of reflection, the exact amount and its phase being a consequence of manufacturing tolerance and therefore known only as a probability distribution. The problem can usually be approximated sufficiently well if we quantize the possible reflections. That is, we assume that the reflections have one of a finite set of magnitudes and a finite set of phases, with known probability distributions. We can then ask: What is the probable input standing wave ratio, and the probable variance around this value? This is a question of how the various individual reflections will successively combine. That the rules of combination are somewhat complicated—vectorial addition if the reflections are small enough, and worse if they are large, or accumulate to a large standing wave ratio—may be nasty in detail, but does not alter the principle.

A large number of other problems could be cited. Some are of tremendous importance. (For example, Darwin's principle of survival of the fittest is, in detail, a Markoff process involving the successive generations.) However, suffice it to say these problems arise whenever one wishes to know something about the end result of the successive application of random processes.

We may categorize all such problems as involving a system that can exist in a finite number of states. At intervals, which may be regular or not, events happen which may change the state of the system. The effect of a given event cannot be predicted exactly, but only as the set of probabilities associated with the possible transitions. These probabilities are, in general, functions of the state preceding the event, but are not functions of any other observable data. We want to know something about the probable situation after a given number of such events. Or we want to know the probable number of events that will occur before the system is in a given state or set of states. Such a problem is called a *Markoff* or *random walk* or *drunkard's walk* problem.

1. STATE VECTOR

To tackle such a problem, we set up a state vector whose dimensionality equals the total number of possible states of the system. In the gambler's case, he may have anywhere from \$0 to \$$M$ in, say, \$1 steps. Hence we establish an $(M + 1)$-dimensional vector, each component representing one possible state.

We may order these components in any way. In the gambler's case, it is natural to order the states according to the gambler's bankroll. The first component may represent his having the maximum amount, \$$M$, the next \$$(M - 1)$, and so on, to the last component which represents him being broke, with \$0. Or vice versa. This is a matter of convenience only, however, and has no mathematical significance. In the cases of the atomic pile or the reflections on a transmission line, there is no such simple order suggested. But all that is required is that we know what state corresponds to each entry.

If we know that at a given time the gambler has exactly \$$N$, then we set the Nth component of the vector equal to unity, and all other components equal to zero. We call such a situation a *pure state*.

If we do not know exactly what the gambler has, but only the probabilities, then we enter those probabilities. If the probability that he has \$$N$ is p_N, then we write the vector

$$
\mathbf{x} = \begin{pmatrix} p_M \\ \vdots \\ p_2 \\ p_1 \\ p_0 \end{pmatrix}
\tag{1}
$$

We call this a *mixed state*.

For a given vector **x** to represent a state, whether pure or mixed, it must have certain properties:

(a) Its components are all real.
(b) Every component is nonnegative.
(c) The sum of its components must equal unity, since the system must be in some one of the states listed.

A vector with these properties we call a *probability vector*.

We need also to consider vectors that are not probability vectors. In particular, we shall need vectors that are the difference between two probability vectors.

We define the norm of a vector as the algebraic sum of its components:

$$\| \mathbf{x} \| = \sum_i x_i \tag{2}$$

This is a somewhat unusual definition of norm, but it is the one that suits our purpose here.

We recall the definition of a norm given on page 61. The vectors that we will want to consider will all have norms that are nonnegative definite. The norm as given is a linear function so that $\| \alpha\mathbf{x} \| = \alpha\| \mathbf{x} \|$. And Minkowski's inequality does hold. In fact, we can go further and replace the inequality by an equality:

$$\| \mathbf{x} + \mathbf{y} \| = \| \mathbf{x} \| + \| \mathbf{y} \| \tag{3}$$

A probability vector has unit norm. A vector formed as the difference of two probability vectors has zero norm. Hence such a vector cannot be nonnegative—i.e., not all of its components can be nonnegative.

2. TRANSITION OR MARKOFF MATRIX

We next consider what happens when our gambler plays the game (or the neutron collides, or we move our attention one length back along the transmission line).

Suppose, first, that he started with exactly \$n. After one play there are various amounts that he may have, with various probabilities. Suppose that the probability that after one play, he ends up with exactly \$m is p_{mn}.

Or p_{mn} is the probability that the neutron is at position m after collision, if it started at position n. Or p_{mn} is the probability that the complex reflection coefficient has the value that we index as #m, if it has the value indicated by #n one section further along the line.

The value p_{mn} is the *transition probability* from state n to state m. Suppose, now, we do not know that the gambler had, intially, exactly \$$n$. Suppose we only know that there was a probability x_n that he had this sum. Then after one play, the combined probability that he started with \$$n$ and ended with \$$m$ is the product of the probabilities, $p_{mn}x_n$. Then the total probability y_m that he has exactly \$$m$ after one play is the sum of all such quantities, over the range of possible initial states:

$$y_m = \sum_n p_{mn}x_n \qquad (4)$$

Equation (4) is the expression for the product of a matrix by a vector. Hence we can write the totality of such equations for all values of m by the vector equation

$$\mathbf{y} = \mathbf{P}\mathbf{x} \qquad (5)$$

where $\mathbf{P}$ is the matrix of transition probabilities.

The matrix $\mathbf{P}$ is called a *transition* or *Markoff matrix*.

Suppose we consider the situation after s plays, and indicate the gambler's state by $\mathbf{x}(s)$. Let $\mathbf{x}_k$ be the pure state in which the kth component is unity, all others zero. This corresponds to exact knowledge of the amount of money the gambler has at that time.

After one more play, the gambler is in the state $\mathbf{x}(s+1)$. If he started in $\mathbf{x}_k$, he has

$$\mathbf{x}(s+1) = \mathbf{P}\mathbf{x}_k = \begin{pmatrix} p_{Mk} \\ \vdots \\ p_{1k} \\ p_{0k} \end{pmatrix} \qquad (6)$$

Since this is a possible situation, the vector $\mathbf{x}(s+1)$ must be a probability vector, even though one describing a mixed state. But it is simply the kth column of $\mathbf{P}$.

Hence a necessary and sufficient condition for $\mathbf{P}$ to be a Markoff matrix is that each of its columns shall be a probability vector—all its components are real and nonnegative, and the sum of the coefficients in each of its columns must be unity.[1]

---

[1] There is some confusion in the literature as to just what is called a Markoff matrix. Sometimes p_{mn} is taken as the probability that state m arose from state n, and the Markoff matrix is the matrix of these probability terms. In this case, each row must be a probability vector, since state m must have arisen from some state.

3. EIGENVECTORS OF A MARKOFF MATRIX

In the following we shall assume simple structure. This is not necessarily true and the possibility of generalized eigenvectors can be taken account of without too much elaboration, but we shall confine ourselves to the simpler case.

Consider an eigenvector $\mathbf{x}_i$ which is also a probability vector. Then it is a possible state of the system, and $\mathbf{x}(s)$ in Eq. (5) may be this vector:

$$\mathbf{x}(s) = \mathbf{x}_i$$
$$\mathbf{P}\mathbf{x}_i = \lambda_i \mathbf{x}_i \tag{7}$$

and

$$\mathbf{x}(s + 1) = \lambda_i \mathbf{x}_i$$

However $\mathbf{x}(s + 1)$ is then also a probability vector. Since the norms of both $\mathbf{x}(s)$ and $\mathbf{x}(s + 1)$ must be unity, λ_i must be unity. The eigenvalue corresponding to any eigenvector that is also a probability vector must be unity.

This does not prove that there is necessarily such a vector that is both an eigenvector of $\mathbf{P}$ and a probability vector. This can be proven, however. It can also be proven that there can be no eigenvectors whose eigenvalue has a magnitude greater than unity. This is perhaps not unreasonable. The existence of such a vector means that there exists a limiting situation. If the game is repeated a large number of times, it will generally approach asymptotically a constant distribution of probabilities. (There are exceptions to this, however.)

Consider as a specific example the gambler who plays until he is either broke or else has accumulated \$$M$ when he, hypothetically, quits. In this case, there are two eigenvectors with unit eigenvalues representing these two pure states:

$$\mathbf{x}_1 = \mathrm{col}(1, 0, 0, ..., 0) \tag{8}$$

$$\mathbf{x}_2 = \mathrm{col}(0, 0, ..., 0, 1) \tag{9}$$

When he reaches either state, the game goes on without him, so that the state is unchanged by further action of the game. Hence these are eigenvectors with unit eigenvalue.

Suppose, in addition, there are the eigenvectors $\mathbf{x}_3$, ..., $\mathbf{x}_n$ making up a complete set. Then any initial vector, whether a pure state or not, can be expanded on these eigenvectors:

$$\mathbf{x}(0) = \sum_i a_i \mathbf{x}_i = a_1 \mathbf{x}_1 + a_2 \mathbf{x}_2 + \cdots \tag{10}$$

After playing the game once, the gambler's state is

$$\mathbf{x}(1) = \sum_i a_i \mathbf{P} \mathbf{x}_i = \sum a_i \lambda_i \mathbf{x}_i \tag{11}$$

and after m times

$$\mathbf{x}(m) = \sum a_i \lambda_i{}^m \mathbf{x}_i \tag{12}$$

The initial state was a probability vector. So, too, are the states after each successive play. Hence $\| \mathbf{x}(m) \| = 1$ for all m. It is evident, and can be proven rigorously, that every eigenvector whose eigenvalue is not unity must have zero norm

$$\| \mathbf{x}_i \| = 0 \qquad \text{if} \quad \lambda_i \neq 1 \tag{13}$$

Otherwise we cannot hope to maintain the norm at unity with successive applications of $\mathbf{P}$.

Consider, furthermore, the $\mathbf{x}_i$ whose λ_i is the largest of the set of λ's which are not equal to unity. If this $|\lambda_i| > 1$, then as m increases, this eigenvector must eventually dominate all others. Since the norm of this eigenvector is zero, at least one of its components must be negative. Hence, if such a vector existed, $\mathbf{x}(m)$ would eventually have a negative component. Since $\mathbf{x}(m)$ is a probability vector this is impossible. Hence all the eigenvalues of $\mathbf{P}$ must have magnitude not greater than unity:

$$|\lambda_i| \leqslant 1 \qquad \text{for all } \lambda_i \tag{14}$$

In the case of the gambler, if $\mathbf{x}_1$ and $\mathbf{x}_2$ are the only eigenvectors with unit eigenvalue, then after a sufficiently large number of plays, the contributions of the $\mathbf{x}_3$, ..., $\mathbf{x}_n$ parts of $\mathbf{x}(m)$ in Eq. (10) become vanishingly small, so that

$$\lim_{m \to \infty} \mathbf{x}(m) = a_1 \mathbf{x}_1 + a_2 \mathbf{x}_2 \tag{15}$$

The probability of his ultimately winning $\$M$ is a_1, and that of his ultimately going broke is a_2, the coefficients of the corresponding vectors in the expansion of the initial state on the eigenvectors.

The above is not intended to be a rigorous proof but is rather a plausibility statement. The theorem can, however, be rigorously proven. To summarize, we state the theorem as follows:

If $\mathbf{P}$ is a Markoff matrix that is semisimple, then it has at least one eigenvector with unit eigenvalue and which can be chosen to be a probability vector. All other eigenvectors have eigenvalues whose magnitudes are not greater than unity. Those with eigenvalues whose magnitude is less then unity have zero norm.

It must be possible to find at least one eigenvector with unit eigenvalue that is a probability vector. This need not be a pure state. Neither does it follow that every eigenvector with unit eigenvalue is normalizable to a probability vector. In the gambler's problem, we had two eigenvectors with unit eigenvalue that were pure states, x_1 and x_2, given by Eqs. (9) and (10). Since they are degenerate, any linear combination of them is an eigenvector with unit eigenvalue. But $(x_1 - x_2)$, while still such an eigenvector, has zero norm and so is unnormalizable. Also, $(2x_1 - x_2)$ is such an eigenvector which does have unit norm, but is not nonnegative, and so is not a probability vector.

As another example, consider the transition matrix

$$\mathbf{P} = \begin{pmatrix} 0 & 1 \\ 1 & 0 \end{pmatrix} \tag{16}$$

This is a Markoff matrix since each column adds to unity and all terms are nonnegative. Each pure state is turned into the other by its application. The eigenvector with unit eigenvalue, adjusted by a scalar factor to have unit norm, is

$$x_1 = \begin{pmatrix} \frac{1}{2} \\ \frac{1}{2} \end{pmatrix} \tag{17}$$

and indicates an equal probability of the two pure states.

The other eigenvector is

$$x_2 = \begin{pmatrix} 1 \\ -1 \end{pmatrix} \tag{18}$$

and has an eigenvalue of -1. Its norm is, as expected, zero.

We may note that in this case, an arbitrary initial vector does not approach a determined limit. Its expansion in terms of x_1 and x_2 will in general contain some finite amount of x_2. Since $|\lambda_2| = 1$, successive application of $\mathbf{P}$ does not cause this component to decay, but simply to alternate its sign. Hence the state oscillates. Even in such a case where the system does not approach a limiting condition, we can show rigorously that its average state, averaged over successive applications of $\mathbf{P}$, does approach a limit which is composed of the eigenvectors of eigenvalue unity.

4. RECIPROCAL EIGENVECTORS

It is of interest to consider the reciprocal eigenvectors. These, it will be remembered, are the vectors y_i such that

$$y_i^\dagger x_j = \delta_{ij} \tag{19}$$

Then, since

$$\mathbf{y}_i{}^\dagger \mathbf{P} \mathbf{x}_j = \lambda_j \mathbf{y}_i{}^\dagger \mathbf{x}_j = \lambda_j \delta_{ij} = \lambda_i$$

it follows that

$$\mathbf{y}_i{}^\dagger \mathbf{P} = \mu_i \mathbf{y}_i{}^\dagger$$

or

$$\mathbf{P}^\dagger \mathbf{y}_i = \mu_i{}^* \mathbf{y}_i \tag{20}$$

so that the $\mathbf{y}_i$ are the eigenvectors of the adjoint matrix under the unitary inner product relation.

Then, since

$$\mathbf{y}_i{}^\dagger \mathbf{P} \mathbf{x}_i = \mu_i \mathbf{y}_i{}^\dagger \mathbf{x}_i = \lambda_i \mathbf{y}_i{}^\dagger \mathbf{x}_i \tag{21}$$

it follows that $\mu_i = \lambda_i$.

Since the columns of $\mathbf{P}$ add to unity, it is immediately evident that the vector

$$\mathbf{y}_i = \frac{1}{n} \begin{pmatrix} 1 \\ 1 \\ \vdots \\ 1 \end{pmatrix} \tag{22}$$

is a reciprocal eigenvector of $\mathbf{P}$ with eigenvalue unity, or an eigenvector of the adjoint, $\mathbf{P}^\dagger$. We are able to write down immediately and explicitly one of the inverse eigenvectors of any Markoff matrix. It is, furthermore, an eigenvector with unit eigenvalue and unit norm.

5. NONNEGATIVE AND POSITIVE MATRICES

The class of Markoff matrices is a special case of a broader class which are known as nonnegative matrices. A matrix is said to be nonnegative if all of its coefficients are real and $\geqslant 0$.

If all of the terms are positive, none being zero, the matrix is said to be positive.

Note that this has nothing to do with positive definiteness.

Such matrices have an important subclassification according to whether they are *reducible* or not. We use the term *reducible* here in a similar, but slightly different sense from that we mentioned before (Chapter VIII, Section 1). We call a Markoff matrix *reducible* if we can permute the order of its basis vectors in such a way as to put it into the form

$$\begin{pmatrix} \mathbf{A} & \mathbf{B} \\ \mathbf{0} & \mathbf{C} \end{pmatrix} \tag{23}$$

where $\mathbf{A}$ and $\mathbf{C}$ are square matrices. Otherwise, we call it *irreducible*.

Such a permutation of the basis vectors can be accomplished by a similarity transformation with an operator $\mathbf{T}$ that is a permutation matrix—i.e., a matrix in which each row and each column has only a single nonzero term, which is unity. We do not, however, permit a general change of basis since this might upset the property of a given vector being a probability vector.

The class of irreducible nonnegative matrices have some remarkable spectral properties that are a generalization of those we have cited for Markoff matrices. These are given by the theorem of Perron as generalized by Frobenius which we shall not prove:

Theorem.   *An irreducible nonnegative matrix always has a positive real eigenvalue λ that has multiplicity one. The magnitudes of all other eigenvalues do not exceed λ. To λ there corresponds a reciprocal eigenvector that can be normalized to have coordinates that are all real and positive.*

Furthermore, if the matrix has k eigenvalues, λ_0, λ_i, ..., λ_{k-1}, all of magnitude λ, then these eigenvalues are all distinct and are roots of

$$\lambda^k - \lambda_0{}^k = 0. \tag{24}$$

Likewise, all other eigenvalues are simple and occur in sets that are similarly related.

If $k > 1$, then the matrix can, by a permutation, be put into the form

$$\begin{pmatrix} 0 & 0 & 0 & \cdots & & \mathbf{A}_{1k} \\ \mathbf{A}_{21} & 0 & 0 & \cdots & & 0 \\ 0 & \mathbf{A}_{32} & 0 & \cdots & & 0 \\ \vdots & & & & & \\ 0 & 0 & 0 & \cdots & \mathbf{A}_{kk-1} & 0 \end{pmatrix} \tag{25}$$

where the $\mathbf{0}$'s along the main diagonal are scalars or square matrices.

The simple matrix of Eq. (16) is irreducible. The only possible permutation of the order of the states does not change it, so that it cannot, in this manner, be put into the form of Eq. (25).

The matrix of the gambler's problem, on the other hand, must be reducible. If the gambler goes broke, or wins his predetermined amount, then no further change can occur. Hence, if the states of $\mathbf{x}$ are ordered with \$0 at the bottom and the maximum amount at the top, the first column of $\mathbf{P}$ has all zeros except the top element which is unity. Likewise the last column is all zeros except the bottom element which is unity. Hence, with this sequence of the basis vectors, the matrix is in the form of Eq. (23) since it can be partitioned into 1×1 and $(n-1) \times (n-1)$ blocks on the main diagonal that are square, and the $n \times 1$ block in the lower left is null. We have already seen that in this particular case the unit eigenvalue has at least multiplicity two, and generates at least two eigenvectors.

A weaker form of the theorem of Perron and Frobenius can be proven for reducible matrices. Specifically, we can show that, in this case, there still exists a λ_0 which is real and positive, and such that it is not exceeded by the magnitude of any other eigenvalue, and such that there corresponds a nonnegative reciprocal vector. We do not know that λ_0 is nondegenerate, nor do we know the interrelation between eigenvalues of the same magnitude.

6. CONCLUSIONS

The class of Markoff matrices gives us the means of studying various problems which involve probabilistically determined processes.

In addition, they provide a class of matrices about which a great deal can be inferred on general grounds. We know, for example, much about the spectrum of eigenvalues and the corresponding eigenvectors or reciprocal eigenvectors. It is therefore sometimes worthwhile even in nonprobabilistic problems to consider if the basis can be renormalized so as to make the matrices involved either Markoff matrices or their transposes. If we can can do this, then the theory of this class of matrices can be employed even though the physical problem has nothing to do with a Markoff process.

We have not attempted here the mathematical proof of the theorems involved. Instead we have discussed them on the basis of a hypothetical game and attempted in this way to make them plausible.

Exercises

1.   Suppose a gambler has \$200 to begin with. Suppose he quits when he is either broke, or has \$400. Suppose the game pays even money on any bet, and gives him a probability p of winning any single bet. What is his expectation of winning the \$400 he wants if he (a) bets his \$200 on a single play? (b) makes \$100 bets? (c) makes \$50 bets? How should he play if the game is favorable $(p > \frac{1}{2})$? How if it is unfavorable $(p < \frac{1}{2})$?

2.   Consider a Markoff matrix of the form

$$
\mathbf{A} =
\begin{pmatrix}
1 & b & 0 & 0 & 0 & & & & \\
0 & a & b & 0 & 0 & & & & \\
0 & c & a & b & 0 & & & & \\
0 & 0 & c & a & & b & & & \\
& & & & \ddots & & & & \\
& & & & & 0 & c & a & b & 0 \\
& & & & & 0 & 0 & c & a & 0 \\
& & & & & 0 & 0 & 0 & c & 1
\end{pmatrix}
$$

where a, b, c are real and positive and

$$a + b + c = 1$$

Find an explicit expression for the eigenvalues (cf. Chapter XVII, Exercise 1). Show that they are real and have magnitude less than or equal to unity. Find the eigenvectors. Show that their norms have the values deduced in the text.

3.   Show that if $\mathbf{P}$ and $\mathbf{Q}$ are Markoff matrices, then

$$\mathbf{X} = a\mathbf{P} + (1 - a)\mathbf{Q}$$

is a Markoff matrix where a is in the range $0 \leqslant a \leqslant 1$.

4.   Prove that if $\mathbf{P}$ and $\mathbf{Q}$ are Markoff matrices, then so is $\mathbf{PQ}$.

5.   Show that if $\mathbf{u}$ is a real vector whose norm [in the sense of Eq. (2)] is zero, then the algebraic sum of the components of any column of $\mathbf{uv}^T$, where $\mathbf{v}$ is any real vector, is zero. Use the dyad expansion to show that if $\mathbf{A}$ is a *positive* semisimple matrix whose eigenvectors are $\mathbf{x}_1$, $\mathbf{x}_2$, ..., $\mathbf{x}_n$, with eigenvalues $\lambda_1 = 1$ and λ_2, λ_3, ..., λ_n any suitable values, and with norms $\| x_1 \| = 1$, $\| x_2 \| = \| x_3 \| = \cdots = \| x_n \| = 0$, then $\mathbf{A}$ is a Markoff matrix.

CHAPTER XIX

Stability

We shall here consider an important class of problems that involve determining whether or not a given system is stable. The system may be described by a vector differential equation of the form

$$\frac{d\mathbf{x}(t)}{dt} = \mathbf{P}\mathbf{x}(t) \tag{1}$$

The question that arises is: What can happen as t becomes indefinitely large? If, for any admissable initial condition, $\lim_{t \to \infty} \mathbf{x}(t) = \mathbf{0}$, then the system is *stable*. If there is an admissable initial condition for which at least some components of $\mathbf{x}(t)$ become infinite, then the system is *unstable*. It may also happen that for some initial condition, $\mathbf{x}(t)$ remains bounded but does not approach the zero vector. For example, $\mathbf{x}(t)$ might be constant. In this case, the system is neither stable nor unstable.

The problem may arise by considering what happens if the system is perturbed from a known equilibrium state. Even if the system is non-linear, if its behavior is sufficiently smooth, then the perturbation problem is a linear one, and the question arises as to whether or not the system is stable against any physically possible perturbation.

In the above, we have spoken of "admissable" initial conditons. Obviously, we are interested only in physically possible initial conditions and it is these we call *admissable*. We shall here do no more than point out the possibility that there may be physical constraints that limit the range of admissable states. Usually in such cases it is possible to take account of such constraints by a proper choice of the coordinate system —i.e., by the choice of basis—and by limiting the dimensionality of the problem. In what follows, we shall assume that this has been done, if necessary, and that we are concerned with the stability of the system for any initial condition, $\mathbf{x}(0)$.

Since our principal subject here is stability, we have written Eq. (1) with time as the independent variable. The problem is, of course, mathematically equivalent if the independent variable is z instead. In this case, the system is distributed along the z axis, and the question is whether or not any input signal amplifies with increasing z (the unstable case) or propagates without attenuation (neither stable nor unstable).

Also, in what follows, we shall be concerned with **P** constant except when otherwise stated. As has been repeatedly mentioned, the problem is vastly more difficult if this is not so, and the class of problems with constant **P** is itself of great importance.

We can solve Eq. (1), with **P** constant, as

$$\mathbf{x}(t) = \exp(\mathbf{P}t)\mathbf{x}(0) \tag{2}$$

If the dimensionality of the system is reasonably small, this solution is not only possible in principal, but quite practical. However, it is often the case that the dimensionality is quite large. If we are concerned with the question of the stability of a power distribution network, or the vibrational stability—flutter—of an aircraft wing, the number of degrees of freedom that have to be studied may be of the order of 100 or more. We therefore want criteria for the stability of Eq. (1) that do not involve the explicit calculation of the solution of Eq. (2).

It is this problem that will concern us here.

1. THE BASIC THEOREM FOR STABILITY

The basic theorem that applies to this question is the following:

Theorem.   *A system described by Eq.* (1) *with* **P** *constant is stable for all initial conditions if and only if all the eigenvalues of* **P** *have negative real parts—i.e., are in the left-hand plane of* λ.

If we make a transformation of basis according to

$$\mathbf{x}(t) = \mathbf{S}\mathbf{u}(t) \tag{3}$$

where **S** is nonsingular and constant, then Eq. (1) becomes

$$\frac{d\mathbf{u}}{dt} = (\mathbf{S}^{-1}\mathbf{P}\mathbf{S})\mathbf{u} = \mathbf{P}'\mathbf{u} \tag{4}$$

so that **P** is transformed by a similarity transformation. We choose **S** so that **P'** is in the Jordan canonical form.

If **P'** is diagonal—i.e., if **P** was semisimple—the theorem is evident since

$$\mathbf{u}(t) = \mathrm{diag}(e^{\lambda_1 t}, e^{\lambda_2 t}, ...)\mathbf{u}(0) = \mathbf{M}'(t)\mathbf{u}(0) \tag{5}$$

and the condition is necessary and sufficient to make the diagonal matrix, $\mathbf{M}'(t)$, go to the null matrix.

If $\mathbf{P}$ is not semisimple, then $\mathbf{P}'$ is quasidiagonal with Jordan blocks along the diagonal. It is sufficient to consider an equation of the form of Eq. (4) where $\mathbf{P}'$ is itself a Jordan block:

$$\mathbf{P}' = \begin{pmatrix} \lambda & 1 & 0 & 0 & & \\ 0 & \lambda & 1 & 0 & & \\ 0 & 0 & \lambda & 1 & & \\ & & & & \ddots & \\ & & & & & \lambda \end{pmatrix} \tag{6}$$

or

$$\mathbf{P}'_{ii} = \lambda$$

$$\mathbf{P}'_{i,i+1} = 1$$

$$\mathbf{P}'_{i,j} = 0 \qquad \text{otherwise} \tag{6'}$$

We assert that the solution to Eq. (4) is

$$\mathbf{u}(t) = \mathbf{M}'(t)\mathbf{u}(0)$$

$$\mathbf{M}'(t) = e^{\lambda t} \begin{pmatrix} 1 & t & t^2/2! & t^3/3! & \cdots \\ 0 & 1 & t & t^2/2! & \\ 0 & 0 & 1 & t & \end{pmatrix} \tag{7}$$

or

$$\mathbf{M}'_{ij} = \frac{e^{\lambda t} t^{j-i}}{(j-i)!} \qquad \text{if} \quad j \geqslant i$$

$$= 0 \qquad \text{if} \quad j < i \tag{7'}$$

We see that

$$\frac{d\mathbf{M}'_{ij}}{dt} = \lambda e^{\lambda t} \qquad \text{if} \quad j = i$$

$$= e^{\lambda t} \left(\frac{\lambda t^{j-i}}{(j-i)!} + \frac{t^{j-i-1}}{(j-i-1)!} \right) \qquad \text{if} \quad j \geqslant i+1$$

$$= 0 \qquad \text{if} \quad j < i \tag{8}$$

and this is also what we obtain by evaluating $(\mathbf{PM})_{ij}$. Hence Eq. (7) is the solution to Eq. (5).

Since for any finite n the exponential factor of $t^n e^{\lambda t}$ dominates for sufficiently large t if λ is not pure imaginary, the theorem is proven.

The problem of determining the stability of Eq. (1) is that of determining whether or not all the eigenvalues of $\mathbf{P}$ have negative real parts.

We make the following definition:

Definition. *P is said to be* **stable,** *or a* **stability matrix** *if all of its eigenvalues have negative real parts.*

2. ROUTH-HURWITZ METHOD

Given a matrix $\mathbf{P}$, we wish to determine whether it has eigenvalues with positive real parts. Suppose we can obtain its characteristic equation. Admittedly this can be a formidable problem if $\mathbf{P}$ is large and does not have many zeros or other regularities that we can exploit. However, supposing this can be done, we have a polynomial of degree n in λ which, in most situations of interest, will be a real polynomial—i.e., one with real coefficients but not necessarily real roots. If n is large, we still face a difficult problem in determining where its roots lie. It is this problem for which the Routh-Hurwitz method was designed.

We shall here outline the method without proof, both because the proof is rather long and because it involves function theory more than matrix algebra.

We shall write the characteristic polynomial as

$$p(\lambda) = a_0\lambda^n + b_0\lambda^{n-1} + a_1\lambda^{n-2} + b_1\lambda^{n-3} + \cdots$$
$$+ a_k\lambda^{n-2k} + b_k\lambda^{n-2k-1} + \cdots \tag{9}$$

and let

$$a_k = 0 \quad \text{if} \quad k > \tfrac{1}{2}n$$
$$b_k = 0 \quad \text{if} \quad k > \tfrac{1}{2}(n-1)$$

We assume that all a_k and b_k are real. We shall also assume that $p(\lambda)$ has no roots that are pure imaginary. The technique that we shall give can be elaborated to take care of this case, but we shall not worry about it here.

We form the *Hurwitz matrix* $\mathbf{H}$ as the $n \times n$ matrix

$$\mathbf{H} = \begin{pmatrix} b_0 & b_1 & b_2 & b_3 & \cdots & b_{n-1} \\ a_0 & a_1 & a_2 & a_3 & \cdots & a_{n-1} \\ 0 & b_0 & b_1 & b_2 & \cdots & b_{n-2} \\ 0 & a_0 & a_1 & a_2 & \cdots & a_{n-2} \\ 0 & 0 & b_0 & b_1 & \cdots & b_{n-3} \\ 0 & 0 & a_0 & a_1 & \cdots & a_{n-3} \\ 0 & 0 & 0 & b_0 & \cdots & b_{n-4} \end{pmatrix} \tag{10}$$

$$\cdots$$

We triangulate this matrix. We start by subtracting a_0/b_0 times the first, third, fifth, etc., rows from the second, fourth, sixth, etc., rows, respectively, obtaining

$$\begin{pmatrix} b_0 & b_1 & b_2 & b_3 & \cdots & b_{n-1} \\ 0 & c_0 & c_1 & c_2 & \cdots & c_{n-2} \\ 0 & b_0 & b_1 & b_2 & \cdots & b_{n-2} \\ 0 & 0 & c_0 & c_1 & \cdots & c_{n-3} \\ & & & \cdots & & \end{pmatrix} \tag{11}$$

Then we subtract (b_0/c_0) times the second, fourth, etc., from the third, fifth, etc., rows, respectively. Continuing the process, we ultimately arrive at what is sometimes called the *Routh matrix* **R**:

$$\mathbf{R} = \begin{pmatrix} b_0 & b_1 & b_2 & \cdots \\ 0 & c_0 & c_1 & \cdots \\ 0 & 0 & d_0 & \cdots \end{pmatrix} \tag{12}$$

We have then Routh's theorem:

Theorem. *The number of roots of Eq. (9) in the right-hand plane—i.e., with positive real part—is equal to the number of changes of sign in the sequence*

$$a_0, b_0, c_0, d_0, \ldots$$

and Routh's criterion:

Theorem. *A polynomial, Eq. (9) has all of its eigenvalues in the left-hand plane—i.e., with negative real part—if all of the terms $a_0, b_0, c_0, \ldots$ are nonzero and have the same sign.*

In the above, we have tacitly assumed that none of the terms b_0, c_0, d_0, etc., vanish, since the triangulation process requires that we divide by them. This is the so-called *regular* case. If one does vanish, but not all of the terms in that row vanish, then we replace the zero in that position by a small real number ϵ and carry it through. It will be found that it makes no difference whether we take ϵ as small positive or negative.

To illustrate the regular case, consider the equation

$$(\lambda^2 + \lambda + 1)(\lambda^2 + \lambda - 1) = \lambda^4 + 2\lambda^3 + \lambda^2 - 1 = 0$$

which evidently has only a single root with positive real part. We have

$$\mathbf{H} = \begin{pmatrix} 2 & 0 & 0 & 0 \\ 1 & 1 & -1 & 0 \\ 0 & 2 & 0 & 0 \\ 0 & 1 & 1 & -1 \end{pmatrix}$$

Triangulating this we get

$$\mathbf{H} \to \begin{pmatrix} 2 & 0 & 0 & 0 \\ 0 & 1 & -1 & 0 \\ 0 & 2 & 0 & 0 \\ 0 & 0 & 1 & -1 \end{pmatrix} \to \begin{pmatrix} 2 & 0 & 0 & 0 \\ 0 & 1 & -1 & 0 \\ 0 & 0 & 2 & 0 \\ 0 & 0 & 1 & -1 \end{pmatrix} \to \begin{pmatrix} 2 & 0 & 0 & 0 \\ 0 & 1 & -1 & 0 \\ 0 & 0 & 2 & 0 \\ 0 & 0 & 0 & -1 \end{pmatrix}$$

The coefficients therefore are

$$1, \quad 2, \quad 1, \quad 2, \quad -1$$

and have only a single change of sign as expected.

To illustrate the procedure when one of the key terms vanishes, take the equation

$$\lambda^4 + 2\lambda^3 - \lambda^2 - 2\lambda - 3 = (\lambda^2 + \lambda - 3)(\lambda^2 + \lambda + 1) = 0$$

which, again, has only one root with positive real part.

The Hurwitz matrix is

$$\mathbf{H} = \begin{pmatrix} 2 & -2 & 0 & 0 \\ 1 & -1 & -3 & 0 \\ 0 & 2 & -2 & 0 \\ 0 & 1 & -1 & -3 \end{pmatrix}$$

At the first step in the triangulation, this becomes

$$\begin{pmatrix} 2 & -2 & 0 & 0 \\ 0 & 0 & -3 & 0 \\ 0 & 2 & -2 & 0 \\ 0 & 0 & 0 & -3 \end{pmatrix}$$

and the process is in difficulty since $c_0 = 0$. We set $c_0 = \epsilon$ and proceed:

$$\begin{pmatrix} 2 & -2 & 0 & 0 \\ 0 & \epsilon & -3 & 0 \\ 0 & 2 & -2 & 0 \\ 0 & 0 & \epsilon & -3 \end{pmatrix} \to \begin{pmatrix} 2 & -2 & 0 & 0 \\ 0 & \epsilon & -3 & 0 \\ 0 & 0 & -2 + 6/\epsilon & 0 \\ 0 & 0 & \epsilon & -3 \end{pmatrix} \to \begin{pmatrix} 2 & -2 & 0 & 0 \\ 0 & \epsilon & -3 & 0 \\ 0 & 0 & -2 + 6/\epsilon & 0 \\ 0 & 0 & 0 & -3 \end{pmatrix}$$

so that the key coefficients become

$$1, \quad 2, \quad \epsilon, \quad -2 + b/\epsilon, \quad -3$$

If ϵ is small positive, the signs are $(+ + + + -)$. If it small negative, the signs are $(+ + - - -)$. In either case there is only a single change of sign.

We have not, of course, proven the validity of any part of this process. Neither have we considered all possible complications. We have not considered the possibility of roots on the imaginery axis. Neither have we considered what to do if all of one row vanishes at some step. These situations can be taken care of by a suitable elaboration of the process. However, the intent here is not to be exhaustive, but to sketch in the process in a form that is applicable to most of the situations that arise in practice.

3. HURWITZ DETERMINANTS

The more usual formulation of the method given above is through the Hurwitz determinants. These are the determinants Δk, of order k formed from the Hurwitz matrix (of order n):

$$\Delta_1 = b_0$$

$$\Delta_2 = \begin{vmatrix} b_0 & b_1 \\ a_0 & a_1 \end{vmatrix}$$

$$\Delta_3 = \begin{vmatrix} b_0 & b_1 & b_2 \\ a_0 & a_1 & a_2 \\ 0 & b_0 & b_1 \end{vmatrix}$$

etc. (13)

If the polynomial, Eq. (9) is written so that a_0 is positive, then the Routh-Hurwitz criterion for all of its roots to have negative real parts is that

$$\Delta_i > 0, \quad \text{all} \quad i \leqslant n \tag{14}$$

It may be observed that the process of computing these determinants involves the same sequence of operations as are involved in triangulating **H** and determining the resultant diagonal elements.

4. CRITERION OF LIENARD AND CHIPART

Consideration of the Hurwitz determinants, Eq. (13) shows that a necessary condition for Eq. (9) to have all its roots have negative real part is that all of the coefficients of Eq. (8) have the same sign—i.e., all be positive if we standardize so that a_0 is positive.

This is not, however, a sufficient condition. For example

$$\lambda^3 + \lambda^2 + \lambda + 6 = (\lambda + 2)(\lambda^2 - \lambda + 3) = 0$$

has the roots

$$\lambda = -2 \quad \text{and} \quad \tfrac{1}{2}(1 \pm j \sqrt{11})$$

If, then, the polynomial has different signs in it, we know immediately that it cannot have all of its roots with negative real parts. If its coefficients are all positive, then we can apply the criterion developed by Lienard and Chipart.

To state this criterion we will change the symbology slightly to

$$p(\lambda) = a_0\lambda^n + a_1\lambda^{n-1} + \cdots + a_n \qquad (a_0 > 0) \tag{15}$$

so that the ith order Hurwitz determinant is

$$\Delta_i = \begin{vmatrix} a_1 & a_3 & \cdots & \\ a_0 & a_2 & \cdots & \\ 0 & a_1 & \cdots & \\ 0 & a_0 & \cdots & \\ & & \cdots & a_i \end{vmatrix}$$

$$a_k = 0 \qquad \text{if} \quad k > n \tag{16}$$

The Lienard-Chipart criterion then is:

Theorem. *All of the roots of Eq.* (15) *have negative real parts if and only if one of the following four conditions is true (if one is true all are true):*

I. $a_{n-2k+2} > 0,$ $\Delta_{2k-1} > 0,$ $1 \leqslant k \leqslant n/2$

II. $a_{n-2k+2} > 0,$ $\Delta_{2k} > 0,$ $1 \leqslant k \leqslant n/2$

III. $a_n > 0, \quad a_{n-2k-1} > 0,$ $\Delta_{2k-1} > 0,$ $1 \leqslant k \leqslant n/2$

IV. $a_n > 0, \quad a_{n-2k-1} > 0,$ $\Delta_{2k} > 0,$ $1 \leqslant k \leqslant n/2$
$$\tag{17}$$

Again we shall give no proof of this theorem.

The advantage of this criterion over that of Hurwitz is that it requires the computation of only half of the Hurwitz determinants. This can give a considerable saving of effort if the degree of the polynomial is large.

This type of approach to the problem has received extensive attention in the field. It has been our purpose to call attention to this fact so that when faced with such a problem the student will at least know that such a theory exists.

We will now move on to other aspects of the problem of stability.

5. LYAPUNOV'S SECOND METHOD

Returning to the original problem, which is that of determining when a system described by Eq. (1) is stable for any initial condition, there is one method of broad applicability that is available. This is Lyapunov's second, or direct, method.

Suppose we have a constant, hermitian matrix $\mathbf{L}$ which is positive definite. The *Lyapunov function* s given by

$$s = \mathbf{x}^\dagger \mathbf{L} \mathbf{x} \tag{18}$$

is positive real for any $\mathbf{x}$ except $\mathbf{x} = 0$, at which it vanishes.

Let us differentiate s with respect to t along a curve that is a solution to Eq. (1):

$$\frac{ds}{dt} = \frac{d\mathbf{x}^\dagger}{dt} \mathbf{L}\mathbf{x} + \mathbf{x}^\dagger \mathbf{L} \frac{d\mathbf{x}}{dt}$$

$$= \mathbf{x}^\dagger(\mathbf{P}^\dagger \mathbf{L} + \mathbf{L}\mathbf{P})\mathbf{x} = \mathbf{x}^\dagger \mathbf{M} \mathbf{x} \tag{19}$$

Now the matrix

$$\mathbf{M} = \mathbf{L}\mathbf{P} + \mathbf{P}^\dagger \mathbf{L} \tag{20}$$

is hermitian, since

$$\mathbf{M}^\dagger = (\mathbf{L}\mathbf{P} + \mathbf{P}^\dagger \mathbf{L})^\dagger = \mathbf{P}^\dagger \mathbf{L} + \mathbf{L}\mathbf{P} = \mathbf{M} \tag{21}$$

Therefore ds/dt is real.

Suppose $\mathbf{L}$ has been chosen so that $\mathbf{M}$ is negative definite. If the trajectories starts at any point $\mathbf{x}_0$, then s starts at some positive quantity, s_0. Subsequently $s(t)$ is monotone decreasing. But s has the lower bound of zero at $\mathbf{x} = 0$. Hence s is at least confined between s_0 and 0, and $\mathbf{x}(t)$ ($t > 0$) is confined inside the contour for which $s(\mathbf{x}) = s_0$.

Actually, s must go to zero, so that $\mathbf{x}$ must go assymtotically to $\mathbf{x} = 0$.

To see this, we recall the variational determination of the eigenvalues of a hermitian matrix (see Chapter III, Section 18) and see that for any $\mathbf{x}$

$$\frac{s}{\mathbf{x}^\dagger \mathbf{x}} = \frac{\mathbf{x}^\dagger \mathbf{L} \mathbf{x}}{\mathbf{x}^\dagger \mathbf{x}} \geqslant \lambda_m > 0 \tag{22}$$

where λ_m is the smallest eigenvalue of $\mathbf{L}$, which is positive real since $\mathbf{L}$ is a positive definite hermitian matrix. Likewise, we have

$$\frac{\mathbf{x}^\dagger \mathbf{M} \mathbf{x}}{\mathbf{x}^\dagger \mathbf{x}} \leqslant \mu_m < 0 \tag{23}$$

where μ_m is the least negative eigenvalue of $\mathbf{M}$.

Then we see that

$$\frac{ds}{dt} = \mathbf{x}^\dagger \mathbf{M} \mathbf{x} \leqslant \mu_m \mathbf{x}^\dagger \mathbf{x} \leqslant \frac{\mu_m}{\lambda_m} s = -k_m s$$

where

$$k_m = -\mu_m/\lambda_m > 0 \tag{24}$$

Hence

$$\leqslant e^{-k_m t} s_0 \tag{25}$$

which goes to zero as t goes to $+\infty$.

These conclusions are valid even when $\mathbf{P}$ is not constant, except that Eq. (20) for $\mathbf{M}$ now includes the term $d\mathbf{L}/dt$, and we must require that $\mathbf{M}$ not only be negative definite at all t, but that its eigenvalues have an upper bound that is less than zero. We can use this negative upper bound in Eq. (23) in place of μ_m, and obtain Eq. (25).

The process given can be generalized to nonlinear equations and to more complicated functions than the quadratic form used for $s(\mathbf{x})$. One must then set up additional conditions to assure that $s(t)$ actually goes to zero and does not simply approach some finite limit (indicating at least the possibility of a limit cycle) but the principle remains the same.

The difficulty with the method is, of course, the determination of $\mathbf{L}$, or of the Lyapunov function $s(\mathbf{x})$. There is no general process for doing this, although processes have been developed for various classes of problems. Generally speaking, however, it becomes a process of trial and error, or inspiration.

As a help in the search for Lyapunov functions, we can observe that $s(\mathbf{x})$ has properties like the stored energy of the system. If the energy decays from any initial condition, then evidently the equilibrium condition is the condition of lowest energy and the system is stable. It is sometimes possible to compute the stored energy and show that it is a Lyapunov function. Otherwise, we may be able to weight various classes of energy in such a way that the resultant *reduced energy* is a Lyapunov function.

As an example of the general process, consider the system described by Eq. (1) with

$$\mathbf{P} = \begin{pmatrix} j\omega + \mu & e^{j\theta} + j\kappa \\ -e^{-j\theta} - j\kappa & -j\omega - \eta \end{pmatrix}$$

where ω, θ, μ, η, and κ are real constants.

We wish to find conditions on μ, η, and κ such that the system is stable.

One suitable Lyapunov function is

$$s = \mathbf{x}^\dagger \mathbf{x}$$

i.e.,

$$\mathbf{L} = \mathbf{I}$$

This is hermitian and positive definite. We form $\mathbf{M}$:

$$\mathbf{M} = \mathbf{LP} + \mathbf{P^{\dagger}L} = 2 \begin{pmatrix} \mu & j\kappa \\ -j\kappa & -\eta \end{pmatrix}$$

$\mathbf{M}$ will be negative definite if the trace, which is the sum of the two roots, is negative and the determinant, which is the product, is positive

$$\mu - \eta < 0, \qquad -\mu\eta - \kappa^2 > 0$$

If μ, η, and κ are functions of time, then to assure stability we must have finite lower bounds on the magnitudes:

$$\mu - \eta \leqslant -\epsilon_0, \qquad -\mu\eta - \kappa^2 \geqslant \delta_0$$

where ϵ_0 and δ_0 are nonzero positive quantities.

These are not necessary conditions, since other Lyapunov functions will lead to other conditions, but they are sufficient. If $\mathbf{P}$ satisfies these conditions, then the system will be stable.

6. A METRIC AS LYAPUNOV MATRIX

We may note the similarity of $\mathbf{M}$, in Eq. (20), to some of the expressions involving a metric $\mathbf{K}$.

Suppose we have a metric $\mathbf{K}$ such that the inner product it defines is proper. Then $\mathbf{K}$ is positive definite and $\mathbf{x^{\dagger}Kx}$ fulfills the first requirement of a Lyapunov function. The second requirement is that

$$\mathbf{M} = \mathbf{KP} + \mathbf{P^{\dagger}K} \tag{26}$$

shall be negative definite.

Let

$$\begin{aligned} \mathbf{P}_1 &= \tfrac{1}{2}(\mathbf{P} + \mathbf{K^{-1}P^{\dagger}K}) \\ \mathbf{P}_2 &= \tfrac{1}{2}(\mathbf{P} - \mathbf{K^{-1}P^{\dagger}K}) \end{aligned} \tag{27}$$

so that $\mathbf{P}_1$ is K-hermitian and $\mathbf{P}_2$ K-skew-hermitian

$$\mathbf{KP}_1 - \mathbf{P}_1^{\dagger}\mathbf{K} = 0 \tag{28}$$

$$\mathbf{KP}_2 + \mathbf{P}_2^{\dagger}\mathbf{K} = 0 \tag{29}$$

and

$$\mathbf{P} = \mathbf{P}_1 + \mathbf{P}_2 \tag{30}$$

Substituting Eq. (30) in Eq. (26) and using Eq. (28), we find

$$\mathbf{M} = \mathbf{KP}_1 + \mathbf{P}_1^{\dagger}\mathbf{K} = 2\mathbf{KP}_1$$

Therefore the second requirement is that $\mathbf{KP}_1$ shall be negative definite.

If we are able to find a *proper* metric $\mathbf{K}$ such that $\mathbf{KP}_1$, where $\mathbf{P}_1$ is the K-hermitian part of $\mathbf{P}$, is negative definite, then $(\mathbf{x}^\dagger\mathbf{Kx})$ is a Lyapunov function and the system is stable.

7. CONCLUSIONS

We have here considered the problem of determining the stability of a dynamic system. Since we are confining ourselves to linear systems, or to the linearized approximation of a system, the question of whether or not the system is stable is answered when we know whether or not all of the roots of $\mathbf{P}$ have negative real parts.

If the system is of sufficiently small dimension, then there is no problem. We can, if we like, simply compute the eigenvalues and look at them.

Unfortunately, the problem generally arises in situations that preclude such a straightforward approach. It may be that the dimensionality is too large so that the exact calculation of the eigenvalues becomes prohibitively wasteful of effort. Or it may be that we are not asking about a particular system, but rather for conditions on a general type of system that will assure stability.

Two general tools for these questions are available to us. If it is possible, and feasible, to obtain the characteristic equation, then there are tests to determine if the system is stable. These derive from the Routh-Hurwitz theory and include such procedures as the Lienard-Chipart criterion. These methods can still involve a large amount of effort if the order of the polynomial is large, but at least they are much superior to the detailed calculation of all the eigenvalues.

The other tool is the use of the second method of Lyapunov. This is a method that is rather beautiful in its generality, but does depend on finding a suitable Lyapunov function. Unfortunately, there is no general systematic method of finding one. However, when one can be found, the logic is quite straightforward. Further, the Lyapunov function is likely to express some sort of reduced energy of the system which is physically important.

Exercises

1. Find general conditions on a, b, c, and d that will assure us that the equation

$$x^4 + ax^3 + bx^2 + cx + d = 0$$

will have only roots with negative real parts.

2. What happens if we attempt to apply the Routh-Hurwitz method to

   (a) $x^3 + ax^2 + x + a = 0$
   (b) $x^4 + ax^3 + (b + 1)\, x^2 + ax + b = 0$

where a and b are nonzero. Try also the modification for the irregular case.

   (*Note*: Both equations have the factor $x^2 + 1$. Hence they each have a pair of roots on the imaginary axis.)

3. Let

$$\mathbf{P} = \begin{pmatrix} j\omega + \mu & e^{j\theta} + j\kappa \\ -e^{-j\theta} - j\kappa & -j\omega - \eta \end{pmatrix}$$

as before. What conditions for stability do we obtain by Lyapunov's second method using

$$\mathbf{L} = \begin{pmatrix} a & 0 \\ 0 & b \end{pmatrix}$$

where a and b are positive numbers?

References and Recommended Texts

The following is an acknowledgment of some of the sources that we have found valuable, and a recommendation of various materials for further study. The field of matrix algebra is broad and its applications have been extremely varied. The following list, therefore, is an essentially personal one—these are the books that we have found useful. We can only apologize to the authors of possibly excellent books or papers that we have not used, and to workers in various specialized subfields that have not directly concerned us.

Chapter I–VIII

F. R. Gantmacher, *The Theory of Matrices*, Vols. I and II, Chelsea, New York, 1959, translated from the Russian by K. A. Hirsch. This contains most of the basic theory, including some that we have not used here. The treatment is rigorous, but not so abstract or generalized as to be unintelligible. The treatment is fairly compact, however, so that we consider it a better reference than text book.

R. Bellman, *Introduction to Matrix Analysis*, McGraw-Hill, New York, 1960. This book contains a broad development of the basic theory, although generally not at as a deep a level as we would like. Also, the approach is from the concept of real quadratic forms. The development therefore does not follow the route that we prefer. Nevertheless, it is a useful book in that it contains a clear exposition of a wide range of theory and application.

Academician V. I. Smirnov's *Linear Algebra and Group Theory*, revised, adapted, and edited by R. A. Silverman. McGraw-Hill, New York, 1961. This book contains a clear development of those parts of matrix theory that are a necessary prelude to the basic concepts of group theory. Its scope is therefore limited, but, within that scope, the exposition is excellent.

B. Friedman, *Principles and Techniques of Applied Mathematics*, Wiley, New York, 1956. While this text is concerned primarily with infinitely dimensioned linear vector spaces and differential or integral operators, it gives a useful development of the basic concepts and theories on linear vector spaces.

R. R. Stoll, *Linear Algebra and Matrix Theory*, McGraw-Hill, New York, 1952, contains a good development of the foundations of the subject.

P. R. Halmos, *Finite Dimensional Vector Spaces*, Van Nostrand, Princeton, New Jersey, 1958. This book is primarily a mathematical text. It is useful in providing a careful and clear exposition of various aspects of the theory which are not normally treated but which sometimes are of great value—e.g., the theory of projectors (Chapter XI).

W. H. Louisell, *Coupled Mode and Parametric Electronics*, Wiley, New York, 1960, is the standard reference on one of the areas of principal application. The book is not written in matrix terms, but the application is obvious.

R. H. Dicke and J. P. Wittke, *Introduction to Quantum Mechanics*, Addison-Wesley, Reading, Massachusetts, 1960. This is a good introduction to quantum mechanics which uses the matrix formulation fairly extensively.

A. Messiah, *Quantum Mechanics* Vols. 1 and 2, North-Holland Publ. Co., Amsterdam, 1961 and 1962. These books give an extensive treatment of quantum mechanics, and of the analytic techniques that are used there. Much of the analysis is by matrix methods, although often infinitely dimensional matrices.

V. Faddeeva, *Computational Methods of Linear Algebra*, translated by C. D. Benster, Dover, New York, 1959, is the principal reference on computational methods—an area that we have not attempted to cover here. Other techniques have been developed since, but most are refinements on Faddeeva's methods.

Chapter IX

The improper inner product has received very little attention anywheres. We can refer to our own papers in *Proc. I.R.E.* **49**, 488-497 (1961); and *J. Appl. Phys.* **31**, 1988–1996, 2028-2036 (1960); **32**, 1145–1151, 1736-1743 (1961); **33**, 2398–2399 (1962). The indefinite metric has also been used by E. C. G. Sudarshen, *Phys. Rev.* **123** 2183–2193 (1961) and by Schnitzer and Sudarshen, *Phys. Rev.* **123**, 2193–2201 (1961) in quantum mechanics. It has also been very important in relativity—see, for example:

J. L. Synge, *Relativity: The Special Theory*, North Holland Publ. Co., Amsterdam, 1960.

Chapter X

The dyad expansion is not entirely new, but we have not seen its systematic exploitation elsewhere. Some of the theory is used in:

P. M. Morse and H. Feshbach, *Methods of Theoretical Physics*, McGraw-Hill, New York, 1953.

It is also used in quantum mechanics under the guise of the Dirac notation. For this, see Dicke and Wittke, and Messiah, *loc. cit.* Part of the theory is also given in Friedman, *loc. cit.*, and elsewhere.

Chapter XI

Projectors are used extensively in quantum mechanics. For this the reader can look to Dicke and Wittke and, particularly, Messiah, *loc cit.* The subject is also treated abstractly in Halmos, *loc. cit.*

Chapter XII

The particular treatment of singular operators given here is, as far as we know, unique, although we have found Friedman, *loc. cit.*, a useful source for some of the theorems.

An alternative approach, which leads to essentially the same results, has been developed by J. S. Frame and his co-workers. A summary of this method by Frame was published in *Spectrum* 1, 208–220 (March 1964).

Chapter XIII

For the application of matrices to group theory and the development of the associated Lie algebra, some of the basic theory is given in Smirnov, *loc. cit.* We can also refer the student to:

E. P. Wigner, *Group Theory and Its Application to the Quantum Mechanics of Atomic Spectra*, Academic Press, New York, 1959.

For the deeper levels of this subject, see:

N. Jacobson, *Lie Algebras*, Wiley (Interscience), New York, 1962.

L. P. Eisenhart, *Continuous Groups of Transformations*, Dover, New York, 1961. (Original copyright 1933.)

M. Hausner and S. Sternberg, *The Structure of Semisimple Lie Algebras*, a report by RIAS, Inc., 1958, ASTIA Doc. No. 203673.

H. Weyl, *The Classical Groups, Their Invariants and Representations*, Princeton Univ. Press, Princeton, New Jersey, 1946.

Unfortunately, all of these references are essentially mathematical in their approach, and so require intensive study. There does not seem to be any intermediate text.

Chapter XIV

These subjects are covered in Bellman, *loc. cit.* For the application to group theory, see Smirnov and Wigner, *loc. cit.*

Chapter XV

For the basic theory, see Gantmacher, *loc. cit.* As an example of its use, see E. S. Cassedy and A. A. Oliner, *Proc. IEEE* **51**, 1342–1358 (1963).

Chapter XVI

The underlying physical theory here is that of the electromagnetic field, for which there are many excellent texts. Our attention was first drawn to the power of polarization coordinates by A. E. Siegman, *J. Appl. Phys.* **31**, 17–26 (1960).

Chapter XVII

For the basic theory on Sturm-Liouville systems, see Morse and Feshbach, *loc. cit.*, or
R. Courant and D. Hilbert, *Methods of Mathematical Physics*, Vol. I, Wiley (Interscience), New York, 1953.
For the use of the Cauchy Index, see Gantmacher, *loc. cit.*
For the use of a finite grid as an approximation to the continuous case, see:
R. S. Varga, *Matrix Iterative Analysis*, Prentice-Hall, Englewood Cliffs, New Jersey, 1962.

Chapter XVIII

For the simple theory, see Bellman, *loc. cit.* For the deeper analysis, and the further extension of the theory to what are called "totally nonnegative" matrices and "oscillatory" matrices, see Gantmacher, *loc. cit.*

Chapter XIX

The material on stability theory is fairly well scattered. Bellman, *loc. cit.*, gives some of it. Gantmacher, *loc. cit.*, gives a fairly extensive discussion of the Routh-Hurwitz method and related procedures. Lyapunov's second, or direct, method is developed in considerable detail in:
J. LaSalle and S. Lefschetz, *Stability by Liapunov's Direct Method with Applications*, Academic Press, New York, 1961.

SUBJECT INDEX